THE ALOES OF TROPICAL AFRICA
AND MADAGASCAR

THE AUTHOR'S JOURNEYS IN SEARCH OF ALOE

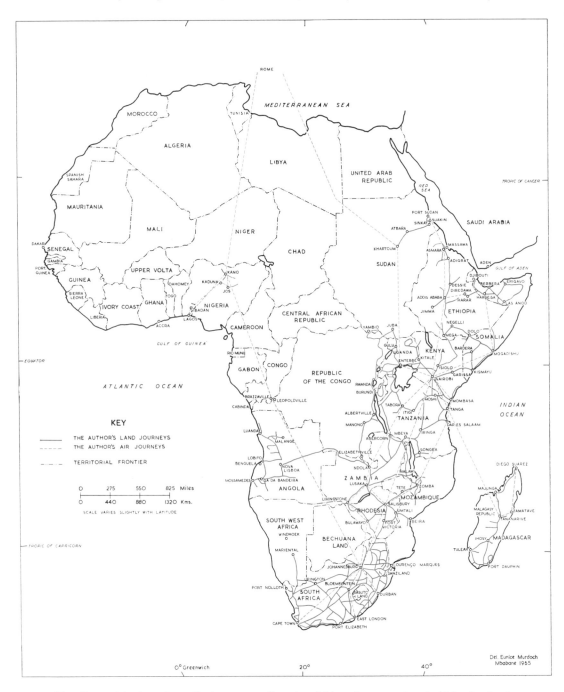

Dr. Reynolds has travelled more miles in Africa in search of (Aloe) plants than any other plant collector living or dead. — *The Secretaries, The Linnean Society of London. 8 August 1960.*

THE
ALOES
OF
TROPICAL AFRICA
AND
MADAGASCAR

By

GILBERT WESTACOTT REYNOLDS

HON. D.SC. (CAPE TOWN), F.L.S.

Published by

THE TRUSTEES
THE ALOES BOOK FUND

P.O. BOX 234, MBABANE, SWAZILAND

September 1966

PRINTED IN SOUTH AFRICA
BY CAPE AND TRANSVAAL PRINTERS LIMITED
CAPE TOWN

PREFACE

Berger's Monograph in Engler's *Pflanzenreich* Liliac.-Aloin (1908) listed 181 species of Aloe, as then known. Since then, investigation of the South African species progressed comparatively rapidly, and culminated in the publication in 1950 of *The Aloes of South Africa* which listed 132 species, excluding Tropical species.

Because of tremendous distances, and lack of ground communications, progress in the rest of Africa has been much slower. It is only in the last 25 years or so that many parts of Africa have been more rapidly opened up – and then, mostly because of World War II. Since then, botanical workers have been able to penetrate much further afield and discover many unexpected new species of Aloe in remote corners.

With the passing in 1950 of Mr. H. Basil Christian ("Ewanrigg" near Salisbury, Rhodesia) who, in his day, contributed much to the increase of knowledge of the Aloes of Tropical Africa, and with *The Aloes of South Africa* off my hands, the urge to investigate and monograph the Aloes of all Africa, and Madagascar, began to assert itself – soon irresistibly.

One has only to glance at a map of Africa to recognize the immensity of the continent, while to try and grasp how widespread the genus Aloe was distributed, and even to think of attempting to trace them, was not only a sobering influence, but made me wonder whether I could ever complete such a task in the years left to me. I think it was the magnitude of the challenge that decided me to attempt it, and once started, there was no turning back, no matter what problems and obstacles arose, and there were many.

The descriptions of many early species were vague, incomplete, and sometimes misleading, while there were no figures of many of them. Most of Berger's figures in Engler's *Pflanzenreich* (1908) were conjured up from pressed herbarium material, and were often more misleading than helpful. Again, much of the Aloe material at Berlin was unfortunately destroyed during the last war, while such type material as did exist elsewhere frequently proved to be fragmentary, incomplete and, often exasperating. In several instances species had been described with habit of growth and leaves unknown, while in a few even the flowers were unknown.

It soon became clear that nothing less than a personal visit to the cited type localities – wherever they might be – could ever enable to me solve the problems of the identity of those species, or at least to attempt it. And so, in periodic expeditions from 1951 to 1960, I covered over 40,000 miles on the roads of Africa and Madagascar, in quest of Aloes at their type localities, and wherever else I could find them. Where possible, I traversed some parts of the routes taken by early botanical travellers, to check where they went and what they could have found. I have sought Aloe from the Cape of Good Hope to the Gulf of Aden and the Red Sea, and from the Indian Ocean to the Atlantic, as is shown on the accompanying map – see Frontispiece.

On the whole, I was very successful tracing many species at their type localities, securing photographs, and preparing herbarium specimens.

A. schweinfurthii Bak. on Jebel Bangenze in the SW corner of the Sudan, and *A. percrassa* Tod. on the Kohaito Plateau in Eritrea, were two species I had the good fortune to find in flower – so were *A. camperi* Schweinf. and *A. elegans* Tod. also from Eritrea.

With the identity of these four "Key" species established, and with the mystery of the identity of *A. abyssinica* Lam. solved (thanks to Professor J. Millot), further investigations were much simplified.

I have always believed that the "picture tells the story" infinitely better than pages of cold print. Hence, apart from 106 colour plates, a considerable number of photographs – mostly of plants in their natural surroundings, has been reproduced. I have also concentrated on photographing flowers with pedicels and bracts natural size, and sometimes various flowers gathered at random to show how perianths vary in shape and size. This has been done in an endeavour to assist the student to identify his specimen, but identification is by no means as simple as might seem.

Most species vary considerably under different conditions, and no one photograph can ever depict all the various forms of a species. Some vary through intermediates from one to the next and it is rarely, if ever, possible to know just where one ends and the next begins.

There is much difference of opinion. There is no fixation of characters, and no measuring stick by which species can be determined.

A reliable concept of a good species depends infinitely more on a worker with considerable field experience, who has observed how species vary under different conditions of environment, soil, climate, rainfall, altitude, etc., and who has learnt to recognise the points of resemblance that bring them together, than it ever will on one armed with a millimeter rule in a herbarium.

Throughout this work, the policy adopted has been one of judicious "lumping" based on personal knowledge of species as they grow wild and vary in their natural habitats.

I was indeed fortunate to complete my travels in Africa before the "troubles" erupted. Today it would be impossible to travel freely and safely in some parts of Africa where Aloe abounds.

This work is not complete. There are still several new species to be described from the Congo, Tanzania, Moçambique, Kenya, Somalia and Ethiopia when flowers become available. When this will be is problematical, and one cannot postpone publication indefinitely. If any of these species flower in time for descriptions to be included in this work, they will be found in an Appendix.

This work treats 197 species in Tropical Africa and Madagascar. Included in this total are nine species which also occur in South, and South West Africa. They are *A. aculeata* Pole Evans, *A. aborescens* Mill., *A. chabaudii* Schonl., *A. cryptopoda* Bak., *A. globuligemma* Pole Evans, *A. hereroensis* Engler, *A. littoralis* Bak. (=*A. rubrolutea* Schinz), *A. myriacantha* (Haw) R & S, and *A. zebrina* Bak.

Allowing for these nine species, and adding the 132 species included in *The Aloes of South Africa* plus four described subsequently (*A. modesta* Reynolds, *A. monotropa* Verdoorn, *A. soutpansbergensis* Verdoorn and *A. prinslooi* Verdoorn) establishes that 324 species of Aloe are known at present.

The cultivation of Aloe plants is now rapidly becoming a world-wide hobby, and it is my hope that those who use this book will derive as much joy from its pages, as I have had in producing it.

AUTHOR'S ACKNOWLEDGMENTS

(Alphabetically)

BALL, Mr. John, Melsetter, Rhodesia, for conducting me along the Chimanimani Mountains and to "The Corner", Eastern Rhodesia, for flowering plants that enabled *A. howmanii* to be described, and for much other useful help.

BALLY, Mr. P. R. O., formerly Botanist at the Coryndon Museum, Nairobi, for organizing expeditions through parts of Tanzania, Kenya, Uganda, Southern Ethiopia and Somalia, for unstinted hospitality whenever I was in Nairobi, for many excellent photographs and Aloe plants from a wide area in north-eastern Africa, for considerable assistance during our travels together, and for much help in many other directions over many years.

BULLOCK, Mr. E. J., Bulawayo, Rhodesia, for distribution records of the Rhodesian Aloes, for several plants that enabled *A. musapana* and *A. ballii* to be described when they flowered at Mbabane, Swaziland, and for other species with photographs and data.

CLASSEN, Mr. George A., Nairobi, Kenya, for a large number of Aloe plants mostly from outlying parts of Kenya, some being new and awaiting description, for Kodachromes and much data, painstakingly assembled, and for plants that enabled *A. classenii* to be described.

CODD, Dr. L. E., Chief, Botanical Research Institute, Pretoria, for placing the facilities of the National Herbarium, Pretoria, freely at my disposal, for many photographs from early botanical works, for a considerable number of prints made from my negatives and used for most of the black and white figures in this book, and for much other assistance.

COMPTON, Professor R. H., formerly Director, National Botanical Gardens, Kirstenbosch, near Cape Town, for making available the pages of the *Journal of South African Botany* for the publication of new species, for his services as Chairman of the Board of Trustees, for invaluable encouragement and assistance in many directions over many years, and for his ever-available constructive criticisms and interest in the publication of this work.

DESCOINGS, Mr. Bernard, formerly Botanist at the Institute Scientifique de Madagascar, Tananarive, for many kindnesses and much considerate help during our travels together in Madagascar, for photographs and specimens; also for plants of *A. buettneri* from near Brazzaville, Congo.

DYER, Dr. R. A., formerly Chief, Botanical Research Institute, Pretoria, for placing the facilities of the Institute freely at my disposal, for many photographs, for his helpful suggestions, encouragement and untiring personal interest in the production of this book, and invaluable assistance and guidance as a Trustee in matters of finance and publication.

FERNANDES, Dr. A., Director Centro de Botânica, Lisbon, for sending his LISC Aloe sheets for study, and for much other help with the Aloes of Angola.

GILLETT, Mr. Jan B., Botanist in Charge, East African Herbarium, Nairobi, worked along the southern boundary of Ethiopia in 1952 with the Kenya-Ethiopian Boundary Commission when he sent many Aloe plants to me with photographs and field notes. I am grateful for this and for help in other directions from Kew and from Nairobi.

GREENWAY, Dr. P. J. (formerly Botanist in Charge, East African Herbarium, Nairobi, Kenya), for many plants of East African Aloes, with much data, for the facilities of the East African Herbarium, and for hospitality and much assistance whenever I passed through Nairobi.

GUERRA, Eng. Guilherme, Director of Agriculture and Forests, Loanda, Angola, for plants and data, and for every assistance during my travels in Angola.

GUNN, Miss M., Librarian, Botanical Research Institute, Pretoria, for the facilities of the Library, for checking many references, for her assistance in bibliographical research, and for her ever available help in other ways.

HUMBERT, Professor H., Director of the Muséum National d'Histoire Naturelle, Paris, for sending several of Perrier de la Bathie's type specimens to me for study, and for his observations on some species.

KEAY, Mr. R. W. J., formerly Director of Forests, Ibadan, Nigeria, for arranging transport and itineraries for studying the three species of Aloe in various parts of Nigeria, for hospitality and every assistance while I was there, for many Aloe plants and much data, and especially for his researches that established that *A. barteri* Bak. was a mixture of species. His paper *The Nigerian Species of Aloe* in *Kew Bull.* 17:1, 65 (1963) which discussed, *inter alia*, the Aloe species described by Chevalier in *Rev. Bot. Appliq.* 31: 591–598 (1952), finally cleared up the confusion concerning their identity.

LAVRANOS, Mr. John, Bryanston, Johannesburg, for many plants, material, copious field notes and considerable assistance with the Aloes of Arabia in general. He visited south-western Arabia and the Hadhramaut in August 1962, and again, accompanied by Professor W. Rauh, in March 1964. As a result of these journeys he described six new species of Aloe in *Journ. S.A. Bot.* 31: 55–81 (1965). These species together with *A. lavranosii* Reynolds from the Amiri Highlands near Dhala, about 87 miles north of Aden, have now been included in this present work. In the same publication Mr. Lavranos reviewed the botanical background of the Aloes of Arabia from Forskal 1762–63 to the present day, and his findings have also been incorporated in this work. Had it not been for Mr. Lavranos's contribution, the Aloes of Arabia would have been poorly represented.

LEACH, Mr. Larry C., Greendale, Rhodesia, and Nelspruit Eastern Transvaal, for a large number of Aloe plants from many parts of Rhodesia, Malawi, Moçambique, Tanzania and elsewhere, with Kodachromes and copious field notes, and for much assistance in other directions over many years. Mr. Leach has also collected and distributed a considerable number of Aloe and other succulent specimens to several Herbaria, especially PRE and SRGH.

LEANDRI, Mr. J., Sub-Director, Muséum National d'Histoire Natural, Paris, for photographs, sketches and descriptions, and for sending several type specimens of Aloe to me for examination.

MacLEAY, Dr. K. N. G., formerly Department of Botany, University College of Khartoum (now at the University of Basutoland, Bechuanaland and Swaziland, Roma, Basutoland) for hospitality, considerable assistance with my travels in the Sudan, for photographs and data and many plants of Aloe from several parts of the Sudan, including the Imatongs which enabled *A. macleayi* to be described.

MENDES, Dr. E. J., Centro de Botânica, Lisbon, for data concerning the Aloes of Angola, for several Aloe plants, especially one of the long-sought-for *A. metallica* Engl. et Gilg. from the Cuchi District, and *A. mendesii* Reynolds from the Serra da Chela south-west of Sá da Bandeira, also for some excellent photographs used in this work, and for much other assistance.

Millot, Professor J., formerly Director of The Institut Scientifique de Madagascar, Tsimbazaza – Tananarive (now Director of the Musée de l'Homme, Paris), for arranging my visit to Madagascar to investigate the Aloes, for warm hospitality, and for providing every possible facility and assistance during my travels in Madagascar.

Milne-Redhead, Mr. E., Deputy Keeper of the Herbarium and Library, Royal Botanic Gardens, Kew, for very considerable assistance over many years including many photographs, much data, research, helpful suggestions, hospitality while I was at Kew, and considerably more besides.

Munch, Mr. and Mrs. R. C., Rusape, Rhodesia, for many Aloe plants and much data, for conducting me to Zembe Mountain in Moçambique where *A. decurva* Reynolds was found, and along the Chimanimani Mountains east of Melsetter, Rhodesia, where *A. munchii* Christian and other species were photographed, and for plants that enabled *A. hazeliana* to be described.

Paulian, Dr. R., formerly Deputy Director, Institut Scientifique de Madagascar, Tsimbazaza – Tananarive (now Directeur, Institut d'Etudes Centre-Africaines, Brazzaville) for providing transport throughout my travels in Madagascar, for photographs, many Aloe specimens, for translations of some early French works, for helpful advice and considerable assistance in many other directions.

Plowes, Mr. D. C. H., Umtali, Rhodesia, for many Rhodesian Aloes, especially from Musapa and the Chimanimanis, for much data, for several Kodachromes, from two of which (*A. howmanii* Reynolds and *A. excelsa* Berger) colour plates were made, and for plants and data enabling me to describe *A. plowesii*.

Rauh, Professor W., Institute for Systematic Botany, University of Heidelberg, West Germany, for copious field-notes and data, plants, Kodachromes and very excellent photographs of Malgache and Arabian Aloes used in this book, and for his whole-hearted co-operation.

Richards, Mrs. H. M., Abercorn, Zambia, for Aloe plants, mostly from Zambia and Western Tanganyika, and especially for several plants of the "bulbous" *A. richardsiae* Reynolds which enabled that species to be described.

Robyns, Professor W., Director, Jardin Botanique de l'Etat, Brussels, for sending several sheets for study of the Aloes of the former Belgian Congo, for several photographs, and for arranging every assistance when I investigated the Aloes of the Belgian Congo in 1954.

Rycroft, Professor H. B., Director, National Botanic Gardens, Kirstenbosch, near Cape Town, for making the pages of *The Journal of South African Botany* freely available for the publication of descriptions of many new species of Aloe discovered during my African expeditions, for his services and guidance as a Trustee, and for his enthusiastic help in other ways.

Smuts, the late Dr. N. R. For helpful suggestions and advice over many years, and especially for companionship and assistance during our travels by caravan through Tanzania and Angola.

South African Council for Scientific and Industrial Research, Pretoria, for travelling grants that enabled me to investigate the Aloes almost throughout the continent of Africa, and in Madagascar, for grants that defrayed the cost of the majority of the 106 colour plates included in the book, and for other financial assistance that eased my burden. Had it not been for the generous financial encouragement of the C.S.I.R. this book would not have been produced in its present scope.

Taylor, Sir George, Director, Royal Botanic Gardens, Kew, for placing the facilities of Kew freely at my disposal while I was there working on Aloe, and for much assistance in many other directions.

Tweedie, Mrs. E. M., Kitale, Kenya, for considerable assistance with the Aloes of East Africa, for many plants and herbarium specimens with descriptions and data, for warm hospitality when I visited "Mutamayo", and especially for organising a very rewarding trip through most parts of Karamoja, Northern Uganda, to study the Aloes.

VERDOORN, Miss Inez C., Botanical Research Institute, Pretoria, for much assistance in many directions – especially with the species described and being investigated by the late Mr. H. Basil Christian, of Ewanrigg, near Salisbury, Rhodesia.

VESEY-FITZGERALD, Mr. L. D. E. F. (formerly Principal Scientific Officer, International Red Locust Control Services, Abercorn, Zambia), for much assistance with the Aloes of the Abercorn District (especially *A. nuttii* Bak. from its type locality) and parts of Western Tanganyika, for taking me to Kalambo Falls where *A. veseyi* Reynolds grows on precipice faces, and for every hospitality and help whenever I visited Abercorn.

WILD, Dr. H., Chief Botanist, Branch of Botany, Salisbury, Rhodesia, for the facilities of the Herbarium, for sending a large number of SRGH Aloe sheets to me for study, for photographs, several plants, and ever-available help with the Rhodesian Aloes.

WILSON, Mr. John T., Ecologist, Moroto, Karamoja, Uganda, for photographs, plants and help with the Aloes of Karamoja, and – notwithstanding a broken arm set in plaster – for leading me 3,000 ft. up a spur of Mt. Moroto to Imagit Peak, to photograph and collect *A. wilsonii*.

AND THERE IS STILL ONE to whom I perhaps owe most. As with *The Aloes of South Africa*, so with this present work she has often been left at home alone to care for the family while I have been away sometimes for weeks or months at a time. She has always been a source of encouragement, without complaint. To my own wife I do indeed owe most.

LIST OF SUBSCRIBERS

A

Ackermann, J. J.

Adelaide Botanic Garden, S. Australia

Albert R. Mann Library, New York

Amato, N. N.

Anderson, Ken R.

Anderson, P. H.

Anderson, Mrs. S. A. G.

Andriés, H. E.

Anglo-Transvaal Consolidated Investment Co. Ltd.

Argus Printing and Publishing Company Limited, Johannesburg

Arnold Arboretum of Harvard University, Mass.

Ashton, Hugh

Auckland Municipal Reference Library, New Zealand

Austin, Bill

B

Bailey Hortorium, Cornell University, N.Y.

Bain, K. A. R.

Balderson, G. C.

Bally, P. R. O.

Barker, Miss W. F.

Barnard, H. S.

Barnard, Dr. P. J.

Barrow, Sir Malcolm P.

Bathoen II, Paramount Chief Kgosi, C.B.E.

Bayer, Professor A. W.

Bayley, Mrs. T. E.

Beard, Dr. J. S.

Beasley, A. J.

Beck, F. G.

Bentum, P. A.

Bernstein, B. L.

Berry, Dr. Guy F.

Beukes, P.

Bird, Dr. Allan

Black, Mrs. Dugald

Block, Dr. B.

Bloemfontein Public Library

Booysen, P. G.

Bornman, Chris. H.

Borok, Dr. G.

Botha, Dr. Chris. L.

Bourke, M. E.

Botanischer Staatssammlung, München

Bowker, H. M.

Bowyer, H. L.

Bradley, R. M.

Brandt, Dr. H. D.

Brayshaw, B. M.

British Museum (Natural History), London

Britten, Mr. & Mrs. A. B.

Brooker, J. H., Colombia

Brooklyn Botanic Garden Library, New York

Brossy, Dr. J- J.

Brown, Mr. & Mrs. Eion R. McL.

Brown, J. R., Calif.

Brown, Ralph C.

Bruyns-Haylett, Dr. J. P.

Buchholz, S. A.

Buckland, A. G.

Bullock, E. J.

Burgers, H. T.

Burns, Mrs. A.

Bursey, B. P.

Burton, Mrs. Helen

Butcher, Ronald R.

Butlin, Mrs. P. C.

C

Cactus and Succulent Society of N.S.W., Australia

Cady, Leo I., Australia

Cambridge University Botanic Garden, England

Campbell, Mrs. I. E.

Cannell, I. C.

Cape and Transvaal Printers Ltd.

Carnegie Library, Girls' High School, Pietermaritzburg

Carp, Bernard

Carr, J. D.

Carr, Mrs. Nola

Centro de Botânica, Lisbon

Charlton, M. V.

Chew, J. A.

Childs, Mr. & Mrs. S. E.

Chiazzari, W. L.

Christelis, D.

Claassen, Mrs. M. C.

Classen, George A.

Codd, Dr. L. E.

Coetzee, Mrs. G.

Cooke, E. H.

Cowen, Maurice

Cox, Graham Campbell

Crasnow, Mrs. A.

Crawford, B. D.

Crawford, J. B. S.

Crawford, J. L.

Croesér, Major Michael P. L.

Cronwright, G. M. C.

Crook, Mrs. Lucy K. A.

Cullinan, D.

Cunliff, Mr. & Mrs. K. M.

Currie, L. H.

D

Dahlstrand, K. A.

Daniels, Gilbert S.

Davey, Dr. Evelyn

Davidson, Dr. J. Findlay

Davis, Paul

De Beer, J. H.

De Bruyn, H. J.

De Bruyn, M. J.

Dednam, G.

De Jager, Mr. & Mrs. C.
De Lorm, Mr. & Mrs. R. A.
Delport, G. C.
De Mooy, C. and Zonen, N. V. Holland
Desert Botanical Garden, Phoenix, Arizona
De Souza, Dr. C. W. L.
De Souza, Dr. J. J. L.
De Vaal, Dr. P. S.
De Villiers, Ben
De Villiers, Dr. Marquard
De Villiers, Mrs. P. W.
De Vries, Hugo, Laboratories Library, Amsterdam
De Wet Nel, The Hon., M.D.C.
De Winter, Dr. B.
Dicks, Alan V. R.
Dickson, C. G. C.
Diggle, Mrs. M.
Dinkelmann, Dr. E. E.
Dippenaar, Dr. J. F.
Dixen, Hans, B. S. H. Denmark
Dommisse, Dr. & Mrs. George F.
Donnelly, B. G.
Drost, N. J.
Dunstan, Dr. T.
Dunstan, William J.
Du Plessis, E.
Du Plessis, Dr. & Mev. G. G.
Durban Teachers' Training College, Principal
During, F. W. H.
Dyer, Dr. R. A.

E

East London Municipal Library
Elphinstone, F.
Erasmus, P. M. S. J.
Erens, J.
Ernst, Dr. D. S.

F

Fannin, Dr. John
Fievet, Gerard, Madagascar

Faul, Sid
Fischer. Dr. Alwin G.
Fisher-Jeffes, Mrs. D.
Flack, E. Victor
Ford, A. H.
Förs, Henrik
Fouche, Dr. G. W.
Foulcher-Delbosc., Lauzun
Fourie, Dr. A. M.
Fraser, F. J.
Franklin, W. L. Stuart
Fraser, George G.
Friedländer & Sohn. R.

G

Garb. Phil
Gettliffe, R.
Gilbert, Mrs. W. H.
Gilfillan, N. H.
Gill, Dr. C. C., Winnepeg
Gillatt, Mrs. F. S. V.
Gillett, Jan B., Nairobi
Gillett, Mrs. G. K.
Glass, Charles, Calif.
Glatthaar, Mrs. M. M.
Goulding, A. K.
Goerbert, F. R.
Gordon, Mr. P. S. L.
Gouws, P. J.
Granelli, Miss G. A.
Grobbelaar, Dr. & Mrs. C. J.
Grobler, J. M.
Grobler, Mev. M. J.
Guenther, Egon

H

Hall, Mrs. Hugh D.
Hall, Jimmie
Hall, L. H. & Sons Ltd.
Hardy, David S.
Harland, Mrs. Sybil, Australia
Harrison, E. R.
Harwin, Dr. & Mrs. R. M.
Haselton, Scott E., Calif.
Havenaar, A. P.
Hawkins, L. A. W.
Hazlewood, W., Australia

Heij, D., Holland
Hepburn, A. I. M.
Herbin, G. A.
Herbst, Mrs. Helena J.
Hersov, B. E.
Hertzog, The Hon. Dr. A.
Higgins, Mrs. Vera
Hindson, B. R.
Hobson, J. R.
Hoffe, Brig. C. M.
Hoheisen, H. O.
Holley, Geoffrey E. W.
Holmes, R.
Holtz, Dr. H.
Hoogenhout, Mrs. Joyce
Horsham, Ronald J. E.
Horsthemke, S.
Horwood, F. K.
Hosken, F. W.
Howick of Glendale, Lord
Hubbard, C. S.
Hume, M. E.
Humphriss, Deryck
Huntington Botanical Gardens, San Marino
Hutchison, Paul C., University of California
Hyslop, Mrs. Tuli

I

Instituto Botanico della Universita, Napoli

J

Jackson, T. H. E., Kitale
Jacobsen, Dr. H., Kiel
Jacqueman, Mrs. Eleanor
James, J. R.
Jardine Botanique de l'Etat, Brussels
Jardin de Aclimatacion de la Orotava, Tenerife
Jardine Exotique, Monte Carlo
Jeffery, R. G.
Jeffes, Dr. Don L. F.
Jenkins, Mrs. E.
Jeppe, Barbara
Johannes, G. A.

Johannesburg Parks and Recreation Dept.
Johannesburg Public Library
Johns, Mrs. P.
Johnstone, A. H.
Jonck, Prof. L. M.
Jones, Dr. A. J.
Jones, Dr. Hugh I.
Jooste, Mev. A. M.
Joubert, Dr. C. J.
Joubert, Dr. J. A.
Joubert, Dr. J. M. L.

K

Kamstra, M. W.
Karim, Dr. Goolam M.
Kenya Horticultural Society, Nairobi
Kidd, William Henry
Kietzman, Mr. & Mrs. A. L.
Kimberley, Michael J.
Kirby, Mrs. G. E., Kent.
Kirchhoff & Co. (Pty) Ltd., F.
Klapwijk, Menno
Kling, Dr. K. G.
Knoll, Mrs. Valerie
Kodak (South Africa) (Pty) Ltd., Cape Town
Koeleman, A.
Kok, I. B.
Koston, John
Koston, Paul
Kraiser, E. W.
Kroonstad Municipality, O.F.S.
Kruger, H. G.
Krugersdorp Town Council
Kuschke, A. E.
Kuschke, Dr. Erich
Kuenzler, Horst., New Mexico

L

Lake, N. Ross
Lamb, Edgar and Brian M.
Lang, Frederick M.
Lapping, K.
Lategan, Prof. F. V.
Laughton, F. S.

Lavranos, Mrs. J. S.
Lawrence, Miss E.
Leach, Mrs. Christine
Leach, Larry C.
Le May, B. C.
Levitt, R. E.
Levien, Dr. M.
Lewis, J., Surrey
Lewis, John, B.M.
Library of Congress, Washington, D.C.
Library of Parliament, Cape Town
Liebenberg, P. J.
Livraria Cunha, Coimbra, Portugal
Livraria Lopes da Silva, Porto, Portugal
Livingstone Museum, Zambia
Louw, Mrs. M. C.
Louw, T. J.
Louw, Dr. W. J.
Lovell, Mr. & Mrs. Leo
Lubbers, Mr. & Mrs. G. E. K.

M

Macintosh, A. H.
Mackenzie, Ian
Mac Neillie, C. L.
Macpherson, Mr. & Mrs. Stuart
Mac Robert, N. J.
Mc Bride, C. J.
Mc Ewan, Oliver
Mc Ewan, Mr. & Mrs. W. S.
Mc Intosh, A. R. D. (Pty) Ltd.
Mc Kechnie, W. E.
Magener, G.
Maggs, Col. E. O'C.
Magnuson, Cal & Maureen
Marais, Dr. Ben
Marais, H. S.
Marais, J. S. N.
Maritz, F. I.
Marnier-Lapostolle, Julien
Marshall, G. W.
Martin, Mrs. C. M.
Mason, L. Maurice

Massachusetts Horticultural Society Library
Matthews, J. W.
Matthey, A.
Maughan-Brown, N. C.
Mauve, Mrs. A.
Meeser, Dr. M. J. N.
Mendes, Dr. E. J., Lisbon
Menell, Arthur
Meintjes, Miss B.
Meyer, Dr. George
Miami University Library, U.S.A.
Michigan State University Library, U.S.A.
Middelmann, Walter and Ruth
Minne, Dr. S. L.
Missouri Botanical Garden, U.S.A.
Mockford, Miss G. E.
Mockford, Harold H.
Mogg, Dr. A. O. D.
Moore, Miss G.
Morgan, H. K.
Morris, Alan
Mostert, P. A. M.
Moubray, Duncan M.
Mullavey, F. T.
Muller, Benjamin
Muller, Mrs. H. M.
Müller, J. L.
Munch, R. C.

N

Napton, John R.
National Botanic Gardens, Dublin
National Museums of Rhodesia, Salisbury
National Parks and Wild Life Management Salisbury, Rhodesia
Natural Resources Board, Rhodesia
Naturhistorischen Museum, Botanische Abteilung, Vienna
Naude, Hennie
Newey, Capt. A. F., (Tod.)

Newton, L. E.
Nicholson, H. B.
Nigrini, L. P.
Nilsson, Sven
Noble, R. J., Calif.
Noël, Dr. A. R. A.
Northover, E. C.

O

Oberholster, Mrs. J. C.
Oliver, E. G. H.
OPPENHEIMER, H. F.

P

Palmer, Mrs. R. D.
Parker, Mrs. Jean
Patz, Dr. I. M.
Paulian, Prof. R., Abidjan
Payne, Mrs. M. R.
Peatling, T. V.
Pellatt, Mr. & Mrs. T. M.
Pennsylvania Horticultural
    Society, Philadelphia
Perlman, Dr. Michael
Pert, Charles W.
Pethick, Gordon
Pienaar, P. H.
Pieterse, J. A.
Pillman, A. H.
Pim, Miss Joane, L.I.L.A.
Pocock, T. N.
Ponting, Mrs. M.
Porter, Arthur
Potgieter, H. P.
Potgieter, Mrs. Marie
Powell, M. N.
Powell, Tom, New York
Press, Sydney
Pretoria, Director of Parks
    and Recreation
Pretorius, Dr. E. J.
Pretorius, Dr. H. P.
Pretorius, W. H.
Pringle, V. L.
Prins, F. J.
Prinsloo, C. W.
Prinsloo, Mrs. J. M.
Proctor, John, Tanzania

Q

Queen Elizabeth School,
    Salisbury
Quinton-Smith, O.
Quy, Mrs. C. E.

R

Rabie, D. C.
Rabie, S. W.
Rae, John
Raynor, Mrs. W. E.
Read, B. L.
Read, Everard W.
Reinhard, A.
Reitz, F. W.
Renny, A. T.
Resende, Prof. Dr. Flavio
Reynolds, Miss Beryl I.
Reynolds, Miss Elizabeth A.
Reynolds, Miss Janet M.
Reynolds, Mrs. K. J.
Rich, Mrs. M. E.
Richardson, M. E.
Riley, Prof. Herbert P.
Riley, Mrs. R. M.
Rissik, H.
Rissik, Ulrich
Roger, Alan Stuart
Rompel, Dr. H.
Rourke, J. P.
Roux, C. L. M.
Roux, Dr. W. P. R.
Royal Botanic Gardens, Kew
Royal Botanic Gardens and
    National   Herbarium,
    South Yarra, Australia
Royds, G. S. Ltd.
Russell, J. Hamilton
Rycroft, Prof. H. B.
Rijksherbarium Library, Lei-
    den

S

S.A. Public Library, Cape
    Town
Saunders, R. C.
Schouten, Mrs. M. A.
Schroeder, Donald Arthur
Schroder, Lionel
Schwellnus, Otto E.
Scott, John

Serjeant, Philip
Siemers, A. H.
Simpson, A. O.
Sinclair, Esther and Bernard
Slabbert, S. W. B.
Slotow, Dr. M.
Smit, A. C. T.
Smith, D. N.
Smith, Graeme
Smith, Mrs. M.
Smook, C. Harold
Sonnenberg, J. P. J.
South African Railways Re-
    ference Library, Johannes-
    burg
Söyrinki, Prof. Dr. Niilo,
    Oulu
Städt   Sukkulentensamm-
    lung, Zurich
Stander, W. W.
Star, The, Johannesburg
Starke-Ayres,   Mowbray,
    Cape Town
Steuart, Ian Philson
Stidolph, P. A.
Strauss, Dr. K.
Stretton, Sandy
Strid, Ake
Stutterheim, Mrs. M. E.
Suid-Afrikaanse Aalwyn- en
    Vetplantvereniging, Pre-
    toria
Swanepoel, C. H.
Swart, Mrs. E. A.
Swart, Mrs. J.
Swart, Mrs. Zandra
S.W.A. Scientific Society,
    Windhoek
Sweet, Nathan C., Jun.

T

Taeuber, E.
Tait, Mrs. P. C.
Tate, Mrs. Joyce
Taylor, Hugh K.
Theiler, Dr. Gertrud
Thompson, K.A.
Thompson, L. C.
Thorncroft, N. G.
Tingle, A. C.
Townsend, Mrs. V. R.
Transvaal Horticultural So-
    ciety, Johannesburg

Tregidga, J. A.
Turner, I. S.
Tweedie, Mrs. E. M.
Twello Kwekery, Barberton

U

Umtali Horticultural Society, Rhodesia
United Tobacco Cos. (South) Ltd., Johannesburg
University College, Nairobi
University College Library, Nairobi
University College of Rhodesia, Salisbury
Université de Liege, Belgium
University of California Biomedical Library
University of Florida, Hume Library, U.S.A.
University of Tennessee Library, U.S.A.
University of Texas Library, U.S.A.
University of the Witwatersrand Library, Johannesburg
University of Washington Library, Seattle
Universiteit van Pretoria, Departement van Algemene Plantkunde
Uys, Reynard

V

Van Amstel, J.
Van Bergen, Dr. Colijn
Van den Berg, Lizeke en Han
Van der Merwe, Dr. A. le R.
Van der Merwe, Mrs. E. C.
Van der Merwe, J. H.
Van der Schijff, Prof. H. P.
Van der Walt, P. C. L.
Van Dyk, D. S.
Van Eck, Dr. H. J.
Van Heerden, Barney
Van Hoepen, Dr. E. J.
Van Hoogstraten, Dr. R. C. J.
Van Rensburg, A. B. J.
Van Son, Dr. G.
Van Tienhoven, Wil
Van Wyk, Mrs. C.
Van Tubergen, C. G. Ltd., Holland
Van Zyl, Dr. J. V.
Van Zyl, P. J. C.
Verdoorn, Miss Inez C.
Vermooten, Dr. Vincent, Texas
Vigne, Chidlow
Viljoen, Dr. J. L.
Visser, F. A. F.
Voorspuy, Mrs. H. J.
Vorenberg, H. W. & Co. (Pty) Ltd.
Vosloo, G. L.
Vygekraal Nature Reserve, Witfield, Transvaal

W

Wade, F. D.
Wakelin, Dr. John
Walker, Eric
Walmsley, W. C.
Walters, Dr. I. B.
Waterfield, Miss R. G.
Watmough, Dr. R. H.
Watson, John Myrryne
Weinberg, P.
Weilbach, Dr. C. N.
Wessels, A. J. J.
Wessels, Daisy
Weyers, Louis
Wheeldon, H. G.
Whitmore, F. C.
Whyte, W. K.
Wicks, Mrs. Joan
Wilhelmij, H.
Williams, E. G. K.
Williams, Ion
Wilkes, Maria, Calif.
Wilson, John G.
Wilson, P. M. C.
Wilson, Vivian J.
Wiseman, Frank M.
Witt, Mrs. Hilda
Woodhall, F. G.

Z

Zaaiman, Dr. Ign. M.

LIST OF COLOUR PLATES

(Alphabetically)

PLATE			PAGE	PLATE			PAGE
53	A. ACULEATA · ·	· Rhodesia	242	4	A. INYANGENSIS ·	· Rhodesia	23
103	A. ANTANDROI · ·	Madagascar	491	11	A. JACKSONII · ·	S. Ethiopia	54
91	A. BAKERI · · ·	Madagascar	415	10	A. JUCUNDA · · ·	Somalia N.	49
89	A. BELLATULA ·	Madagascar	403	85	A. KEDONGENSIS ·	· · Kenya	376
61	A. BERHANA · ·	N. Ethiopia	279	21	A. LATERITIA · ·	Congo (Leo)	97
58	A. BREVISCAPA ·	Somalia N.	267	55	A. LAVRANOSII · ·	· Arabia	252
96	A. BULBILLIFERA var. PAULIANAE			73	A. LITTORALIS · ·	· Angola	318
		Madagascar	457	67	A. MACLEAYI · ·	S.E. Sudan	299
6	A. BUCHANANII · ·	Malawi	30	20	A. MACROCARPA ·	N. Ethiopia	92
8	A. BUETTNERI (yellow)	Malawi	42	101	A. MACROCLADA ·	Madagascar	484
9	A. BUETTNERI (scarlet)	· Congo	43	36	A. MACROSIPHON	NW. Tanzania	177
23	A. BUKOBANA · ·	· Tanzania	108	69	A. MARSABITENSIS ·	N. Uganda	304
46	A. CALIDOPHILA ·	S. Ethiopia	218	53	A. MAWII · · ·	· Malawi	237
79	A. CAMERONII · ·	· Malawi	349	15	A. MCLOUGHLINII ·	· Ethiopia	65
79	A. CAMERONII var. DEDZANA			70	A. MEDISHIANA ·	Somalia N.	307
		Malawi	349	65	A. MEGALACANTHA (red)		
45	A. CAMPERI · · ·	N. Ethiopia	213			Somalia N.	295
98	A. CAPITATA · · ·	Madagascar	467	66	A. MEGALACANTHA (yellow)		
99	A. CAPITATA var. QUARTZITICOLA					Somalia N.	296
		Madagascar	471	68	A. MICRODONTA ·	Somalia S.	301
22	A. CHABAUDII · ·	· Rhodesia	104	102	A. MILLOTII · ·	Madagascar	489
38	A. CHRISTIANII · ·	· Malawi	187	24	A. MILNE-REDHEADII	NW. Zambia	110
35	A. CONFUSA · ·	· Tanzania	167	62	A. MONTICOLA · ·	N. Ethiopia	281
100	A. CONIFERA · ·	Madagascar	479	18	A. MOROGOROENSIS	· Tanzania	72
37	A. CRYPTOPODA ·	Moçambique	182	57	A. MUBENDIENSIS ·	· Uganda	260
84	A. DAWEI · ·	Kenya, Uganda	370	74	A. MUNCHII ·	· E. Rhodesia	321
54	A. DECURVA · ·	Moçambique	247	1	A. MYRIACANTHA ·	· Tanzania	8
90	A. DESCOINGSII ·	Madagascar	412	25	A. MZIMBANA · ·	N. Malawi	113
77	A. DESERTI · · ·	Tanzania	338	86	A. NGOBITENSIS ·	· Kenya	378
33	A. DHALENSIS · ·	· Arabia	141	28	A. NIEBUHRIANA ·	· Arabia	121
105	A. DIVARICATA ·	Madagascar	504	7	A. NUTTII ·	Mbeya, Tanzania	33
17	A. DOROTHEAE · ·	· Tanzania	70	87	A. NYERIENSIS ·	· · Kenya	381
43	A. ELEGANS (orange)	N. Ethiopia	204	51	A. ORTHOLOPHA ·	· Rhodesia	235
44	A. ELEGANS (scarlet)	· Eritrea	205	92	A. PARALLELIFOLIA	Madagascar	418
81	A. ELGONICA · ·	· Kenya	361	88	A. PARVULA · ·	Madagascar	399
32	A. EREMOPHILA · ·	· Arabia	138	14	A. PECKII · ·	Somalia N.	62
13	A. ERENSII ·	Turkana, Kenya	60	60	A. PERCRASSA · ·	· Eritrea	273
72	A. EXCELSA · · ·	· Rhodesia	315	16	A. PIROTTAE · ·	Somalia N.	67
82	A. FLEXILIFOLIA ·	· Tanzania	363	83	A. RABAIENSIS · ·	· Kenya	367
39	A. FORBESII · ·	· Socotra	194	80	A. RETROSPICIENS ·	Somalia N.	357
71	A. GRACILICAULIS ·	N. Somalia	309	5	A. RHODESIANA ·	· Rhodesia	27
19	A. GRAMINICOLA ·	· Kenya	79	29	A. RIGENS · · ·	Somalia N.	124
27	A. GRATA · · ·	· Angola	117	26	A. RIVAE · · ·	S. Ethiopia	115
49	A. GUERRAI · · ·	· Angola	229	75	A. RUPICOLA · ·	· Angola	323
78	A. HILDEBRANDTII ·	Somalia N.	341	63	A. SCHWEINFURTHII	SW. Sudan	290
3	A. HOWMANII · ·	· Rhodesia	18	64	A. SCHWEINFURTHII		
95	A. IMALOTENSIS ·	Madagascar	446		var. LABWORANA ·	· Uganda	293
47	A. INERMIS · · ·	· Arabia	221	40	A. SCOBINIFOLIA (red)	Somalia N.	198
104	A. INTERMEDIA · ·	Madagascar	502				

PLATE		PAGE
41	A. SCOBINIFOLIA (yellow) Somalia N.	199
50	A. SECUNDIFLORA · · Tanzania	231
56	A. SERETI · · · Congo (Leo)	257
42	A. SINKATANA · · · · Sudan	201
12	A. SOMALIENSIS · · Somalia N.	57
34	A. SPLENDENS · · · Arabia	161
97	A. SUAREZENSIS · Madagascar	460
30	A. TOMENTOSA · · Somalia N.	128

PLATE		PAGE
2	A. TORREI · · · Moçambique	14
31	A. TRICHOSANTHA · · Eritrea	132
48	A. TURKANENSIS · · N. Kenya	225
59	A. TWEEDIAE Karamoja, Uganda	270
106	A. VAOMBE · · · Madagascar	510
93	A. VERSICOLOR · · Madagascar	422
94	A. VIGUIERI · · Madagascar	441
76	A. VOLKENSII · · · Uganda	328

TABLE OF CONTENTS

PAGE

Map of Author's Travels ... ... *frontispiece*

Preface vii

Author's Acknowledgments ix

List of Sponsors and Subscribers xiii

List of Colour Plates xix

PART 1

TROPICAL AFRICA

(Including Arabia, Socotra)

PAGE

ALOE L.—Generic Characters 1

Introductory Notes 1

KEY TO THE GROUPS (with typical species):

GROUP 1. Grass Aloes (*A. myriacantha*) 6

GROUP 2. *Leptoaloe* (*A. nuttii*) 9

GROUP 3. "Bulbous" species (*A. buettneri*) 36

GROUP 4. Perianth striped (*A. peckii*) 47

GROUP 5. *A. dorotheae* and allies 68

GROUP 6. *Saponariae* (*A. lateritia*) 75

GROUP 7. *Hereroenses* (*A. hereroensis*) 100

GROUP 8. Perianth trigonously indented above the ovary (*A. chabaudii*) 102

GROUP 9. *Verae* (*A. barbadensis*) 118

GROUP 10. Pendent species (*A. veseyi*) 162

GROUP 11. *Latebracteatae* (*A. cryptopoda*) 173

GROUP 12. *A. christianii* and allies 183

GROUP 13. Perianths clavate (*A. camperi*) 190

GROUP 14. Flowers secund (*A. secundiflora*) 219

GROUP 15. Racemes bottle-brush-like (*A. aculeata*) 241

GROUP 16. Large compact rosettes (*A. percrassa*) 249

GROUP 17. Leaves spreading, canaliculate (*A. megalacantha*) 283

GROUP 18. Tall-stemmed species (*A. volkensii*) 305

GROUP 19. Shrubs (*A. dawei*) 330

GROUP 20. Trees (*A. eminens*) 384

PART 2

MADAGASCAR

	PAGE
Map of Author's Travels	390
Introduction	391

KEY TO THE GROUPS (with typical species):

			PAGE
GROUP	1.	Very small plants (*A. haworthioides*)	394
GROUP	2.	Leaves distichous (*A. compressa*)	424
GROUP	3.	Leaves ± 10 times longer than broad, inflorescence mostly simple (*A. schomeri*)	429
GROUP	4.	Leaves mostly lineate (*A. deltoideodonta*)	432
GROUP	5.	Rosettes large, inflorescence branched (*A. bulbillifera*)	450
GROUP	6.	Racemes globose or capitate, lowest pedicels the shortest (*A. capitata*)	461
GROUP	7.	Racemes densely cylindric (*A. macroclada*)	476
GROUP	8.	Shrubs (*A. acutissima*)	486
GROUP	9.	Tall simple stem (*A. vaombe*)	508

PART 3

SPECIES IMPERFECTLY KNOWN

	PAGE
A. abyssinica Lam. etc.	519
Index	531

PART I

ALOE L.

Aloe L. *Spec. plant.* 1: 319 (1753) *pro parte;* Haworth in *Trans. Linn. Soc.* 7: (1804) *pro parte;* Duval, *Plant. succ. hort. Alenc.* 5 (1809); Haw. *Synops.pl.succ.* 74 (1812); J. A. et J. H. Schultes in R. & S. *Syst. Veg.* 7: (1829) *pro parte;* Salm Dyck *Monogr. gen. Al.* (1836–63) *pro parte;* Kunth *Enum. pl.* 4: 492 (1843) *pro parte;* Baker in *Journ. Linn. Soc.* 18: 152 (1880); Benth. et Hook. f. *Gen. Plant.* 3: 776 (1883); Bak. in Th. Dyer, *Fl. capens.* 6: 302 (1896), et in *Fl. Trop. Afr.* 454 (1898); Schonland in *Rec. Alb. Mus.* I: 33 (1903), 120 (1904), 282 (1905); Berger in Engler *Bot. Jahrb.* 36: 42 (1905), 38: 84 (1905), in Engler *Pflanzenr.* Liliac.-Aloin. 159 (1908); Perrier de la Bâthie in *Mem. Soc. Linn. Norm.* 1 (1): 17 (1926), in *Flora Madag.* Liliac. 77 (1938); Reynolds in *Aloes S. Afr.* 103 (1950), in *Aloes Madag. Revis.* 8 (1958).—*Kumara* Medicus *Theod.* 69, *t. 4* (1786).—*Catevala* Medic. *Theod.* 67 (1786) *pro parte.*—*Rhipidodendron* Willd. in *Ges. Naturf. Fr. Berl. Magaz.* 5: 164 (1811).—*Pachidendron* Haw. *Revis.* 35 (1821).—*Bowiea* Haw. in *Phil. Mag.* 122 (1827) *pro parte.*—*Busipho.* Salisb. *Gen. Pl.* 76 (1866) *fide* Berger.—*Ptyas* Salisb. *l.c.* 76, *fide* Berger.—*Leptaloe* Stapf in *Bot. Mag. t.* 9300 (1933).

GENERIC CHARACTERS

Perianth 6-lobed, tubular, straight to more or less curved, cylinderical or constricted above the ovary, thence enlarging towards the throat, sometimes clavate, cylindric-ventricose, cylindric-campanulate, rarely bilabiate. *Segments* 6, more or less of equal length and similar shape; the 3 outer free to base or connate into a short to long tube, with apices acute to obtuse, straight or more usually spreading to recurved, with 3 or more median nerves, usually narrower and more fleshy than the inner; the 3 inner segments sometimes free, usually dorsally adnate to the 3 outer for about half their length but with margins free, 1-nerved or with 3 or more congested nerves forming a keel, usually broader than the outer and with more obtuse more spreading apices.

Filaments filiform-flattened, the 3 inner narrower and lengthening in advance of the 3 outer, usually broader at base, gradually more slender upwards. *Anthers* linear to oblong.

Ovary ovate, oblong, broadly trigonal, 6-grooved.

Style filiform, at length longer than the filaments, with small capitate stigma. *Ovules* numerous, superposed in 2 rows in the loculi. *Capsule* papyraceous or slightly woody, oblong to sub-cylindrical or globose, with loculicidal dehiscence. *Seeds* many, irregularly triquetrous to flattened. *Testa* grey or black.

Plants more or less succulent, acaulescent, shrubby to arborescent. *Leaves* distichous to multifarious, basally amplexicaul, narrowly linear, long-deltoid, lanceolate to ensiform, glabrous to spiny both sides, with margins rarely entire, sometimes ciliate, mostly sinuate-dentate.

Inflorescence terminal or lateral, simple or branched, with racemes capitate to long-cylindrical. *Flowers* short to long-pedicillate, rarely sessile. *Perianth* sometimes stipitate or tapering into the pedicel, red, brown, yellow, orange, or whitish. *Capsules* erect, dehiscing from the apex.

TROPICAL AFRICAN SPECIES

(Including Arabia, Socotra)

The Tropical African species of Aloe, including Arabia and Socotra, but excluding varieties and *species non satis cognitae* (and Madagascar which are treated in Part 2) total 151.

Of these, three species occur only on Socotra, while 17 occur in Arabia, two of which – *A. inermis* Forsk., and *A. tomentosa* Deflers – are also found in Somalia N., on the African mainland.

This means 133 species are found on the mainland of Africa north of the Limopopo River, the Republic of South Africa's northern border.

Excluding the Lydenburg and Pietersburg districts of the Transvaal, Africa's richest Aloe area in numbers of species and in quantities of plants is undoubtedly from Eritrea (where *A. camperi*

1

Schw. puts up a great show in May) through Ethiopia to Somalia N. (formerly Somaliland Prot.) where *A. megalacantha* Bak. grows in considerable numbers near Boroma and Hargeisa, with *A. scobinifolia* Reynolds et Bally in unbelievable quantities near Erigavo.

Aloes grow in sandy desert from a few feet above sea-level (*A. massawana* Reynolds near Massawa, Eritrea) to mountain slopes at an altitude of 9,000 ft. and more (*A. percrassa* Tod. N. Ethiopia). It is of interest to note that *A. percrassa* has not been found below 8,000 ft.

In size, species range from the "grass-aloe" *A. myriacanth* Haw R & S 9 in. high to the tall 40—50 ft. tree *A. eminens* Reynolds et Bally north of Erigavo in Somalia N.

Such distinctive species as *A. jucunda* Reynolds (Gaan Libah, Somalia N.), *A. jacksonii* Reynolds (S. Ethiopia), *A. peckii* Bally et Verdoorn (Somalia N.) with its remarkably striped flowers, *A. buettneri* Berger with its "bulb" can always be recognised immediately, while others, especially the spotted-leafed maculates in Group 6 often present great difficulties in identification.

There is scarcely a district in Africa which has not its own characteristic Aloe. Some species are very localized, while others have a tremendous range. As examples, the "grass-aloe" *A. myriacantha* (Haw), R & S grows from the Albany Dist. of the Cape through Zululand, E. Rhodesia, Malawi, Tanzania, Kenya to Uganda and Rwanda, while the "bulb" Aloe, *A. buettneri* Berger is found in Zambia, Malawi, Congo (Leo), Congo (Brazzaville), Angola, Nigeria, Ghana and westwards to Mali – a range of no less than 3,500 miles.

In their various geographical stations, in shade or in sun, Aloe plants vary so much in size, length and width of leaf, markings, density and length of racemes, length of pedicels and flowers that it is impossible to give precise measurements, or to devise any Key to the Groups and Species that would be infallible, and from which the student could "run" any specimen to an exact identification.

All that can be done is to offer the subjoined list of Groups with brief diagnoses, and citing a typical species.

KEY TO THE GROUPS

(Key to the Species under each Group)

GROUP 1. "GRASS ALOES" (Section *Graminialoe* Reynolds).

Plants small, acaulescent, with fusiform roots. *Leaves* 6—10 rosulate, narrowly linear. *Inflorescence* simple. *Peduncle* sterile-bracteate in upper half. *Raceme* capitate or conic-capitate. *Pedicels* 10—20mm. long. *Perianth* 10—20mm. long, basally substipitate, the mouth trigonous upturned, rarely bilabiate; *outer segments* free.

Type species: *A. myriacantha* (Haw.) R & S – the only tropical species in this group; also occurs in South Africa   ..   ..   Page 6

GROUP 2. (LEPTOALOE Berger)

Plants acaulescent or short-stemmed. *Leaves* distichous or rosulate, narrowly linear to broader and more fleshy, rigid or flabby; *margins* minutely dentate, rarely entire. *Inflorescence* simple. *Bracts* small to large, sometimes clasping their pedicels. *Pedicels* 10—35mm. long, often the colour of the perianth. *Perianth* salmon-pink to scarlet with green tips, 24—40mm. long (except *A. ballii* 14mm. long); *outer segments* free to base (except *A. nuttii* which is often connate to the middle). *Genitalia* not, or very shortly, exserted.

Type species: *A. nuttii* Bak. In Tropical Africa 11 species, of which none occur in South Africa; 18 species in South Africa of which none occur N. of the Republic ..   ..   Page 9

GROUP 3. PLANTS WITH UNDERGROUND "BULBS" (Section *Bulbiformes* Christian).

Leaves rosulate, deciduous, the leaf bases markedly dilating below ground and forming prominent bulb-like swellings. *Inflorescence* simple or branched.

Type species: *A. buettneri* Berger. Three species in Tropical Africa, none in Madagascar; one species in South Africa (*A. kniphofioides* Berger)   ..   ..   Page 36

GROUP 4. PLANTS WITH STRIPED PERIANTH

Plants small, acaulescent (except *A. jacksonii*) solitary or in small to large dense groups. *Leaves* rosulate, fleshy, deltoid, ensiform or lanceolate, spotted both sides. *Inflorescence* simple in the small species, branched in the larger. *Bracts* very small. *Pedicels* short (5—10mm. long). *Perianth* cylindric-trigonous, 20—30mm. long; *outer segments* connate to the middle or higher; whole perianth usually clearly white-striped to base.

Type species: *A. peckii* Bally et Verdoorn   ..   ..   Page 47
See Group 6 for *A. greatheadii* Schonl. and Group 9 for *A. massawana* Reynolds.

GROUP 5. *Plants* rather small with compact rosettes, or larger with

open rosettes, acaulescent, mostly suckering freely forming dense groups. *Leaves* lanceolate. *Inflorescence* simple or sparingly branched. *Pedicels* short. *Bracts* very small. *Perianth* narrowly cylindric, not striped, 35—38mm. long; *outer segments* connate to the middle or higher.

Type species: *A. dorotheae* Berger   ..   ..   Page 68

GROUP 6. PERIANTH WITH PRONOUNCED BASAL INFLATION, ABRUPTLY CONSTRICTED ABOVE THE OVARY, THENCE ENLARGING TO THE THROAT. (Series *Saponariae* Berger).

Plants of medium size, acaulescent or with short stem, solitary or in groups. *Leaves* densely rosulate, usually spotted on one or both surfaces; *margins* mostly sinuate-dentate, armed with pungent teeth. *Inflorescence* mostly a branched panicle. *Racemes* from densely capitate to laxly cylindric-acuminate. *Pedicels* short (5mm.) to long (30mm.). *Perianth* 25—40mm. long.

Type species: *A. lateritia* Engler. Tropical species: 10, of which 4 also occur in the Republic of South Africa ..   ..   Page 75

GROUP 7. (Series *Hereroenses* Reynolds)

Plants acaulescent or short-stemmed. *Leaves* rosulate, lanceolate-deltoid. *Margins* sinuate-dentate. *Inflorescence* a branched panicle. *Racemes* capitate. *Pedicels* longer than the perianth. *Perianth* cylindric-trigonous shortly stipitate, straight; *outer segments* free to the middle.

One species only, *A. hereroensis* Engler (S. Angola). Occurs much more abundantly in South West Africa, and South Africa   ..   ..   Page 100

GROUP 8. PERIANTH TRIGONOUSLY INDENTED ABOVE THE OVARY. (Series *Aethiopicae* Berger *pro parte*)

Plants acaulescent or shortly caulescent. *Leaves* densely rosulate, not too copiously spotted, flat to slightly canaliculate. *Inflorescence* a few- to many-branched panicle. *Racemes* subcapitate to elongate. *Pedicels* half as long as the perianth or as long. *Bracts* small.

Type species: *A. chabaudii* Schonl. Tropical species: 6, of which *A. chabaudii* also occurs in the Republic of South Africa   ..   ..   Page 102

GROUP 9. SERIES *VERAE* BERGER EMENDED

Plants acaulous rarely caulescent, solitary or in groups. *Leaves* densely rosulate, long-attenuate, fleshy, glaucous, rarely spotted. *Inflorescence* short or tall, simple or few-branched, branches erect, rarely many-branched. *Raceme* mostly narrowly cylindric, sublax to subdense. *Pedicels* averaging 5—8mm. *Bracts* reflexed, often twice as long as the pedicels. *Perianth* cylindric-trigonous, averaging 25—30mm. long, mouth slightly upturned, red, orange or yellow, varying from glabrous to pubescent and tomentose-villose; *outer segments* connate to the middle and higher.

Type species: *A. barbadensis* Mill. Tropical species: 17, mostly from N. Africa and Arabia; none in Madagascar or South Africa.   ..   ..   Page 118

GROUP 10. PLANTS PENDENT OR SEMI-PENDENT.

Stems mostly slender, simple or branched, in some the apical 20—30cm. laxly foliate, the leaf basal sheaths 10—20mm. apart, in others leaves densely rosulate. *Inflorescence* simple or 3—4-branched, pendent, with only the racemes ascending or arcuate-ascending.

Type species: *A. veseyi* Reynolds   ..   ..   Page 162

GROUP 11. BRACTS LARGE, BROADLY OVATE OR SUBOR-BICULAR (Series *Latebracteatae* Berger *pro parte*)

Plants acaulescent or shortly caulescent. *Leaves* densely rosulate, mostly ensiform, spotted or unspotted. *Inflorescence* branched. *Bracts* large, broadly ovate or suborbicular, mostly longer than the pedicels. *Perianth* cylindric-ventricose, 30—35mm. long, smooth except in *A. venusta* which is minutely pubescent.

Type species: *A. cryptopoda* Bak. Tropical species 4 ..   ..   ..   Page 173

GROUP 12. *Plants* acaulescent or short-stemmed. *Leaves* densely rosulate narrowly lanceolate, not spotted, obscurely lineate. *Inflorescence* a branched panicle under 1m. tall or 2—2·60m. high. *Racemes* cylindric-acuminate. *Pedicels* 8—25mm. long. *Perianth* cylindric-trigonous, 38—45mm. long; *outer segments* almost free, or connate to beyond the middle.

Type species: *A. christianii* Reynolds. Tropical species: 3, of which *A. pretoriensis* also occurs in South Africa   ..   ..   Page 183

GROUP 13. PLANTS WITH PERIANTHS CLAVATE

Plants small to large, acaulescent to caulescent, solitary or of shrubby growth. *Leaves* densely rosulate, or amplexicaul and spaced along the apical portion of stems; *margins* dentate (except in *A. scobinifolia*). *Inflorescence* a branched panicle. *Racemes* capitate or elongate, densely or laxly flowered. *Bracts* small. *Perianth* clavate, 20—30mm. long, yellow, orange or scarlet.

Type species: *A. camperii* Schweinf. Tropical species: 10, of which 2 from Socotra   ..   ..   Page 190

GROUP 14. RACEMES OBLIQUE, FLOWERS ± SECUND (Sub-Sect. *Ortholophae* Christian, emended)

Plants acaulescent, sometimes shortly caulescent. *Leaves* laxly to densely rosulate, spreading or incurved, green or glaucous. *Inflorescence* erect or suboblique, simple or divaricately many-branched. *Racemes* oblique to almost horizontally disposed, sublaxly to densely flowered; the flowers secund or almost so. *Bracts* small. *Pedicels* short. *Perianth* cylindric-trigonous, ventricose or clavate; *outer segments* connate for one-quarter to two-thirds their length. *Anthers* shortly to long-exserted.

Type species: *A. secundiflora* Engler. Tropical species: 7, of which one, *A. globuligemma* also occurs in South Africa in considerable numbers .. .. Page 219

GROUP 15. RACEMES DENSELY FLOWERED, BOTTLE-BRUSH-LIKE, FLOWERS SESSILE OR VERY SHORTLY PEDICEL-LATE

Plants with little or no stem. *Leaves* large, compactly rosulate or spreading-recurved. *Inflorescence* simple or few-branched. *Bracts* small to very large. *Pedicels* 0—4mm. long. *Perianth* mostly cylindric-ventricose, up to 40mm. long; *outer segments* free to the middle or to near base. *Filaments* long-exserted.

Type species: *A. aculeata* Pole Evans, Rhodesia .. .. .. Page 241

GROUP 16. MEDIUM TO LARGE PLANTS WITH DENSELY ROSULATE LEAVES FORMING RATHER COMPACT ROSETTES

Stems none or short, decumbent or erect. *Bracts* minute to large. *Pedicels* up to 20mm. long. *Perianth* cylindric-trigonous, yellow or red; *outer segments* free for quarter to half their length.

Type species: *A. percrassa* Tod. Tropical species: 13, of which one in Arabia .. .. Page 249

GROUP 17. MEDIUM TO LARGE PLANTS WITH LEAVES SPREADING TO RECURVED, SLIGHTLY TO DEEPLY CANALICULATE

Plants acaulescent, or with erect or decumbent stems, 50—80cm. long. *Leaves* up to 80cm. long, 16cm. broad at base, forming open (not compact) rosettes. *Inflorescence* mostly many-branched and about 1m. high. *Racemes* sublax to dense, sometimes slightly secund. *Bracts* inconspicuous. *Pedicels* mostly 10mm. long. *Perianth* cylindric-trigonous, straight, yellow-orange or scarlet, 22—36mm. long.

Type species: *A. megalacantha* Bak. Tropical species: 8 .. .. Page 283

GROUP 18. PLANTS TALL-STEMMED, SIMPLE OR FEW-BRANCHED FROM BASE (Sect. *Pachydendron* Haw. *pro parte*)

Plants with stems simple or few-branched from base, 2—6m. and more high; smooth or densely bearded with dried remains of old leaves. *Leaves* rosulate, mostly large, spreading to recurved, often canaliculate, smooth or partly spiny. *Inflorescence* mostly a many-branched panicle with erect or oblique racemes. *Racemes* cylindric, conical or subcapitate, sublaxly to very densely flowered, mostly erect, sometimes suberect to oblique (*A. excelsa*), or oblique with flowers slightly secund (*A. ballyi*). *Bracts* small to large. *Pedicels* short to long. *Perianth* cylindric, scarlet-orange or yellow, short (18mm.) to long (42—45mm.).

Type species: *A. volkensii* Engler. Tropical species: 9, of which one species, *A. gillilandii* Reynolds from Arabia ..   ..   Page 305

GROUP 19. SHRUBS

Plants of shrubby growth, from low undershrubs with short stems, to large shrubby plants 3—4m. high, sometimes forming dense thickets several metres across. *Inflorescence* branched. *Racemes* capitate to long cylindric-acuminate. *Pedicels* 30—35mm. long. *Bracts* from minute to large. *Perianth* from 20mm. long, yellow (*A. retrospiciens*) to scarlet and 48mm. long (*A. cameronii*).

Typical species: *A. dawei*, *A. nyeriensis*. Tropical species: 22, of which one species, *A. arborescens*, occurs considerably more abundantly in South Africa   ..   ..   Page 330

GROUP 20. TALL TREES, DICHOTOMOUSLY BRANCHED AND REBRANCHED

Leaves densely rosulate, deeply canaliculate and recurved. *Inflorescence* branched. *Racemes* cylindric. *Pedicels* short. *Bracts* small to large. *Perianth* 25—40mm., cylindric.

Type species: *A. eminens* Reynolds. Tropical species: 2—*A. eminens* from Somalia North, and *A. sabaea* from the Western Yemeni Escarpment   ..   ..   Page 384

GROUP 1

(Section *Graminialoe* Reynolds)

"GRASS ALOE"

Plants small, acaulescent. *Roots* fusiform. *Leaves* 6—10 distichous or rosulate, narrowly linear. *Inflorescence* simple. *Peduncle* slender, sterile-bracteate in upper half. *Raceme* capitate or conic-capitate. *Pedicels* 10—20mm. long. *Perianth* 10—20mm. long, basally substipitate, mouth trigonous or bilabiate, usually upturned. *Segments* free to base.

Type species: *A. myriacantha* (Haw.) R & S – the only tropical species in this group. Also occurs in South Africa together with 4 other species – see *Aloes of South Africa* 110–120 (1950).

1. **A. myriacantha** (Haw.) R & S in *Syst. Veg.* 7: 704 (1829); Kunth *Enum. pl.* 4: 516 (1843); Baker in *Journ. Linn. Soc.* 18: 156 (1880), in Th. Dyer *Fl. Capens.* 6: 306 (1896); Schonland in *Rec. Alb. Mus.* 1: 35 (1903); Berger in Engler *Pflanzenr.* Liliac.-Aloin. 166 (1908); Reynolds in *Journ. S.A. Bot.* 13: 100 (1947), in *Aloes S. Afr.* 116 (1950), in *Journ. S.A. Bot.* 19: 25 (1953), in *Aloes of Nyasaland* 43 (1954).
—— *Bowiea myriacantha* Haw. in *Phil. Mag.* 122 (1827).
—— *A. graminifolia* Berger in Engler's *Bot. Jahrb.* 38: 84 (1905), in *Pflanzenr.* Liliac.-Aloin. 166 (1908).
—— *A. caricina* Berger in Engler's *Bot. Jahrb.* 38: 85 (1905), in *Pflanzenr.* 166 (1908). – *Note* Berger cites Uhlig 1079 for both *A. graminifolia* and *A. caricina.*
—— *Leptaloe myriacantha* (Haw.) Stapf in *Bot. Mag. t.* 9300 (1933); Christian in *Fl. Pl. S. Afr.* 20: 799 (1940); Reynolds in *Journ. S.A. Bot.* 13: 100 (1947).

—— *A. johnstonii* Bak. in *Trans. Linn. Soc.* ser. 2, Bot. 2, 351, *t.* 63 (1887), in Th. Dyer *Fl. Trop. Afr.* 7: 456 (1898); Durand et Schinz *Consp. Fl. Afr.* 5: 308 (1893); Engler *Pflanzenr. Ost-Afr.* 140 (1895); Berger in Engler's *Pflanzenr.* Liliac.-Aloin. 167 (1908); Reynolds in *Journ. S.A. Bot.* 13: 100 (1947), et 19: 25 (1953).

DESCRIPTION: Plant small, acaulescent with fusiform roots.

Leaves 8—12, rosulate, narrowly linear, usually sub-erect, about 25cm. long, 8—10 mm. broad, dilating and becoming imbricate-amplexicaul near ground level; *upper surface* dull green, canaliculate, with a few white spots in lower quarter; *lower surface* obtusely keeled, dull green, more copiously spotted near base, the spots somewhat tuberculate-sub-spinulescent; *margins* with minute white cartilaginous teeth that are more crowded and larger (·5mm.—1mm.) near base, smaller to obsolescent and more distant upwards.

Inflorescence simple, occasionally 2, 20—25cm. high.

Peduncle terete, 4mm. thick, clothed with several ovate long-acuminate sterile-bracts in upper two-thirds, the lowest sub-amplexicaul and up to 20mm. long.

Raceme capitate, densely flowered, about 4·5cm. long, 6cm. diameter, 20—30-flowered, the buds and flowers usually dull reddish-pink or vinaceous, rarely greenish-white.

Bracts ovate long-acuminate, as long as the pedicels.

Pedicels the lowest 15mm. long, shorter upwards.

Perianth cylindric-trigonous, 15—20mm. long, basally sub-stipitate and tapering into the pedicel, the mouth distinctly bi-labiate and upturned; *outer segments* free to base, the apices sub-acute, 3-nerved, the nerves obscurely dull vinaceous; *inner segments* broader than the outer, with more obtuse apices.

Genitals not, or very shortly exserted; *ovary* 4—5mm. long, 2mm. diameter, finely 6-grooved. (Plate 1, Figs. 1—2).

FIG. 1.

A. myriacantha (Haw.) R. & S. Plant from the Kirk Range, 57 miles south of Dedza, Ncheu Dist., Malawi. Flowering in Johannesburg. Height 28cm.

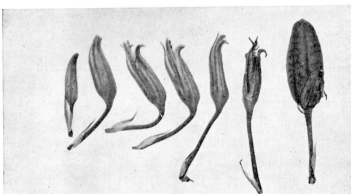

FIG. 2.

A. myriacantha (Haw.) R. & S. Flowers natural size, from bud to fruit stages.

PLATE 1

ALOE MYRIACANTHA   (Haw.) R. & S.
14 miles NE of Sao Hill, 47 miles SW of Iringa, Tanzania (Tanganyika),
alt. 6,200 ft., cult. Johannesburg. Height 12″.

RHODESIA. *Melsetter Dist.*, Cashel, 3 March 1957, F. C. Greatrex in GHS 74592! (SRGH). *Umtali Dist.* Odzani Heights, 5,000 ft., 24 March 1957, N. C. Chase 6367! (K, PRE, SRGH). *Inyanga Dist.* 21 February 1946, H. Wild 847! (SRGH); Mororo River, 18 March 1952, J. C. Hopkins in GHS 35983! (SRGH, PRE); Inyanga, 6,000 ft., 21 February 1960, Lady Beatrice Drewe 64! (SRGH).

MALAWI (NYASALAND). Kirk Range, 7 miles N of Goche Village, 70 miles S of Dedza, 4,900 ft., fruiting 19 May 1956, Reynolds 8185 (PRE).

TANZANIA. *Southern Highlands Prov.:* 14 miles NE of Sao Hill, 6,100 ft., cult. Johannesburg, fl. 24 April 1956, Reynolds 7528! (K, PRE). *Central Prov.* Mpwapwa Dist., Kiboriani Mountain, 16 June 1937, Mr. and Mrs. Hornby 792! (EA); Seed ex Kiboriani Mountain. cult. Amani, 19 April 1932, P. J. Greenway 2946! (EA). *Northern Prov.:* Malanja, Ngorongoro, 8,000 ft., 17 Nov. 1957, Tanner 3794! (K); Steppe between Kilimanjaro and Meru at Maji ya Chumvi, 1000 m., 2 Dec. 1901, Uhlig 789! isosyntype of *A. graminifolia* Berger (EA). *North-Western Prov.:* Uzinza west of Mwanza, 4,000 ft., 9 April 1937, B. D. Burtt 6531! (K, BM).

KENYA. Taveta, 2,000 ft., H. H. Johnston s.n.!—type of *A. johnstonii* Bak.—(K, BM); Chyulu Hills, 5,500 ft., 8 May 1938, P. R. O. Bally 565! (K, EA); Ngong near Nairobi, 7,000 ft., 24 Nov. 1930, Miss E. P. Napier 548! (K, EA); Nairobi, St. Austins, on open grassy slopes, 25 March 1941, A. G. McLoughlin 674! (PRE); Machakos, Yatta Plains, cult. Pretoria, fl. March 1940, I. B. Pole Evans et J. Erens 1099! (PRE)—type of *Fl. Pl. S. Afr.* 20: Plate 799 (1940). Nairobi National Park, 5,500 ft., 2 Dec. 1956, Verdcourt 389! (K, EA); Nairobi Golf Course, 5,400 ft., 5 May 1952, Reynolds 6616! (K, PRE); Langata, 5 miles S of Nairobi, 6 May 1952, Reynolds 6620! (PRE); Lukenya, 24 miles ESE of Nairobi, 17 May 1952, Dr. Piers s.n.! (EA); Kassarani on Thika Rd., 3 June 1952, E. Kirrika 177! (K, EA).

UGANDA. ANKOLE: Gazaya, 5,000 ft., May 1929, J. D. Snowdon 1912! (K); Mbarara, 5,000 ft., March 1939, J. W. Purseglove 654 (K); Ruisi River, 4,300 ft., 29 March 1951, J. Jarrett 456! (K, PRE, EA); Mbarara, 19 Aug. 1957, Lind 2182! (K); Sanga Rest Camp, 4,400 ft., Oct. 1932, W. J. Eggeling 593! (K); Hills on Kigezi-Ankole border, Nyarusanje and Kisisi, 27 March 1952, E. D. Norman 18! (EA).

RWANDA. Kagera National Parc, Ruwita, 1600 m., Jan. 1938, Jean Lebrun 9618 (K! BM! BR). In *Bulletin du Jardin Botanique de l'Etat* 31: fasc. 3, 407, Brussels, 30 Sept. 1961, Dr. G. Troupin lists the following: *Region du Mutara:* Colline Nyakabira, 1420 m., April 1958, Troupin 7156 (BR, LWO, YBI); 3 Km. N de Nyagatare, alt. 1400 m., April 1957, Troupin 3089 (BR, LWO, YBI, EA. K!. NY); Kakitumba. alt. 1300 m., Feb. 1955, Christiaensen 834 (BR, LWO, YBI); Parc National de la Kagera, Uruwita, alt. 1600 m., Jan. 1938, Jean Lebrun 9618 (BR), Jan. 1958, Troupin 5839 (BR, LWO, YBI); Colline Lukonji alt. 1430 m., April 1938, Troupin 6773 (BR, LWO, YBI).

A. myriacantha was first collected by James Bowie, probably during his fourth journey from the Cape which took him eastwards to the Kowie River where he was on 15 March 1822. Type locality is not known, but in all probability it is in the Albany (Grahamstown) Dist. of the Eastern Cape, South Africa. There is a painting at Kew of Bowie's plant inscribed "Imported in 1823 from the Cape of Good Hope by Mr. Bowie". In 1827 it was first described as *Bowiea myriacantha* Haw., but was re-named *Aloe myriacantha* (Haw.) R & S in 1829.

Sometimes called a grass aloe, *A. myriacantha* grows mostly in stony ground in short grasslands, and when not in flower or fruit is almost impossible to find.

This species has a tremendous distribution from Grahamstown in the Cape northwards through Zululand to the eastern mountainous parts of southern Rhodesia (Melsetter, Musapa Mountain, Odzani Heights, Inyanga Downs), to the Kirk Range south of Dedza in Malawi. In Tanzania (Tanganyika) it has been collected in the Mporotos, along Sao Hill, on Kiboriani Mountain in the Mpwapwa Dist., slopes of Kilimanjaro where it was collected by H.H. (later Sir Harry) Johnston in 1884. It grows near Mwanza (Uzinza), while the Duke of Mecklenburg found it flowering in June 1907, on the Kiboroga steppe, Bukoba Dist., west of Lake Victoria.

In Kenya, *A. myriacantha* has been found by Mr. Peter Bally on the Chyulu Hills (north-east of Kilimanjaro); and also found near Nairobi, Langata, Ngong, Lukenya, Machakos, Nanyuki. Gilgil, Menengai near Nakuru, and the East Cherangani Range. In Uganda there are several localities in Ankole, while some localities are known in the Kagera National Park in the north-eastern parts of Ruanda. Further south, in Burundi, the author has collected plants seven miles south-west of Kiteza at 5,700 ft. on the road to Usumbura. This is a range of 3,000 miles, and gives *A. myriacantha* the widest distribution of all the Aloes – with the exception of *A. buettneri* Berger.

Flowering Period: Depending on rains and locality, from February to April in southern localities to May–June in Kenya and Uganda.

Native Name: Nyakaryayata in the Ankole tongue of Uganda – J. Jarrett.

GROUP 2

(*Leptoaloe* Berger)

Plants acaulescent or with short stems. *Leaves* distichous or rosulate, narrowly linear to broader and more fleshy, rigid or flabby; *margins* minutely dentate, rarely entire. *Inflorescence* simple. *Bracts* small to large, sometimes clasping their pedicels. *Pedicels* 10—35mm. long, often the colour of the perianth. *Parianth* salmon-pink to scarlet with green tips, 24—40mm. long (except *A. ballii* 12—16mm. long); *outer segments* free to base (except in *A. nuttii* which is frequently connate to the middle). *Genitalia* not or very shortly exserted.

Type species: *A. nuttii* Bak.

Eleven species in Tropical Africa, none in Madagascar. (Eighteen species in the Republic of South Africa.)

Not one of the 11 species in Tropical Africa occurs in the Republic of South Africa, and not one of the 18 South African species has been found north of South Africa's northern border. The Limpopo Valley therefore seems to provide a two-way barrier for the species in this group, and yet, it provided no distribution barrier to the small *A. myriacantha* (Haw.) R & S which ranges from the Albany Dist. (Grahamstown) in the south, through Zululand, Rhodesia, Malawi (Nyasaland), Tanzania, Kenya, Uganda, Ruanda and Burundi – over 3,000 miles.

The richest area for species in this group is the eastern mountainous parts of Rhodesia, 8 of the 11 species being found from the southern end of the Chimanimanis to the northern parts of the Inyanga Downs. One of these species *A. ballii* has cylindric-campanulate perianths only 12—16mm. long, that are almost indistinguishable from the Madagascar species *A. bellatula* Reynolds. In leaf characters there is no resemblance whatever.

Of the remaining 3 species, *A. torrei* Verdoorn et Christian (which closely resembles the eastern Transvaal *A. chortolirioides* Berger) grows on Namuli Peaks, 110 miles north of Quelimane, Moçambique, while *A. buchananii* Bak. is a Shire Highlands and Kirk Range Malawi (Nyasaland) species.

The last, *A. nuttii* Bak. first collected at Fwambo near Abercorn, Zambia (Northern Rhodesia) near the southern end of Lake Tanganyika, has been found in northern Malawi (Nyasaland), southern Tanzania (Tanganyika) in the Mbeya, Njombe, and Sao Hill districts, the Copper Belt of Zambia and Elizabethville in the Congo. It has also been collected in Angola west of Matonchi and Mwinilunga near the Zambia border, and considerably farther west between Longa and Serpa Pinto in the Cubango Dist., Angola. It is noteworthy that no species in this group have been found north of the southern parts of Tanzania (Tanganyika), in Kenya or Uganda. The Northern Prov. of Kenya, Somalia, and the Sudan are too arid and sandy. The mountains of Eritrea and Ethiopia seemed likely places, but no plants in this group have ever been found in those regions.

Note. For descriptions, figures, and some colour plates of the 16 species found in South Africa see *Aloes of South Africa* 121–155 (1950). The two species described after 1950 are *A. modesta* Reynolds in *Journ. S.A. Bot.* 22: 86 (1956), and *A. soutpansbergensis* Verdoorn in *Fl. Plants. Afr.* 35: pl. 1931 (1962).

KEY TO THE SPECIES

1. LEAVES DISTICHOUS

A. *Perianth under 20mm. long:*
  (*a*) Stem 20—30cm. long, inflorescence spreading horizontally to obliquely downwards, pedicels longer than their 12—16mm. perianths .. ..   2 *A. ballii*

B. *Perianth 25—40mm. long:*
  (*a*) Plants acaulescent, leaves fleshy:
    1. Leaves rigidly suberect, 15—20cm. long, 10mm. broad, pedicels 10—12mm., perianth 30mm. .. ..   6 *A. wildii*
  (*b*) Plants with stems, leaves linear:
    1. Stems 20cm. and more long, leaves 15cm. long, 12mm. broad, margins with 1—2mm. broad translucent hyaline border, pedicels 12—15mm., perianth 24mm., whole plant pendent .. ..   5 *A. howmanii*
    2. Stems 20cm. long, leaves 30—40cm. long, 15mm. broad, pedicels 15—18mm., perianth 30mm. .. ..   7 *A. musapana*
    3. Stems 25cm. and more, leaves 20cm. long, 15—20mm. broad, pedicels 25—30mm., perianth 35—40mm., young buds at first covered with large imbricate bracts .. ..   8 *A. inyangensis*

4. Stems erect, 50cm. and more high, the apical 10—20cm. laxly foliate, the leaves alternately opposite, pedicels 13mm., perianth 25mm. long ..   ..   9 *A. hazeliana*

2. LEAVES DISTICHOUS IN YOUNG PLANTS

Sometimes becoming rosulate with age: Stem none or short, leaves 60—75cm. long, 5cm. broad, gradually narrowing, inflorescence 60—80cm., racemes 15—20cm. pedicels 30—35mm., perianth 30mm. long, narrower at mouth ..   ..   11 *A. buchananii*

3. LEAVES ALWAYS ROSULATE

A. *Plants with many tufted stems 10—15cm. long:*
Leaves narrowly linear, 30—40cm. long, 5mm. broad, deflexed, bracts 13mm. enfolding 20mm. pedicels, perianth 27mm.   ..   ..   ..   3 *A. torrei*
B. *Plants acaulescent or almost so:*
    1. Leaves 20—30cm. long, 6—10mm. broad, inflorescence 30—40cm., raceme 10cm., pedicels 30mm., perianth 30—35mm.   4 *A. plowesii*
    2. Leaves 25—30cm. long, 4—5cm. broad, raceme cylindric-conic, 12—15cm. long, bracts 20mm., pedicels 25—30mm. long, perianth narrowly cylindric, 35mm.   ..   ..   ..   10 *A. rhodesiana*
    3. Leaves 30—40cm. long, 2cm. broad near base, inflorescence 60cm. high, racemes 15—20cm., pedicels 35mm. long, perianth 40mm. salmon-pink ..   ..   12 *A. nuttii*

2. **A. ballii** Reynolds in *Journ. S.A. Bot.* 30: 123 (1964)

DESCRIPTION: *Plant* small, usually pendulous, developing long spirally-coiled smooth stems 1—1·5m. long when hanging down sheer rock faces, the terminal viable portion 20—30cm. long, 9mm. diam.

Leaves 8—10 distichous, basally amplexicaul, 20—30cm. long, 10mm. broad near base, gradually narrowing to an acute apex; *upper surface* canaliculate, green, with several white or very pale green elongated spots scattered in lower quarter; *lower surface* convex, green, usually copiously white-spotted near base; *margins* with minute white teeth about 2—4mm. apart low down, obsolescent upwards.

Inflorescence simple, 50—60cm. long, produced obliquely to horizontally or obliquely downwards, with the raceme sometimes slightly up-turned.

FIG. 3.

A. ballii Reynolds. Plant from the Haroni Gorge, southern end of the Chimanimani Mountains, Melsetter Dist., Rhodesia. Flowering at Mbabane Swaziland. × ⅛ approx.

2

Peduncle basally plano-convex and 5mm. broad, terete and 3mm. thick upwards, clothed with a few sterile bracts that are ovate-acute, 5mm. long, 3mm. broad, 3—5-nerved, the racemose portion the colour of the perianth and pedicels.

Raceme cylindric-acuminate, 12—18cm. long, 4cm. diam. at base, sub-laxly 40—50-flowered, youngest buds erect, open flowers nutant.

Bracts ovate-acute, 3mm. long, 2mm. broad, thin, 3—5-nerved.

Pedicels very slender, 14—20mm. long, longer than, and the colour of the perianth.

Perianth 12—16mm. long, cylindric slightly campanulate, flame-scarlet to pale reddish-orange, basally tapering into the pedicel, 4mm. diam. across the ovary, enlarging a little to a wide open mouth; *outer segments* free to base, apices slightly spreading; *inner segments* with 3 crowded nerves forming a scarlet keel throughout.

Filaments almost white, the 3 inner narrower and lengthening before the 3 outer with their *anthers* not exserted. *Stigma* at length not exserted. *Ovary* green, 2·5mm. long, 1·5mm. diam. (Figs. 3–4).

Fig. 4.

A. ballii Reynolds. Raceme and flowers 1/1. at the angle produced.

RHODESIA. *Melsetter Dist.*, Haroni Gorge, at the confluence of the Haroni and Chisenga Rivers (South of the Chimanimani Range), alt. 1,250 ft., cult. hort. Bullock Bulawayo, fl. 13 Oct. 1963, Bullock 37/1 holotype (SRGH); cult. Mbabane Swaziland fl. 9 Feb. 1964, Bullock et Reynolds 10115, isotype (K, BM, PRE).

A. ballii was named after Mr. John Ball of Melsetter, Rhodesia, who discovered it in November 1962 in a deep gorge at the confluence of the Haroni and Chisenga Rivers at the southern end of the Chimanimani Range. This locality is one and three-quarter miles north-west of Point 74 on the Moçambique–Rhodesian border at 1,250 ft.

Subsequently Mr. E. J. Bullock of Bulawayo visited the locality with Mr. Ball, and he wrote "Plants were found growing in leaf mould and sand amongst tussocks of grass wedged in crevices of large quartzite rocks and on sheer rock faces. When the stem is a few inches long it starts sending out its distichous leaves slightly out of line with the previous ones so that the plant develops a twist. When this happens to a plant growing over the edge of a rock face the stem develops a spiral twist. In moist conditions a long 'dead' spiral stem may suspend the viable stem like a coil spring. From the original growing point to the viable stem the length of this 'dead' part of stem may be up to 150cm.".

In cultivation, numerous shoots appear at random along the growing stem, while the inflorescence is produced obliquely to horizontally, or obliquely downwards.

The most striking character of *A. ballii* is its long racemes with short cylindric-campanulate flowers only 12—16mm. long, the pedicels being slightly longer.

No other African species of Aloe is known with such flowers, but the Madagascar species *A. bellatula* Reynolds has flowers that are almost identical, but in leaf clusters and leaves there is no resemblance whatever. In leaf characters only, *A. ballii* seems nearest allied to *A. musapana* Reynolds on Musapa Mountain which is 10 miles north of Melsetter.

3. **A. torrei** Verdoorn et Christian in *Fl. Pl. Afr.* 25: pl. 987 (1946)

DESCRIPTION based on plants from type locality when flowering in Mbabane, Swaziland.

Plants with 20 to 40 or more densely tufted stems 10—15cm. long, 10—15mm. diam., branching from base.

Leaves about 10, rosulate, narrowly linear, 40—45cm. long, 5mm. broad, widening abruptly to 15mm. broad when the imbricate sheathing portion clasps the stem, all leaves limp and deflexed and more or less hanging downwards; *upper surface* green, rather deeply canaliculate, with a few spots low down; *lower surface* green, rounded, with numerous crowded lenticular white spotting near base, the spots sometimes slightly tuberculate; *margins* with exceedingly narrow cartilaginous edge with minute teeth about 1—2mm. apart.

Inflorescence simple, averaging 50cm. tall, sometimes 2—3 consecutively.

Peduncle basally plano-convex and 6 mm. broad, terete and 5mm. thick upwards, with a few sterile bracts below the raceme, the lowest amplexicaul, ovate-acute, 15mm. long, 10mm. broad at middle, slightly fleshy, many-nerved, smaller upwards.

Raceme cylindric slightly acuminate, 9cm. long, 4—5cm. diam., about 10-flowered, buds flame-scarlet, grey-green tipped, open flowers nutant.

Bracts the lowest clasping the pedicel, ovate-acute, 15mm. long, 7mm. broad at the middle when pressed flat, slightly fleshy, many-nerved.

Pedicels the lowest 15mm. long, the colour of the perianth.

Perianth 30mm. long, scarlet, grey-green at mouth, cylindric-trigonous, slightly ventricose and 6—7mm. diam. at the middle, tapering to the pedicel and shortly stipitate, narrower at the mouth; *outer segments* free to base, thinner at the edges, 3—5-nerved, the apices subacute; *inner segments* free, with broad very pale pink border, and with 3 crowded nerves forming a keel that is salmon, the apical 5mm. greenish.

Filaments very pale lemon, the 3 inner narrower and lengthening before the 3 outer with their *anthers* in turn not exserted; *stigma* at length scarcely exserted; *ovary* very pale green, 5mm. long, 2mm. diam. (Plate 2, Figs 5—7).

Fɪɢ. 5.

Part of Namuli Peaks, taken from Lioma just north of Vila Junqueiro (Gurue) Zambezia Dist.,
Moçambique; type locality of *A. torrei* Verdoorn et Christian.
Photo: Mr. L. C. Leach.

MoçᴀᴍʙɪQᴜᴇ. Gurue Mountains, Quelimane, cult. Pretoria, fl. March 1944, da Torre, holotype (PRE 27239); *Zambezia Dist.*, Namuli Peaks near Vila Junqueiro (Gurue) about 170 miles north of Quelimane, c. 37° 02′ E, 15° 22′ S, c. 5,000 ft., fl. 26 July 1962, L. C. Leach et E. A. Schelpe 11479 (SRGH); cult. hort. Leach Greendale Salisbury, fl. Feb.–March 1963, Leach et Schelpe 11479 (BM, BOL, BRLU, COI, EA, G, K, LISC, LM, PRE).

A. torrei was named after Dr. Rocha da Torre who for many years has studied the flora of Moçambique, where he has collected extensively.

In July 1962, Mr. L. C. Leach and Dr. E. A. Schelpe visited the type locality and found that plants grew in grass on exposed granite slopes and were comparatively common over a rather restricted area on the west face of Namuli Peaks. This locality is approximately 250 miles west of Lumbo on the coast (Port of Moçambique), 170 miles north of Quelimane, and 110 miles north-east of Mt. Mlanje, Malawi.

Mr. Leach found that plants developed 40 and more densely tufted stems about 10—15cm. long, and 10—15mm. thick. Leaves are only 5mm. broad, and up to 40—45cm. long.

A. torrei is nearest allied to the Eastern Transvaal (South Africa) species *A. chortolirioides* Berger (see *Aloes of South Africa* 124 (1950)) from which it differs in having longer narrower

PLATE 2

ALOE TORREI   Verdoorn et Christian.

Plant collected by Mr. L. C. Leach on Namuli Peaks near Vila Junqueiro
(Garue) Zambezia Dist., Moçambique (Type locality). Grown at Mbabane,
Swaziland. Height 60cm.

Fɪɢ. 6.

A. torrei Verdoorn et Christian. Plant flowering in Mr. L. C. Leach's gardens at Greendale, Salisbury – a portion of a plant that originally had 40 stems.

Photo: Mr. L. C. Leach

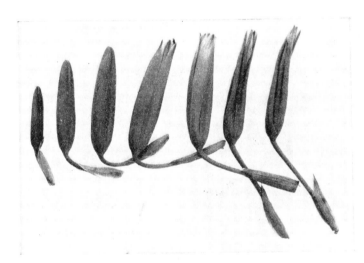

Fɪɢ. 7.

A. torrei Verdoorn et Christian. Flowers natural size.

more flabby leaves, a taller inflorescence, longer laxer racemes, and shorter more ventricose perianths.

In cultivation, plants do much better in large tins and watered, than in open ground where there is a tendency to dry out.

4. **A. plowesii** Reynolds in *Journ. S.A. Bot.* 30: 71 (1964)

Plant small, acaulescent, with fusiform roots.

Leaves about 10, rosulate, basally dilated and imbricate-amplexicaul near ground level, narrowly linear upwards, 20—30cm. long, 6—10mm. broad, gradually narrowing to an acute apex, suberect to spreading; *upper surface* dull green, canaliculate, with a few scattered spots in lower portion; *lower surface* carinate, dull green, with numerous crowded small white spots low down; *margins* with minute ·5mm. long white teeth that are slightly larger and closer low down, smaller, more distant and obsolescent upwards.

Inflorescence simple, 30—45cm. tall.

Peduncle 8mm. thick, with 6—8 sterile bracts that are ovate-acute, long-pointed, 6mm. broad, 15—20mm. long, 3—5-nerved.

Raceme cylindric-conical, up to 10cm. long, 6cm. diam., the apical buds denser and at first hidden by imbricate bracts, open flowers cernuous to nutant.

Bracts the lowest clasping the pedicel, ovate-acute when pressed flat and about 15mm. long, 7mm. broad, 3—5-nerved.

Pedicels 30mm. long, the colour of the perianth.

Perianth scarlet, paler to greenish at mouth, cylindric-trigonous, 30—35mm. long, basally obtuse and shortly stipitate, 8mm. diam. across the ovary; *outer segments* free to base, greenish at apex, obscurely 3—5-nerved; *inner segments* slightly broader than the outer with a scarlet keel throughout, the apices broader and more spreading than the outer.

Filaments fililiform-flattened, very pale lemon, the 3 inner narrower and lengthening before the 3 outer with their *anthers* in turn exserted 1—2mm.; *stigma* at length exserted 2mm.; *ovary* green, 7mm. long, 2·5mm. diam. (Figs. 8, 9).

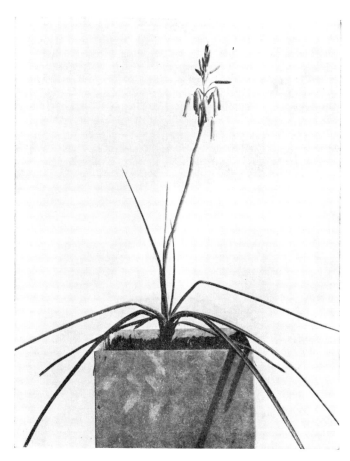

Fig. 8.

A. plowesii Reynolds. Plant from track to Mountain Club hut, Chimanimani Mts., Melsetter Dist., Rhodesia, cultivated at Mbabane, Swaziland – very robust form. Height 45cm.

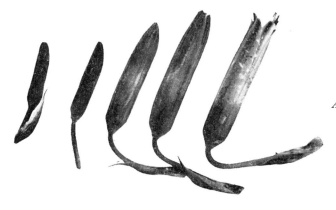

Fig. 9.

A. plowesii Reynolds. Flowers natura size.

RHODESIA. Chimanimani Mountains, along footpath to Mountain Club Hut among sandstone boulders in short grass, alt. 5,000—5,800 ft., fl. 14 Oct. 1962, D. C. H. Plowes 2273! holotype (SRGH); Oct. 1960, Plowes 1213! (SRGH); Chimanimani Mountains, fl. August 1947, Munch 8 (SRGH 32424); Gully above upper Haroni, rocky grassland, 4,800—5,000 ft., fl. 3 Feb. 1957, J. B. Phipps 447! (SRGH); Plant coll. Plowes along track to Mountain Club Hut, cult. Mbabane, Swaziland, very robust form, fl. 12 December 1963, Plowes et Reynolds 10049! (PRE).

MOÇAMBIQUE. Manica, Sofala, Chimanimani Mountains, fl. 9 July 1949, Pedro et Pedrogaõ 7393! (PRE).

A. plowesii was named after Mr. D. C. H. Plowes of Umtaḷi, who has contributed much to the advancement of botanical knowledge in Rhodesia. He found plants growing among sandstone boulders in short grass at the head of Dead Cow Gulch, and along the path to the Mountain Club huts, sometimes in association with *A. wildii*, from 5,000 ft. to 5,800 ft. There are two forms of *A. plowesii*, (1) a weaker form with shorter narrower (6mm.) more erect leaves growing in grass, and (2) a more robust form with longer broader (10mm.) more flabby leaves with a taller inflorescence. The weaker form has been collected by Mr. J. A. Whellan in numbers on the steep hillside along Martins Falls, which lie about three and a half miles east of Point 71 (Binga), just over the border in Moçambique.

When not flowering, plants of *A. plowesii* with their narrow rosulate suberect keeled leaves could very easily be mistaken for *A. myriacantha* (Haw.) R & S, but the flowers resemble those of *A. wildii* and *A. inyangensis* which are in all ways different. *A. wildii* has 6—8 leaves that are distichous and 10—15mm. broad, and could hardly be confused.

5. **A. howmanii** Reynolds in *Kirkia* 1: 156 (Feb. 1961)

DESCRIPTION: *Plant* succulent, with few or several stems, pendent on cliff faces, or overhanging ledges.

Stems simple or branched from base, 20—30cm. long, 12mm. diam.

Leaves 6—12, distichous, basally sheathing-imbricate, linear, 15—20cm. long, 12—15mm. broad, mostly falcately decurved; *upper surface* green, without spots or markings, flat at base, slightly convex upwards; *lower surface* green, usually without spots but sometimes with a few small white spots near base; *margins* parallel, with a 1·5mm. broad translucent hyaline border, entire or with minute teeth about 2—4mm. distant; leaf apex obtuse, shortly cuspidate.

Inflorescence simple, 20—25cm. long, hanging downwards, with the raceme upturned.

Peduncle basally plano-convex and 6—7mm. broad, slightly compressed laterally and 4mm. diam. below the raceme, clothed with a few scattered broadly ovate-acute sterile-bracts.

Raceme subcapitate, cylindric, slightly conic, 4—5cm. long, sublaxly about 12—18-flowered, the buds denser and suberectly spreading, open flowers slightly laxer, nutant to subpendulous.

Bracts ovate-acute, 3—4mm. long, 2mm. broad, subscarious, 3-nerved.

Pedicels 10—15mm. long, the colour of the perianth.

Perianth flame-scarlet, 24mm. long, cylindric slightly ventricose, basally obconic and shortly stipitate, 5mm. diam. across the ovary, slightly narrowed at the green-tipped mouth; *outer segments* free to base; *inner segments* free, broader than the outer, with a prominent scarlet keel turning green at the more obtuse, more spreading apices.

Filaments pale lemon, the 3 inner narrower and lengthening before the 3 outer with their *anthers* in turn exserted 1—2mm.; *style* pale yellow, with *stigma* at length exserted 1—2mm.; *ovary* pale-orange, 3mm. long, 1·5mm. diam. (Plate 3, Fig. 10).

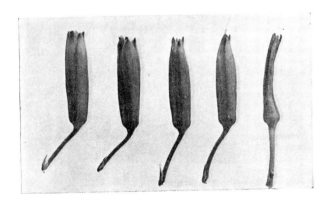

FIG. 10.

A. howmanii Reynolds. Flowers natural size.

RHODESIA. *Melsetter Dist.*, Chimanimani Mountains, 6,000 ft., fl. 1 May 1957, J. S. Ball 646 (PRE, holotype; SRGH without flowers); Sept. 1945, R. C. Munch 4! (SRGH); fl. 6 June 1949, H. Wild 2881! (K, PRE, SRGH); fl. May 1956, K. Coates Palgrave in GHS 70624 (SRGH).

A. howmanii was named after Mr. Roger Howman, who was Native Commissioner at Ndanga and Zaka until 1939, and later at Melsetter.

PLATE 3

ALOE HOWMANII   Reynolds.

Plant on the Chimanimani Mts. E of Melsetter, Rhodesia, × ⅓ approx.
From a Kodachrome by Mr. D. C. H. Plowes.

During the Easter holidays of 1940, Mr. Howman visited the Chimanimani Mountains (east of Melsetter) and collected plants of "a small aloe hanging on cliff faces, mostly in inaccessible places so that they could only be reached by lying down and reaching over the edge".

Plants have subsequently been collected by Dr. H. Wild, Mr. J. A. Whellan, Mr. R. C. Munch, Mr. John Ball, Mr. E. J. Bullock, myself and others, mostly at the top of the very steep gully of the main ascent of the Chimanimanis at an altitude of 5,500—6,000 ft.

Mr. Ball has found plants on steep upper slopes of Point 71, at 7,800 ft., the highest point of the Chimanimanis – now known as Binga. *A. howmanii* extends from the Bundi Gorge through the second range of the Chimanimanis northwards for 10 miles to the Musapa Gap. Mr. Whellan has found it on the cliffs of Mawenje (Turret Towers), 2 miles eastwards from Binga.

A. howmanii grows mostly in inaccessible places on sheer rock faces, out of reach of grass fires, and mostly on south slopes getting little or no sun in the winter months. Stems and leaf clusters are pendant with only the raceme upturned. Leaves are fleshy and somewhat biconvex in cross-section, while their margins have a distinctly translucent hyaline border about 1·5mm. broad, which shows up clearly when viewed against the light. These characters, and shorter flowers distinguish *A. howmanii* from its nearest ally, *A. musapana* Reynolds.

Plants flower in late April and May, and rarely, if ever, survive in cultivation.

6. **A. wildii** (Reynl.) Reynolds in *Kirkia* 4: 13 (1964).

—— *A. torrei* Verdoorn et Christian var. *wildii* Reynolds in *Kirkia* 1: 158, *t.* 16 (Feb. 1961).

DESCRIPTION: *Plant* acaulescent, solitary or with a few shoots from ground level forming small groups.

Leaves about 6, distichous, rather rigidly suberect, averaging 15—20cm. (rarely 30cm.) long, basally imbricate-sheathing, thence linear upwards and 5—10mm. broad; *upper surface* slightly canaliculate, dull green with brownish tinge, with a few scattered small white spots low down; *lower surface* convex, similar in colour to upper surface, copiously white-spotted low down, fewer upwards, the spots exceedingly shortly spinulescent; *margins* with very small soft white cartilaginous teeth about ·5mm. long, 1—2mm. apart, larger and more crowded low down, smaller to obsolescent upwards.

Inflorescence simple, averaging 25—30cm. tall (sometimes up to 50cm. tall in very robust specimens).

Peduncle 5mm. diam., clothed with a few sterile-bracts, the lowest shortly ovate-acute, 5mm. long and broad, thin, 3—5-nerved.

Raceme 6—7cm. long, 5cm. diam., about 12—16-flowered, the buds suberect and denser, open flower subpendulous and laxer.

FIG. 11.

A botanical treasure-house – the Chimanimani Mtns., east of Melsetter, Rhodesia. Home of *A. wildii, A. plowesii, A. howmanii, A. musapana, A. hazeliana, A. swynnertonii* (formerly known as *A. chimanimaniensis*), also *A. munchii* and *A. arborescens*.

Bracts dull-pink, ovate-acute, 5mm. long, 2—3mm. broad, thin, subscarious, 3-nerved.

Pedicels nutant at apex, 10—15mm. long, the colour of the perianth.

Perianth bright orange-scarlet, green-tipped, cylindric-ventricose, 30—40mm. long, basally tapering into the pedicel and shortly stipitate; *outer segments* free to base; *inner segments* carinate, broader than the outer, and with more obtuse more spreading apices.

Filaments filiform-flattened, the 3 inner narrower and lengthening before the 3 outer with their *anthers* in turn exserted 0—1mm.; *stigma* at length exserted 1—2mm.; *ovary* dull yellow, 3mm. long, 1·5mm. diam. (Figs. 11–13).

Fig. 12.

A. wildii (Reynl.) Reynolds. From "The Corner", and along the Chimanimanis.
Height 30cm., (12″).

Fig. 13.

A. wildii (Reynl.) Reynolds. Flowers 1/1 from bud to post-pollination stage.

RHODESIA. *Melsetter Dist.*, Chimanimani Mountains, Martin Forest Reserve, The Corner, 5,000 ft., fl. 9 Oct. 1950, H. Wild 3541! (K, PRE, SRGH holotype); Skeleton Pass, cult. et fl. Greendale, 16 Sept. 1959, L. C. Leach 9360! (SRGH, PRE); ex The Corner, cult. Johannesburg, fl. 22 Sept. 1954, G. W. Reynolds 6247! (PRE); above base of Long Gully, on lower slopes of end range in open Protea scrub, Sept. 1955, R. Watmough 140! (SRGH); The Corner, 8 Oct. 1950, N. C. Chase 2946! (BM, SRGH) 31145.

A. wildii was at first wrongly described as a variety of *A. torrei* Verdoorn et Christian which had been described from a young plant that flowered in Pretoria, when the authors did not know then that old adult plants developed 30—40 tufted stems, and that the nearest affinity was *A. chortolirioides* Berger, found in the Eastern Transvaal and Swaziland.

A. wildii is a very distinctive little species characterized by having no stem, sometimes developing into a multiple-headed plant, with 6—8 leaves that are distichous, suberect to spreading, 15—25cm. long, somewhat strap-shaped and 10—15mm. broad, with a simple inflorescence resembling that of *A. musapana* Reynolds and *A. inyangensis* Christian.

A. wildii has been found at The Corner, and along the main Chimanimani range, especially along the main path from the Mountain Hut to Binga Peak – the highest point of the range.

Mr. J. A. Whellan found *A. wildii* was "common almost everywhere on the Rhodesian side of the border, especially ascending Mawenje, to about 7,000 ft. It extends across Skeleton Pass into Moçambique."

Plants do well in cultivation, and can be watered rather freely in the summer months.

7. **A. musapana** Reynolds in *Journ. S.A. Bot.* 30: 125 (1964)

DESCRIPTION: *Plant* mostly pendent, with several stems up to 20cm. long, 1cm. diam., with numerous shoots near base or higher, forming dense groups.

Leaves distichous, about 10, basally amplexicaul, spreading to falcately decurved, linear, gradually narrowing to an acute apex, 15mm. broad near base, 30—40cm. long; *upper surface* dark green, canaliculate with or without a few white spots low down; *lower surface* convex, copiously spotted near base, the spots dirty-white, lenticular; *margins* with white cartilaginous teeth that are minute near base, obsolescent upwards.

Inflorescence simple, 30—40cm. long.

Peduncle rather slender, basally plano-convex and 5mm. broad, terete and 4mm. thick upwards, with a few sterile-bracts that are ovate-acute, thin, scarious, brownish, 12mm. long, 7mm. broad, many-nerved.

Racemes cylindric-acuminate, 15cm. long, 6cm. broad, subdensely flowered, the youngest buds suberect, scarlet with greenish tips, open flowers pendulous, scarlet, pale greenish at mouth.

Bracts ovate-acute, the lowest 10mm. long, 6mm. broad at base, thin, scarious, many-nerved.

Pedicels 20mm. long, slender, the colour of the perianth.

Perianth scarlet, sometimes bright orange, pale green at mouth, cylindric slightly trigonous, 28—30mm. long, 6mm. diam. across the ovary, slightly enlarging to the throat; *outer segments* free to base, obscurely 3-nerved, the apices subacute; *inner segments* broader than the outer, thin at the edge, with 3 crowded nerves forming a scarlet keel turning green at the broader apices.

Filaments filiform-flattened, very pale rose, the 3 inner narrower and lengthening before the 3 outer with their *anthers* in turn exserted 1—2mm.; *stigma* at length exserted 2 mm.; *ovary* pale olive, 5mm. long, 2mm. diam. (Figs. 14–15).

RHODESIA. *Melsetter Dist.*, Musapa Mountain, 10 miles north of Melsetter, alt. 6,500 ft., cult. Bulawayo, fl. 10 March 1963, E. J. Bullock, 36/1 holotype (SRGH); cult. Mbabane, Swaziland, fl. 30 March 1964, Bullock et Reynolds 10092, isotype (PRE, K).

FIG. 14.

A. musapana Reynolds. Plant collected by Mr. E. J. Bullock on Musapa Mtn., 10 miles north of Melsetter, Rhodesia, alt. 6,500 ft. Flowering in the author's gardens Mbabane, Swaziland.

Fig. 15.

A. musapana Reynolds. Flowers 1/1 from
bud to post-pollination stages.

A. musapana was named after the locality where Mr. E. J. Bullock of Bulawayo first found plants in January 1960, namely Musapa Mountain (7,040 ft.) which is 10 miles north of Melsetter and west of the northern end of the Chimanimani Range, in the eastern parts of Rhodesia. Mr. Bullock found plants on northern, north-western and southern sheer rock faces on Musapa Mountain in conditions of full summer and winter sunshine, at an altitude of between 6,250 and 6,750 ft., also on Groen Kop near by, to the south.

A. musapana appears to be nearest allied to the weaker forms of *A. inyangensis* Christian from which it differs in having leaves with much smaller marginal teeth, a much slenderer peduncle, with much smaller sterile bracts. The youngest buds of *A. musapana* are not at first hidden by large imbricate bracts as they are in *A. inyangensis,* while the bracts are smaller, the pedicels are shorter (20mm. against 25—30mm.) and the perianth is also slenderer and shorter i.e. 30mm. against 35—40mm. long.

In cultivation, plants increase rather quickly, especially if watered, and flower prolifically.

8. A. inyangensis Christian in *Fl. Pl. S. Afr.* 16: Plate 640 (1936)

DESCRIPTION: Based on cultivated plants of average size from the summit of Inyangani Mountain.

Plant succulent, usually with many densely tufted stems about 20cm. long, 15—20mm. diam., branching near base and with numerous shoots at random sometimes forming dense patches of 1—2m. across.

Leaves about 8—10, laxly distichous and basally imbricate-amplexicaul, averaging 15—20cm. long, 15mm. broad near base; *upper surface* canaliculate and more or less involute, dark green with or without a few scattered spots low down; *lower surface* rounded, dark green, usually copiously spotted near base, the spots very pale green, lenticular, sometimes with slight tubercules in the centre of the spots; *margins* ciliate-denticulate, with white cartilaginous edge with minute teeth ·5mm. long, 1—2mm. apart, larger low down, smaller to obsolescent upwards.

Inflorescence simple, averaging 30—35cm. tall.

Peduncle plano-convex at base and 7mm. broad, 5mm. thick upwards, with a few sterile-bracts, the lowest ovate-acute thin, dry, 20mm. long, 12mm. broad, many-nerved.

Racemes cylindric-acuminate, 6—8cm. long, sublaxly about 16-flowered, the youngest buds at first covered by large densely imbricate bracts, open flowers subpendulous.

Bracts the lowest lanceolate-attenuate, 25mm. long, 9mm. broad, thin, subscarious, many-nerved.

Pedicels averaging 30mm. long, the reddish colour of the perianth.

Perianth bright scarlet-red, greenish at mouth, 35—40mm. long, cylindric-trigonous, about 7mm. diam. across the ovary; *outer segments* free to base, the apices green, subacute, slightly spreading; *inner segments* broader than the outer, thin and white at the edges, with 3 crowded nerves forming a scarlet keel turning greenish at the more obtuse apex.

Filaments pale lemon, the 3 inner narrower and lengthening before the 3 outer with their *anthers* not exserted; *stigma* at length exserted 0—1mm.; *ovary* pale olive-yellow, 7mm. long, 2·5mm. diam. (Plate 4, Figs. 16–17).

RHODESIA. Rokotso, Inyanga Mountains, alt. 6,500 ft., March 1936, C. P. Piers in Nat. Herb. 28428, holotype (PRE)—the type of *Fl. Pl. S. Afr.* Pl. 640.

Inyanga Downs. Covering rock faces at 6,000 ft., fl. June 1932, Eyles 7001! (K, SRGH); north of Troutbeck among rocks on mountain top, May 1957, L. C. Leach 268! (PRE, K, SRGH); 2 miles S of Rhodes Hotel, 6,400 ft., 21 April 1953, N. C. Chase 5000! (BM, PRE, SRGH); Inyanga, 3 June 1961, L. C. Leach 1140! (SRGH); Isuwe, E of Inyangani Mountain, 5,000 ft., May 1961, D. C. H. Plowes 2178! (SRGH); Pungwe Falls (about 12 miles ESE of Rhodes Estates) May 1946, R. C. Munch in GHS 32429 (SRGH). *Umtali Dist.:* Castle Beacon, Vumba, 8 April 1958, D. C. H. Plowes 2021! (SRGH, PRE).

A. inyangensis was first collected by Mr. C. P. Piers, Government Surveyor, in February 1931, on Rokotso, Inyanga Mountains, where it formed large clumps 8—9 ft. across, on the tops and sides of bare flattish outcrops, at 6,500 ft. It occurs abundantly along the top of Inyangani Mountain,

PLATE 4

ALOE INYANGENSIS   Christian.

Near World's View, 4 miles W of Troutbeck Inn., Inyanga, Rhodesia,
alt. 7,350 ft. $\times \frac{1}{3}$ approx.

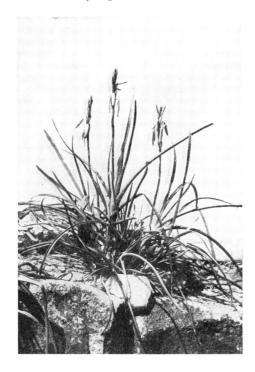

Fig. 16.

A. inyangensis Christian. Collected by Mr. D. C. H. Plowes at the top of Inyangani Mtn., Rhodesia – flowering at Mbabane, Swaziland. Height 33cm.

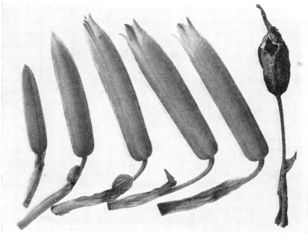

Fig. 17.

A. inyangensis Christian. Flowers 1/1 from bud to fruit stages – from a plant near World's View, Inyanga, Rhodesia.

at 7,500 ft., and Mr. D. C. H. Plowes has found it at Isuwe to the east of that mountain. The Inyanga Downs is the headquarters of *A. inyangensis*, where plants grow on Fort Hill, Bideford Estate, mountain 6 miles north of Troutbeck, near World's View, 4 miles west of Troutbeck, at Mtarazi Falls, in the Pungwe Falls area about 12 miles east-south-east of Rhodes Estate. Further south in the Umtali Dist. some very robust growth forms grow at Castle Beacon, Vumba Mountain.

A. inyangensis has not so far been found along the Chimanimanis east of Melsetter, but a near ally, *A. musapana* Reynolds occurs on Musapa Mountain, about 10 miles north of Melsetter.

In some localities and especially in old plants cultivated for some years, *A. inyangensis* develops stems 50cm. and more long, and 25—30mm. thick, while leaves reach 50cm. long, and 35—40mm. broad at base. These robust forms have very large densely imbricate bracts, covering the buds. In all forms the stems are mostly oblique to sprawling, and branch at base or higher, often with several offshoots at random, forming large clumps.

Flowering time is Feb.–April.

This species is well worth growing, and increases rapidly, especially if watered in the summer months.

NATURAL HYBRID

A. arborescens × *A. inyangensis* was originally collected in profusion among both parents by Mr. E. C. Bertram on a hilltop on Inyanga Downs, about 16 miles north-east of Inyanga Village. This cross also increases rapidly in cultivation. There are some large plants at Ewanrigg, near Salisbury.

9. **A. hazeliana** Reynolds in *Journ. S.A. Bot.* 25: 279 (1959)

DESCRIPTION: *Plant* of compact slender growth, with few to several stems from ground level.

Stems slender erect, up to 50cm. long, 15mm. diam., with the apical 15cm. rather laxly foliate.

Leaves about 12, distichous, linear, up to 20 cm. long, 10—15mm. broad, suberect to spreading, straight or slightly curved, the basally sheathing portion 10—15mm. long; *upper surface* flat to slightly canaliculate, unspotted or sometimes with a few small scattered pale green elliptical spots; *lower surface* green, rounded, with numerous crowded smaller pale green spots low down, the sheaths copiously spotted; *margins* with a very narrow somewhat hyaline edge armed with firm white deltoid teeth about ·5mm. long, and 5mm. apart low down, smaller to obsolescent upwards with the leaf apices obtuse, cuspidate, and minutely dentate.

Inflorescence simple, 30—40cm. long, produced laterally.

Peduncle slender, basally flattened and 6—8mm. broad, green, with a few broadly ovate-cuspidate sterile bracts.

Raceme laxly about 18-flowered, 8—10cm. long, 4cm. diam., the youngest buds greyish-tipped and suberectly spreading, open flowers pendent.

Bracts ovate-acute, 4mm. long, 3mm. broad at base, slightly fleshy, obscurely 3-nerved.

Pedicels the lowest 13mm. long, shorter upwards, the scarlet colour of the perianth.

Perianth scarlet, green-tipped, 25mm. long, cylindric-trigonous, basally obtuse and shortly stipitate, 6mm. diam. across the ovary, thence trigonous upwards; *outer segments* free to base, obscurely 3-nerved, the apices greenish, subacute, slightly spreading; *inner segments* broader than the outer, with broad pale marginal border and 3 crowded nerves forming a scarlet keel, the apices more obtuse and more spreading than the outer.

Filaments filiform-flattened, the 3 inner narrower and lengthening before the 3 outer with their *anthers* in turn not or exceedingly shortly exserted; *stigma* at length exserted 1—2mm.; *ovary* pale orange, 5mm. long, 2mm. diam. (Figs. 18–19).

FIG. 18.

A. hazeliana Reynolds. Collected by Mrs. Hazel Munch in the S.W. parts of the Chimanimani Mtns., Rhodesia. Flowering in Johannesburg. × ¼ approx.

FIG. 19.

A. hazeliana Reynolds. Flowers 1/1 from bud to
fruit stages.

RHODESIA. *Melsetter Dist.*, Chimanimani Mountains, coll. Mrs. Hazel Munch, cult. Johannesburg, fl. 3 May 1959, Reynolds 9031 holotype (PRE) isotype (K); cult. "Mona" near Rusape, Rhodesia, fl. 5 May 1959, Munch 6/138 (K).

A. hazeliana was named after Mrs. Hazel Munch who first collected plants in September 1945 on the Chimanimani Mountains about 20 miles south-east of Melsetter in Rhodesia. Plants were found at altitudes from 5,000 to 7,000 ft. on both sides of the Rhodesia-Moçambique border, mostly in pockets of soil on rocks and in rock fissures. Mr. J. A. Whellan has collected *A. hazeliana* about half way from the mountain hut to Martins Falls, in Moçambique.

A. hazeliana is a plant of compact growth with few to several slender erect stems from ground level; the stems average 30—45cm. in length and are not branched above ground level. A striking character of *A. hazeliana* is that the apical 10—20cm. of stems is laxly foliate, the leaves always being distichous—alternately opposite. The sheaths are 10—20mm. long, and are copiously white-spotted, while racemes vary from laxer to denser.

Its nearest ally is *A. inyangensis* Christian which occurs further north in the Inyanga Dist. and elsewhere, but has never been found on the detached Chimanimani Range.

A. inyangensis differs from *A. hazeliana* in forming considerably larger denser clumps that are sometimes several feet across, and in having shorter, thicker stems, leaves more densely crowded, longer bracts and pedicels, and flowers 35—40mm. long.

10. **A. rhodesiana** Rendle in *Journ. Linn. Soc. Bot.* 40: 215 (1911)

—— *A. eylesii* Christian in *Fl. Pl. S. Afr.* 16: Plate 638 (1936)

DESCRIPTION: Based on plants among rocks 2 miles S of Pungwe Falls View, 17 miles S of Rhodes Hotel, Inyanga, Rhodesia.

Plants with fusiform roots, acaulescent or with short stem 10cm. long, 3—4cm. thick, solitary or 2—3 branched at base.

Leaves 8—12, densely rosulate, suberect to slightly spreading, basally dilating, imbricate and 4—5 cm. broad, gradually narrowing to the apex, up to 25—30cm. long when not burnt by grass fires; *upper surface* dull green, flat to very slightly canaliculate, usually without spots or markings; *lower surface* convex, mostly without spots or markings but sometimes with a few small whitish elliptic spots very low down; *margins* with a very narrow white cartilaginous edge with minute firm white teeth about ·5—1mm. long low down, 1—4mm. apart, smaller and obsolescent upwards.

Inflorescence simple, sometimes 2—3 from a rosette, averaging 40—45cm. high.

Peduncle basally plano-convex and 13mm. broad with several sterile-bracts, the lowest ovate-acute, thin, 20mm. long, 10—12mm. broad, many-nerved.

Raceme cylindric-acuminate, 12—15cm. long, 8cm. diam., buds suberect and partly hidden by imbricate bracts, salmon-pink grey-green tipped, denser near apex, laxer downwards.

Bracts ovate-acute, cuspidate, 20mm. long, 11mm. broad, thin, subscarious, many-nerved.

Pedicels lowest up to 30mm. long, the colour of the perianth.

Perianth salmon-pink, cylindric-trigonous, averaging 35mm. long, basally obconic and tapering to the pedicel, 6mm. diam. across the ovary; *outer segments* free to base, obscurely 3-nerved, the apices slightly spreading; *inner segments* thinner at the edges, keeled salmon-pink greenish at apex, apices broader and more spreading than the inner.

Filaments filiform-flattened, the 3 inner narrower and lengthening before the 3 outer with their *anthers* in turn exserted 0—1mm.; *stigma* at length exserted 1—2mm.; *ovary* pale green, 5mm. long, 2mm. diam. (Plate 5, Figs 20–21).

RHODESIA. Melsetter S. Rhodesia, from the Umvumvumvu River to Mt. Pene, 6,000 ft., 10 Oct. 1908, Swynnerton 6047! holotype (BM); Gazaland, Mt. Pene or Singwekwe, SE Rhodesia, 7,000 ft., Oct. 12–14 1908, Swynnerton 6048! (BM); Summit of Inyangani Mountain c. 2400m., 14 Feb. 1931, Norlindh et Weinmarck 5020! (BM); Central Patrol and north, 29 June 1934, Gilliland 523 B! (BM); *Inyanga Dist.*, 15 Dec. 1947, J. C. Hopkins B1606! (SRGH); Inyanga, open grassland on steep slope next to kloof above Nyamziwa River, 19 Oct. 1946, J. M. Rattray 890! (SRGH); slopes of Inyangani

PLATE 5

ALOE RHODESIANA   Rendle.

Plant from the Melsetter district, Rhodesia, flowering in Johannesburg.
Height 60cm.

3

FIG. 20.

A. rhodesiana Rendle. Plants near Pungwe Falls, 17 miles south of Rhodes Hotel, Inyanga, Rhodesia, at alt. 6,200 ft. Height 40cm.

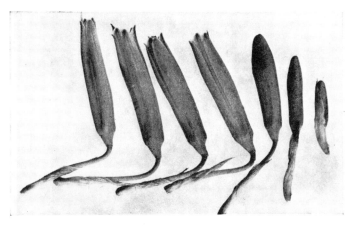

FIG. 21.

A. rhodesiana Rendle. Flowers 1/1 from a plant in the Pungwe Falls area.

Mountain, 6,500—7,000 ft., 24 Oct. 1935, Eyles 8516! as *A. eylesii* Christian (PRE, K); Foot of Inyangani Mountain in open grassland, scapes 1 ft. 6 in., flowers bright red, 23 Oct. 1946, H. Wild 1558! (SRGH 16103, PRE); Inyanga, near Troutbeck, 7,000 ft., cult. Geendale, 10 March 1958, L. C. Leach 270! (SRGH); near Pungwe Falls, 17 miles south of Rhodes Hotel 6 200 ft., 18 July 1950, Reynolds 8209! (SRGH, PRE, K). Umtali, Vumba, Castle Beacon, 10 June 1957, L. C. Leach 291! (SRGH). *Melsetter Dist.:* Mutsarara Farm, 16 miles S of Melsetter, form with distichous leaves, fl. 2 Nov. 1950, A. D. Crook M258 (SRGH, K, PRE).

Moçambique. Manica and Sofala, Serra da Gorongosa, 6 Oct. 1946, J. Simeo 994 (LM, PRE).

   A. rhodesiana was first collected by Swynnerton in October 1908 and is one of the species described in "A contribution to our knowledge of the Flora of Gazaland; being an account of collections made by C. F. M. Swynnerton Esq. F.L.S." by Dr. A. B. Rendle in *Journ. Linn. Soc. Bot.* 40: 215 (1911).
   Type locality: Melsetter, south-east Rhodesia, 6,000 ft., from the Umvumvumvu River to Mt. Pene. *Note:* The Umvumvumvu River flows westwards into the Odzi River, north of the Sabi River confluence, while Mt. Pene (5,660 ft.) lies about 13 miles south of Melsetter.

A. rhodesiana grows on the farm Mutsarara 16 miles south of Melsetter, also at Skyline 12 miles west of Melsetter, 12 miles south-east, and elsewhere in that area. It has been found in the Umtali Dist., near Castle Beacon, Vumba Mountains, further north in the Stapelford Forest Reserve, near Pungwe Falls and Mtarazi Falls, Mt. Inyangani, Rhodes Estate, Troutbeck and beyond to Black Mountain, Inyanga Downs.

A. rhodesiana has been reported from the Moçambique side of the border, and has also been collected further north on Gorongoza Mountain which lies north of the Umtali–Beira road in Moçambique.

Plants are found mostly in rocky or stony ground, either singly or with 3—4 short stems.

11. **A. buchananii** Baker in *Kew Bull.* 119 (1895), in Th. Dyer *Fl. Trop. Afr.* 7 : 457 (1898); Berger in Engler's *Pflanzenr.* Liliac.-Aloin. 167 (1908); Christian in *Fl. Pl. S. Afr.* 20: Pl. 763 (1940); Reynolds in *Aloes of Nyasaland* 5 (1954)

DESCRIPTION: Based on plants along the Limbe-Cholo road, Shire Highlands, and near Goche Village, Kirk Range, Malawi (Nyasaland). *Plant* succulent, with fusiform roots. *Stem* none or up to 20cm. long, 4—5cm. thick, usually with old dried leaf bases persistent.

Leaves 12—16 distichous, or becoming rosulate, suberectly spreading, sometimes deflexed, averaging 60cm. long, 4—6cm. broad near base, basally dilated and imbricate-amplexicaul; *upper surface* deeply canaliculate, green, with a few scattered elongated dull white spots towards base, *lower surface* rounded, green, more copiously and more distinctly lenticular white-spotted near base, usually with a small tubercle in the centre of each spot; *margins* minutely denticulate, with a narrow translucent cartilaginous edge, armed with minute teeth ·5 mm. long and 8—15 mm. apart low down, obsolete in upper part of leaf.

Inflorescence 1—2, simple, 60—80cm. high.

Peduncle green, basally 10—15mm. broad, terete upwards, with numerous sterile-bracts from the middle upwards, the lowest ovate-acuminate, amplexicaul, 30mm. long, 15—20mm. broad, thin, subscarious, many-nerved.

Raceme cylindric-acuminate, averaging 15—20cm. long, 7cm. diam. at base, the apical buds at first covered by large densely imbricate bracts, exposed buds erectly spreading, open flowers pendulous.

Bracts pale pink, lowest 25—30mm. long, 10—12mm. broad, rather fleshy, ovate-acute, apiculate, many-nerved.

Pedicels 35—40mm. long, the colour of the perianth.

Perianth salmon-pink or light coral-red, turning greenish at the mouth, averaging 30 mm. long, about 10—11mm. diam. across, the ovary and narrowing to the mouth, slightly stipitate at base; *outer segments* free, or very shortly connate, obscurely about 7-nerved, the apices subacute; *inner segments* broader than the outer, white with 3 crowded nerves forming a pink keel turning greenish at the more obtuse apices.

Genitals not, or scarcely exserted.

Ovary pale green, 8mm. long, 4mm. diam. (Plate 6, Figs. 22–24).

FIG. 22.

A. buchananii Bak. Plant from Bvumbwe, 9 miles south of Limbe, Malawi, flowering in Blantyre. Distichous form. Height 70cm.

ALOE BUCHANANII   Baker.

Rosulate form on the Kirk Range, 70 miles S of Dedza, Ncheu Dist.,
Central Prov., Malawi (Nyasaland). Flowering in May, height 70cm.

FIG. 23.

A. buchananii Bak. Flowers 1/1 from a plant on the Kirk Range, south of Dedza, Malawi – See Colour Plate.

MALAWI (NYASALAND). Shire Highlands, received from Buchanan in 1892, fl. at Kew Gardens Dec. 18, 1894—Type specimen! (K).

SOUTHERN PROVINCE. Shire Highlands, 12 miles S of Limbe, cult. Pretoria, fl. 3 June 1938, I. B. Pole Evans and J. Erens 540! (K, PRE); Bvumbwe, 9 miles S of Limbe, 3,800 ft., in woodland, 17 May 1956, G. W. Reynolds 8172! (K, PRE, SRGH, EA); Zomba, 16 June 1957, L. C. Leach 370, G.H.S. 76953 (SRGH); Zomba Plateau, Brachystegia woodland,1500m., 4 June 1946, L. J. Brass 16228! (K, SRGH). Mt. Mlanje: on Chamke-Likabula path, 4,000 ft., without date T. D. Chapman (SRGS)..

CENTRAL PROVINCE. *Ncheu Dist.:* Chirobwe, 1580m., 18 March 1955, A. W. Excell, F. A. Mendonca and H. Wild 1021! (SRGH); Kirk Range, near Goche Village, 70 miles south of Dedza, 5,000 ft., 19 May 1956, Reynolds 8183! (K, PRE, SRGH).

FIG. 24.

A. buchananii Bak. Flowers 1/1 from various plants at random showing variation.
Photo: The late H. B. Christian.

In its varying localities, *A. buchananii* (originally spelt *A. buchanani*) is a very variable species, and has so far been found only in Malawi (Nyasaland).

In the Shire Highlands, Southern Prov., plants are rather smaller and almost always distichous. They are to be found along the Limbe–Cholo road, on Mt. Mlanje, on Chiradzulu between Limbe and Zomba, near Zomba and on Zomba Plateau.

In the Ncheu Dist. of the Central Prov. plants are generally larger and vary from leaves distichous to mostly rosulate. On the Lake View road, 22 miles north of Ncheu (7 miles south-east of Lizulu and 26 miles south-east of Dedza) some remarkably robust forms were found at 5,000 ft. Three miles from Dedza the author found a plant with 9 tufted stems—but this is unusual. Although plants with tufted stems do occur, the most frequent form is solitary or with 2—3 stems.

It seems that the headquarters of *A. buchananii* are along the Kirk Range, especially from 10 miles north to 10 miles south of Goche Village, which is 60–80 miles south of Dedza, at 4,800—5,200 feet.

Although distichous forms are met with, the most frequent on the Kirk Range is leaves rosulate. Whether with leaves distichous or rosulate, the perianth of *A. buchananii* averages 30mm. in length and are always broader at base (10—12mm.) and narrower at the mouth. This is one of the characters which distinguish it from *A. nuttii*.

Flowering time: Mostly April and May.

Local native name: *Maluwa* in Chinyanja, which applies to almost any flower.

12. **A nuttii** Baker in *Hook. Ic. Pl. t.* 2513 (1897), in Th. Dyer *Fl. Trop. Afr.* 7: 457 (1898); Berger in Engler's *Pflanzenr.* Liliac.-Aloin. 170 (1908); Christian in *Fl. Pl. S. Afr.* 20: Pl. 762 (1940) – *Non* Reynolds in *Aloes of Nyasaland* 8 (1954) – Plants near Dedza, Nyasaland, subsequently proved to be rosulate forms of *A. buchananii* Bak.

—— *A. brunneo-punctata* Engler et Gilg. in Baum (Warburg) *Kuneni-Sambesi Expedition* p. 189, Fig. 89 (1903); Berger in Engler's *Pflanzenr.* Liliac.-Aloin. 170 (1908).

—— *A. corbisieri* De Wildeman in *Contrib. Fl. Katanga* 29 (1921).

—— *A. mketiensis* Christian in *Fl. Pl. S. Afr.* 20: Plate 785 (1940); Reynolds in *Aloes of Nyasaland* 43 (1954).

DESCRIPTION based on plants from the type locality (Fwambo) near Abercorn, Zambia (N. Rhodesia), and on large numbers on mountains north of Mbeya, Tanganyika:

Plants succulent, growing singly, or with 2—3 stems, or sometimes with up to 12 and more tufted stems, the stems varying from very short to 10—20cm. long, 4—5cm. thick.

Leaves 16—20, always rosulate, erectly spreading, sometimes deflexed at about the middle, the dilated basal part 3—4cm. broad, abruptly narrowed to 15—20 mm. broad near base, thence linear-tapering to a slender point and averaging 40—50cm. long; *upper surface* canaliculate, green, sometimes obscurely lineate, usually with a few dull pale greenish lenticular spots low down; *lower surface* rounded, not at all keeled, green, usually copiously spotted near base, the spots lenticular, and often with a very small spinulescent tubercle in the centre of the largest spots; *margins* with a very narrow ·5—1mm. broad white cartilaginous border with soft white cartilaginous teeth that are about 1mm. long and more crowded low down, becoming smaller and more distant towards middle of leaf, and obsolescent towards apex.

Inflorescence 1—2, simple, 60—80cm. tall.

Peduncle basally plano-convex and 10—15mm. broad, terete upwards and clothed with several sterile-bracts that are ovate-acute, 15—20mm. long, 10—15mm. broad, thin, brownish, subscarious, many-nerved.

Raceme cylindric-acuminate, averaging 15—20cm. long (sometimes 25cm. long), 8—9cm. diam., the youngest buds at first entirely covered by large densely imbricate bracts, open flowers nutant to subpendulous.

Bracts clasping the pedicel, ovate-acute, averaging 15—20mm. long, about 10mm. broad at middle when pressed flat, sometimes as long as the pedicel, thin, scarious, many-nerved.

Pedicels 30—35mm. long, the colour of the perianth, nutant at apex.

Perianth peach-red, strawberry-pink or salmon-pink, 38—40—42mm. long, cylindric slightly trigonous, rather fleshy, basally obtuse and shortly stipitate, about 9mm. diam. across the ovary; *outer segments* varying from free for one-quarter their length to free to the middle or to near base, faintly 7—9-nerved, greenish at apex; *inner segments* thin at the edges, with more obtuse more spreading apices.

Filaments pale lemon; *anthers* not exserted; *style* at length exserted 0—1mm.; *ovary* pale orange-green, 7—8mm. long, 3mm. diam. (Plate 7, Figs. 25–29).

TANZANIA (TANGANYIKA). SOUTHERN HIGHLANDS PROV. *Mbeya Dist.*: Kyimbila (near Tukuyu) N of Lake Nyasa, 13 Nov. 1913, A. Stolz 2300! (K, BM); Chunya Ridge, 8,000 ft., 26 Jan. 1937, B. D. Burtt 6390! (K, BM); Mbeya Range, 8,000 ft., cult. Pretoria fl. 3 June 1938, Pole Evans et Erens 742! (PRE, BR, K)—the type of *Fl. Pl. S. Afr.* 20: pl. 762 (1940); Rocky slopes 24 miles N of Mbeya at 6,500 ft., c. 8° 47′ S, 33° 34′ E, cult. Johannesburg, fl. 30 April 1955, Reynolds 7539! (PRE, K, EA); 9 miles N of Mbeya, grassy mountain slopes at 7,600 ft., fl. 21 June 1958, Reynolds 8664! (PRE, K, EA), cult. Johannesburg, fl. 15 May 1960, Reynolds 8664! (SRGH); Mbeya Peak, common on western ridges of mountain, cult. Muguga, June 1962, D. Kerfoot 3779! (EA). *Njombe Dist.*: Elton Plateau, 5 Jan. 1957, Mrs. H. M. Richards 7481! (K); 20 miles SE of Njombe at 5300 ft., fl. 24 June 1958, Reynolds 8689! (PRE, K); 32 km. S of Njombe, 1620 m., 6 July 1956, Milne-Redhead et Taylor 10994! (K). *Sao Hill Dist.*: Sao Highlands, north of Mketi (?Mkewe), cult. Pretoria, fl. March 1939, I. B. Pole Evans et J. Erens 795! in Nat. Herb. 24803 (PRE)—type of *A. mketiensis* Christian in *Fl. Pl. S. Afr.* 20: Pl. 785 (1940); Coll. 12 miles SW of Sao Hill, 6,000 ft., cult. Johannesburg, fl. 8 April 1959, Reynolds 8713! (PRE, K). *Iringa Dist.*: Mt. Image, 50 miles NE of Iringa a little N of Morogoro Road, 6,700 ft., 3 March 1962, fairly common, scattered in montane grassland, Polhill et Paulo 1668! (K, PRE, EA). *Western Prov. Sumbawanga Dist.*: Kito (Chito) Mountain, near N. Rhodesia border, 1800 m., 21 April 1961, Mrs. H. M. Richards 13796 (EA).

MALAWI (NYASALAND). *Northern Prov.*: Nchena Chena spur, Nyika Plateau, 2000 m., 10 Aug. 1946, L. J. Brass 17147! (K); 20 Aug. 1946, L. J. Brass 17369! (K). Kondowe to Karonga, 2,000—6,000 ft., July 1894, A. Whyte! (K). Eastern slopes of the Nyika above Nchena Chena, 7,000 ft., cult. Blantyre, fl. 20 May 1956, Reynolds 8187! (PRE, K).

PLATE 7

ALOE NUTTII   Baker.

A form from mountain slopes N of Mbeya, Southern Highlands
Prov., Tanzania (Tanganyika), flowering in Johannesburg. Height 65cm.

Fig. 25.   Fig. 26.

A. nuttii Bak.

Fig. 25. Plant from between Abercorn and Fwambo (type loc.) Northern Prov., Zambia, flowering in Johannesburg, Height 60cm.

Fig. 26. Plant from 25 miles SSE of Elisabethville, Katanga, Congo, near Welgelegen, type loc. of *A. corbisieri* De Wild. Height 70cm.

Fig. 27.   Fig. 28.

A. nuttii Bak.

Fig. 27. Plants near the valley of the Cambumbe River, Bié – Cuando – Cubango Dist., Angola. Height 70cm.
Fig. 28. Showing spotting of leaves dorsally, near base.

Photos: Dr. E. J. Mendes.

ZAMBIA (NORTHERN RHODESIA). *Northern Prov., Abercorn Dist.:* Fwambo, S of Lake Tanganyika at about 5,250 ft., in *Hook. Icon Pl.* V. 26 t. 2513 (1897), Coll. and comm. Mr. W. H. Nutt 1896! holotype (K), also mounted on same sheet: Fwambo, 1894, Alexander Carson 29! (K); bush above Inono stream, 5,000 ft., 28 Feb. 1935, Mrs. H. M. Richards 4711! (K); Abercorn, 28 March 1955, Excell, Mendonça and Wild 1236! (SRGH); Abercorn, high plateau between Senga Hill and Kambole Mission, 5,500 ft., 6 June 1936, B. D. Burtt 5878! (K); Abercorn—Fwambo Road, cult. Johannesburg, fl. 3 May 1959, G. W. Reynolds 8653! (PRE, K); Abercorn, Brachystegia woodland, 5,500 ft., 9 March 1950, A. A. Bullock 2615! (K, BR, EA). *Western Prov. Copper Belt:* Kitwe, Kamfinsa River, 23 Feb. 1958, D. B. Fanshaw 4281! (K). *North Western Prov.:* 5 miles W of Mwinilunga, 26 Jan. 1938, Milne-Redhead 4363! (K). *Note:* Mwinilunga is in the far north-western corner of Zambia, some 300 miles W of the Copper Belt.

CONGO (LEO). *Katanga:* Elisabethville. Welgelegen, flowers rose coloured, 1912, Corbisier n. 623!—holotype of *A. corbisieri* De Wildeman (BR), 25 km. SSE from Elisabethville, 1 March 1954, A. Schmitz 4599! (BR); *Jadotville Dist.:* Kambove, near road to Panda, 17 March 1926, W. Robyns 1722! (BR). *Note:* Welgelegen is a small railway station 197 km. from the Sakania—Ndola border on road to Elisabethville and 56 km. S of Elisabethville.

ANGOLA. *Bié Dist.:* Moxico. In Brachystegia-Isoberlinia woodland between River Kanyezhi and River Kaboli, 20 Jan. 1938, Milne-Redhead 4260! (K). *Note:* This is about 40 miles W of Mwinilunga (N. Rhodesia), and some 340 miles W of the N. Rhodesian Copper Belt. *Bié:* Near Longa, above the Quiriri—Longa Junction, 1250 m., fl. 2 Feb. 1900, H. Baum 698—(holotype of *A. brunneo-punctata* Engler et Gilg.) (B), isotype (K, BM). *Note:* This is approximately 14° 50′ S, 18° 33′ E. *Bié*, Cuando, Cubango, *Menongue:* 50 km. E of Caiundo on road to Vila Serpa Pinto, alt. 1300 m., 4 Feb. 1960, E. J. Mendes 2354! (LISC); Vila Serpa Pinto, valley of the Cambumbe River, c. 1420 m., 15 Feb. 1960, E. J. Mendes 2575! (LISC); valley of the Luassinga River, between Longa and Serpa Pinto, fruiting 22 March 1960, E. J. Mendes 3243! (LISC).

FIG. 29.

A. nuttii Bak. Flowers 1/1 from a plant collected near Fwambo, east of Abercorn, Northern Prov., Zambia (type loc.)

Type locality: Fwambo, about 10 miles east of Abercorn in Zambia (N. Rhodesia), eastwards from the southern tip of L. Tanganyika, alt. 5,250 ft. The type material at Kew includes the upper portion of a leaf only, and Baker (in his second publication) was not correct in describing the leaf as unspotted with marginal teeth obsolete. This has misled many workers. Leaves of *A. nuttii* are always denticulate in lower half, more noticeably nearer base.

Baker (*F.T.A.* 7: 457) described the perianth as having "tube half as long as the segments" which means segments free for two-thirds their length. Plants from near Fwambo had outer segments free to the middle, while in plants near each other on mountains north of Mbeya the author has seen considerable variation in perianths with outer segments free for 8m. only, free to the middle, and free almost to base. This has also been observed in plants along Sao Hill in the Southern Highlands of Tanzania. Here, the length and shape of flowers also varied, hence *A. mketiensis* Christian goes into synonymy.

Several plants from Welgelegen, 25 miles SSE of Elisabethville in the Congo (type locality of *A. corbisieri* De Wild), flowered in Johannesburg and proved to be forms of *A. nuttii*, hence this too goes into synonymy.

Dr. E. J. Mendes, Centro de Botânica Lisbon, has collected several plants of *A. brunneo-punctata* from near its type locality in Angola. His excellent material (LISC) leaves no doubt that *A. brunneo-punctata* must also go into synonymy.

A. nutti varies considerably in its growth forms. Near Abercorn, 5,000 ft., plants occur mostly in sandy soil in Brachystegia—Isoberlinia woodland, and grow singly or with stems 2—3-branched at ground level. This is the largest form, and has longer leaves, taller inflorescences, and flowers averaging 38—40mm. long.

On mountains north of Mbeya in Tanzania, especially on a rocky slope 24 miles from Mbeya on road to Lupa Goldfields, large numbers of *A. nuttii* were found varying from single-stemmed plants to specimens with 9—12 and more densely tufted stems, each up to 20cm. long. In this latter form leaves were always shorter and narrower. Hence, the greater the number of stems, the shorter and narrower the leaves produced.

Native Names: Nibeets (Uhehe) Tanzania. *Dilenga* Elisabethville, Congo; Zambia: *Tembwisya* in the local Mambwe tongue of Abercorn, and *Iwata* in the Namwanga tongue of Isoka, east of Kasama.

Flowering period mostly January to March, depending on locality, and the rains.

A. nuttii is nearest allied to the Malawi species *A. buchananii* Bak, but the latter usually has larger leaves that are often distichous, and shorter flowers averaging 30mm. long that are markedly broader at base and narrower at the mouth.

GROUP 3

(Section *Bulbiformes* Christian).

PLANTS WITH UNDERGROUND "BULBS"

Leaves rosulate, deciduous, the leaf bases dilating below ground and forming bulb-like swellings; *inflorescence* simple or branched.

Type species: *A. buettneri* Berger. 3 species in Tropical Africa, none in Madagascar; 1 species in South Africa (*A. kniphofioides* Berger).

KEY TO THE SPECIES

1. SMALL PLANTS

"Bulb" 30mm. diam., leaves 15mm. broad, margins ciliate with ·5—1mm. teeth; *inflorescence* simple or 1-branched, 40cm. high:
  (a) *Raceme* lax, 25cm. long, pedicels 5—7mm., bracts to 25mm. long, perianth 40—48mm. long, outer segments free .. .. .. 13 *A. richardsiae*
  (b) *Raceme* 7—10cm. long, pedicels 4—5mm. long, bracts 8—10mm. long, perianth 30mm., outer segments free for 8mm... .. 14 *A. bullockii*

2. LARGE PLANTS

"Bulb" 8—10cm. diam., leaves 9—10cm. broad, canaliculate, inflorescence 3—5-branched, 70—90cm. high, pedicels 20—25mm. long:
  (a) Racemes 10—15cm. long, perianth 38mm. long, outer segments free for 10mm. .. .. 15 *A. buettneri*

13. **A. richardsiae** Reynolds in *Journ. S.A. Bot.* 30: 67 (1964)

DESCRIPTION: *Plant* with thick fleshy narrowly long-attenuate (not fusiform) roots, and with an underground bulb-like swelling about 35mm. long, 30mm. diam.

Leaves 8—10, rosulate, rather fleshy, suberectly to obliquely spreading, 20—25cm. long, 15mm. broad when pressed flat; *upper surface* canaliculate, green, obscurely lineate, unspotted; *lower surface* rounded, lineate, without spots; *margins* ciliate with white firm cartilaginous deltoid crowded teeth that are ·5mm. long, 1—2mm. distant.

Inflorescence simple, 35—45cm. tall.

Peduncle brown, basally plano-convex, 8—9mm. broad, with a few scattered sterile bracts, the lowest up to 5mm. long, 8mm. broad, gradually attenuate, long pointed, many-nerved.

Raceme narrowly cylindric-acuminate, very laxly flowered, about 25cm. long, 5—6cm. diam., the youngest buds at first hidden by long imbricate bracts, the lowest open flowers pendulous.

Bracts narrowly ovate-acute, 25—30mm. long, 7—8mm. broad, thin, white, scarious, many-nerved.

Pedicels 5—7mm. long, nutant at apex.

Perianth pale orange-scarlet, up to 48mm. long, 7—8mm. across the ovary, slightly narrowed above the ovary, thence slightly decurved and slightly enlarging to the throat and narrowing again to a laterally compressed rather closed mouth; *outer segments* free for 15mm. (approximately one-third their length), obscurely 3-nerved; *inner segments* free but dorsally adnate to the outer for two-thirds their length, with 3 crowded nerves forming a slight keel, the apices rather obtuse.

Filaments pale lemon, filiform-flattened, the 3 inner narrower and lengthening before the 3 outer with their *anthers* in turn exserted 1—2mm.; *style* pale lemon, with *stigma* at length exserted 3mm.; *ovary* very pale olive-green, 5mm. long, 3mm. diam. (Figs. 30—32).

Fig. 30.

A. richardsiae Reynolds. Plant × 2/3 showing underground bulbous swelling, and tapering (not fusiform) roots.

Fig. 31.

A. richardsiae Reynolds. Plant × 1/5 approx.

TANZANIA (TANGANYIKA). *Iringa Dist.*, Ipogoro—M'kawa track, Sao Hill, c. 3,500 ft., 12 December 1961, Mrs. H. M. Richards 15604! holotype (K), isotype (PRE). "Grass clearing in woodland, wet mud, dry in dry season. Growing in many thousands, a wonderful sight. Leaves narrow, flowers vermilion, tip yellow. Roots bulbous." Cult. Mbabane, Swaziland, fl. 5 Oct. 1963, Richards et Reynolds 9971 (K); fl. 17 Nov. 1963, Richards et Reynolds 10003 (PRE).

A. richardsiae was named after Mrs. H. M. Richards who is one of the most outstanding collectors there has ever been in Tropical Africa. She started collecting in 1951 (at an age when most men had already retired), and in the following 14 years collected over 20,000 gatherings, many from places hitherto unknown botanically, mostly in the backwoods of Zambia and Tanganyika.

Mrs. Richards and Mr. John Proctor discovered considerable numbers of plants flowering in December 1961 in a very out of the way place, namely along the Ipogoro–M'kawa track. A carefully prepared map by Mr. Proctor shows the Aloe area about 12 miles SW of Madibira Mission, beyond the Ndembera River, and NE of Ipogoro, at approximately 8° 16″ S, 34° 44″ E, which is about 50 miles due west of Sao Hill as the crow flies, at 3,500 ft. Mr. Proctor noticed plants in an area about 5 miles long and 2 miles wide.

FIG. 32.

A. richardsiae Reynolds. Portion of raceme with bract, pedicel, and flower 1/1.

A. richardsiae is distinguished by having an underground bulb-like swelling, and is closely related to *A. bullockii* Reynolds from the Kahama District in North-western Tanganyika, but it differs in having much narrower, more fleshy, leaves (10—15mm. broad against 30mm.), a very laxly flowered raceme that is three times as long (25—30cm. against 7—10cm.), considerably longer bracts (25—30mm. long against 8—10mm.), and longer flowers. The bulb-like swelling in *A. richardsiae* is much more pronounced when flowering in the rainy season than it is in the dry months.

14. **A. bullockii** Reynolds in *Journ. S.A. Bot.* 27: 73, pl. 11, 12 (1961)

DESCRIPTION: *Plant* with thick fusiform roots and with an underground bulb, 3cm. tall and 3—4cm. diam. at the middle.
    Leaves 8—10, rosulate, spreading to recurved, linear-lanceolate, 10cm. long and 2cm. broad when flowering at the end of the dry season, reaching 20cm. long, 3cm. broad at the middle in the rainy season; *upper surface* canaliculate, green, lineate, the lines alternately lighter and deeper green in colour, without spots; *lower surface* rounded, similar to upper surface in colour and lineation; *margins* with continuous cartilaginous narrow edge ciliate with crowded soft pale-pink teeth about ·5—1mm. long, ·5—1mm. apart.
    Inflorescence simple or 1-branched, 35—50cm. tall.

Peduncle plano-convex and 8mm. broad at base; when 1-branched the branch subtended at base by a scarious, thin many-nerved bract 12mm. long, 5mm. broad.

Raceme cylindric, slightly acuminate, 7—10mm. long, about 5cm. diam.

Bracts broadly ovate-acute, deflexed, 8—10mm. long, 5—6mm. broad, thin, scarious, white, 3—5-nerved.

Pedicels 4—5mm. long.

Perianth pale scarlet to coral-red, 30mm. long, basally flat, 6mm. diam. across the ovary, constricted to 4mm. above the ovary, thence enlarging and slightly contracted at the throat; *outer segments* free for 8mm., obscurely nerved, the apices subacute; *inner segments* orange, broader than the outer, with pale-scarlet keel, and more obtuse apices.

Filaments lemon, the 3 inner narrower and lengthening before the 3 outer with their *anthers* in turn exserted 3mm.; *stigma* at length exserted 4—5mm.; *ovary* pale brown, 3·5mm. long, 2·5mm. diam. (Figs. 33–36).

Fig. 33.

A. bullockii Reynolds. Flowering plant in natural habitat. Height 45cm.

Photo: Mr. A. A. Bullock.

Tanzania. *Kahama Dist.:* 15 miles south of Mbugwe, c. 3° 32′ S, 31° 15′ E, alt. 4,000 ft., fl. 5 August 1950, A. A. Bullock 3076 holotype (K); *Buha Dist.:* Murungu—Nyamgalika, c. 4° 14′ S, 31° 11′ E, alt. 4,000 ft., fl. 20 August 1950, Bullock 3195! (K); coll. Bullock 15 miles south of Mbugwe, cult. Bryanston, Johannesburg, fl. 23 Aug. 1960, Reynolds 9525 (PRE).

A. bullockii was named after Mr. A. A. Bullock of Kew, who discovered it in August 1950 in burnt woodland fringing the east "bank" of the Mogowosi River, which runs almost north to south in a botanically little-known area which is depopulated because of sleeping sickness.

Mr. Bullock found plants 15 miles S of Mbugwe in the Kahama District, and also further south in the Buha District, flowering after bush fires in August 1950.

A. bullockii is one of the very few species of Aloe having an underground bulb-like swelling, and is nearest allied to *A. richardsiae* Reynolds from about 50 miles due west of Sao Hill which is also in Tanzania. The latter differs in having much narrower more fleshy leaves (10—15mm. broad against 30mm.), a very lax raceme that is three times as long (25—30cm. against 7—10cm.), considerably longer bracts, and longer flowers.

Another noteworthy characteristic of *A. bullockii* is that, when plants flower towards the end of the long dry season, the leaves have dried back to 10cm. long, while six months later, after heavy rains, leaves develop to 20cm. in length and are more spreading recurved. The "bulb" is also larger after rains.

FIG. 34.

A. bullockii Reynolds. Uprooted plants showing bulbs and fusiform roots × ¼ approx.
Photo: Mr. A. A. Bullock.

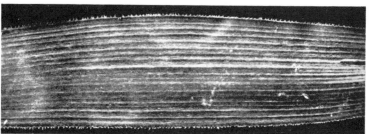

FIG. 35.
A. bullockii Reynolds. Portion of leaf (after rains) 1/1.

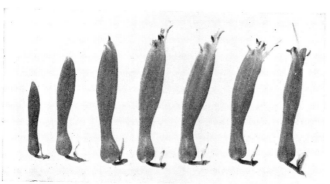

FIG. 36.

A. bullockii Reynolds.
Flowers natural size.

15. **A. buettneri** Berger in Engler's *Bot. Jahrb.* 36: 60 (1905, in Engler's *Pflanzenr.* Liliac.-Aloin. 241 (1908); R. W. J. Keay in *Kew Bull.* 17: 67 (1963).

—— *A. paedogona* Berger in *Journ. Bot.* 44: 57 (1906), in Engler's *Pflanzenr.* Liliac.-Aloin. 240 (1908).

—— *A. bulbicaulis* Christian in *Fl. Pl. S. Afr.* 16: Pl. 630 (1936); Reynolds in *Aloes of Nyasaland* 12 (1954).

—— *A. barteri* Bak. in *Journ. Linn. Soc. Bot.* 18: 168 (1880), *pro parte*, in *Fl. Trop. Afr.* 7: 464 (1898), *pro parte*, in *Fl. W. Trop. Afr.* 2: 345 (1936) *pro parte – fide* Keay.

—— *A. barteri* Bak. var. *sudanica* A. Chev. in *Rev. Bot. Appliq.* 31: 592 t. 33/B (1952), *descr. gall. tant. – fide* Keay.

—— *A. barteri* Bak. var. *dahomensis* A. Chev. in *Rev. Bot. Appliq.* 31: 594 (1952), *descr. gall. tant. – fide* Keay.

—— *A. paludicola* A. Chev. l.c. 597, t. 33C. (1952) *descr. gall. tant.*; in *Et. Fl. Centr. Afr.* 1: 313 (1913), *nomen nudum – fide* Keay.

DESCRIPTION based on personal observations in Zambia, Congo Republic, Angola, Nigeria, and on cultivated plants from elsewhere.

Plant succulent, growing singly, acaulescent, with leaf bases dilating below ground level and forming a bulb-like swelling, the "bulb" 8—10cm. diam., 6—8cm. long, sometimes with a somewhat woody stem below the "bulb" reaching 5—10cm. long, 3—4cm. thick in old specimens.

Leaves about 16, rosulate, somewhat leathery, deciduous, 35—55cm. long (40—45cm. the average), about 8cm. broad at base, widening a little and 9—10cm. broad in upper third, thence narrowing to an acute apex, the youngest leaves erectly spreading, oldest leaves spreading to slightly recurved; *upper surface* green, usually unspotted, obscurely lineate, slightly canaliculate; *lower surface* rounded, green, obscurely lineate, usually not spotted; *margins* with very narrow white to pale pink cartilaginous edge armed with firm cartilaginous teeth varying from 1·5mm. long and 3—5mm. apart low down to 10mm. apart higher up in south-eastern localities, to margins sinuate-dentate with teeth 3—4mm. long and 10—15mm. apart in the far north-western localities.

Inflorescence 2—3 consecutively, averaging 70—90cm. high, 3—5-branched from just above the middle.

Peduncle thick, scarcely flattened at base 20—30mm. diam., without sterile-bracts below the first branch, but the branches with a few sterile-bracts below the racemes.

Racemes sub-capitate and 10cm. long to cylindric-conic and 15cm. long, about 7cm. diam., the buds suberect, open flowers nutant to pendulous.

Bracts broadly deltoid-acute, or lanceolate-acuminate, clasping the pedicel, 10—15mm. long, 6—8mm. broad at base, deep brownish, 5—7-nerved.

Pedicels 20—25mm. long.

Perianth varying from greenish-yellow or olive-buff to pinkish-brown and dull to bright red, averaging 38mm. long, basally obconic, with globose inflation 9—11mm. diam. across the ovary, thence gradually narrowing to 6—8mm. above the ovary and gradually enlarging to 9—11mm. at two-thirds the length of the perianth, thence again contracted to the throat, with a wide-open mouth; *outer segments* free for 9—10mm., with pale margins and obscurely to prominently 3—5-nerved to base; *inner segments* free but dorsally adnate to the outer for three-quarters their length, the apices broader and more spreading than the outer; the perianth smooth or sometimes costate (ribbed).

Filaments pale lemon, filiform-flattened, with their *anthers* exserted 0—1mm.; *stigma* at length exserted 1mm.; *ovary* green, 5mm. long, 3mm. diam. (Plates 8—9, Figs. 37—43).

TOGO. Near Bismarckburg Experimental Station, 31 July 1890, Büttner s.n. holotype of *A. buettneri* Berger (B).

MALI. Diondiou, near Bobo-Dioulasso, 11 June 1899, Chevalier 1014 (P, syntype of *A. barteri* var. *sudanica*). Between Kita and Badinko, 3 Jan. 1899, Chevalier 115 (P, syntype of *A. barteri* var. *sudanica*)—*fide* R. W. J. Keay.

GHANA. Togo. Kpeve Agricultural Station, 24 Dec. 1926, Howes 1073 (K). Near Kintampo, June 1933, Vigne 3046! (K).

DAHOMEY. Atacora Mountains, from Natitingou to Bokorona, 21 June 1910, Chevalier 24217 (P, holotype of *A. barteri* var. *dahomensis*).

W. NIGERIA. Iseyin, 11 May 1958, Hambler 455! (K). Savannah, near Ado Awaiye, Feb. 1948, Keay & Brenan in FHI 22403! (FHI, K, SRGH). Olokemeji, 13 June 1946, Jones & Keay in FHI 18816 (FHI).

N. NIGERIA. *Zaria Prov.*, Anara Forest Reserve, 19 Oct. 1947, Keay in FHI 5488! (FHI, K), same plant fl. Sept. 1948 (SRGH). Same locality, cult. Ibadan, 4 July 1949, Keay in F.H.I. 32969! (K, FHI). *Niger Prov.*, about 80 km. N of Zungeru on the Bernin Gwari road, 11 June 1949, Latilo in F.H.I. 25329! (FHI, K). *Oyo Prov.*, Ado Rock, S of Iseyin, 10 June 1949, Latilo in F.H.I. 25328! (FHI, K). Oyo, 10 June 1949, Keay in F.H.I. 25328, 4 July 1949, Keay in F.H.I. 32970 and 9 July 1949, Keay in F.H.I. 32971, 32972 (K). *Oyo Prov.*, in open savannah, Feb. 1948, Keay in F.H.I. 22403! (K).

SHARI. South of Baguirmi, near Madabo, 30 July 1903, Chevalier 9475 (P, holotype of *A. paludicola*)—*fide* R. W. J. Keay.

REPUBLIC DU CONGO. Coll. B. Descoings, near the Loa River, 10km. WSW of Brazzaville, c. 4° 20′ S, 15° 10′ E, alt. 310 m., cult. Mbabane, Swaziland, fl. 22 March 1964, Reynolds 9909 (K, PRE).

ANGOLA. *Benguela Dist.*, grasslands at 5,900 ft., 124 miles E of Lobito, c. 12° 22′ S, 15° 08′ E, fl. in Johannesburg 31 March 1960, Reynolds 9328 (PRE, K, SRGH). *Malange Dist.*, Malange, June 1903, Gossweiler 946! holotype of *A. paedogona* Berger (BM), isotype (K). *Bié Dist.*, 4 miles E of Chinguar between Silva Porto and Nova Lisboa, fl. in Johannesburg 31 Jan. 1960, again 10 March 1960, Reynolds 9234! (K, PRE). *Huila Dist.*: Ganguelas, Vila Artur de Paiva (Vila da Ponte) 25 Jan. 1960, E. J. Mendes 2175! (LISC).

PLATE 8

ALOE BUETTNERI   Berger.

Young plant from Northern Malawi (Nyasaland), flowering in Johannesburg. Height 60cm.

PLATE 9

ALOE BUETTNERI   Berger.

Plant from 10km. WSW of Brazzaville, Congo, flowering at Mbabane,
Swaziland in March 1964. Height 85cm.

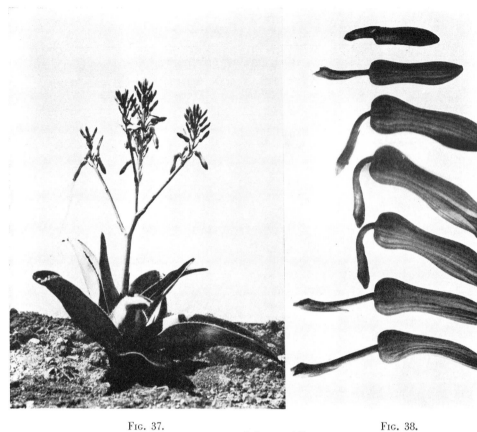

Fig. 37.

Fig. 38.

A. buettneri Berger.

The type plant of *A. bulbicaulis* Christian (from Misundu   Flowers natural size – less constricted above the
Siding N. Zambia) flowering at Ewanrigg, near Salisbury.   ovary than usual.

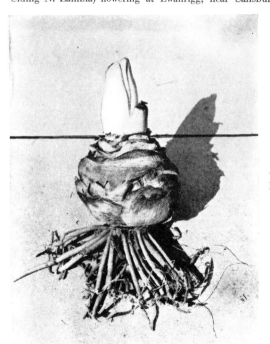

Fig. 39.

A. buettneri Berger. This "bulb" from N. Malawi,
produced the yellow-flowered young plant depicted on
Plate 8. The line indicates ground level.

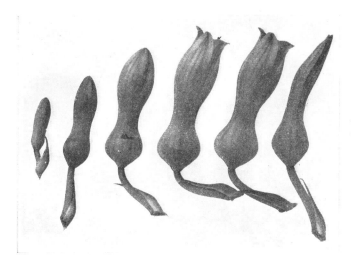

Fig. 40.

A. buettneri Berger. Flowers 1/1, from the scarlet-flowered plant from near Brazza-ville, Congo, depicted on Plate 9.

Fig. 41.

A. buettneri Berger. A form with spotted leaves and prominent marginal teeth near Sampa, NW Ashanti, Ghana. Height 60cm.
Photo: Dr. C. D. Adams.

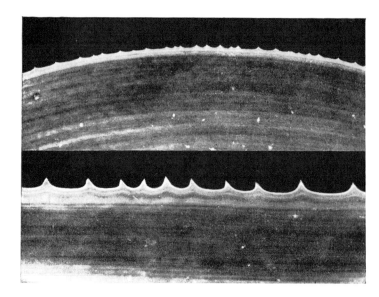

FIG. 42.

A. buettneri Berger. Showing variation in leaf margins. *Upper:* From a plant near Ndola, Zambia. *Lower:* From a plant near Malange, Angola, 1/1.

FIG. 43.

A. buettneri Berger. Flowers 1/1 from a plant near Chinguar, between Silva Porto and Nova Lisboa, Angola.

CONGO REPUBLIC. Katanga, 5 miles NE of Elisabethville, 4,000 ft., fruiting 7 May 1954, Reynolds 7227! (K, BR); 6 miles NE of Elisabethville, 1 March 1954, O. Schmitz 4600! (PRE); Kitenge, between Kabongo and Kabalo, 16 Oct. 1955, O. Schmitz 5014 (PRE). *Note:* Kabongo is 140 miles NE of Kamina, SW of Kabalo, and W of Manono. Large numbers are found E of Manono.

MALAWI. *Northern Prov.:* South edge of Vwaza Marsh, 2 miles W of N.A. Katumbi, in Huwe country, N of Njakwa, cult. Johannesburg, fl. 14 Feb 1953, Reynolds 6749A (K, PRE).

ZAMBIA. *Western Prov.:* Misundu Siding on N. Rhodesia-Belgian Congo border, 4,200 ft., cult. Pretoria, Christian in Nat. Herb. 20587, holotype of *A. bulbicaulis* Christian (PRE); Ndola, 8 Jan. 1955, Fanshaw 1780! (K). *North West Prov.:* Woodland around Matonchi farm, 22 Oct. 1937, E. Milne-Redhead 2903A (K). *Note:* This locality is about 30 miles W of Mwinilunga and over 300 miles W of the North Rhodesian Copper Belt, almost on the Angola border.

A. buettneri was originally described "Habit of growth and leaves unknown", hence a most important character, the underground "bulb", was not recorded. It has only recently been established that the two later described species *A. paedogona* Berger from Malange, Angola, and *A. bulbicaulis* Christian from the Zambia–Congo border are forms of one and the same species.

Plants are found over a tremendous area, from North Malawi, Lake Mweru southwards to the Copper Belt of Zambia, westwards to Angola where it grows in abundance along the watershed and elsewhere in Angola. In the Congo Republic, Katanga, from Elisabethville northwards to the

Parc National de l'Upemba, Manono and Kabalo (west of Albertville); from Elisabethville north-westwards to Kamina, Luluabourg, Leopoldville to near Matadi, and abundant in the Binza–Kimwenza areas; across the R. Congo near Brazzaville and elsewhere in the Republic du Congo; northwards through the Cameroons, Shari, Nigeria, Dahomey, Togo, Ghana and to Mali (late French Sudan) where it occurs near Bobo–Dioulasso and further west near Kita. From the Copper Belt in Zambia to Kita in Mali is at least 3,500 miles which is the widest distribution range of any species of Aloe in Africa.

Habitat varies from Brachystegia–Isoberlinia woodland, Guinea Savannah and grasslands, to low-lying places that become water-logged for a month or two in the rainy season. In Zambia, near Mwinilunga, plants were observed growing on dry termite mounds. The leaves dry back and disappear in winter.

There is a gradual change in form from one end of the range to the other. For example, in the furthest south-eastern limits of distribution (Copper Belt in Zambia, Elisabethville in Congo and N. Malawi) the "bulb" is larger, leaves are unspotted, margins have a narrow cartilaginous edge with small teeth only 1—1·5mm. long, and the flowers are yellowish. In the Leopoldville and Brazzaville areas the "bulbs" are smaller, and the flowers are reddish, while in upper Ashanti, Ghana, leaves are found rather copiously spotted on both surfaces, with the margins horny, sinuate-dentate with pungent teeth 3—4mm. long.

No matter how other characters may vary, it can be stated that *A. buettneri* can always be identi-fied by the unusual shape of its flowers with globose basal swelling, a fixed character unique in the genus.

At Malange, Angola, *A. paedogona* Berger was described with inflorescence reaching 2m. This was caused merely by plants growing in 5—6 ft. grass (*Hyparrhenia* sp.). A few miles away, in shorter grass, the usual 70—80cm. inflorescences were found.

NATIVE NAMES. Angola: *Kikalangu-Kibela* in the Kimbundu tongue of Malange – Gossweiler in *Nomes Indigenas de Plantas de Angola*, p. 491 (1953). *Note:* In the new spelling Qu replaces K. (Malange is ESE of Luanda at c. 9° 32′ S, 16° 21′ E).

CONGO REPUBLIC. Katanga: *Maposo* in the Kisanga tongue, at Lusinga, Parc National de l'Upemba near Mitwaba. Mali: The general name *Baza* among the Senoufo. The juice of the leaves is sometimes used in the preparation of arrow poison mixed with *Strophanthus* seeds. Called *Boi* in Bambara, near Kita. Sap exuding from cut leaves is used as a cicatrising agent for leg wounds.—Prof. A. Chevalier.

GROUP 4

SMALL PLANTS WITH ± STRIPED FLOWERS

Plants small, acaulescent (except in *A. jacksonii*), growing singly or in small to large dense groups. *Leaves* rosulate, fleshy, deltoid, ensiform or lanceolate, spotted both sides. *Inflorescence* simple or branched. *Bracts* very small. *Pedicels* short (5—10mm.). *Perianth* cylindric-trigonous, 20—30mm. long, *outer segments* connate to middle or higher.

Type species: *A. peckii* Bally et Verdoorn.

The 8 species in this group are characterized by being acaulescent (except in *A. jacksonii*) and by having small to larger leaves usually copiously spotted both sides, very small bracts, short pedicels, cylindric flowers that are more or less clearly white-striped to base. *A. peckii* with its conspicuously reddish-brown striped flowers is unique in the genus. *A. greatheadii* has flowers clearly white-striped from base to apex, but the flowers are not cylindric – see under Group 6, *Saponariae*. *A. massawana* also has striped flowers – see under Group 9, *Verae*.

KEY TO THE SPECIES

A. INFLORESCENCE SIMPLE, 30CM. HIGH

Small plants suckering freely, forming dense groups, perianth 25—27mm long:
1. Plants acaulescent, leaves 4cm. long .. ..   16 *A. jucunda*
2. Plants with slender stems, 10—20cm. long, leaves 10—15cm. long .. ..   18 *A. jacksonii*

Small plants, solitary or in very small groups:
3. Leaves 12cm. long, 25—30mm. broad .. ..   17 *A. hemmingii*

B. INFLORESCENCE A BRANCHED PANICLE, 1M. HIGH

LARGER ACAULESCENT PLANTS:
1. *Perianth "squat", 20—24mm. long:*
   (*a*) Leaves ensiform, 40—50cm. long, 7cm. broad, glossy or polished-like .. ..   22 *A. mcloughlinii*
2. *Perianth cylindric-trigonous, 25—30mm. long:* ..
   (*a*) Leaves 20cm. long, 7cm. broad, inflorescence 60cm. high, perianth flesh pink with a bloom .. ..   20 *A. erensii*
   (*b*) Leaves 16cm. long, 6cm. broad, 2cm. thick; perianth straw-coloured, conspicuously red-brown striped from base to apex ..   21 *A. peckii*
   (*c*) Leaves narrowly lanceolate, 20cm. long, 7cm. broad, brownish-green, slightly glossy, perianth pink-scarlet, 28—30mm. .. ..   19 *A. somaliensis*
   (*d*) Plants larger, leaves marbled with age, inflorescence much more branched, racemes shorter and denser, perianth deeper red   19A var. *marmorata*
   (*e*) Leaves ensiform, chocolate-brown with white lenticular markings, margins involute, perianth pink-scarlet, 30mm. ..   23 *A. pirottae*

16. **A jucunda** Reynolds in *Journ. S.A. Bot.* 19: 21 (1953) with Plate XI; Verdoorn in *Fl. Pl. Afr.* 35: Pl. 1390 (1962).

DESCRIPTION based on plants at the type locality, Gaan Libah, Somalia North (formerly Somaliland Prot.).

Plant very small, succulent, with cylindric (*not* fusiform roots, acaulescent or with very short stem, suckering freely and forming dense groups 30—50cm. and more across, the rosettes averaging 8cm. diam.

Leaves about 12, densely rosulate, broadly ovate-acuminate, spreading to recurved, 4cm. long, 2—5cm. broad at base, rather fleshy; *upper surface* dark green and flat low down, turning brownish and channelled in upper half, with numerous pale-green to dull-white spots throughout, the spots lenticular, sometimes confluent, smaller and more crowded low down, larger and fewer upwards; *lower surface* rounded, deep green, copiously spotted throughout, the spots smaller and much more numerous than on upper surface; *margins* armed with horny, reddish-brown, pungent, deltoid teeth up to 2mm. long, 3—4mm. distant, the interspaces rounded; the teeth smaller near base of leaf, largest near the middle and smaller towards apex, with a few minute spines dorsally in median line of leaf near apex.

Inflorescence simple, 33cm. high.

Peduncle plano-convex and 5mm. broad at base, gradually becoming terete upwards; clothed with about 6 sterile-bracts, the lowest deltoid-acute, 9mm. long, 4mm. broad at base, thin, dirty-white, subscarious, 5-nerved.

Raceme 13cm. long, 5cm. diam. low down, sublaxly about 20-flowered, the youngest buds suberect, grey-green striped in upper third and more crowded, the older buds spreading, with the open flowers nutant and more laxly disposed (10—15mm. distant).

Bracts lowest ovate-acute, 5mm. long, 3mm. broad at base, thin, scarious, dirty-white, 3-nerved.

Pedicels lowest 7mm. long, of a deeper pink colour than the base of the perianth.

Perianth 20mm. long, pale rose-pink (nearest coral-pink R.C.S. 13), cylindric, basally flat or exceedingly shortly stipitate, 7mm. diam. across the ovary, thence very slightly narrowed and slightly trigonous, the throat paler to whitish, the mouth white open; *outer segments* free for 7mm., white, with 3 pink nerves, the apices subacute, spreading; *inner segments* free but dorsally adnate to the outer for two-thirds their length, broader than the outer, white, with 3 congested nerves throughout, the nerves deep pink turning greenish at apex, the apices more obtuse and more spreading than the outer.

Filaments lemon-yellow, filiform-flattened, the 3 inner narrower and lengthening before the 3 outer, with their *anthers* in turn exserted 2mm.; *style* filiform, yellow, with the *stigma* at length exserted 2—3mm.; *ovary* pale olive-green, 5mm. long, 2·5mm. diam., obtusely tapering into the style. (Plate 10, Figs. 44—48).

SOMALIA NORTH (formerly Somaliland Prot.). Gaan Libah, c. 9° 55′ N, 44° 18′ E, coll. P. R. O. Bally no. 7157, cult. Johannesburg, fl. 31 Jan. 1953, Reynolds 6223, holotype (PRE); fl. again 24 May 1953, Reynolds 6223 (K); Gaan Libah, 12 miles NW of Ghor, 3,500 ft., 20 Sept. 1957, Reynolds 8473 (K, PRE); Gaan Libah East at Gerbakele, 5,500 ft., type locality, 20 Sept. 1957, Bally B11719! (K, G, EA); plant cult. Div. of Bot. Gardens Pretoria, fl. Jan. 1961, figured for *Fl. Pl. Afr.* 35: Plate 1390 (1962), No. 29013 in Nat. Herb. (PRE)

This charming little Aloe was discovered by Mr. P. R. O. Bally (at that time botanist at the Coryndon Museum, Nairobi) on Gaan Libah, which is about 25 miles W of Upper Sheikh (on

PLATE 10

ALOE JUCUNDA   Reynolds.

On Gaan Libah, 12 miles NW of Ghor, Somalia North, alt. 5,300 ft.
Height 9″.

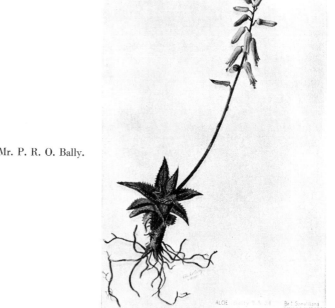

Fig. 44.

A. jucunda Reynolds. From a painting by Mr. P. R. O. Bally.

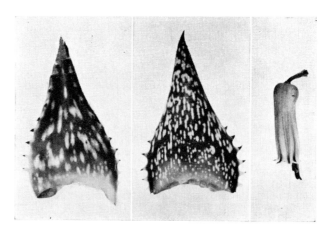

Fig. 45.   Fig. 46.   Fig. 47.

A. jucunda Reynolds.
Fig. 45. Upper surface of leaf, × 1/1.
Fig. 46. Lower surface of leaf, × 1/1.
Fig. 47. Flower natural size.

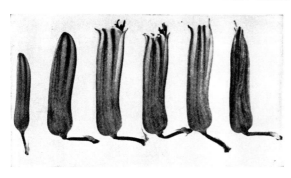

Fig. 48.

A. jucunda Reynolds. Flowers natural size.

the Berbera–Burao road), and 5 miles E of Mandera on the Berbera–Hargeisa road. In September 1957 the author visited Gaan Libah with Mr. Bally. Plants were found mostly facing north near the edge of the escarpment, on limestone, and mostly under partial shade of *Buxus hildebrandtii*, at 5,300 ft.

    A. jucunda is a most distinctive little Aloe with rather squat rose-pink flowers, the rosettes of leaves being only about 8—9cm. across, which makes it one of the smallest rosulate species in the genus. *A. descoingsii* Reynolds from near Tulear, Madagascar, has very similar rosettes of leaves, but the rosettes are much smaller, and the flowers bear no resemblance whatever to those of *A. jucunda*. Plants do well in a greenhouse, or with partial shade, and produce successive inflorescences.

17. **A. hemmingii** Reynolds et Bally in *Journ. S.A. Bot.* 30: 221 (1964)

DESCRIPTION: *Plant* succulent, solitary or in small groups, acaulescent or with very short stem.

    Leaves about 10, densely rosulate, spreading to slightly recurved near apex, ovate or lanceolate-attenuate, 10—12cm. long, 3—3·5cm. broad near base; *upper surface* flat near base, slightly canaliculate and with margins somewhat involute near apex, brownish-green with numerous dull white elongated streaks, throughout; *lower surface* convex, similar in colour to upper surface, but with the white lenticular streaks or blotches smaller and more numerous throughout; *margins* armed with pungent deltoid teeth that are whitish near base, brown-tipped at apex, smaller near base and apex, largest at middle of leaf where they average 2mm. long, 4—6mm. apart, sometimes with a few small teeth dorsally in median line near apex.

    Inflorescence simple, averaging 30—35cm. long.

    Peduncle slender, basally plano-convex and 5mm. broad, upwards terete and 3·5mm. thick, dull brownish, with a few sterile-bracts.

    Raceme cylindric, 10—15cm. long, 5cm. diam. laxly about 18-flowered, the buds grey-green tipped and suberect, open flowers rose-red, nutant to pendulous.

    Bracts ovate-acuminate, 8mm. long, 3mm. broad, thin, scarious, 5-nerved.

    Pedicels 6—8mm. long.

FIG. 49.

A. hemmingii Reynolds et Bally. Cultivated plant from Sheikh Pass, Golis Range, S of Berbera, Somalia North. Height 40cm.

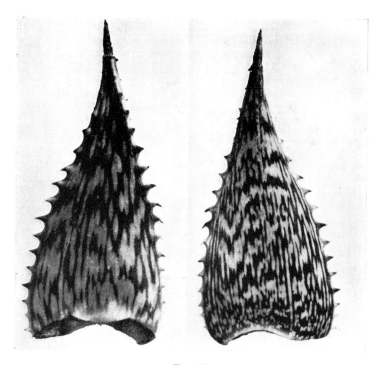

Fig. 50.

A. hemmingii Reynolds et Bally.
Leaves natural size. *Left:* upper
surface. *Right:* lower surface.

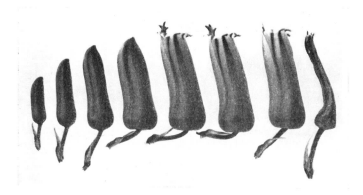

Fig. 51.

A. hemmingii Reynolds et Bally.
Flowers natural size.

Perianth flamingo-pink or pale rose-red, minutely spotted, cylindric-trigonous, 24mm. long, 8mm. across the ovary, thence cylindric-trigonous upwards; *outer segments* free for 7mm., 3-nerved to base, and with broad white borders giving the perianth a white-striped effect; the apices subacute, slightly spreading; *inner segments* broader than the outer with broader white border, and broader more obtuse spreading apices.

Filaments pale lemon, filiform-flattened, the 3 inner narrower and lengthening before the 3 outer with their *anthers* in turn exserted 2—3mm.; *stigma* at length exserted 3—4mm.; *ovary* yellowish-olive, 5mm. long, 2mm. diam. (Figs. 49-51).

SOMALIA NORTH. Sheikh Pass, Golis Range, 1 June 1949, Bally 7146 holotype (EA); near Sheikh Pass coll. Bally, B7146, cult. Johannesburg, fl. 19 Feb. 1955, Reynolds 7207 (PRE); *Borama Dist.* Loli Mudeda, 8 miles NW of Borama, 3 Oct. 1954, Bally B9961 (EA).

This distinctive species was named after Mr. C. F. Hemming, who for many years travelled extensively with the Desert Locust Survey throughout Somalia North (formerly Somaliland Prot.), Somalia South, Northern Kenya, parts of Ethiopia, and S. Arabia. He collected extensively in remote places, including many plants of Aloe. Mr. P. R. O. Bally collected plants of *A. hemmingii* in May 1949 near the top of Sheikh Pass in the Golis Range, south of Berbera (B.7146), and in October 1954 he found the same species flowering at Loli Mudeda, 8 miles NW of Borama, which is about 84 miles west of Hargeisa.

A. hemmingii is nearest allied to *A. jucunda* Reynolds, but the latter is a much smaller plant that suckers freely and forms dense groups; it has much smaller leaves with different markings, and slightly smaller flowers.

The flowers of *A. hemmingii* have broad, whitish borders to the outer segments which give them a somewhat white-striped effect.

18. **A. jacksonii** Reynolds in *Journ. S.A. Bot.* 21: 59 (1955)

DESCRIPTION: A small soboliferous, caespitose, succulent plant forming compact groups up to 30—50cm. and more across.

Stem simple or branched at base, erect or sprawling, up to 10—20cm. long, 8—10mm. diam.

Leaves 5—7 at apex of stems, narrowly subulate-attenuate, 10—15cm. long, 10—14mm. broad near base, basally sheathing, with short striate-internodes, youngest leaves suberect, older leaves spreading and with an obtuse apex bearing 1—2 firm white spines about 1—2mm. long; *upper surface* slightly concave low down, more caniculate upwards (more fleshy and plano-convex in cross-section in watered cultivated plants), dull green with several dull very pale-green lenticular spots irregularly scattered mostly in lower half of leaf; *lower surface* rounded, dull greyish-green with numerous dull pale-greenish lenticular markings or spots irregularly scattered, or sometimes arranged in broken transverse bands; *margins* straight, with isolated, firm, deltoid, white teeth which are reddish-brown tipped and about 1mm. long low down, 3—6mm. distant, becoming smaller to obsolescent upwards. *Sap* dries yellow.

Inflorescence simple, averaging 30 cm. tall.

Peduncle plano-convex and 4mm. broad at base, terete and 2mm. diam. below the raceme, with about 5 sterile bracts, the lowest ovate-acuminate, thin white, 5-nerved, 7mm. long, 5mm. broad, gradually smaller upwards.

Raceme cylindric, 6—8cm. long, laxly 16—20-flowered, youngest buds suberect, open flowers pendulous, the apex a small tuft of wilted bracts.

Bracts ovate-acuminate, 4mm. long, 2·5mm. broad at base, thin, subscarious, white, 3-nerved.

Pedicels 5—7mm. long.

Perianth bright scarlet-red or scarlet, paler to almost white at the mouth, 27mm. long, cylindric-trigonous, basally flat, 8—9mm. diam. over the ovary, thence narrowing very slightly to the throat with the mouth wide open; *outer segments* free for 6—7mm. with white edges, 3-nerved, the apices subacute spreading; *inner segments* broader than the outer, and with more obtuse more spreading apices.

Filaments yellow, filiform-flattened, the 3 inner narrower and lengthening before the 3 outer, with their *anthers* in turn exserted 2mm.; *style* filiform, with *stigma* at length exserted 3mm.; *ovary* pale olive, 5mm. long, 2mm. diam. (Plate 11, Figs. 52—54).

ETHIOPIA. *Ogaden Prov.*: El Carre, c. 5° 50′ N, 42° 07′ E, coll. T. H. E. Jackson, cult. Johannesburg, fl. 7 June 1953, Reynolds 6224 holotype (PRE); ex El Carre, coll. T. H. E. Jackson, Reynolds 7296 (K); flowering stem from plant coll. T. H. E. Jackson at El Carre, cult. Kapretwa, Kitale, Kenya, fl. 25 Oct. 1955, Reynolds 8005 (K); El Carre, cult. Sept. 1954, T. H. E. Jackson in CMN 18505 (EA).

A. jacksonii was named after Mr. T. H. E. Jackson who discovered it in 1943, at El Carre, when he was Acting Senior Civil Affairs Officer during the last war. El Carre lies WSW of Gabredarre, at a point about 120 miles north of Dolo, in the Ogaden Province of Southern Ethiopia.

Mr. Jackson stated "El Carre is a strange rock outcrop with precipitous sides, and our station was built below the precipice. There is a steep path winding up a cleft, and the Aloes were found along the edge at the top."

A. jacksonii is almost indistinguishable from *A. jucunda* in simple inflorescence, pedicels, bracts and flowers, but it differs considerably in leaf characters, the leaves being narrowly subulate-attenuate, 10—15cm. long and only about 12mm. broad. The flowers are also very near those of *A. erensii* and *A. somaliensis*, but the latter have very different leaves.

Cultivated plants need a little shade; they may be watered, and usually flower prolifically.

PLATE 11

ALOE JACKSONII   Reynolds.

Plant from El Carre, Ogaden, Southern Ethiopia. Height 50cm.

Fig. 52.

A. jacksonii Reynolds. Group flowering in the gardens of Mr. T. H. E. Jackson, near Kitale Kenya.

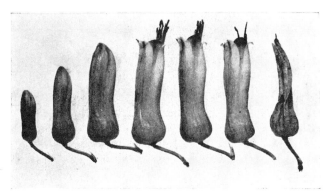

Fig. 54.

A. acksonii Reynolds.
Flowers 1/1.

Fig. 53.

Fig. 53. *Left* upper surface of leaf 1/1. *Right* lower surface 1/1.

19. **A. somaliensis** W. Watson in *Gard. Chron.* 26: 430 (1899); C. Wright in *Kew Bull.* 135 (1901); Berger in *Monatsschrift f. Kakteenkunde* 14: 120 (1904) *cum fig.*; in *Pflanzenr.* Liliac.-Aloin. 236 (1908); Reynolds in *Journ. S.A. Bot.* 24: 163, Pl. 11, 12 (1958) — Non *Miss. Biolog. Borana* 4: 348, t. 119 (1939). This is a totally different species in Sect. *Saponariae.*

DESCRIPTION: *Plant* succulent, growing singly or forming small groups. *Stem* none or short.

Leaves 12—16, densely rosulate, usually narrowly lanceolate, spreading to slightly recurved, averaging 20cm. long, 7cm. broad at base, 8—10mm. thick; *upper surface* flat low down, slightly canaliculate upwards, rather glossy brownish-green with numerous pale green lenticular spots throughout; *lower surface* convex, paler brownish-green than upper surface, and with more numerous, more crowded, sometimes confluent lenticular spots throughout; *margins* sinuate-dentate, the teeth reddish-brown, pungent, deltoid, averaging 4mm. long, 8—10mm. apart, the interspaces paler; *sap* dries brown.

Inflorescence a branched panicle, 60—80cm. high, usually produced suberectly to obliquely.

Peduncle plano-convex and 10—12mm. broad at base, terete upwards, averaging 5—8-branched from below the middle, the lowest branches sometimes with 1—2 branchlets.

Racemes cylindric, sublaxly flowered, 15—20cm. long, 5—6cm. diam., when erect the flowers evenly distributed around the axis, with youngest buds suberect, older buds horizontally disposed, open flowers nutant; in oblique racemes the flowers usually subsecund.

Bracts ovate-attenuate, about 8mm. long, 4mm. broad, thin, scarious, white, many-nerved.

Pedicels the lowest averaging 8mm. long.

Perianth pinkish-scarlet, turning paler after pollination, cylindric-trigonous, 28—30mm. long, basally flat to obtuse, 9mm. diam. across the ovary, thence very slightly narrowed on the underside only, slightly narrowed to the mouth, the whole perianth minutely speckled; *outer segments* free for 10mm., obscurely 3-nerved to base, the apices subacute and slightly spreading; *inner segments* broader than the outer, with a broad pale border and keeled in upper third, the keel the colour of the perianth, the apices more obtuse and more spreading than the outer.

Filaments lemon, the 3 inner narrower and lengthening before the 3 outer with their *anthers* in turn exserted 1—2mm; *stigma* at length exserted 3mm.; *ovary* olive-green, 6mm. long, 3mm. diam. (Plate 12, Fig. 55).

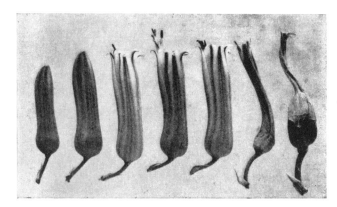

FIG. 55.

A. somaliensis Watson. Flowers 1/1 from a plant 4 miles SE of Boroma Somalia North – see Colour Plate.

SOMALIA NORTH (previously Somaliland Prot.). Cult. Kew from seeds gathered by Miss Edith Cole n. 261/1895! type (K); cult. Kew, 3 March 1905, Miss Edith Cole! (K); Sheikh, 21 Feb. 1929, E. Burne n. 4! (K) probably belongs here; Sandstone rocks north of Hargeisa, 9° 34′ N, 44° E, alt. 4,300 ft., fl. 23 Sept. 1932, J. B. Gillett 3996! (K); Fodjar Escarpments W of Sheikh, 23 Feb. 1951, Bally B9669 (EA), same loc. fl. 13 Feb. 1954, Bally B9669 (K); Ged Debti, 20 miles N of Hargeisa, 2 Oct. 1957, Bally 11770! (EA, K); Aderiale hill, 25 miles N of Hargeisa, 2 Oct. 1957, Bally 11784 (EA, K); 4 miles SE of Borama, 24 Oct. 1957, Bally (EA); 4 miles SE of Borama, 72 miles from Hargeisa, c. 9° 55′ N, 43° 12′ E, alt. 5,100 ft., 30 Aug. 1957, Reynolds 8363 (K, PRE, EA); 7 miles NW of Borama, 4,600 ft., 1 Sept. 1957, Reynolds 8381 (K, PRE, EA).

NATIVE NAME: Mr. J. B. Gillett records that the Somali name is *Daar biyu*, biyu meaning water.

In 1894–95, Miss Edith Cole (accompanying Mr. and Mrs. E. Lort-Phillips and Mr. F. Gillet Gunnis) undertook a botanical journey from Berbera on the coast of Somaliland Protectorate (now Somalia North) southwards to the Golis Range, where they ascended to over 5,000 feet.

Subsequently, in 1899, *Aloe somaliensis* was described by Watson from plants raised at Kew from seeds that had been gathered by Miss Edith Cole on that journey. In the light of present-day knowledge, it seems that the locality where Miss Cole collected the seeds was above Sheikh Pass in the neighbourhood of Upper Sheikh.

The first to collect plants in the wild state and to prepare herbarium specimens of *A. somaliensis* appears to be Mr. J. B. Gillett, who found the species on sandstone rocks north of Hargeisa, at 4,300 ft., on 23 Sept. 1932. His No. 3996 (K) is typical.

PLATE 12

ALOE SOMALIENSIS W. Watson.
Plant 4 miles SE of Borama, 72 miles W of Hargeisa, Somalia North.
Height 70cm.

During the author's investigations throughout the then Protectorate, he found that the largest numbers of *A. somaliensis* occurred 4 miles south-east and 7 miles north-west of Borama, which is 72 miles and 83 miles respectively, west of Hargeisa, at 5,100 ft. and 4,600 ft., flowering in September 1957, in large numbers. Mr. P. R. O. Bally has also found it near Borama, on the lower part of Fodjor escarpment, west of Sheikh, near Upper Sheikh, and on Wagger mountain east of Sheikh.

The plant between Mega and Moyale in Borama, Southern Ethiopia, figured and named *A. somaliensis* in *Missione Biologica nel Paese Dei Borana* 4: 348, fig. 119 (1938), is not that species at all, but something very different.

A. somaliensis is closely related to the much smaller *A. jucunda*, which grows on Gaan Libah in Somaliland, there being scarcely any difference in bracts, pedicels, flowers.

19A. **A. somaliensis** Watson var. **marmorata** Reynolds et Bally in *Journ. S.A. Bot.* 30: 222 (1964).

DESCRIPTION: *Plant* succulent, acaulescent or with very short *stem*, solitary or in small groups of 3—4.

Leaves about 16—20, densely rosulate, ascending, spreading near apex, narrowly lanceolate-attenuate, up to 40cm. long, 6—8cm. broad; *upper surface* scarcely canaliculate, dark green, obscurely speckled, with diffuse darker green longitudinal markings giving the leaf a marbled effect; *lower surface* rounded, otherwise as in the upper surface; *margins* armed with brown deltoid teeth 4mm. long, 4—6mm. apart low down, 10mm. apart higher up.

Inflorescence a many-branched panicle, up to 85cm. high, up to 4 produced simultaneously.

Peduncle dark olive-green with pale grey longitudinal striations, basally flattened and 20mm. broad, up to 16-branched from low down, the lowest sometimes with 1—4 secondary branchlets.

Racemes 4—6cm. long, rather densely flowered, the buds pink, with olive tips, open flowers bright red, the segments turning ivory-white with age.

Bracts triangular, 6—7mm. long, 3—4mm. broad at base, 3—5-nerved.

Pedicels 10mm. long.

Perianth bright red, cylindric, 26mm. long; *outer segments* free to the middle.

Genitals shortly exserted. (Figs. 56–58).

FIG. 56.   FIG. 57.

A. somaliensis Watson var *marmorata* Reynolds et Bally.

FIG. 56. At upper Sheikh, Somalia North, height 85 cm; inflorescence entangled in the branches of *Acacia etbaica*.—Photo Mr. P. R. O. Bally.

FIG. 57. Plant from Upper Sheikh flowering at Mbabane. Height 80cm.

SOMALIA NORTH. Near Upper Sheikh, mostly in shade of *Acacia etbaica*, fl. 7 Oct. 1958, P. R. O. Bally 11793!, holotype (K), isotypes (EA, PRE), coll. Upper Sheikh (Golis Range S of Berbera), cult. Mbabane, Swaziland, fl. 21 June 1964, Reynolds 8353 (K, PRE).

FIG. 58.

A. somaliensis Watson var. *marmorata*
Reynolds et Bally. Flowers 1/1 from the
Fig. 57 plant.

This interesting variety of *A. somaliensis* was found by Mr. P. R. O. Bally on the flat alluvial plain in the neighbourhood of Upper Sheikh—which is south of Berbera (on the Gulf of Aden) on the road to Burao—locally common, mostly under spreading low-growing bushes of *Acacia etbaica*. In this habitat, the inflorescences become entangled in the branches and photographs give poor detail. (I have collected it myself, not flowering, near Sheikh. – G.W.R.).

The var. *marmorata* is a larger plant than *A. somaliensis* and has darker green leaves with a different pattern of markings which with age, give the leaves a marbled effect. The inflorescence is considerably more branched, the racemes are shorter and denser flowered, the flowers are deeper red (not pinkish) while the free segments turn ivory-white at maturity.

20. **A. erensii** Christian in *Fl. Pl. S. Afr.* 20: Plate 797 (1940).

DESCRIPTION: *Plant* succulent, acaulescent.

Leaves about 16—19, densely rosulate, ascending, slightly incurved, ovate-acute, gradually attenuate from above the middle, 21cm. long, 8cm. broad above the base, 1·3cm. thick in the middle; *upper surface* green, sometimes milky-green, obscurely lineate, with clearly defined white elliptical spots, slightly concave in the middle and convex towards the margins; *lower surface* convex, the same colour as the upper, with the non-confluent spots in irregular transverse bands; *margins* with a narrow whitish translucent border armed with small flat, whitish deltoid spreading teeth, 1·5mm. long, and usually 4—6mm. apart, the interspaces straight.

Inflorescence erect, or arising more or less obliquely, branched from below the middle with about 6—7 branches.

Peduncle light brown, naked, laterally compressed, 7mm. diam. on the one axis, 4mm. diam. on the other; *branches* slender 3·5mm. diam., obliquely spreading, the lowest 28cm. long and sub-branched.

Racemes the terminal 21cm. long, the lateral shorter, gradually acuminate with the flowers sub-secund and from lax to sub-dense.

Floral bracts ovate-acuminate, scarious, 3-nerved, 6mm. long.

Pedicels erect-spreading, at length cernuous, 8—9mm. long.

Perianth flesh-pink with a bloom, the base flat, 29mm. long, 10mm. diam. over the ovary, straight or very slightly constricted on the upper side, on the lower side gradually constricted above the ovary to 8mm. diam. and widened again to 9mm. diam., trigonous; *outer segments* free for 13mm., pale at the margins, 3-nerved, apices sub-acute, hardly spreading; *inner segments* white on margins with a 3-nerved flesh-pink median line, free on margins, dorsifixed to the outer, the apices sub-obtuse nearly straight.

Stamens with the filaments white, shading to citron-yellow above; *anthers* apricot-orange, shortly exserted; *ovary* lettuce-green, 6mm. long, 3mm. diam., acuminate; *style* citron-yellow, included.—H. Basil Christian. (Plate 13, Fig. 59).

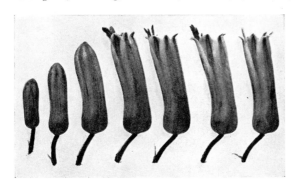

FIG. 59.

A. erensii Christian. Flowers 1/1 from a plant from
Lokitaung Gorge, Turkana, Kenya.

PLATE 13

ALOE ERENSII   Christian.

Plant from gorge between Lokitaung and Lake Rudolph, Turkana,
Kenya, flowering in the author's garden. Height 50cm.

KENYA. Turkana. In gorge between Lokitaung and Lake Rudolph, cult. Division of Botany and Plant Pathology, Pretoria, fl. Feb. 1940, Pole-Evans et Erens no. 1587 in National Herbarium, Pretoria No. 26354 holotype (PRE); between Lokitaung and Lake Rudolph, 4-branched, 31 July 1938, Pole Evans et Erens 1587! (PRE).
SUDAN. *Equatoria Prov.:* coll. J. G. Williams at Kamathia, 2,200 ft., cult. Nairobi, fl. May 1953, Reynolds 7002 (PRE, EA).

A. erensii was named after Mr. J. Erens, who collected plants in July 1938, when he accompanied Dr. I. B. Pole-Evans on the Pole-Evans Central and East Tropical African Expedition. Plants were found in the gorge between Lokitaung and Lake Rudolph, between Lodwar and Todenyang, west of Lake Rudolph in the northern Turkana of Kenya.

Mr. John Williams, Ornithologist at the Coryndon Museum, Nairobi, has found *A. erensii* north of Todenyang, across the border at Kamathia in the far SE corner of the Sudan at 2,200 ft., and c. 4° 53' N, 35° 21' E. (He also found *A. marsabitensis* Verdoorn et Christian at that locality.)

Mr. Williams records (*in litt.*) that he found *A. erensii* "common at head of gorge at Lokitaung, abundant in rock crevices and on precipitous cliffs. The gorge starts at Lokitaung and extends for about 6 miles down to the plains. Rosettes up to a maximum of 20cm. across. Plants solitary, or sometimes form compact groups of up to a dozen plants."

In cultivation, with more water, plants produce rosettes of leaves twice as large as in the arid wild state, it seems.

21. A. peckii Bally et Verdoorn in *Fl. Pl. Afr.* 31: Plate 1214 (1956).

DESCRIPTION: Based on personal observations in 1957 of large numbers of plants along the road from Erigavo northwestwards to the Tabah Gap (Surud), Somalia North (formerly Somaliland Prot.).
Plants acaulescent, solitary or in small groups, sometimes forming dense groups of 20 and more compact rosettes.
Leaves 14—16, densely rosulate, fleshy, rather compact, with the apical portion slightly spreading, averaging 16cm. long, 6cm. broad at base, about 2cm. thick; *upper surface* rather flat, olive-green, usually with numerous elongated whitish-green spots, sometimes light green without markings; *lower surface* rounded, similar in colour and markings to the upper surface; *margins* sinuate-dentate, often with continuous horny brown edge with pungent deltoid brownish teeth about 3—4mm. long, 6—10mm. apart. *Sap* dries deep brown.
Inflorescence a branched panicle, 60—80cm. high.
Peduncle grey-green with many conspicuous broken longitudinal lines to the first branch, the lines clearer low down more obscure upwards, basally plano-convex and 14mm. broad, terete upwards, 6—8-branched from the middle or lower, the lowest 1—2 branches sometimes re-branched.
Racemes cylindric, 15—20cm. long, 5—6cm. diam., youngest buds suberect and denser, open flowers pendulous and a little laxer.
Bracts narrowly ovate-attenuate, somewhat membranous, thin, scarious, 10—12mm. long, 4mm. broad, pale brown, 7—9-nerved.
Pedicels green, 10mm. long.
Perianth conspicuously 6-striped longitudinally, straw coloured to greenish-yellow, cylindric-trigonous, 25—30mm. long, basally flat and slightly stipitate, 7mm. diam. across the ovary, very slightly narrowed above the ovary, thence very slightly enlarging to a wide open mouth; *outer segments* free to the middle (about 14mm.), with broad pale marginal border and with 3 crowded reddish-brown nerves confluent at apex, more spaced to base; *inner segments* themselves free but dorsally adnate to the outer to the middle, with 3 crowded nerves forming a conspicuous keel throughout.
Filaments pale lemon, the 3 inner narrower and lengthening before the 3 outer, with their *anthers* in turn exserted 2—3mm.; *stigma* at length exserted 3—4mm.; *ovary* green, 6mm. long, 3mm. diam. (Plate 14, Figs. 60—62).

SOMALIA NORTH (formerly Somaliland Prot.): Erigavo, cult. Nairobi, fl. Dec. 1951, E. A. Peck in herb. Bally 4283! in CMN holotype (EA), in National Herb., Pretoria no. 28584!, isotype (PRE); Erigavo, a few miles N towards Daloh, 5,100 ft., 2 Nov. 1954, Bally 10297 (K, G, EA); Erigavo, 7 Nov. 1957, Bally, 10359 (G, EA); Al Madu Range, below Agasur, 5,000 ft., 10 Oct. 1956 Bally 11005 (K!, EA, G), at Geldin, 4,600 ft., 15 Oct. 1956 Bally 11119 (K!, EA); Erigavo Grazing Reserve, 5,000 ft., fl. 8 Sept. 1957, Reynolds 8398 (K!, EA); 7 miles NW of Erigavo, Euphorbia flats, abundant, 9 Sept. 1957, Reynolds 8406 (K!, EA); 9 miles N of Erigavo, 26 Sept. 1960, Hemming 1938 (EA); Erigavo, leg. Bally, cult. Pretoria, 19 April 1958, in Nat. Herb. No. 29510 (PRE!).

A. peckii was named after Major E. A. Peck who was in charge of Veterinary and Agricultural Services in British Somaliland for some time before and after the last war. It was Mr. P. R. O. Bally (at that time botanist at the Coryndon Museum, Nairobi) who, in November 1954 found where Major Peck had originally collected his plants, namely in the Grazing Reserve and elsewhere near Erigavo.

In October 1956, Mr. Bally explored the eastern parts of the Al Madu Range and found large numbers of *A. peckii* in the Ahl Mountains near Geldin and below Agasur. He found that in that region leaves were narrower and thinner. These localities are in the far north-eastern parts of the territory, not far from the Somalia border.

The most striking character of *A. peckii* is the conspicuously striped flowers. The perianth is yellowish or straw-coloured. The 3 crowded red-brown nerves from base to apex of the outer segments, with the narrower greenish dorsal keel of the inner segments visible from base to apex give a most distinctive reddish-brown and green striped effect to the flowers which is unique in the genus.

PLATE 14

ALOE PECKII   Bally et Verdoorn.
Eight miles NW of Erigavo, Somalia North, alt. 1,830m. Height 90cm.

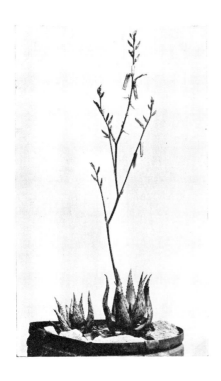

Fig. 60.

A. peckii Bally et Verdoorn. Young plant collected by Mr. Peter Bally near Geldin, Eastern Al Madu, Somalia North, flowering in Johannesburg. Height 1m.

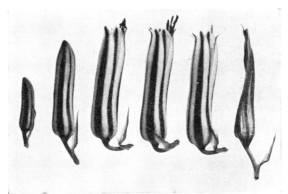

Fig. 62.

A. peckii Bally et Verdoorn.

Fig. 62. Flowers 1/1 from a plant near Erigavo, Somalia North.

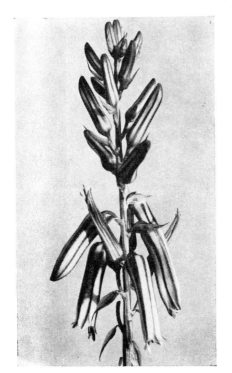

Fig. 61. Portion of raceme × 9/10.

Fig. 61.

Plants are sometimes found with their inflorescence entangled in thorn bushes.

The Somalis call *A. peckii Daar* and, it is reported, they use the leaf sap as an ingredient for eye drops.

22. **A. mcloughlinii** Christian in *Fl. Pl. Afr.* 28: Plate 1112 (1951)

DESCRIPTION: Based on personal observations 5 miles west of Dire Dawa, Harar Prov., Ethiopia.

Plant succulent, acaulescent, or with very short stem, sometimes growing singly, usually in groups of about 4—6 plants.

Leaves 16—20, densely rosulate, ascending to slight-spreading and a little recurved near the apices, about 40—50cm. long, 7 cm. broad at base, gradually attenuate; *upper surface* flat low down, slightly canaliculate towards apex, green, somewhat glossy, with numerous very pale green narrow elongated lenticular markings throughout; *lower surface* convex, paler green, with more numerous very pale green markings that are longer, larger, and sometimes confluent; *margins* sinuate-dentate, armed with deltoid firm to subpungent teeth that are paler at base, reddish-brown tipped, about 3—5mm. long, 10—15mm. apart from the middle upwards, smaller and more crowded towards base of leaf.

Inflorescence a branched panicle 1—1·2m. high.

Peduncle plano-convex and 15mm. broad at base, compactly 6—9-branched from about the middle, the lowest 1—2 branches sometimes with 1—2 branchlets, marked below the first branch with obscure elongated narrow lenticular lines.

Racemes cylindric-acuminate, rather laxly flowered, the terminal 15cm. long, 6cm. diam., laterals a little shorter, buds suberect and grey-green tipped, open flowers cernuous to sub-pendulous.

Bracts small, deltoid-acute, averaging 5mm. long, 2mm. broad, thin, scarious, white, 5-nerved.

Pedicels averaging 10mm. long, the colour of the base of the perianth.

Perianth strawberry-red with a slight bloom, cylindric-trigonous, straight, 20—24mm. long, basally flat to slightly obtuse, 9—10mm. diam. across the ovary, thence exceedingly slightly narrowed below the middle and widening again to the slightly up-turned mouth; *outer segments* free for two-thirds their length (16mm.), not free to base, with thin almost white marginal border giving the flower a white-striped effect, the segments 3-nerved, their apices subacute spreading; *inner segments* themselves free but dorsally adnate to the outer for one-quarter their length, broader than the outer, almost wh te with 3 crowded nerves forming a reddish keel turning greenish at apex, the apices more obtuse and more spreading.

Filaments pale lemon; *anthers* in turn exserted 4mm.; *stigma* at length exserted 5mm.; *ovary* pale green, 6mm. long, 2·5mm. diam. (Plate 15, Figs. 63–64).

ETHIOPIA. *Harar Prov.:* Dire Dawa, McLoughlin 826 in National Herbarium No. 28464 (PRE); cult. Herb. Christian No. 1170 holotype; 4 miles W of Dire Dawa, 11 Sept. 1957, Bally 11649 (K, EA, G); 5 miles W of Dire Dawa, c. 9° 36′ N, 41° 49′ E, alt. 3,800 ft., fl. 8 May 1956, Reynolds 8154 (K, PRE, EA).

FIG. 63.

A. mcloughlinii Christian. Plant 5 miles west of Dire Dawa, Harar Prov., Ethiopia, 3,800 ft. Height 1·5m.

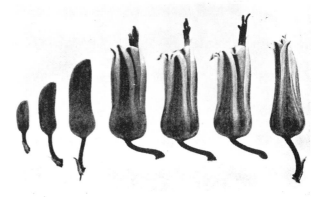

FIG. 64.

A. mcloughlinii Christian. Flowers natural size.

PLATE 15

ALOE MCLOUGHLINII   Christian.

Four miles W of Dire Dawa, Harar Prov., Ethiopia. Alt. 1,160m. Height
110cm.

A. mcloughlinii was named after Major A. G. McLoughlin who collected plants west of Dire Dawa, in Harar Province, Ethiopia, in June 1941, and sent them to the National Herbarium, Pretoria.

This very distinctive species is readily recognised by its long, narrow, fleshy leaves that have a polished look about them, and by their very narrow lenticular elongated pale-green markings copiously scattered on both surfaces. In this respect, leaves bear a striking resemblance to those of *A. macrosiphon* Baker from near the south and south-west shores of Lake Victoria in Tanganyika but the flowers are very different. The flowers of *A. mcloughlinii* are remarkably "squat", being rather flat at base, 10mm. diam. across the ovary and only 20—25mm. long, while the broad white borders of the outer segments give the flowers a white-striped effect.

Large numbers of *A. mcloughlinii* grow 4—5 miles and further west from Dire Dawa along the Awash road, sometimes in association with the shrubby *A. megalacantha* Bak., hybrids being occasionally seen.

Plants also grow along the Harar road, SE of Dire Dawa, to near Harla Village, 9 miles away, sometimes socially with *A. harlana* Reynolds. Some plants seen, not flowering, appeared to be crosses.

23. **A. pirottae** Berger in Engler's *Bot. Jahrb.* 36: 65 (1905), in Engler's *Pflanzenr.* Liliac.-Aloin. 266 (1908); Chiovenda in *Result. Sci. Miss. Stefani.* 1: 171 (1916) – excl. fig. 24D which is *A. microdonta* Chiovenda; Reynolds in *Journ. S.A. Bot.* 20: 35 (1954)

DESCRIPTION based on observations in S. Ethiopia, Somalia North and South.
Plant succulent, rarely solitary, usually in small groups of 3—6 plants. *Stem* none or negligible.
Leaves rosulate, sometimes trifarious when young, 12—16, ensiform, spreading and recurved, averaging 40—50cm. long, 8—9cm. broad at base when pressed flat, gradually narrowing to an acute apex; *upper surface* mostly chocolate-brown in dry season, greener after rains, copiously marked throughout with elliptical or lenticular dull whitish spots, flattish near base, deeply canaliculate upwards with the margins sometimes involute and touching each other; *lower surface* rounded, similar to the upper in colour and markings; *margins* armed with whitish deltoid teeth that are pale-brown tipped, 2—3mm. long and 10mm. apart near base, gradually smaller and more distant upwards, obsolescent towards apex. *Sap* dries brown.
Inflorescence a branched panicle 1—1·2m. high.
Peduncle basally plano-convex and 10—15mm. broad, terete upwards, brown with a bloom, about 8-branched from about the middle, the lowest 1—2 branches sometimes with 1 or 2 branchlets, the whole inflorescence sometimes producing 12 racemes.
Racemes cylindric, 12—15cm. long, 5—6cm. diam., sublaxly flowered, the buds suberect, greenish at apex and grey-striped for 6mm., open flowers nutant.
Bracts ovate-acute, 5mm. long, 4mm. broad, white, scarious, 5-nerved.
Pedicels averaging 5—7mm. long.
Perianth pinkish-scarlet, cylindric-trigonous, very slightly curved, 30mm. long, basally rather flat, 8mm. diam. across the ovary, narrowed to 6 mm. above the ovary, thence trigonously enlarging a little to a markedly trigonous mouth; *outer segments* free for 8mm., with broad whitish marginal border, clearly 3-nerved from base to apex; *inner segments* themselves free but dorsally adnate to the outer to the middle.
Anthers exserted 2—3mm.; *stigma* at length exserted 3—4mm.; *ovary* green, 6mm. long, 2·5mm. diam. (Plate 16, Figs. 65—66).

"SOMALILAND. Savati, River Lagonomi, on dry stony places, 25 March 1893, Riva 1682".

(*Note:* After travelling from Berbera (on the coast) to Hargeisa (capital of Somalia North, formerly British Somaliland), and to Imi (in Ethiopia, southwards from Hargeisa), Riva reached the Webi (River) Gestro, and Dolo in March 1893. Riva was in Dolo at least until 16 April 1893, and Riva 1682 is dated 25 March 1893, which implies that "Savati, River Lagonomi" would be somewhat near Dolo, Dolo being at c. 4° 10′ N, 42° 08′ E. The precise type locality remains unknown, but it is probably near or north of Dolo on the east side of the Ganale Doria or the Webi Gestro, in the Ogaden, S. Ethiopia.)

SOMALIA NORTH. 1 mile E of Kirit, 25 Oct. 1954, Bally 10198 (K!, EA), 5 miles E of Kirit, 26 Sept. 1956, Bally 10847 (K!, EA); Redabeth S of Hargeisa 19 Oct. 1954, Bally 10194 (EA); between El Afwein and Erigavo, 4,000 ft., cult. Div. of Bot., Pretoria, fl. 1958 Reynolds 8392 (PRE); 24 miles N of El Afwein, 4,000 ft. in bud 1 Sept. 1957 Reynolds 8392 (PRE, K).

SOMALIA SOUTH. Under thorn bushes, 6 miles S of Bardera on E side of Juba River, leaf only, not fl., Reynolds 7102 (PRE).

DISTRIBUTION: *Kenya*, near Buna in the N.F.D.; east of Mtito Andei on Mombasa Road; near Voi. *Ethiopia*: Between Neghelli and Dolo. *Somalia South*: Occasional from Lugh Ferandi to Iscia Bardoa and Bardera; plentiful 6 and 12 miles west of Bardera, and frequent along the Bardera—Margherita road on east side of the Juba River, mostly in arid thorn country; 90 miles north of

PLATE 16

ALOE PIROTTAE   Berger.

1 mile W of Kirit, Somalia North. Fl. 25 October 1954. Height 1m.
From a Kodachrome by Mr. P. R. O. Bally.

Fig. 65.
A. pirottae Berger. Under thorn bushes (not flowering) 6 miles south of Bardera, east of the Juba River, Somalia. Alt. 450 ft.

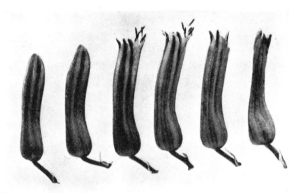

Fig. 66.

A. pirottae Berger. Flowers 1/1, from a plant 24 miles north of El Afwein, 41 miles S of Erigavo, Somalia North, at 4,000 ft. alt. – The furthest north known.

Mogadishu. *Somalia North* (formerly Somaliland Prot.): Burao, Ainabo, Kirit, east and west of Wadamayo, the furthest north seen being between El Afwein and Erigavo.

A. pirottae is found over a considerable area, usually in small groups, rarely in the open, most frequently under thorn bushes with the inflorescence becoming entangled in the branches. Sometimes young plants have leaves almost trifarious, but become rosulote with age. The leaves are chocolate-brown or chocolate-greenish, copiously spotted both sides, and are usually deeply channelled with the margins involute and sometimes touching each other, thus giving the leaf a somewhat tubular effect. The perianth outer segments have a broad whitish marginal border which gives the flowers a white-striped appearance. Nine miles west of Ainabo (2,500 ft.) crosses with *A. rigens* var. *glabrescencens* occur.

GROUP 5

Rather small plants with compact rosettes about 25cm. diam., or larger, and forming open rosettes, acaulescent, suckering freely, forming dense groups. *Leaves* lanceolate, with or without spots. *Inflorescence* simple or sparingly branched. *Pedicels* short (7mm.). *Bracts* very small. *Perianth* narrowly cylindric, not striped, 35—38mm. long. *Outer segments* ± connate to the middle or higher.

Three species: *A. dorotheae*, *A. morogoroensis*, *A. greenwayi* – all from Tanzania (Tanganyika).

The species in this small group have longer unstriped cylindric flowers than group 4, and bracts too small for Group 9 (Berger's *Verae*).

KEY TO THE SPECIES

A. SMALLER ACAULESCENT PLANTS FORMING DENSE GROUPS, ROSETTES COMPACT, INFLORESCENCE 50—60CM. HIGH

    1. Inflorescence mostly simple, racemes 10—12cm. long, pedicels 6mm., bracts 3mm., perianth scarlet or yellow 33—36mm. .. ..   24 *A. dorotheae*

    2. Inflorescence 1—3-branched, racemes 20—25cm., pedicels 8—10mm., perianth 35mm. long .. ..   25 *A. morogoroensis*

B. LARGER SHORTLY CAULESCENT PLANTS

    1. Inflorescence 1—3-branched, 50—60 cm. Raceme 15—20cm. long, pedicels 8—10mm., bracts 10mm. long, perianth 30mm. long   26 *A. greenwayi*

24. **A. dorotheae** Berger in Engler's *Pflanzenr.* Liliac.-Aloin. 263 (1908)

DESCRIPTION based on large numbers at Kideliko Rock, 4 miles S of Handeni, Tanga Prov., Tanganyika.

    Plants acaulescent, or shortly caulescent, suckering freely and forming large dense groups.

    Leaves 16—20, densely rosulate, averaging 25cm. long, 5cm. broad, 7—8mm. thick, gradually narrowing to an acute apex, erectly spreading to spreading; *upper surface* rather flat, green, turning somewhat brownish-red, usually with several elongated lenticular spots in lower half, sometimes without spots; *lower surface* convex, paler green, more copiously spotted throughout with smaller more crowded very pale green elongated spots; *margins* sinuate-dentate, the teeth pale, firm, 4—5mm. long, 10mm. apart low down, shorter upwards.

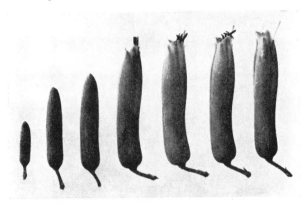

FIG. 67.

A. dorotheae Berger. Flowers 1/1, from a red-flowered plant.

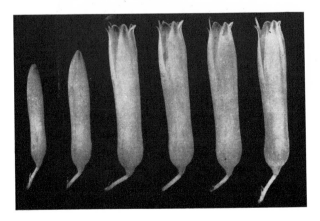

FIG. 68.

A. dorotheae Berger. Flowers 1/1, from a yellow-flowered plant.

PLATE 17

ALOE DOROTHEAE   Berger.

Near Kideliko Rock, 4 miles S of Handeni, Tanga Prov., Tanzania
(Tanganyika). Alt. 660 m. Height 50—60cm.

Inflorescence simple, rarely with a short branch, averaging 50—60cm. high.

Peduncle basally flattened and 10—12mm. broad, terete upwards with a few sterile bracts, the lowest being 5mm. long, 8mm. broad, thin, scarious, 3—5-nerved.

Raceme sub-laxly flowered, cylindric, slightly acuminate, averaging 10—12cm. long, 5cm. diam., buds suberect, older buds spreading, open flowers nutant.

Bracts 3mm. long, 2mm. broad, thin, dry, 3-nerved.

Pedicels 6mm. long, the colour of the perianth whether yellow or scarlet.

Perianth yellow or scarlet, greenish at mouth, cylindric, slightly trigonous, 33—36mm. long, basally obtuse and shortly stipitate, 7mm. diam. across the ovary, slightly enlarging trigonously to the open mouth; *outer segments* free for one-third to one-half their length (11—12mm.), thinner at the edges, obscurely 3-nerved, apices greenish, slightly spreading; *inner segments* themselves free but dorsally adnate to the outer for two-thirds their length, broader and with 3 crowded nerves forming a keel in upper third.

Filaments filiform-flattened, the 3 inner narrowed and lengthening before the 3 outer with their *anthers* in turn exserted 2—3mm.; *stigma* at length exserted 4—5mm.; *ovary* greenish-brown, 4mm. long, 2mm. broad (Plate 17, Figs. 67–68).

TANZANIA. *Tanga Prov.:* Friedrich Hoffmannsplantage, introduced alive by Goertze to the Royal Botanic Gardens, Berlin, in 1890(?). Flowered at La Mortola in March 1907—A. Berger. (*Note:* Habit of growth unknown; no figures. No type material, collectors' number, date, or Herbarium is given by Berger, while the late Prof. G. Werdemann stated (in litt.) that there is no type specimen in Berlin-Dahlem.) *Tanga Prov.:* Plant cult. Botanic Gardens Dahlem, fl. 31 July 1914, H. Strauss n. 435, Friedrich Hoffmannsplantage, situated in the hinterland of Tanga, in the lowland, in the vicinity of Pangani Falls (B); foot of Kideliko Rock, 4 miles S of Handeni, 46 miles SW of Korogwe, alt. 660 m., fl. 1 July 1958, Reynolds 8746 (PRE, K, EA); same locality, 1948, Bally 11342 (EA, G).

Berger states he named this attractive species after a Miss Dorothy Westhead of London.

The type locality, Friedrich Hoffmans Plantations are now Kwamdulu Estate on the south bank of the Pangani River. The whole area is now under sisal and those who know the estate well say there is not an Aloe plant to be found for miles. Dr. P. J. Greenway and Mr. P. R. O. Bally have both searched the area in vain for plants of *A. dorotheae*.

Since the Kideliko Rock plants match the Strauss specimen named *A. dorotheae* Berger in Berlin-Dahlem, they are accepted as being typical of the species.

25. **A. morogoroensis** Christian in *Journ. S.A. Bot.* 6: 181, Plate 20 (1940), in *Fl. Plants Afr.* 25: Plate 991 (1946).

DESCRIPTION: *Plants* acaulescent, densely soboliferous.

Leaves about 20, rosulate, arcuate-ascending, lanceolate-attenuate, up to 30cm. long, 5—6cm. broad, 1cm. thick; *upper surface* bright glossy green changing to copper colour in the dry season, not spotted, concave becoming chanelled towards the apex; *lower surface* convex, turning copper coloured at the tips in the dry season; *margins* with a narrow white cartilaginous border armed with flat, white-tipped deltoid teeth inclining forward, 4—5mm. long, about 12mm. apart at the middle, more distant upwards.

Inflorescence erect, simple or 1—3-branched, up to 55cm. high, one or two to a rosette in succession.

Peduncle pale brown, branched from about the middle, laterally compressed and 8—10mm. broad at base; *branches* slender, 4mm. diam., 15cm. long—often longer—ascending or arcuate-erect.

Raceme conico-cylindric, sub-dense, 20—25cm. long, the buds red, tipped with dark green, erectly spreading, mature flowers pendulous.

Bracts ovate-acute, 6mm. long, 3mm. broad, scarious, many-nerved.

Pedicels 8—10mm. long, those of mature flowers pendulous.

Perianth coral-red, changing to greenish-yellow at apex, cylindric, straight, up to 35mm. long, the base stipitate, 6mm. diam. over the ovary, slightly constricted towards the middle on underside only, again widened to 8mm., and then contracted towards the throat, laterally compressed to 7mm.; *outer segments* free for 15mm., coral-red shading to greenish-yellow at apices, obscurely many-nerved, apices slightly spreading; *inner segments* free on margin, dorsi-fixed to tube, pinkish-white with a broad many-nerved red median line shading to greenish-yellow at apex and with slightly spreading apices.

Filaments yellow, included; *anthers* included; *style* yellow, included; *ovary* pale green or pale brown, 6mm. long, 3mm. diam. (Plate 18, Figs. 69–71).

TANZANIA. On rocky cliffs near Morogoro, coll. July 1935, B. D. Burt 5718, fl. Ewanrigg July 1938, Christian 811, holotype (SRGH), isotype (K, BM); *Morogoro Dist.*, Mkumbe Hill, Burtt 5173 (K, BM, SRGH); Ex Morogoro, plant from type stock fl. June 1945 in Pretoria, Christian 811, in National Herbarium, Pretoria No. 27464 (PRE)—figured in *Fl. Pl. S. Afr.*, Plate 991 (1946). Originally distributed by Mr. Christian, cult. Pretoria, 15 July 1959, No. 29520 in Nat. Herb. (PRE).

TYPE LOCALITY: Rocky cliffs near Morogoro, which is a town 130 miles W of Dar es Salaam, in Tanzania. *A. morogoroensis* grows on the Uluguru Mts. to the south of Morogoro and is reported to occur on the Usambara mountains, on Mt. Luemba near Kilosa, and the Inselbergs, Masai Steppes (I have not found anything matching *A. morogoroensis* anywhere on the Western Usambaras – G.W.R.).

The leaves are a bright glossy green, more or less changing to copper-colour in the dry season, and it has the advantage of being, as far as we know, entirely resistant to that scourge of Aloe gardens, the Aloe Rust. Although one of the smaller species of Aloe, it suckers so freely and forms

PLATE 18

ALOE MOROGOROENSIS   Christian.

Increases from the original type plant, flowering at Ewangrigg, near
Salisbury, Rhodesia. Height 60cm.

FIG. 69.

A. morogoroensis Christian. The type plant at Ewanrigg
– originally collected by D. B. Burtt on rocky cliffs
near Morogoro, Tanganyika.
Photo: H. B. Christian.

FIG. 70.

A. morogoroensis Christian. Plant from the original type stock
flowering in the author's garden.

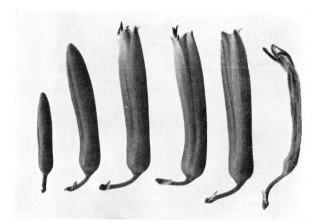

FIG. 71.

A. morogoroensis Christian. Flowers natural size.

FIG. 72.

A. greenwayi Reynolds. Plants at Kifungilo, 12 miles east of Lushoto, Western Usambaras, Tanganyika, 5,300 feet, fl. 2 July 1958. Height, 80 cm.

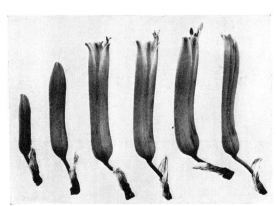

FIG. 73.

A. greenwayi Reynolds. Flowers 1/1 from bud to post-anthesis stages.

such big clumps that it makes a fine show when in flower in June–July, and it is very well worth cultivating in any Aloe garden. – H. B. Christian.

Since first grown at Ewanrigg, near Salisbury, *A. morogoroensis* has increased in considerable numbers and has been distributed far and wide.

The accompanying colour plate is of a small group from the original type plant stock flowering at Ewanrigg.

26. **A. greenwayi** Reynolds in *Journ. S.A. Bot.* 30: 229 (1964)

DESCRIPTION: *Plants* solitary or in small groups, acaulescent or with stem up to 30cm. long—longer when hanging down rock faces.

Leaves about 16, densely rosulate, up to 30cm. long, 6cm. broad, spreading and forming rather open rosettes; *upper surface* flat to slightly canaliculate, dull green flushed reddish-bronze, usually with a few scattered very pale green spots; *lower surface* convex, paler green, copiously spotted throughout with numerous very small pale green elongated spots; *margins* armed with small deltoid pungent teeth about 2mm. long, 5—8mm. apart.

Inflorescence about 60 cm. high, mostly 1—2-branched from about the middle.

Racemes cylindric-acuminate, the terminal sometimes 20cm. long, but usually about 15cm. long with the lateral a little shorter, 5—6cm. broad, rather densely flowered.

Bracts ovate-acute to lanceolate-acute, about 10mm. long, 4—5mm. broad, thin, scarious, dirty-white, rather brittle, 7—9-nerved.

Pedicels 8—10 mm. long, sometimes 12mm. after anthesis.

Perianth reddish-orange to yellow, cylindric-trigonous, 30mm. long, basally obtuse and slightly stipitate, 5—6mm. diam. across the ovary, thence very slightly narrowed on the underside only, the mouth wide open: *outer segments* free for 10mm., obscurely 3-nerved, paler at the margins, greenish tipped; *inner segments* broader than the outer and with broad white border, with 3 crowded nerves forming a keel and with more obtuse more spreading apices.

Filaments filiform-flattened, the 3 inner narrower and lengthening before the 3 outer, with their *anthers* in turn exserted 1—2mm.; *stigma* at length exserted 2—3mm. (Figs. 72—73).

TANZANIA. *Tanga Prov.:* Western Usambaras, Kifungilo, 12 miles E of Lushoto, 5,300 ft., fl. 2 July 1958, Reynolds 8759 (holotype PRE, isotypes K, EA); Coll. Kifungilo, Western Usambaras, cult. Hort. Moreau, Amani, 7 April 1942, Greenway 6452 (EA); Coll. World's View, Shume, cult. Hort. Greenway, Amani, 25 Nov. 1946, Greenway 7892 (EA).

This species was named after Dr. P. J. Greenway who was formerly Botanist at the East African Agriculture Research Institute, Amani, Tanzania, and latterly Botanist in charge of the East African Herbarium, Nairobi, Kenya, who has contributed very considerably to the advancement of botanical knowledge of East Africa.

A. greenwayi appears to be nearest allied to *A. morogorensis* Christian from which it differs in being a larger plant with a stem up to 50cm. long (longer when hanging down cliff faces), and in having larger, more spreading leaves forming open rosettes, shorter more crowded marginal teeth, much larger bracts, and a taller inflorescence.

A. greenwayi grows in numbers on cliff edges of the south-eastern face of the Western Usambaras, and is also found at World's View near Shume, at Kifungilo Mission, 12 miles E of Lushoto, at Gare, while a weaker form occurs on rock faces two miles W of Soni on the road down the pass to Mombo.

The leaves of *A. greenwayi* are usually flushed with reddish-bronze, while flower colours range from lemon-yellow through primrose-yellow to reddish-orange.

GROUP 6

(Series *Saponariae* Berger).

PERIANTHS WITH PRONOUNCED BASAL SWELLING, ABRUPTLY CONSTRICTED ABOVE THE OVARY, THENCE ENLARGING TO THE THROAT

Perianth with pronounced basal swelling, abruptly constricted above the ovary, thence enlarging to the throat, 25—40mm. long. *Plants* of medium size, acaulescent or with short stem. *Leaves* densely rosulate, usually spotted on one or both surfaces, the spots or blotches sometimes arranged in irregular transverse bands; *margins* usually sinuate-dentate, armed with pungent teeth. *Inflorescence* mostly a branched panicle. *Racemes* from capitate and densely flowered to long and laxly flowered. *Pedicels* short or long (5—30mm.). *Perianths* 25—40mm. long.

Type species: *A. lateritia* Engler. *Tropical species:* 10, 4 of which also occur in South Africa.

Thirty-two species occur in South Africa, including four which also occur to the north. This makes a total of 38 maculates in the continent of Africa and they range from near Cape Town in the south to the Gulf of Aden and Eritrea, from Ethiopia to Mali, and the Indian Ocean to the Atlantic. There are none in Madagascar.

Apart from the leaf markings so typical of the maculates, the one outstanding character which distinguishes this group from all others, is the perianth which is conspicuously inflated at base, abruptly constricted above the ovary, thence enlarging to the throat. Sometimes short-billed birds puncture this basal swelling to sip the nectar within.

In their different geographical stations – from sea level to 9,000 ft. – most of the species vary considerably in leaf markings, in length of racemes, and in length and colour of flowers, while much depends on whether plants grow singly or in groups, in shade or exposed sunny places, and on rainfall and the severity of winters.

These species constitute a heterogeneous and frequently most exasperating group, and it is often impossible to know where one species ends and the next begins.

It is impossible to devise a key that would be watertight for all species. At best, all that can be attempted is to select characters of the form most typical of the species as a whole.

The subjoined key is offered as a guide.

KEY TO THE SPECIES

A. Racemes Densely Capitate

1. *Racemes corymbose (flat-topped):*
   (a) Inflorescence 8—10-branched, 1·50m. high, the highest 1— 2 racemes usually higher than the terminal .. ..   31 *A. swynnertonii*
   (b) Inflorescence 3—4-branched, 65cm. high, pedicels and peri-anths 35—40mm. long ....   33 *A. saponaria*

2. *Racemes slightly rounded or conic at apex:*
   (a) Leaves 50cm. long, inflorescence 6—10-branched, 1·70m. high, pedicels 30mm., perianth 35—40mm. long .. ..   32 *A. duckeri*
   (b) Leaves 27cm. long, inflorescence 3—5-branched, 1m. high, pedicels 20mm., perianth 33mm.   .. ..   28 *A. graminicola*
   (c) Inflorescence 4—6-branched, 70cm. high, pedicels 16mm., perianth deep wine-red, 30mm. long .. ..   29 *A. kilifiensis*

B. Racemes Cylindric, Slightly Acuminate

1. *Inflorescence usually simple, 60cm.:*
   Small plants, leaves only 6—7cm. wide, pedicels 17mm., perianth 23mm. .. ..   27 *A. amudatensis*

2. *Inflorescence a branched panicle:*
   (a) Inflorescence 3—5-branched, 1m., racemes 20cm., pedicels 12—15mm., perianth 25mm.   .. ..   35 *A. macrocarpa*
   (b) Inflorescence 4—7-branched, 1·5m., racemes 20cm., perianth 30mm., dull flesh-pink, clearly white-striped to base .. .. ..   30 *A. greatheadii*
   (c) Inflorescence 6—10-branched, 1—1·25m. high, racemes 20cm., pedicels 20—25mm. long, perianth orange-scarlet, 35—38mm. long   36 *A. lateritia*
   (d) Inflorescence 6—10-branched, 1—1·25m. high, racemes 30— 40cm. long, laxly flowered, pedicels 6—7mm., perianth 30mm. ..   34 *A. zebrina*

27. **A. amudatensis** Reynolds in *Journ. S.A. Bot.* 22: 136 (1956)

DESCRIPTION: *Plant* succulent, acaulescent, freely suckering and forming small to large dense groups.

Leaves about 12, densely rosulate, erectly spreading, narrowly lanceolate-attenuate, averaging 22cm. long, 5cm. broad, 8mm. thick low down; *upper surface* dull green, sometimes reddish-brown tinged, slightly canaliculate, with numerous lenticular whitish spots or blotches throughout; *lower surface* convex, milky-green, usually with numerous dull very pale greenish lenticular spots or blotches varying from irregularly scattered to more or less confluent into a series of irregular interrupted transverse wavy bands; *margins* sinuate-dentate, with whitish cartilaginous edge armed with small, firm, rather white, deltoid teeth which average 2mm. long, 5—8mm. apart, pale reddish-brown at apices only.

Inflorescence mostly simple, averaging 50—65cm. high, sometimes with 1—2 branches high up.

Peduncle basally plano-convex and 10mm. broad, terete upwards, brownish-green with a bloom, sometimes with 1 or 2 branches in upper third.

Racemes cylindric, slightly conical, averaging 8cm. long, 6—7cm. diam., sublaxly flowered, the apex a small tuft of dried bracts, youngest buds suberect, grey-green tipped, older buds spreading, open flowers subpendulous.

Bracts narrowly ovate-deltoid, 10mm. long, 3mm. broad, thin, subscarious, 3—5-nerved.

Pedicels averaging 17mm. long, arcuate-spreading, nutant at apex.

Perianth rose-pink to coral-red, averaging 23mm. long, basally inflated and 9mm. diam. across the ovary, thence abruptly constricted to 6mm., thence slightly decurved and enlarging to the throat, the mouth trigonous, wide open; *outer segments* free for 7mm., paler at the margins, obscurely 3-nerved, the apices subacute, slightly spreading; *inner segments* broader than the outer, with more obtuse more spreading apices.

Filaments lemon, filiform-flattened, the 3 inner narrower and lengthening before the 3 outer with their *anthers* in turn exserted 0—1mm.; *style* pale yellow with *stigma* at length exserted 2mm.; *ovary* yellowish-green, 6mm. long, 2mm. diam. (Figs. 74–75).

Fig. 74.

A. amudatensis Reynolds. Plants at Amudat, Upe County, Karamoja, Uganda, c. 1° 58′ N., 34° 57′ E., 4,400 ft., fl. October 1955, height 60cm.

Fig. 75.

A. amudatensis Reynolds. Flowers natural size.

UGANDA. *Northern Prov.*: Karamoja, Upe County, at Amudat, c. 1° 58′ N, 34° 57′ E, 4,400 ft., fl. 21 Oct. 1955, Reynolds 7996 holotype (PRE), isotype (K, EA); Dodoth County, 7 miles W of Loyoro, c. 3° 13′ N, 34° 12′ E, 4,500 ft., fl. 14 Oct. 1955, Reynolds 7965 (PRE); Matheniko County, at Lokitanyala (37 miles N of Amudat), form with yellow flowers, fl. 20 Oct. 1955, Reynolds 7988 (PRE); Tweedie 670 (K).
KENYA. *Northern Prov.*: Coll. Mrs. Beecher near Marsabit, cult. Nairobi, fl. 28 Oct. 1963. Verdcourt H352/63 (EA).

A. amudatensis was collected by Mrs. E. M. Tweedie several years ago and sent to Kew under her number 670. It differs from its nearest East African allies in the Section *Saponariae* by being a smaller plant, and in having narrow leaves only 5—6cm. broad, with white cartilaginous margins armed with small, firm, almost white teeth, only 1—2mm. long. The inflorescence is mostly simple, averaging 50—65cm. tall; sometimes it is 1—2 branched in upper third; and flowers vary in length, and in the diameter of the basal swelling. Plants are acaulescent, sucker freely and form small to large dense groups.

DISTRIBUTION: *A. amudatensis* occurs almost throughout Karamoja, from the Suam River to Amudat (91 miles N of Kitale) in the south, to Moroto, Toror, Kotido, Madang, and south and west of Loyoro in the north. Yellow and orange forms occur at Lokitanyala between the Moroto turn-off and the top of Napau Pass which leads down to Turkana in Kenya. A few plants were seen in Kenya between the foot of the Kacheliba Escarpment and the Suam River.

In Kenya, Mrs. S. B. Beecher, wife of the Archbishop of East Africa, has collected *A. amudatensis* near Marsabit, in the Northern Province.

Crosses with *A. tweediae* occur near Amudat among both parents.

28. **A. graminicola** Reynolds in *Journ. S.A. Bot.* 19: 9 (1953).

DESCRIPTION: *Plant* succulent, solitary, or forming small groups by division, acaulescent.
Leaves about 16, densely rosulate, erectly spreading, lanceolate-attenuate, up to 27cm. long, 7cm. broad at base, the apex dried and twisted; *upper surface* flat or slightly canaliculate, dull green with numerous dull white "H"-shaped spots, the spots irregularly scattered or sometimes more or less arranged in interrupted undulating transverse bands; *lower surface* paler green, with fewer spots, irregularly scattered or in transverse bands; *margins* sinuate-dentate, with horny edge, armed with pale-brown, pungent, deltoid teeth 4—5mm. long, 10—15mm. distant, the interspaces rounded and the colour of the leaf. (*Sap* dries yellow.)
Inflorescence a branched panicle up to 1m. high.
Peduncle brown with a grey powdery bloom, flattened and 2cm. broad low down, terete upwards, 3—5-branched from the middle or higher, the lowest branch subtended at base by a rather fleshy many-nerved bract up to 3cm. long, 12mm. broad at base.
Racemes capitate, densely flowered, the terminal averaging 5cm. long, 8cm. diam., the lateral a little smaller.
Bracts narrowly deltoid-acuminate, thin, scarious, 12mm. long, 2mm. broad at base, 3—5-nerved.
Pedicels averaging 20mm. long.
Perianth scarlet to orange-scarlet (sometimes yellow), paler to yellowish at mouth, averaging 33mm. long, slender, with basal swelling 8mm. diam., constricted above the ovary to 5mm. diam., thence decurved, laterally compressed and enlarging towards the throat; *outer segments* free for 8mm., paler at the margins, the apices subacute, slightly spreading; *inner segments* broader than the outer, with broader thin white borders and more obtuse spreading apices.
Filaments almost white, filiform-flattened, the 3 inner narrower and lengthening before the 3 outer, with their *anthers* in turn exserted 1—2mm.; *style* pale yellow, filiform, with the *stigma* at length exserted 2—3mm.; *ovary* pale green, 6mm. long, 2·5mm. diam., finely 6-grooved; *capsule* 32mm. long, 16mm. diam. at the middle. (Plate 19, Figs. 76, 77).

KENYA. In open grassland 8 miles S of Nanyuki (116 miles N of Nairobi), approx. 0° 5′ S, 37° 04′ E, alt. 6,200 ft., fl. 22 April 1952, Reynolds 6576! holotype (PRE), isotype (K, EA); half-mile N of Nanyuki, alt. 6,300 ft., fl. 22 April 1952, Reynolds 6574! (PRE, K); flat grasslands at Gilgil (74 miles NW of Nairobi), 0° 30′ S, 36° 18′ E, alt. 6,580 ft., fl. 19 April 1952, Reynolds 6551! (K, PRE); flat grasslands near Ol Joro Orok, 33 miles N of Gilgil, 0° 04′ S, 36° 22′ E, alt. 7,780 ft., fl. 20 April 1952, Reynolds 6554! (K, PRE); 8 miles E of Thomson's Falls, 7,600 ft., 20 April 1952, Reynolds 6556 (PRE); Naro Moru (14 miles S of Nanyuki), Aug. 1932, E. R. Napier 2187 (EA); Thomson's Falls, Sept. 1962, Tweedie 2459 (EA).

S. ETHIOPIA. Borana, collected on slopes of Mega Mountain, cult. Johannesburg, fl. 29 April 1954, Reynolds 7033 (PRE)—a form with taller more slender inflorescence.

A. graminicola is nearest allied to *A. lateritia* Engler, which I have studied at the type locality, Rombo, on south-eastern foothills of Kilimanjaro, and over a very wide area, but it differs from it, *inter alia*, in having smaller, denser, capitate racemes of much narrower, more curved flowers. In *A. graminicola* the basal swelling of the perianth is also much smaller and the two species could hardly be confused.

Plants were found near Timau (14 miles north of Nanyuki), and in large numbers 8 miles S of Nanyuki (type locality) in open grasslands, while yellow-flowered forms were noticed further south near Naro Moru. Considerable quantities occur for 30 miles north-westwards from Nyeri, near Thomson's Falls, and from there to Ol Joro Orok. It was also seen in the Rift Valley near Nakuru, Gilgil and Naivasha, flowering in April.

PLATE 19

ALOE GRAMINICOLA Reynolds.

Grasslands 8 miles S of Nanyuki, Kenya. Flowers in June. Height 1m.

FIG. 76.

A. graminicola Reynolds. Plants at Gilgil 74 miles NW of Nairobi, Kenya. Alt. 6,580 ft. Height 80cm.

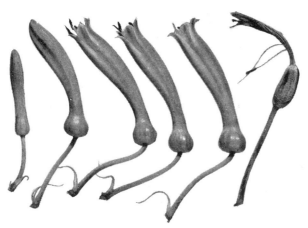

FIG. 77.

A. graminicola Reynolds. Flowers 1/1 from a plant at Gilgil, Kenya – flowers much more slender than in *A. lateritia* Engler.

In all localities visited, *A. graminicola* was found growing in grasslands, which suggested the specific epithet. This species was not seen on rocks, or in dry, arid thorn country. Altitudes from 6,000 ft. to 7,800 ft. in the Kenya Highlands, seem to suit it.

Between Njoro and Elburgon, some 20 miles W of Nakuru, on the road to Mau Summit, it seems that *A. graminicola* grades through intermediates into *A. lateritia*. Beyond the Mau Range, especially for 12 miles before reaching Eldoret, only robust forms of *A. lateritia* were noticed.

29. A. kilifiensis Christian in *Journ. S.A. Bot.* 8: 169, Plate 3 (1942)

DESCRIPTION: A succulent plant, acaulescent.

Leaves c. 15, rosulate, spreading-recurved, from the base long-acuminate or ovate-acuminate, acute, 27cm. long, 7cm. broad at the base. The *upper surface* green, turning copper-coloured in dry season, profusely spotted with scattered oval or H-shaped whitish spots, broadly concave near the base, channelled above, the *lower surface* more profusely spotted with larger confluent spots, convex towards the base, rounded above; the *margins* bounded by a brown horny border, sinuate-dentate, with brown horny deltoid teeth irregularly disposed, 3mm. long, 4mm. apart low down, more distant above.

Inflorescence a panicle up to 57cm. high, erect, branched above the middle.

Peduncle chocolate-coloured, naked, 8mm. diam. in the middle, flattened on one side low down, sub-terete above.

Bract subtending lower branch long-triangular, 20mm. long, 8mm. broad, scarious, 7-nerved.

Branches c. 4—6, arcuate, with one long triangular sterile bract 9mm. long, 4mm. broad, 5-nerved.

Racemes capitate, terminal sub-dense, c. 20-flowered, 8cm. long, 8cm. diam., the buds spreading, the mature flower pendulous.

Floral bracts long-triangular, 14mm. long, 6mm. broad, scarious, 5-nerved.

Pedicels the lower arcuate-erect, 16mm. long, the upper erect-spreading.

Perianth deep wine-red, 30mm. long, 10mm. diam. over the ovary, constricted above the ovary to 6mm. and widened again to 9mm. contracted towards the mouth, laterally compressed to 7mm.; *outer segments* free for 11mm. with a narrow pinkish margin, obscurely 8-nerved, the apices straight, sub-acute, *inner segments* with broad whitish margins, free for 11mm., dorsifixed to tube, apices straight, more obtuse.

Filaments pale yellow, as long as the perianth; *anthers* brown, exserted; *style* pale yellow, included; *ovary* pale green, cylindric-acuminate, 8mm. long, 3mm. diam.—H. B. Christian. (Figs. 78–79).

KENYA. Kilifi (36 miles N of Mombasa) on coral-rag cliff facing the sea, alt. 10—20 ft., Feb. 1937, B. D. Burtt 555H, holotype (SRGH), isotype (K, BM)—*fide* Christian. Coral-rag cliffs at Kilifi, from the type plant coll. J. V. Moggridge, cult. Ewanrigg, fl. 1943, H. B. Christian 767 (PRE); Kilifi, 31 Aug. 1950, Jeffrey 798! (EA).

FIG. 78.

A. kilifiensis Christian. The type plant at Ewanrigg near Salisbury, Rhodesia – from Kilifi, 38 miles north of Mombasa, Kenya. *Photo: The late H. B. Christian.*

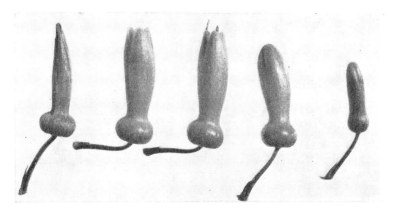

FIG. 79.

A. kilifiensis Christian. Flowers 1/1 from the type plant. *Photos: Mr. H. B. Christian.*

This is one of the Aloes sent to Mr. Christian by the late B. D. Burtt in 1937. It was collected by Mr. J. V. Moggridge. It is readily distinguished from *A. lateritia* Engl. by its more profusely spotted leaves with smaller scattered spots, confluent on lower surface, by the habit of leaves turning copper-coloured in dry season, by the spreading recurved habit of the leaves, by the shape of the flowers which are straight and contracted at the mouth and by the unusual deep wine-red colour of the flowers. It does not sucker and all the plants I have seen are remarkably uniform in habit and character. The photo is of a plant in flower at Ewanrigg in June, 1940. It usually flowers i n February and again in June.—H. B. Christian (*l.c.*).

A. kilifiensis is also reported to grow in a similar habitat near Vipingo, 17 miles south of Kilifi.

The inflorescence averages 80—90cm. in height, and is up to 10-branched from the middle or higher. The flowers are mostly rather glossy deep wine-red.

30. **A. greatheadii** Schonl. in *Rec. Alb. Mus.* 1: 121 (1904) et 289 (1905); Berger in Engler's *Pflanz.* Liliac.–Aloin. 212 (1908); Christian in *Rhod. Agric. Journ. Bull.* 906, p. 14 (1933); Reynolds in *Aloes of Nyasaland* 46 (1954), *Non Fl. Pl. S. Afr.* 10: Plate 369 (1930).

―― *A. pallidiflora* Berger in Engler's *Bot. Jahrb.* 36: 58 (1905), et *Bot. Mag. t.* 8122 (1907) – *fide* Berger.

―― *A. termetophila* (*errore termetophyla*) De Wild. in *Plantae Bequaertianae* p. 30 (1921).

DESCRIPTION: Based on plants over a wide area in S. Rhodesia, Zambia and Elisabethville, Congo.

Plant succulent, varying from solitary to suckering and forming groups. *Stem* none or negligible.

Leaves 16—20, densely rosulate, lanceolate, spreading, 20—30—40cm. long, usually with 10cm. and more of dried twisted apex, 8—12cm. broad; *upper surface* reddish-brown or somewhat glossy dark green, with numerous irregularly scattered elongated whitish spots throughout, sometimes forming broken transverse bands; *lower surface* mostly without spotting, pale green, more or less lineate with interrupted dark green longitudinal lines, especially towards the margins; *margins* sinuate-dentate, with horny brown border armed with reddish-brown deltoid pungent teeth averaging 5—6mm. long, 10—15mm. apart.

Inflorescence a branched panicle up to 1·50m. high, sometimes 2—3 from a rosette.

Peduncle sometimes heavily pruinose, from 3—4 to 6—7-branched above the middle.

Racemes cylindric-acuminate, averaging 20cm. long, 7cm. diam., subdensely flowered, the buds and open flowers flesh-pink, clearly white-striped to base.

Bracts narrowly deltoid-acuminate, about 10mm. long, 3mm. broad at base, scarious, 5-nerved.

Pedicels averaging 15mm. long.

Perianth dull flesh-pink, white-striped, averaging 30mm. long, 7—8mm. diam. across the ovary, constricted to 4·5mm. above the ovary, thence a little decurved and enlarging to the throat and laterally compressed; *outer segments* free for 9mm., with white marginal border and white-striped to base of perianth; *inner segments* free but dorsally adnate to the outer for 20mm., broader than the outer and with broader white marginal border, and more obtuse apices.

Filaments filiform-flattened, the 3 inner narrowed and lengthening before the 3 outer with their *anthers* in turn exserted 1mm.; *stigma* at length exserted 2mm.; *ovary* green, 6mm. long, 2·½mm. diam. (Figs. 80–83).

BECHUANALAND. N.E. Kalahari, Mapellapoede, 18 miles N of Serowe on Ngami Road, 29 Aug. 1903, Schonland 1616! (GRA holotype, PRE).

RHODESIA. 25 miles SW of Enkeldoorn, 3 Sept. 1938, I. B. Pole Evans et J. Erens 1910! (PRE) very typical; near Gwelo, 15 July 1951, Reynolds 6044! (PRE); near Chibakwe River, 56 miles NE of Salisbury, 4 July 1952, Reynolds 6644! (K, PRE); Chindamora Res., 28 miles NNE of Salisbury, 18 June 1958, L. C. Leach 609! (K); *Melsetter Dist.*, Cashel, cult. Greendale, fl. 29 June 1961, L. C. Leach 11147! (SRGH) excellent material; *Umtali Dist.*, 10 miles W of Umtali, July 1959, L. C. Leach 9208! (SRGH), same loc. 23 June 1961, Leach and Wild 11135 (PRE, SRGH); *Chibi Dist.*, near Tokwe Bridge, 21 July 1958, L. C. Leach 590 (SRGH); 14 miles S of Gwelo, 5,000 ft., cult. Greendale, fl. 13 June 1961, L. C. Leach 11108! (PRE, SRGH), fl. 29 June 1961, L. C. Leach 11146! (SRGH).

MOÇAMBIQUE. Manica and Sofala, near Machipanda, 18 June 1959, Leach 9160 (SRGH).

CONGO REPUBLIC (LEO). Katanga. Near Elisabethville, May 1912, Homble 655 holotype of *A. termetophyla* De Wild. (BR). *Katanga Prov.* On termitaria near INEAC Station, Keyberg, 6 miles S of Elisabethville, 4,000 ft., 26 May 1954, Reynolds 7226! (K, BR, PRE); 76 miles NW of Elisabethville (11 miles SE of Jadotville), 4,000 ft., 29 May 1954, Reynolds 7229! (K, BR, PRE); 29 miles N of Kiubo Falls (149 miles N of Jadotville), 30 May 1954, Reynolds 7236! (K, BR, PRE).

A. greatheadii was first collected by Dr. S. Schönland and Dr. J. B. Greathead at Mapellapoede, 18 miles N of Serowe on the road to Lake Ngami, Bechuanaland Protectorate, in Aug. 1903. Since then it has been found to be widely distributed in Rhodesia and Zambia, and in the south-east parts of Katanga, Congo Republic. The type material is from a very weak form, the inflorescence not being typical of the species as a whole. *Note:* Mapellapoede or Mabela-e-Pudi – The goat's nipples.

DISTRIBUTION: Abundant almost throughout Rhodesia; Plumtree, Matopos, Gwanda, Bulawayo–Gwelo to Salisbury, Fort Victoria, Zimbabwe, Birchenough Bridge, Umtali, Odzi, Rusape, Belingwe, Shabani, Mrewa, Ntoko etc.

Fig. 80.   Fig. 81.

A. greatheadii Schonland.

Fig. 80. Plant at Gt. Zimbabwe near Fort Victoria, Rhodesia. Height 5 ft.
Fig. 81. Plant on termite mound at Keyberg, 6 miles S of Elisabethville, Katanga, Congo,
Height 4 ft. *Note:* Rosettes hidden by large *Sansevieria* leaves.

Fig. 82.

A. greatheadii Schonl. Flowers 1/1 from
a plant near Gwelo, Rhodesia – note striping

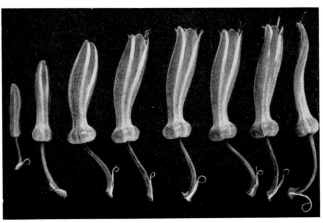

Fig. 83.

A. greatheadii Schonl. Flowers 1/1 from a
plant near Elisabethville, Katanga, Congo
– note striping.

ZAMBIA: Mazabuka, Kapiri Mposhi to Mpika, along the Copper Belt, Chingola, Bancroft, westwards to Solwezi, Mwinilunga and Matonchi near the Angola border.

CONGO (LEO), *Katanga:* Elisabethville to Jadotville and westwards to beyond Kasaji; Jadotville northwards for 150 miles to beyond Kiubu Falls.

NATIVE NAME: *Kizimabupia* in the Kitabwa tongue of Elisabethville Dist. Homble gives the native name as *Itembushia*.

A. *greatheadii* is an exceedingly variable species. In Rhodesia plants are mostly smaller, grow singly, and have taller, more branched inflorescences, while in the Congo near Elisabethville, when growing on termite mounds (which are about 20 ft. high and 30 ft. or more broad) plants sucker and form large groups, leaves are larger, inflorescences are lower and less branched, and racemes tend to be longer.

One striking character of A. *greatheadii* is the buds and open flowers which are mostly an insipid dull flesh-pink colour and are white-striped to base or almost to base. It is this white-striping of the perianth which chiefly distinguishes A. *greatheadii* from its nearest allies.

Mr. Hugh Taylor of Kitwe records *in litt.* "A. *greatheadii* grows on termite mounds near Bancroft, while A. *christianii* grows in the soil between the mounds. A. *christianii* has taken over a couple of termite mounds itself, but the two species do not mingle on the mounds, each keeping instead to its own group of mounds."

31. **A swynnertonii** Rendle in *Journ. Linn. Soc. Bot.* 40: 215 (1911); Reynolds in *Aloes of Nyasaland* 15 (1954).
—— A. *chimanimaniensis* Christian in *Fl. Pl. S. Afr.* 16: Plate 639 (1936); Reynolds in *Aloes S. Afr.* 220 (1950).
—— A. *melsetterensis* Christian in *Fl. Pl. S. Afr.* 18: Plate 697 (1938).

DESCRIPTION: *Plant* succulent, acaulescent or with negligible stem, growing singly or in small groups of 3—4 plants.
Leaves about 20, densely rosulate, lanceolate-attenuate, spreading, averaging 25—30cm. long, plus about 10cm. of the apex dried and twisted, about 8—10cm. broad at base; *upper surface* flat to slightly concave near base, more canaliculate upwards, dark-green, spotted throughout, the spots oblong to confluent H-shaped, arranged more or less in wavy, interrupted transverse bands; *lower surface* convex, paler green, obscurely lineate, usually unspotted; *margins* sinuate-dentate, armed with pungent reddish-brown teeth averaging 4mm. long, 10—15mm. distant. *Sap* dries yellow.
Inflorescence a branched panicle 1·5m.—1·75m. high.
Peduncle brown with a bloom, basally flattened and 20mm. broad, terete upwards, 8—12-branched from above the middle, with the lowest branches sometimes with 1—2 branchlets.
Racemes capitate-corymbose, densely flowered, the terminal about 6—8cm. long, 7—8cm. broad, the youngest buds erect and giving the racemes a flat-topped effect, open flowers pendulous, lateral racemes usually a little smaller with the uppermost 1—2 usually a little higher than the terminal.
Bracts narrowly deltoid, 8mm. long, 3mm. broad at base, thin, scarious with 3 crowded nerves in median line.
Pedicels the colour of the perianth, cernuous, 25—30mm. long.
Perianth flesh-pink to dull coral-red, with a slight bloom, 30mm. long, basally flat, inflated to 8mm. across the ovary, constricted to 5mm. above the ovary, thence slightly decurved, laterally compressed and enlarging to the throat and again slightly contracted at the trigonous mouth; *outer segments* free for 9mm., whitish at the margins giving the perianth a white-striped effect in upper third only, the apices subacute, slightly spreading; *inner segments* broader than the outer and with more obtuse more spreading apices.
Filaments flattened, the 3 inner narrower and lengthening before the 3 outer with their *anthers* in turn exserted 0—2mm.; *stigma* at length exserted 2—3mm.; *ovary* green, 7mm. long, 3mm. diam. (Figs 84—86).

RHODESIA. Gazaland, hills near Chipetzana River, 3,500 ft., 19 April 1907, C. F. M. Swynnerton 722 (holotype BM!, K); *Melsetter Dist.*, along the Chimanimani Mountains on eastern border of Rhodesia, and between Melsetter and Umtali, 4,000—5,000 ft., June 1936, Christian in National Herbarium, Pretoria, No. 21201, holotype of A. *chimanimaniensis* Christian (PRE); in wet vlei 1 mile E of Melsetter Village, July 1937, Christian 275 and in National Herb., Pretoria, No. 23026! holotype of A. *melsetterensis* Christian (PRE); same loc., 27 April 1931, H. B. Christian 3993 in GHS (SRGH, PRE); Chimanimani Mountains, near mountain huts, 5,600 ft., 18 May 1960, Leach 9951! (SRGH); near Nhedziwa Village, 1 mile S of the Umvumvumvu River (51 miles S of Umtali), 3,500 ft., 24 July 1956, Reynolds 8239! (K, PRE, SRGH)—called *Tayu* in the local Manyika tongue; 16 miles N of Chipinga, 3,200 ft., 25 May 1959, L. C. Leach 9033! (K, SRGH); forest between Lusitu and Haroni River, 2,000 ft., 24 April 1962, H. Wild 5723! (PRE, SRGH). *Umtali Dist.*, Christmas Pass, 5 May 1958, L. C. Leach 210! (K, SRGH).

MOÇAMBIQUE. In tall grass 55 miles NE of Benga (E bank of R. Zambezi), 1,000 ft., Reynolds 6651 (K, PRE); 30 miles NE of Tete, cult. Greendale, fl. 21 July 1958, L. C. Leach 392! (PRE, SRGH). *Niassa Dist.*, 30 miles E of Malema in woodland, 2,000 ft., plants with flat rosettes of ensiform leaves, Leach et Rutherford-Smith 10884! (PRE, SRGH).

MALAWI (NYASALAND). *Southern Prov.*, 24 miles E of Mwanza Customs, 1,200 ft., 7 July 1952, Reynolds 6658! (K, PRE); foothills of Kirk Range, 8 miles E of Mwanza, 1,300 ft., 7 July 1952, Reynolds 6656! (K, PRE); 25 miles E of Mwanza, cult. Greendale, July 1956, L. C. Leach 387 (SRGH); Likabula, at foot of Mlanje Mountain, 15 Aug. 1960, L. C. Leach 10455 (SRGH).

TYPE LOCALITY: "Gazaland, hills near Chipetzana River". The Chipetzana River rises on the farm Wolverhampton about 20 miles NNE of Chirinda, and flows southwards near to and parallel with

FIG. 84.   FIG. 85.

A. swynnertonii Rendle.

FIG. 84. Plant near Nkedziwa Village, 10 miles SE of Junction, 51 miles S of Umtali, near the
Umvumvumvu River, Rhodesia. Height 6 ft.

FIG. 85. Plant 20 miles E of Mwanza Customs Post, on road to Blantyre, Southern Malawi. Height 6 ft.

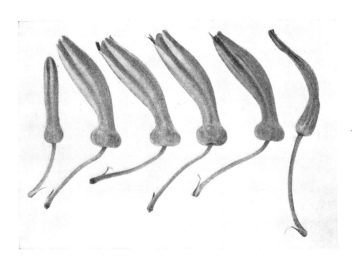

FIG. 86.

A. swynnertonii Rendle. Flowers 1/1 from
the plant depicted on Fig. 84.

the Moçambique border, joining the Busi River about 10 miles NNE of Chirinda. The Chipetzana River is clearly shown on Swynnerton's own map in *Journ. Linn. Soc. Bot.* Vol. 40, opposite p. 12 (1911) – Dr. H. Wild *in litt.*

DISTRIBUTION: From the Chipinga District northwards along the eastern parts of Rhodesia to Melsetter, Umtali and Inyanga at from 3,000 ft. to 6,000 ft.; in Moçambique from SW of Tete to eastwards from Benga (across the Zambezi), along the road to the Malawi border; thence in Malawi from Mwanza Customs for about 30 miles; at the foot of Mlanje Mountain, Cholo Dist., and on hills 15 miles N of Chiromo; also occasional along the Kirk Range, S of Dedza.

A. swynnertoni was named after C. F. M. Swynnerton, renowned for his check-list of land mammals of Tanganyika and for his research into Tsetse control problems. Together with the botanist, B. D. Burtt, who had contributed much material to Kew and to Mr. H. B. Christian at Ewanrigg; both were killed in a tragic air crash near Singida, Tanganyika, in June 1939.

A. swynnertoni can usually be recognised by its leaves being copiously spotted on upper surface and not spotted on lower surface, by its 5—6 ft. branched inflorescence bearing densely flowered capitate-corymbose racemes, the uppermost 1—2 being produced a little higher than the terminal raceme. The flowers vary from dull flesh-pink to redder and usually have a white-striped effect in upper third.

32. **A. duckeri** Christian in *Journ. S.A. Bot.* 6: 179, pl. 19 (1940); Reynolds in *Aloes of Nyasaland* 18 (1954).

DESCRIPTION: Based on personal observations at the type locality, Livingstonia Mission, N. Malawi.
Plant succulent, acaulescent or with short stout stem, solitary.
Leaves about 20, rosulate, lanceolate-attenuate, spreading to slightly recurved, up to 50cm. long, 10—12cm. broad; *upper surface* dull green, somewhat obscurely lined, varying from unspotted to sparingly spotted, flat to slightly canaliculate; *lower surface* paler green, somewhat obscurely lineate, without spots or sometimes with a few scattered whitish elongated spots; *margins* with cartilaginous edge armed with brown deltoid teeth 4—5mm. long, 10—15—20mm. apart.
Inflorescence a branched panicle averaging 1·70m. high, sometimes 2 simultaneously.
Peduncle green, basally plano-convex and 4—5cm. broad, 6—10-branched from above the middle, the lowest branches sometimes with 1—2 branchlets.
Racemes densely flowered, capitate, at first broadly conical, becoming rounded to corymbose, the pedicellate portion 5—6cm. long, 8—10cm. across, youngest buds erectly spreading, open flowers pendulous.
Bracts deltoid, long-pointed, 10—12mm. long, 3mm. broad, thin, dry, 5-nerved.
Pedicels averaging 30mm. long, somewhat arcuate-ascending, nutant at apex.
Perianth mostly scarlet, 35—40mm. long, slightly decurved, basally inflated and about 10mm. diam. across the ovary, abruptly constricted to about 5—6mm. above the ovary, thence enlarging again to the throat and laterally trigonously compressed; *outer segments* free for 11mm., paler at margins, obscurely 3—5-nerved; *inner segments* broader than the outer, keeled with 3—5 crowded nerves.
Filaments filiform-flattened, the 3 inner narrower and lengthening before the 3 outer with their *anthers* in turn exserted 2—3mm.; *ovary* green, 9—10mm. long, 3mm. diam. (Figs. 87–89).

MALAWI (NYASALAND). *Northern Prov.,* near Livingstonia Mission, 3,000 ft., 10 July 1936, B. D. Burtt 5862! (Christian 795) holotype (SRGH), isotype (K, BM). Vipya, 30 miles E of Mzimba, coll. Mrs. H. H. Glover, cult. Nchefu, Cholo, fl. 11 July 1952, Reynolds 6667 (K, PRE); hills near Livingstonia Mission, 4,200 ft., 17 June 1958, Reynolds 8632 (K, PRE, SRGH); on the Nyika, near Chelinda Rest House, 6,800 ft., 18 June 1958, Reynolds 8642 (K, PRE, SRGH).

TANZANIA. *Southern Highlands Prov.:* Mountain slopes 16 miles N of Mbeya, 7,100 ft., 21 June 1958, Reynolds 8666 (K, PRE)—a form with inflorescence lower than usual; 8 miles N of Njombe, 6,500 ft., 23 June 1958, Reynolds 6883 (K, PRE, EA); upland grasslands, 27km. S of Njombe, 1680m., Milne-Redhead and Taylor 11044 (K).

"This Aloe was first collected about seven miles W of Livingstonia Mission, alt. 5,000 ft., in July 1934 by Mr. H. C. Ducker in whose honour it was named, and from whom Mr. Burtt obtained his living material. It is found growing on Brachystegia-covered hills near Livingstonia Mission. The plant sent to me by Mr. Ducker, flowered in the garden at Ewanrigg in July–August 1940"— H. B. Christian.

DISTRIBUTION: Northern Malawi, Vipya Plateau, S of Mzuzu near Ekwendeni, Matipa-Wilindi ridge, Misuku Mountains, near Karonga; abundant on west slopes of hill near Livingstonia Mission which is 46 miles from Njakwa; locally abundant on the Nyika at 6,800—7,000 ft. near the Chelinda Rest House — about 60 miles from Rumpi.

In southern Tanzania *A. duckeri* occurs plentifully near Mwarupinde, E of Mbeya, on road to Tukuyu, and on mountains 16 miles N of Mbeya; from 10—15 miles N of Njombe to about 35 miles S of Njombe. A cross with *A. nuttii* was found among both parents 33 miles S of Njombe.

A. duckeri has been reported from 20 miles E of Mporokoso in Zambia, and from the Luapula-Kalungwishi escarpments where it is said to be plentiful, at about 4,000 ft. alt. (I have not seen plants or material. – G.W.R.).

Fɪɢ. 87.   Fɪɢ. 88.

A. duckeri Christian.

Fɪɢ. 87. Plant from the Wilindi-Wantipi Ridge, Misuku Mts., north of the Nyika, Koronga Dist., Northern Malawi. Grown by the late Mr. W. H. J. Rangeley at Blantyre. Height 6 ft.

Fɪɢ. 88. Plant on the Nyika, 4 miles south of Chelinda Rest House, Northern Malawi, alt. 6,800 ft.

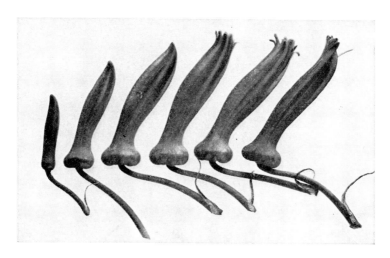

Fɪɢ. 89.

A. duckeri Christian. Flowers natural size.

A. duckeri is variable over its geographical range. In the south (Malawi), leaves are more chan-nelled and recurved and inflorescences reach 6 feet in height; in northern locailities (Tanzania) leaves are more erectly spreading and less channelled, while inflorescences tend to be lower.

Perianth averages 35—40mm. long, and is somewhat decurved, with pedicels averaging 30mm. in length. The pale, almost white, marginal borders of the outer segments give the flowers a rather white-striped effect in upper half.

33. **A. saponaria** (Ait.) Haw. in *Trans. Linn. Soc.* 7: 17 (1804), *Synops. pl. succ.* 83 (1812), *Revis.* 41 (1821), etc. *Note:* For the complete synonymy, pre-Linnean citations, reproductions of early figures, colour plate, figures, medicinal uses, notes on natural hybrids, herbarium material, etc., of the South African forms of *A. saponaria* see *Aloes of S. Africa* pp. 224–231 (1950).

DESCRIPTION based on plants a few miles north of Troutbeck, Inyanga, Rhodesia—the only locality at present known for *A. saponaria* in the tropics. (Vast numbers occur over a wide area in South Africa.)

Plant succulent, acaulescent, always solitary.

Leaves 20—30, densely rosulate, spreading, lanceolate to broadly ovate-lanceolate, up to 22cm. long plus 6cm. of dried twisted apex, 9—11cm. broad at the middle; *upper surface* flat low down, slightly concave upwards, varying from dull to brighter deep green, sometimes with yellowish tinge, and also varying from almost immaculate to clearly spotted with large spots more or less confluent into wavy interrupted transverse bands; *lower surface* convex, usually paler green, and mostly without or with only a few spots. (*Note:* It seems that the most frequent form has upper surface rather copiously spotted, and lower surface not, or sparsely spotted). *Margins* sinuate-dentate, with horny edge armed with prominent pungent deltoid brown teeth that are smaller and more crowded low down, and 6—8mm. long, about 15mm. apart at middle of leaf.

Inflorescence branched, averaging 65 cm. high.

Peduncle basally plano-convex and 20mm. broad, 3—4-branched at the middle (3-branched the average), rarely rebranched.

Racemes capitate-corymbose, 10—12cm. diam., the pedicellate portion 3—4cm. long, produced mostly at the same level, but sometimes with a lateral raceme a little higher than the terminal which is usually the largest; youngest buds suberect, open flowers pendulous.

Pedicels averaging 35—40mm. long, suberectly spreading, nutant at apex.

Bracts narrowly to broadly lanceolate-acuminate, 15—20mm. long, 5mm. broad, thin, scarious, many-nerved.

Perianth orange-scarlet to deep scarlet, averaging 35—40mm. long, with pronounced basal swelling about 9mm. diam. across the ovary, severely constricted above the ovary, thence slightly decurved and enlarging to the throat and slightly compressed laterally; *outer segments* free for 10mm.

Anthers not, or exserted 1mm.; *stigma* at length exserted 1—2mm.; *ovary* green, 8mm. long, 3mm. diam. (Figs. 90–91)

FIG. 90

A. saponaria (Ait.) Haw. On east slopes of Black Mtn., just N of Troutbeck, Inyanga, Rhodesia. Height 3 ft.
Photo: Mr. L. C. Leach.

RHODESIA. Inyanga, a few miles N of Troutbeck, 26 Sept. 1956, L. C. Leach 269! (K, SRGH); downs on rocky dolerite hillside, 6,500 ft. Dec. 1958 D. C. H. Plowes 2060 (K PRE SRGH); 2 miles N of Troutbeck, Oct. 1961, H. Wild 5514! (PRE, SRGH); 3 miles N of Troutbeck, 6,500 ft., fl. 6 Oct. 1959, L. C. Leach 9390A, B, (PRE), 9390C, D, (SRGH).

DISTRIBUTION: Known only in the Inyanga District of Rhodesia, mostly for a few miles north of Troutbeck with the largest numbers on the east slopes of Black Mountain. A few scattered plants seen on road from Troutbeck towards Mt. Inyangani, and on Mt. Inyangani, all at about 6,500 ft. Flowers in October.

A. saponaria is variable in leaf marking, the most frequent form having the upper surface copiously spotted with rather large dull white spots that are more or less arranged in wavy, interrupted transverse bands. The inflorescence is 3—4-branched averaging 65cm. high, with pedicels and flowers each averaging 35—40 mm. long. The racemes are densely capitate-corymbode (flat-topped).

34. **A. zebrina** Baker in *Trans. Linn. Soc.* ser. 2, Bot. 1, 264 (1878), in *Journ. Linn. Soc.* 18: 167 (1880), in Th. Dyer *Fl. Trop. Afr.* 7: 464 (1898); Rendle *Cat. Welwitsch. Afr. Pl.* 1853–61, v. 2: part 1, p. 45 (1899); Berger in Engler's *Pflanzenr.* Liliac.–Aloin. 207 (1908); Christian in *Rhod. Agric. Journ.* Bull. 905, p. 5 (1933); Reynolds in *Aloes S. Afr.* 281 (1950).

—— *A. platyphylla* Bak. in *Trans. Linn. Soc.* ser. 2, Bot. 1, 264 (1878), in *Journ. Linn. Soc.* 18: 167 (1880), in Th. Dyer *Fl. Trop. Afr.* 7: 463 (1898); Rendle *Cat. Welwitsch Afr. Pl.* 1853–61, vol. 2, part 1, p. 45 (1899); Berger in Engler's *Pflanzenr.* Liliac.–Aloin. 207 (1908); Reynolds *Aloes S. Afr.* 281 (1950).

—— *A. lugardiana* Bak. in *Kew Bull.* 135 (1901); Berger in Engler's *Pflanzenr.* Liliac.–Aloin. 207 (1908).

—— *A. baumii* Engler et Gilg. in Warburg (Baum's) *Kunene-Sambesi Exped.* 191–92, Fig. 90 (1903); Berger in *Gard. Chron.* ser. III, 35: 226 (1904); Hemsley in *Bot. Mag. t.* 7948 (1904); Berger (*l. c.*) 207.

—— *A. bamangwatensis* Schönland in *Rec. Alb. Mus.* 1: 122 (1904) – *fide* Berger.

FIG. 91.

A. saponaria (Ait.) Haw. *Left:* Leaf upper surface. *Right:* Under surface × 1/3 approx.
Photo: Mr. L. C. Leach.

DESCRIPTION based on personal observations near Cacuaco and Quicuxe, Luanda, Angola, and elsewhere.

Plant succulent, acaulescent or with very short stem, sometimes solitary, usually suckering and forming small to large groups.

Leaves about 20, spreading, densely rosulate, lanceolate, 20—30 cm. long, 7cm. broad with a few cm. of the apex dried and twisted; *upper surface* rather flat below, slightly canaliculate upwards, somewhat dull green, striate and marked with large oblong whitish spots that are sometimes irregularly scattered, or usually arranged in a series of more or less irregular transverse bands; *lower surface* convex, varying from scarcely to copiously spotted; *margins* sinuate-dentate, armed with stout horny pungent deltoid brownish teeth 4—6mm. long, 10—15mm. apart, the interspaces rounded. *Sap* dries purplish or orange.

Inflorescence a 6—10-branched panicle 1—1·3m. high.

Racemes laxly-flowered, narrowly cylindric, slightly acuminate, 30—40cm. long, 6cm. diam.

Bracts narrowly deltoid, scarious, thin, 3—5-nerved, as long as the pedicel or slightly longer.

Pedicels lowest 6—8mm. long.

Perianth dull reddish, averaging 30mm. long, basally inflated and varying from 7—9mm. diam. across the ovary, abruptly constricted to 4—5mm. above the ovary, thence slightly decurved and enlarging to the throat; *outer segments* free for 7mm., paler at the margins; *inner segments* broader than the outer and with more obtuse apices.

Anthers exserted 1—2mm.; *stigma* at length exserted 2mm.; *ovary* green, 8mm. long, 3mm. diam. (Figs. 92–94).

FIG. 92.   FIG. 93.

A. zebrina Bak.

FIG. 92. Plants near Cacuaco, 10 miles NE of Loanda, Angola. Height 1·4m.

FIG. 93. Plant from Humpata, SW of Sá da Bandeira, Huila Dist., Angola, flowering in Johannesburg. Height 1·5m.

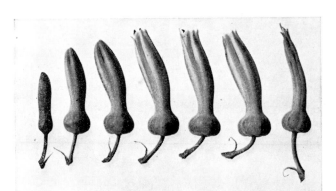

FIG. 94.

A. zebrina Bak. Flowers 1/1 from a plant at Quicuxe, near Loanda, Angola.

ANGOLA. *Loanda Dist.:* Barra do Bengo. Plentiful on dry hills from Quicuxe towards Cacuaco, very social. July 1854, Welwitsch 3721 (Lectotype LISU, syntypes (BM! K!); very plentiful in clayey thickets behind Loanda round Quicuxe. Fl. Jan., Febr., March. Welwitsch 3720 (LISU, BM, K). Icole e Bengo, plentiful in dry places from Funda to Calumguembo, Sept. 1857, Welwitsch 3719 (LISU, BM!). Libongo, flowers a little smaller and tending to a brick-orange red, Welwitsch 3723 (LISU, BM). *Cuanza Norte Dist.:* Pungo Andongo, on banks of the River Caranca, near Sansamanda, fl. 30 April 1857, Welwitsch 3722 (LISU, BM!, K!)—as *A. platyphylla* Bak. *Bié Dist.:* On the Cubango near Chirumba, Oct. 1899, Baum 275 (B)—as *A. baumii* Engler et Gilg.; cult. La Mortola, fl. 19 Nov. 1903, type of *Bot. Mag. t.* 7948 (1904). *Bié Dist.:* Cuando Cubango, Menongue, between Cuchi and Vila Serpo Pinta, valley of the Luassenha Riv. 4 April 1960, E. J. Mendes 3460! (LISC). *Loanda Dist.:* Grasslands near Cacuaco 10 miles NE of Loanda, alt. 250 ft., 12 July 1959, Reynolds 9406 (K, PRE).

BECHUANALAND. 272 miles NW of Molepolole, coll. 30 June 1956, fl. Pretoria, R. Story 4995! (K).

ZAMBIA. *Northern Prov.:* 10 miles SW of Mpika, 16 July 1930, Hutchinson et Gillett 3781! (K); *Southern Prov.*, between Livingstone and Victoria Falls, cult. Johannesburg, fl. 18 April 1959, Reynolds 8987 (K, PRE, SRGH).

RHODESIA. *Gwaai Dist.:* 4 miles NW of Bembusi River Bridge on Bulawayo-Victoria Falls road, 3,500 ft., cult. et fl. Greendale 12 Feb. 1961, L. C. Leach 10720 (PRE, SRGH); *Belingwe Dist.*, 5 miles E of Belingwe, 3700 ft., cult., fll. 24 Feb. 1961, L. C. Leach 10725! (PRE, SRGH); *Salisbury Dist.*, Greendale, 28 Feb. 1955, L. C. Leach 328! (SRGH); *Darwin Dist.*, 5 miles N of Mt. Darwin, plants solitary, 16 March 1961, L. C. Leach 10750 (SRGH).

MOÇAMBIQUE. Manica et Sofala, near Spungabera, cult. Greendale, 8 March 1960, L. C. Leach 9832! (SRGH).

MALAWI (NYASALAND). *Northern Prov.:* 7 miles from Rumpi on Livingstonia Rd., 3,400 ft., 17 June 1958, Reynolds 8633 (PRE, SRGH).

A. zebrina was first collected by Welwitsch in July 1854 near Loanda, on the Atlantic Coast in Angola, and has since been found in abundance almost throughout Angola. In its varying forms it extends southwards well into S.-W. Africa, thence eastwards through Zambia and Rhodesia, and Malawi into Moçambique – almost to the shores of the Indian Ocean. This gives it a range of about 2,000 miles, with the largest numbers in Angola.

A. zebrina occurs as single plants or forming groups, and is variable in leaf markings. The chief distinguishing characters are very laxly flowered racemes, 30cm. and sometimes 40cm. long, with pedicels averaging 6—7mm. long, and perianth averaging 30mm.

Height and branching of the inflorescence are also variable. Flowering time varies according to locality from March–April to June–July.

In Nova Lisboa, Angola, the present author was informed that Europeans and Africans use the leaf-sap of *A. zebrina* as a remedy for dandruff (Portuguese *Caspa*).

Bot. Mag. t. 7948 states "The Kaffirs of Humbe on the Kunene River in the west (Angola) make cakes of the flowers of *Aloe baumii*. They boil and press the flowers for this purpose – but we are not told whether Europeans relish the said cakes."

NATURAL HYBRIDS

Crosses of *A. zebrina* with *A. littoralis* Bak. are not rare where both parents grow socially and flower at the same time. Several such crosses were noticed on the Fortaleza São Filipe hill at Loanda, also much further south, 10 miles NE of Sa da Bandeira in Huila District.

35. **A. macrocarpa** Todaro in *Hort. Bot. Panorm.* 1: 36, t. 9 (1875); Bak. in *Journ. Linn. Soc.* 18: 163 (1880), in Th. Dyer, *Fl. Trop Afr.* 7: 462 (1898); Durand et Schinz, *Consp. Fl. Afr.* 5: 309 (1893); Schweinfurth in *Bull. Herb. Boiss.* 2: app. 2, 69 et 110 (1894); Berger in Engler's *Pflanzenr.* Liliac.–Aloin. 209 (1908); Reynolds in *Journ. S.A. Bot.* 20: 37 (1954); R. W. J. Keay in *Kew Bull.* 17: No. 1, 65 (1963).
—— *A. edulis* A. Chev. in *Expl. Bot. Afr. Occ. Franc.* 1: 645 (1920), in *Rev. Bot. Appliq.* 31: 592, t. 32/A (1952) *descr. gall. tant. – fide* Keay.
—— *A. barteri* Schnell (*non* Baker) in *Ic. Pl. Afr.* Fasc. 1, No. 23 (1953) – *fide* Keay.

DESCRIPTION based on personal observations in Eritrea and Ethiopia.
Plant succulent, acaulescent or with very short stem, growing singly or suckering and forming small groups.
Leaves 16—20, densely rosulate, suberectly spreading, lanceolate to lanceolate-attenuate, 20—30cm. long (sometimes up to 40cm.), 6—7cm. broad; *upper surface* flat to slightly canaliculate, green, with numerous dirty-white or very pale greenish oval spots and blotches throughout, irregularly scattered or in a series of irregular interrupted wavy transverse bands; *lower surface* convex, with numerous pale green blotches throughout, usually arranged in a series of wavy transverse bands; *margins* sinuate-dentate, with cartilaginous margin armed with pale brown subpungent deltoid teeth averaging 3 mm. long and irregularly 8—10mm. apart.
Inflorescence a branched panicle 80—100cm. tall.
Peduncle basally plano-convex and 15—20mm. broad, rather compactly 3—5-branched from about the middle.
Racemes rather laxly flowered, 15—20cm. long, 6cm. diam., laterals a little shorter, buds grey-green tipped and suberectly spreading, open flowers pendulous.
Bracts 8mm. long, 3mm. broad at base, thin, scarious, 3—5-nerved.
Pedicels obliquely spreading, averaging 12—15mm. long.

PLATE 20

ALOE MACROCARPA   Tod.

Near Sambeti Village, 264km. N of Addis Ababa, Shoa Prov.,
Ethiopia. Height 90cm.

FIG. 95.

A. macrocarpa Tod. Reproduction of Todaro's *t* 9 in *Hort.
Bot. Panorm.* 1: 36 (1875) much reduced.
*Photo: By courtesy. The Director Royal Botanic Gardens.
Kew.*

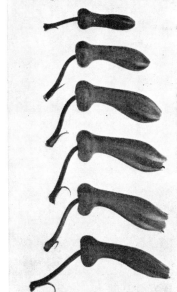

FIG. 96.   FIG. 97.

A. macrocarpa Tod.

FIG. 96. Plant collected by Prof. K. N. G. MacLeay near Heiban, Nuba Mts., Kordofan
Prov., Sudan. flowering in Johannesburg.

FIG. 97. Flowers 1/1 from the plant depicted on Colour Plate 20.

Perianth bright reddish-scarlet, 25mm. long, somewhat glossy, basally inflated and 8mm. diameter across the ovary, abruptly constricted to 5mm. above the ovary, thence slightly decurved and enlarging to the throat and slightly contracted at the mouth; *outer segments* free for 6—7mm., paler at the edges, obscurely 3-nerved, the apices subacute and slightly spreading; *inner segments* with more obtuse apices.

Filaments very pale lemon, the 3 inner narrower and lengthening before the 3 outer with their *anthers* in turn exserted 0—1mm.; *stigma* at length exserted 1mm.; *ovary* pale green, 6mm. long, 2·5mm. diam. (Plate 20, Figs. 95–97).

ERITREA. Amba near Gheleb, 2000m., 13 April 1891, Schweinfurth 1377!; 1436! (K); Mt. Alam Kale, NW of Aiderso, 1800m., 5 April 1892, Schweinfurth et Riva 1488!, 1757! (K); Ambelaco near Maldi, 2000m., 14—18 Feb. 1894, Schweinfurth 157! (K); north side of Mescilit Pass N of Kheren, 4,100 ft., 21 March 1949, Bally 6696! (EA).

ETHIOPIA. *Shoa Prov.*, near Sambeti Village, 133km. S of Dessie (264km. N of Addis Ababa), 4,600 ft., 29 April 1956, Reynolds 8126! (K, PRE, EA).

TYPE LOCALITY: Not known. Todaro merely states "Originates in Abyssinia." Berger states "Introduced into cultivation in 1870 by Schimper, and later by Penzig and Schweinfurth."

The typical form of *A. macrocarpa* has leaves 20—30cm. long and only 6—7cm. broad, and plants occur singly or in groups. The inflorescence averages 80—100cm. in height, racemes laxly flowered and 15—20cm. long, pedicels being 12—15mm. long, with the perianth averaging 25mm. long.

This form is abundant in most parts of Eritrea from the Mescillet Pass, Kheren and Elabet in the north, to Godofelassi, Saganeiti, Adi Ugri and elsewhere in the south. It is found near Axum, Adi Aboon (Adowa) and in the Rift Valley north of Cobbo in Tigre Province of Northern Ethiopia, through the Jurie River valley in Wollo Province to the Shoa Province where it is plentiful at 70km., 90km. and 133km. south of Dessie.

Certain plants west of L. Zwai and near Shashamanne, about 230km. south of Addis Ababa in Arussi Province, Ethiopia, appear to belong here.

35A. Var. **major** Berger in Engler's *Pflanzenr.* Liliac.–Aloin. 210 (1908) – *A. commutata* Engler *Hochgebirgsfl. Trop. Afr.* 164 (1892) *non* Todaro.

Berger states that the var. *major* has larger flowers, 25—35mm. long, and racemes a little longer and laxer. (Figs. 98–99).

FIG. 98.

A. macrocarpa Tod. var. *major* Berger. Collected near Jos Nigeria, flowering in Johannesburg. Height 4 ft.

Fig. 99.

A. macrocarpa Tod. var. *major* Berger. Flowers 1/1 from a plant near Jos, Northern Prov., Nigeria – see Fig. 98.

ETHIOPIA. *Tigre Prov.:* Vongi, above the Lake, 6,000 ft., 6 November 1862, Schimper 798! (BM).

On the assumption that plants are also generally larger, with larger broader leaves, the following material is referred to *A. macrocarpa* Tod. var. *major* Berger:

SUDAN. *Kordofan Prov.:* Nuba Mountains, near Heiban, 800m., coll. Prof. K. N. G. MacLeay, cult. Johannesburg, fl. 8 Feb. 1959, Reynolds 8550 (PRE).

N. NIGERIA. Jos Plateau near Hill Station, Batten-Poole in FHI 12874A! (K, FHI); Jos, cult. Ibadan, 31 May 1948, Keay in FHI 25326! (K, FHI); 29 Aug. 1960, Keay in FHI 22725! (K, FHI); ex Jos Plateau, near Jos, cult. Johannesburg, fl. 10 March 1960, Reynolds 9111 (K, PRE, EA).

UPPER DAHOMEY. Atacora Mountains, Somba country, near Ouandoukouana, among sandstone rocks, 400—600m. alt., 21 June 1910, Chevalier 24157 (P. holotype of *A. edulis* A. Chev.)—*fide* R. W. J. Keay.

In its variable forms *A. macrocarpa* is found almost throughout Eritrea, and in many parts of Ethiopia, westwards through the Sudan (Nuba Mountains, Kordofan) to Nigeria, Dahomey, and as far west as Bamako in Mali – this is a range of about 3,000 miles.

Chevalier records that in Upper Dahomey the flowers of *A. macrocarpa* are eaten by the Sombas, Baribas and Gourmas, and cooked and used for seasoning of meat and starchy foods.

NATIVE NAMES: *Siniani yebo* (Baribo), and *Ifouaman* (Gourma).

A. zebrina Bak. appears to be the nearest ally of *A. macrocarpa*, but differs from it in having longer racemes (30cm.), shorter pedicels (averaging 6mm.), and slightly longer flowers.

36. **A. lateritia** Engler *Pflanzenwelt Ostafrikas* 140 (1895); Baker in Th. Dyer *Fl. Trop. Afr.* 7: 461 (1898); Berger in Engler's *Pflanzenr.* Liliac.–Aloin. 199 (1908).

—— *A. campylosiphon* Berger in *Notizblatt des K. Bot. Gart. Berlin* 4: 151 (1904), in *Gartenwelt* 548 (1906) *cum fig.*

—— *A. amanensis* Berger in Engler's *Bot. Jahrb.* 36: 59 (1903).

—— *A. angiensis* De Wild. in *Plantae Bequaertianae* 24 (1921); Reynolds in *Journ. S.A. Bot.* 20: 179 (1954).

—— *A. bequaerti* De Wild. in *Plantae Bequaertianae* 26 (1921).

—— *A. lanuriensis* De Wild. *l.c.* 27 – *fide* Professor W. Robyns.

—— *A. solaiana* Christian in *Fl. Plants S. Afr.* 20: Plate 781 (1940).

Note: *A. lateritia* is an outstanding example of the type material not being typical of the species as a whole. The type, Volkens 404(B) happens to be an outlying form with short, almost capitate, racemes only about 6cm. long. At the type locality, Rombo, about 24 miles N of Himo at the SE end of Kilimanjaro (Mawenzi), there is considerable variation in leaf size and markings, kind and length of racemes, and length and colour of flowers, the type being described as having perianth "coral-red, not brick-red, and glossy almost as if lacquered." The subjoined description is therefore based on the forms most commonly met with in Tanzania (Tanganyika), Kenya, Uganda and the eastern borders of the Congo Republic.

DESCRIPTION: *Plant* succulent, acaulescent or with very short stem, mostly solitary, sometimes in small groups.

Leaves 16—20, densely rosulate, lanceolate to lanceolate-attenuate, averaging 45cm. long, with a few cms. of the apex dried and coiled or twisted, 8—9cm. broad at base, spreading; *upper surface* flat low down, slightly channelled upwards, dull green to brownish-green, usually copiously spotted with obscure rather large elongated white blotches throughout, sometimes irregularly scattered throughout, the spots sometimes confluent and H-shaped; *lower surface* convex, usually paler green than upper surface and with fewer more obscure blotches irregularly scattered or sometimes arranged in broken transverse bands; *margins* sinuate-dentate, armed with brown pungent deltoid teeth, averaging 3—4mm. long, 10—15mm. apart.

Inflorescence a branched panicle 1—1·25m. tall.

Peduncle basally plano-convex and 15—25mm. broad, with 6—10 branches from above the middle, the lowest branch subtended at base by a thin subscarious ovate-acuminate many-nerved bract 8—12cm. long and 15mm. broad.

Racemes occasionally subcapitate and 8—12cm. long but usually cylindric, slightly acuminate and 20—25cm. long, 8—9cm. diam., the buds suberect, sometimes greenish-tipped, open flowers nutant to subpendulous.

Bracts subscarious, narrowly deltoid, about 10mm. long, 3mm. broad, 3—5-nerved, spreading to recurved at apex.

Pedicels averaging 20—25mm. (sometimes 30mm.) long, usually arcuate-ascending and nutant at apex.

Perianth glossy bright scarlet, orange-scarlet or coral-red, paler at mouth, often not glossy, 35—38mm. long (occasionally 40mm. long), basally flat and 10—11mm. diam. across the ovary, abruptly constricted to 5—6mm. above the ovary, thence enlarging to the throat and laterally compressed trigonously; *outer segments* free for 10mm., paler at margins, 5-nerved, apices subacute, slightly spreading; *inner segments* broader than the outer and with more obtuse more spreading apices.

Filaments lemon, filiform-flattened, the 3 inner narrower and lengthening before the 3 outer, with their *anthers* in turn exserted 1mm.; *stigma* at length exserted 2mm.; *ovary* green, 8mm. long, 3mm. diam. (Plate 21, Figs. 100–103).

Fig. 100.   Fig. 101.

A. lateritia Engler.

Fig. 100. Plant at the type locality Rombo, 15 miles N of Marangu, 24 miles N of Himo, Northern Prov., Tanzania (Tanganyika). Height 1·25m.

Fig. 101. Plants near Solai, 28 miles N of Nakuru, Kenya. Height 1·4m.

Photo: Mr. P. R. O. Bally.

Tanzania. At Rombo near Kilimanjaro, 1400—1500m., 13 June 1893, Volkens 404, holotype (B), isotype (BM). Near Rombo (type loc.) grassy slopes SE end of Kilimanjaro, (Mawenzi), 15 miles N of Marangu, 29 March 1952, Reynolds 6369! (K, PRE, EA); at Himo, 18 miles E of Moshi, 2,700 ft., 29 March 1952, Reynolds 6368! (K, PRE, EA); Dabaga Highlands, Kilolo, 2 Feb. 1962, Polhill et Paolo 1443 (EA), Mt. Bomole, Amani (type loc. *A. amanensis*) 29 Dec. 1956, Verdcourt 1755 (EA); 13km. W of Songea, 990m., 20 Apr. 1956, Milne-Redhead and Taylor 9787! (K); 17·5km. W. of Songea, 960m., 20 April 1956, Milne-Redhead and Taylor 9786! (K); Dry hillsides 4 miles NE of Lushoto, 1650m., 8 April 1953, Drummond and Hemsley 2093! (K, PRE, EA); Mombo-Makuyuni, 1,200 ft., 11 Sept. 1935, Greenway 4080 (PRE, EA). S. Highlands Prov., near Sao Hill, 6,400 ft., 25 June 1960, L. C. Leach 10118 (SRGH); Makumbako, W of Sao Hill, 5,600 ft., 25 June 1960, L. C. Leach 10115 (SRGH); 14 miles NE of Sao Hill, 6,300 ft., 27 June 1958, Reynolds 8716 (K, PRE, EA).

Kenya. NE slopes of Kilimanjaro, 28 Aug. 1956, Bally 10702 (EA); Solai Station, "Lake" Solai, east of Menengai Crater, at foot of Sebukia Hill, cult. Pretoria, fl. Aug. 1939, Pole Evans and Erens in National Herbarium No. 25, 157 (PRE)—type of *A. solaiana* Christian; "Lake" Solai, 28 miles N of Nakuru (type loc. of *A. solaiana* Christian), 5,500 ft., 23 April 1952, Reynolds 6583 (PRE), Bally 8189 (EA); near Makindu, 110 miles SE of Nairobi, 3,250 ft., 14 April 1952,

ALOE LATERITIA   Engler.

A form 27 miles NW of Rwindi, Kivu Province, Congo Republic (Leo.).
Flowers in June. Height 1·20m.

Reynolds 6540 (K, PRE); Taita Hills, cult. Nairobi, 7 Feb. 1953, Bally 8790 (K, EA); 4 miles S of Eldoret (very robust form), 3 April 1952, Reynolds 6607 (K, PRE); Taita Hills, Yale Peak, 2050m., 13 Sept. 1953, Drummond and Hemsley 4289 (K, PRE, EA).

UGANDA. Buganda, Mengo, Kajarsi Forest, Entebbe Road, 3,900 ft., May–June 1930, Chandler 1199 (K); 7 miles S of Kampala, 4 Aug. 1954, Reynolds 7512 (K, PRE); Buganda, Mubende, 6 miles E of Mubende, 27 July 1954, Reynolds 7494 (PRE).

RWANDA. The following *fide* Dr. G. Troupin: Near Mutara, Gabiro-Gatsibu track, 1400m., April 1957, Troupin 3116 (BR, LWO, YBI, EA, K); near Mimuli, near R. Kakitumba, Jan. 1958, Troupin 5745 (BR, LWO, YBI); Parc National de la Kagera, frequent, Bugesera, Nyamabuye, Jan. 1954, Liben 1088 (BR); valley Uruanda, March 1954, Liben 1282 (BR); Biharagu Hill near L. Tshohaha, 1400—1450m., April 1958, Troupin 7048 (BR, LWO, YBI), 7307 (BR, LWO, YBI, NY), neighbourhood of Kindama, 1480m., July 1958, Troupin 7842 (BR, LWO, YBI).

CONGO (LEO). *Upper Katanga:* 25 miles E of Kapona on road to Baudoinville, near Lusaka Mission, 4,000 ft., 5 June 1954, Reynolds 7241 (K, BR, PRE). *Kivu Province:* Rutshuru Territory, Angi, 20 Sept. 1914, J. Bequaert 5789 (BR)—holotype of *A. angiensis* De Wild.; 6 miles NE of Uvira, near L. Tanganyika, 2,700 ft., 11 June 1954, Reynolds 7259 (K, BR, PRE); Kamaniola, 50 miles N of Uvira, 3,100 ft., 16 June 1954, Reynolds 7262 (K, BR, PRE). *Kivu-Nord Dist.:* Hangi (Angi), 6 miles SW of Rutshuru, 4,200 ft., c. 1° 13′ S, 29° 25′ E (type loc. *A. angiensis* De Wild.), 22 June 1954, Reynolds 7265 (K, BR, PRE); Mountain slopes, 27 miles NW of Rwindi, 5,600 ft., 26 June 1954, Reynolds 7269 (K, BR, PRE); near Beni, 7 April 1914, J. Bequaert 3446 (BR)—type of *A. bequaertii* De Wild.; Ruwenzori, in the Lanuri Valley, 2 June 1914, Bequaert 4650, type of *A. lanuriensis* De Wild. (BR)—*fide* Prof. Dr. W. Robyns.

FIG. 102.

A. lateritia Engler. Between Kapona and Moba on road to L. Tanganyika, Katanga Prov., Congo (Leo). Height 1·3m.

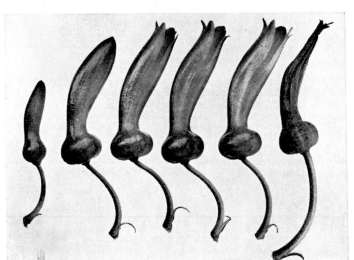

FIG. 103.

A. lateritia Engler. Flowers 1/1 from a plant at Rombo, type loc. – see Fig. 100.

It is wiser, more sensible, and infinitely less confusing to uphold *A. lateritia* as one species only, varying much in its wide distribution range. At the SE localities (Rombo, etc.) racemes are shorter and flowers more glossy coral-red. In Uganda and the eastern borders of Congo Republic racemes average 20—25cm. long, and flowers are not glossy.

NATIVE NAMES: Congo (Leo). *Kidata* in the Kivira tongue of the Bavira tribe of Uvira. *Ngaka* in the Bashu tongue of the tribe at Beni. Rwanda: Between Astrida and Nyanza, *A. lateritia* is known as *Igikakarubamba* in the Kignaruanda tongue of Ruanda. Burundi: *Ngarare* in the Kirundi tongue of the Barundi people of Burundi.

36A. **A. lateritia** Engler var. **kitaliensis** (Reynolds) Reynolds *Comb. nov.* – *A. angiensis* De Wild. var. *kitaliensis* Reynolds in *Journ. S.A. Bot.* 20: 182 (1954).

KENYA. 6 miles SE of Kitale, alt. 6,300 ft., fl. 11 Aug. 1954, Reynolds 7520, holotype (PRE), isotypes (K, EA); 1 mile SE of Kitale, alt. 6,400 ft., fl. 11 Aug. 1954, Reynolds 7519 (PRE, K); NE Elgon foothills, Aug. 1962, Tweedie 2417 (EA). (Figs. 104–105).

FIG. 104.

A. lateritia Engler var. *kitaliensis* (Reynl.) Reynolds. Plant near Kitale, Kenya. Height 1·8m.

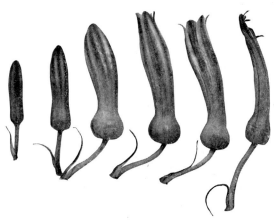

FIG. 105.

A. lateritia Engler var. *kitaliensis* (Reynl.) Reynolds. Flowers natural size.

The variety differs from typical *A. lateritia* in having narrower, denser cylindric-acuminate racemes, denser buds, longer narrowly deltoid bracts as long as their pedicels, shorter pedicels averaging 16mm. long, dull flesh-pink flowers, and 35mm. perianth with less inflated subglobose basal swelling.

Plants were found in numbers near Kitale; on the Kitale–Endebess–Mt. Elgon road; on the Kitale-Elgon link road; on the Kitale Turbo road; repeatedly along the Kitale-Hoey's Bridge road; occasional near Soy and Eldoret. A form with more acuminate racemes occurs in numbers each side of the Kipkarren River, about 11 miles SW of Eldoret on the road to Kapsabet, flowering early in August.

DESCRIPTION: *Plants* solitary, acaulescent or with very short stem.
Leaves about 16, densely rosulate, lanceolate-attenuate, about 40cm. long, 7—9cm. broad, the youngest erectly spreading, oldest spreading and slightly recurved in upper fifth; *upper surface* dull watery-green with numerous greenish-white spots or blotches throughout; the blotches varying from obscurely lenticular to H-shaped, scattered or sometimes arranged in irregular transverse bands; *lower surface* convex, paler green, with fewer blotches; *margins* sinuate-dentate, armed with deltoid pungent pale-brown teeth averaging 3—4mm. long, 10—15mm. distant. *Sap* dries yellow.
Inflorescence a branched panicle 1·1—1·3m. high.
Peduncle plano-convex and 25mm. broad at base, green with a grey powdery bloom, 4—8-branched from the middle or higher.
Racemes cylindric-acuminate, subdensely flowered, the terminal the highest and 20—25cm. long, 8cm. diam., the buds suberect, crowded, older buds spreading, open flowers subpendulous.
Bracts narrowly deltoid-acuminate, 3mm. broad at base, as long as the pedicel.
Pedicels averaging 16mm. long, with apices nutant.
Perianth flesh-pink, averaging 35mm. long, subglobosely inflated at base and averaging 8—9mm. diam. across the ovary, constricted to 5—6mm. above the ovary, thence decurved and enlarging towards the throat; *outer segments* free for 8mm., with paler margins, obscurely nerved, the apices subacute, slightly spreading; *inner segments* broader than the outer and with more obtuse more spreading apices.
Filaments lemon, filiform-flattened, the 3 inner narrower and lengthening before the 3 outer with their *anthers* in turn exserted 0—2mm.; *style* yellow, with *stigma* at length exserted 2—3mm.; *ovary* 8—9mm. long, 3·½mm. diam., green (Figs. 104, 105).

GROUP 7

(Series *Hereroenses* Reynolds)

Plants acaulescent or with short stem. *Leaves* rosulate, lanceolate-deltoid, sometimes with elongated double H-shaped spots. *Margins* sinuate-dentate. *Inflorescence* a branched panicle. *Bracts* narrowly lanceolate long-pointed. *Perianth* cylindric-trigonous, shortly stipitate, straight; *outer segments* free to the middle.

One species only: *A. hereroensis* Engler.

A. hereroensis is found in Southern Angola which is the furthest north known for the species. It occurs abundantly in parts of S.-W. Africa, the type locality being Usakos. Also plentiful in several districts in South Africa from Upington to Bethulie, etc. – see *Aloes of S. Africa* 324–27, with colour plate (1950).

37. **A. hereroensis** Engler in *Bot. Jahrb.* 10: 2 (1888); Baker in *Fl. Trop. Afr.* 7: 462 (1898); Berger in Engler's *Pflanzenr.* Liliac.–Aloin. 204 (1908); Reynolds in *Aloes of S. Africa* 324 (1950) – *A. hereroensis* var. *orpeniae* (Schonl.) Berger (*l.c.*) 204 (1908): Engler et Drude *Veget. Erde.* 9: 2, 326, fig. 224 (1908); *Fl. Pl. S. Afr.* 8: Plate 281 (1928).

DESCRIPTION: *Plants* solitary or in small groups, usually with very short stem.
Leaves about 30, densely rosulate, lanceolate-deltoid, arcuate-ascending, slightly recurved near apex, about 30cm. long, 6cm. broad (sometimes in very old plants reaching 50cm. long, 9cm. broad); *upper surface* flat low down, slightly canaliculate upwards, very glaucous, obscurely lineate to sulcate, usually without spots; *lower surface* convex, similar to upper surface, but sometimes marked with a few to many scattered single or double H-shaped whitish spots throughout; *margins* sinuate, with slight cartilaginous edge armed with reddish-brown to brownish deltoid pungent spreading teeth about 3—4mm. long, 8—10mm. apart.
Inflorescence a many-branched corymbose panicle about 1m. high, frequently 2—3 from a rosette with all the racemes more or less at the same level.
Peduncle branched at the middle or higher with 4—8 arcuate-erect branches the lowest often with 1—2 branchlets, not sterile-bracteate below the first branch.
Racemes densely capitate, corymbose, 6—8cm. long, terminating in a dense conical tuft of imbricate bracts, 8—10cm. broad, unicoloured, the flowers mostly orange-scarlet.
Bracts narrowly lanceolate-deltoid, very long-pointed, thin, scarious white, 3—7-nerved, one-half to two-thirds the length of the pedicel.

Pedicels 30—50mm. long, about 40m. the average, arcuate-ascending with apex nutant.

Perianth orange-scarlet, averaging 38—30mm. long, cylindric-trigonous, narrowing to the throat and with the mouth slightly up-turned; *outer segments* free for 14—16mm. (tube about half the length of the perianth), 3-nerved, the 2 upper segments closely grouped with their subacute apices falcately connivent and upturned; *inner segments* with broad white border and more obtuse spreading apices.

Anthers exserted 2—4mm.; *stigma* at length exserted 5mm.; *ovary* 8mm. long, 3mm. diam. (Figs. 106–107).

ANGOLA. *Huila Dist.:* Stony desert 20 miles NE of Mossamedes, c. 15° 04′ S, 12° 19′ E, alt. 1,000 ft., the last in flower on 28 June 1959, Reynolds 9283 (K, PRE, LUA).

A. hereroensis grows in arid, stony desert conditions of very low rainfall, from 5 to 20 miles NE of Mossamedes on the road inland to Karakul and Sá da Bandeira. In flower it is most attractive, but does not take kindly to cultivation, unless lime is added to the soil.

FIG. 106.

A. hereroensis Engler. 20 miles NE of Maçamedes, Huila Dist., Angola. Height 1m.

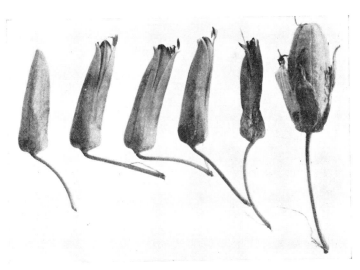

FIG. 107.

A. hereroensis Engler. Flowers natural size.

GROUP 8

(Series *Aethiopicae* Berger *pro parte*)

PERIANTH TRIGONOUSLY INDENTED ABOVE THE OVARY

Plants acaulescent or shortly caulescent. *Leaves* rosulate, not spotted, or copiously spotted, flat to slightly canaliculate. *Inflorescence* branched. *Pedicels* half as short as the perianth or almost the same length. *Bracts* very small, much shorter than the pedicels.

Type species: *A. chabaudii* Schonl. Tropical species: Six.

The species comprising this group are distinguished by having perianths that are markedly trigonously indented above the ovary, as in *A. chabaudii* Schonl.

KEY TO THE SPECIES

A. RACEMES CAPITATE

Rosettes small, with crowded marginal teeth, pedicels 20mm., perianth
25—28mm.   .. ..   43 *A. grata*

B. RACEMES SUBCAPITATE OR BROADLY AND SHORTLY CONICAL

Pedicels 15—17mm., perianth 32mm. .. ..   38B *A. chabaudii* var.
                                                            verekeri

C. RACEMES BROADLY CYLINDRIC

(*a*) *Racemes* 10—15*cm. long, sublaxly flowered:*
    1. Pedicels 20—25mm., perianth 35—40mm. .. ..   38 *A. chabaudii*
    2. Inflorescence oblique, with flowers spreading each side of the
    axis of almost horizontal racemes   .. ..   38A var. *mlanjeana*
    3. Leaves leathery, 50cm. long, 17cm. broad, pedicels 12mm., peri-
    anth thick and fleshy, 33mm. long .. ..   42 *A. rivae*
(*b*) *Racemes subdensely flowered,* 10—12*cm. long:*
    1. Leaves 20cm. long, 7cm. broad, pedicels 16mm. long, perianth
    35mm. .. ..   41 *A. mzimbana*

D. RACEMES NARROWLY CYLINDRIC

1. Racemes 30—40cm. long, laxly flowered, pedicels 12mm. .. ..   39 *A. bukobana*
2. Racemes 20—25cm. long, rather densely flowered, pedicels 18mm.,
perianth 30—35mm. long   .. ..   40 *A. milne-redheadii*

38. **A. chabaudii** Schonl. in *Gard. Chron.* Ser. 3: 38, 102, Fig. 34 (1905); Berger in Engler's *Pflanzenr.* Liliac.–Aloin. 244 (1908); Pole Evans in *Fl. Pl. S. Afr.* 5: Plate 164 (1925); Christian in *Rhod. Agric. Journ.* Bull. 876, p. 3, Feb. (1933); Reynolds in *Aloes of S. Afr.* 339 (1950), in *Aloes of Nyasaland* 23 (1954).

DESCRIPTION based on plants in several localities in Rhodesia:
    Plants acaulescent or shortly caulescent, forming small to large dense groups from suckers and offshoots from base.
    Leaves about 20, densely rosulate, lanceolate, acuminate, up to 50cm. long, 10cm. broad low down; *upper surface* flat low down, slightly canaliculate upwards, dull grey-green to glaucous-green, obscurely lineate, usually without spots, but sometimes with a few small confluent H-shaped spots irregularly scattered; *lower surface* convex, similar to the upper; *margins* with a narrow greyish cartilaginous edge armed with small deltoid teeth 1—2mm. long, 5—10mm. apart low down, more distant upwards.
    Inflorescence a loose somewhat pyramidal panicle with squarrose ascending branches, usually 60—80cm. high, but sometimes reaching 1m. and more in robust specimens.
    Peduncle basally flattened, terete upwards, about 12-branched low down, the branches divaricately spreading almost horizontally with the racemes ascending, the lowest 1—2 branches sometimes with 1—2 branchlets.
    Racemes broadly cylindric slightly acuminate, the terminal 10—15cm. long, 8—10cm. diam., rather laxly 30—40-flowered.

Bracts narrowly ovate-acute or deltoid-acuminate, thin, scarious, 3—5-nerved, 3—5mm. long.

Pedicels slender, the lowest 20—25mm. long, gradually shorter upwards, all obliquely spreading to almost horizontally disposed.

Perianth 35—40mm. long, basally very slightly inflated around the ovary and 7mm. diam., markedly trigonously indented above the ovary and very slightly narrowed, thence slightly decurved and enlarging to the throat, basally obtuse and shortly stipitate; *outer segments* free for 8mm., 3—5-nerved with pale narrow, marginal border and subacute slightly spreading apices; *inner segments* broader than the outer, with crowded nerves in median line, the apices more obtuse and more spreading than the outer.

Filaments filiform-flattened, the 3 inner narrower and lengthening before the 3 outer with their *anthers* in turn exserted 1—2mm.; *stigma* at length exserted 2mm.; *ovary* 6mm. long 2·5mm. diam. (Plate 22 Figs. 108–109).

Fig. 108.

A. chabaudii Schonl. On granite at Zimbabwe Ruins, SE of Fort Victoria, Rhodesia.
Height 75 cm.

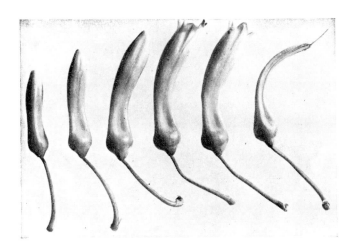

Fig. 109.

A. chabaudii Schonl. Flowers natural size.

PLATE 22

ALOE CHABAUDII　Schonl.

A few miles N of Fort Victoria, Rhodesia. Flowering in July. Height 2′ 9″.

RHODESIA. *Mtoko Dist.*, at foot of granite outcrops, 16 miles NE of Mtoko, 2,000 ft., 5 July 1952, Reynolds 6646! (K, PRE, SRGH); between Lundi and Tokwe River, 1 July 1930, I. B. Pole Evans 2710! (PRE); *Victoria Dist.*, near Lundi, 2,000 ft., 1 Aug. 1952, Reynolds 6730! (K, PRE); *Bulawayo Dist.*, Matoppos, 22 June 1916, Pole Evans 163! (K, PRE); *Mt. Darwin Dist.* between Rusambo and Rukori, 2,400 ft., cult., inflor. 4 ft. 6 in., 4 June 1961, L. C. Leach 11102! (PRE, SRGH); *Salisbury Dist.*, Domboshawa, cult., 1 July 1961, L. C. Leach 11112! (PRE, SRGH); *Umtali Dist.*, 14 miles S of Umtali, cult., 17 June 1961, L. C. Leach 11111! (SRGH, PRE); *Bubi Dist.*, 70 miles NW of Bulawayo, very robust form with 6—7 ft. inflorescence, cult., 21 July 1959, L. C. Leach 9227! (SRGH).

ZAMBIA (Northern Rhodesia). *Southern Prov.*, Cataract Island on N bank of Zambezi River, near Victoria Falls, Sept. 1909, Rev. F. A. Rogers 5288! (SRGH, BOL); *Central Prov.*, between Kafue River and Broken Hill, 3 ft., flowers red, 13 July 1930, J. Hutchinson et J. B. Gillett 3592! (SRGH); 135 miles E of Lusaka, 22 miles W of Luangwa River, 26 July 1952, Reynolds 6713! (PRE); *Eastern Prov.*, 44 miles W of Port Jameson, 24 July 1952, Reynolds 6701! (K, PRE).

CONGO (LEO). *Katanga:* Kiubo Falls on Jadotville-Mitwaba Road, 8 July 1958, A. Schmitz 6359! (PRE).

MALAWI. *Southern Prov.*, 5 miles W of Chiradzulu Mountain between Blantyre and Zomba, cult., 10 June 1958, L. C. Leach 388! (SRGH); *Cholo Dist.*, Nasonia Estate, 10 July 1952, Reynolds 6664! (PRE); *Central Prov.*, 8 miles W of Dedza, 5300 ft., 20 July 1952, Reynolds 6692! (K, PRE).

TANZANIA. *Southern Highlands Prov.:* N side of Kinani River, 69 miles E of Mbeya, 3,800 ft., 27 Aug. 1954, Reynolds 7532! (PRE); *Songea Dist.*, Kipanga Rock, 3 miles S of Lukumbulu (109 miles N of Songea), 1290m., 6 July 1965, Milne-Redhead et Taylor 10970! (K); same locality, 4,300 ft., 26 June 1958, Reynolds 8703! (K, PRE, EA).

MOÇAMBIQUE. Near Vila de Manica, E of Rhodesian border, Aug. 1956, L. C. Leach 404! (PRE, SRGH); N of Vila Gouveia, fl. Pretoria 27 Aug. 1940, I. B. Pole Evans et J. Erens 497! (PRE); 30 miles SW of Tete (= 30 miles NE of Changara Customs) 500 ft., 5 July 1952, Reynolds 6647! (K, PRE); *Zambesi Div.*, W face of Namuli Peaks, 5,000 ft. (Vila Junqueiro, N of Quelimane), Leach et Schelpe 11480! (SRGH); *Niassa Div.*, 6 miles E of Nampula, 1,250 ft., 23 July 1962, Leach et Schelpe 11435! (PRE, SRGH); 17 miles E of Nova Freixo, 1,850 ft., 17 July 1962, Leach et Schelpe 11396! (PRE, SRGH).

TYPE LOCALITY: Rhodesia (S. Rhodesia), precise locality not known. Schonland stated: "This very distinct new species was collected by Mr. J. M. Brown when on a hunting trip to the Zambezi. It was given by him to Mr. John A. Chabaud of Port Elizabeth, in whose garden it flowered, and to whom I owe the opportunity of describing it." Two sheets, without labels or collecting data are at GRA.

A. chabaudii appears to have its specific centre in Rhodesia where it is the commonest and most widely distributed species of Aloe in the Territory. In all localities it is almost invariably found on or at the foot of granite whalebacks and outcrops. It is an exceedingly variable species in size of leaf, height and branching of the inflorescence, length and density of racemes and colour of flowers.

NATURAL CROSSES

1. × *A. aculeata*, among both parents a few miles S of Lundi River on Beit Bridge Road; and Matopos Hills, SE of Bulawayo.

2. × *A. cameronii* has been collected near Great Zimbabwe, SE of Fort Victoria, at Domboshawa, N of Salisbury, and on Zembe Mountain, S of Vila Pery, in Moçambique.

3. × *A. excelsa* has been collected near Zimbabwe, also on Zembe Mountain, S of Vila Pery, in Moçambique.

38A. **A. chabaudii** Schonl. var. **mlanjeana** Christian in *Fl. Plants S. Afr.* 18: Plate 698 (1938); Reynolds in *Aloes of S. Africa* 342 (1950), in *Aloes of Nyasaland* 24, (1954).

Differs from the typical form in having bright green leaves turning dull brick-red in upper part of upper surface only, with horny white line on the margins curving up into the basal part of the teeth. The inflorescence is shorter and is produced obliquely with spreading branches and racemes that cause the flowers to become sub-secund, or sometimes spreading to subpendulous each side of the axis.

Plant acaulescent, suckering from base.

Leaves rosulate about 20, erectly spreading, slightly recurved towards apex, 30—40mm. long, 9cm. broad; *upper surface* green, turning brick-red in upper part, immaculate, obscurely striate; *lower surface* green with reddish tinge at the margins; *margins* bounded by a narrow white horny line with horny brown-tipped teeth 3mm. long, 10—15mm. apart.

Inflorescence a loose panicle, 40—50cm. high, rising obliquely, with 8—12 spreading branches.

Racemes sublax, 16—18cm. long.

Bracts thin scarious, 5mm. long, 5-nerved.

Pedicels spreading, 18—20mm. long.

Perianth coral-red, 30—32mm. long, slightly curved, 9mm. diam. across the ovary, prominently trigonously indented above the ovary; *outer segments* free for 12mm.

Genitalia shortly exserted. (Figs. 110–111).

MALAWI (NYASALAND). *Southern Prov.:* Mlanje Mountain, *Leg.* R. H. Everett, June 1931, fl. Aug. 1937, H. B. Christian 274, in Nat. Herb. No. 23025! (PRE, holotype); ex Mlanje Mountain, cult. Nasonia, fl. 13 July 1952, Reynolds 6665! (K, PRE, SRGH); Nasonia Estate, 13 July 1952 (racemes spreading almost horizontally, flowers pinkish spreading to pendulous), Reynolds 6666 (PRE); Mt. Mlanje, 5,000 ft., flowers orange, 21 July 1958, L. C. Leach 378! (K, PRE, SRGH).

The chief distinguishing character of the var. *mlanjeana* is that the inflorescence is produced obliquely with the racemes spreading almost horizontally, and with the flowers spreading to sub-pendulous.

There is considerable confusion of colour forms and variations in the Cholo District of Southern Malawi.

FIG. 110.

A. chabaudii Schonl. var. *mlanjeana* Christian. Plants from the Likabula Trail, Mlanje Mtn., Malawi; flowering at Mbabane, Swaziland.

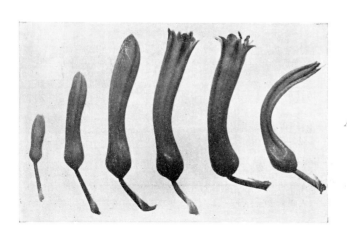

FIG. 111.

A. chabaudii Schonl. var. *mlanjeana* Christian. Flowers natural size.

38B. **A. chabaudii** Schonl. var. **verekeri** Christian in *Fl. Plants S. Afr.* 18: Plate 699 (1938); Reynolds in *Aloes S. Afr.* 342 (1950).

Differs from the typical form in having olive-green leaves turning reddish in upper half in the dry season, leaf margin with narrow whitish cartilaginous edge armed with horny 4mm.-long uncinate teeth, a much-branched inflorescence 75—90cm. high with sub-capitate sometimes shortly and broadly- conical racemes about 8cm. diam.
Pedicels 15—17mm. long.
Perianth 32mm. long, in various shades of yellow and red. (Figs. 112–113).

RHODESIA. Upper end of Sabi Gorge, coll. L. S. A. Vereker, cult. Pretoria, fl. July 1937, No. 23027 in Nat. Herb, holotype (PRE).

MOÇAMBIQUE. Vila de Manica, cult. Greendale, 21 July 1958, L. C. Leach 404 (SRGH, PRE).

The var. *verekeri* was first collected by Mr. L. S. A. Vereker in July 1937, on a small hill at the mouth of the Sabi Gorge in Rhodesia, and as far as present records go it does not seem to be very widespread.

FIG. 112.

A. chabaudii Schonl. var. *verekeri* Christian. Plant collected by Dr. A. O. D. Mogg near Inhambane town, east side of the lagoon, Moçambique, flowering in Johannesburg. Height 5 feet.

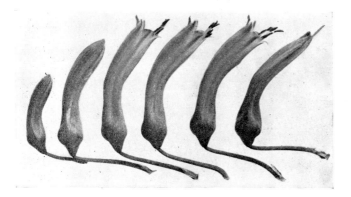

FIG. 113.

A. chabaudii Schonl. var. *verekeri* Christian. Flowers natural size.

6

PLATE 23

ALOE BUKOBANA   Reynolds.
Near Biharamulu, Lake Prov., Tanzania (Tanganyika). Height 75cm.

39. **A. bukobana** Reynolds in *Journ. S.A. Bot.* 10: 169 (1954).

Plant succulent, acaulescent, suckering freely and forming small dense groups.

Leaves about 16, densely rosulate, the youngest suberect, older spreading, lanceolate-attenuate, averaging 30 cm. long, 8 cm. broad at base, about 14mm. thick; *upper surface* dull green with a slight bloom, unspotted, flat low down, very slightly canaliculate towards apex; *lower surface* convex, grey-green, without spots or markings; *margins* sinuate-dentate, armed with firm deltoid brownish-tipped teeth averaging 4mm. long, 10mm. distant, the apex a small spine. Sap dries yellow.

Inflorescence a branched panicle 70—90cm. high, erect or suberect, the whole inflorescence slender with slender branches.

Peduncle basally plano-convex and 10mm. broad, terete upwards, branched below the middle with up to 10 branches, the lowest sometimes with 1—2 branchlets; lowest branch subtended at base by a broadly deltoid subfleshy many-nerved acuminate bract 35mm. long, 14mm. broad.

Racemes very laxly flowered, the terminal averaging 30—40cm. long, narrowly conic-cylindric; the buds grey-green-tipped, spreading, with their pedicels more or less horizontally disposed, open flowers nutant to subpendulous; in oblique racemes, flowers spreading laterally each side of the axis, and not secund.

Bracts small, broadly and shortly ovate-acute, 4mm. long, 3mm. broad, thin, subscarious, 3-nerved.

Pedicels spreading, averaging 12mm. long.

Perianth dull scarlet, paler at mouth, 30—35mm. long, cylindric-trigonous, varying from slightly rounded at base to obtusely tapering into the pedicel, and from not stipitate to shortly stipitate, cylindric and 7—8mm. diam. across the ovary, thence trigonously indented, slightly curved, and enlarging slightly to an open mouth; *outer segments* free for 7mm., paler at the margins, with subacute slightly spreading apices; *inner segments* dorsally adnate to the outer for their greater length, broader than the outer, with more obtuse more spreading apices, and with 3 crowded nerves forming a scarlet keel.

Filaments lemon, filiform-flattened, the 3 inner narrower and lengthening before the 3 outer with their *anthers* in turn exserted 1—2mm.; *style* lemon-yellow, with *stigma* at length exserted 3mm.; *ovary* greenish-yellow, 6mm. long, 3·5mm. diam. (Plate 23, Fig. 114).

FIG. 114.

A. bukobana Reynolds. Flowers 1/1 from a plant on sandstone hill overlooking Bukoba Harbour and Lake Tanganyika – type locality.

TANZANIA. *North-Western Div.:* Bukoba Dist., on sandstone hills overlooking Bukoba Harbour and Lake Victoria, alt. 3,900 ft., 1 Aug. 1954, Reynolds 7507! holotype (PRE), isotype (K, EA); ex Bukoba, cult. Mutamayo, fl. August 1962, Mrs. Tweedie 2414! (EA); 2½ miles S of Biharamulu, 4,800 ft., 16 July 1958, Reynolds 8886 (K, PRE, EA); 18 miles N of Biharamulu, 4,500 ft. (80 miles S of Bukoba) 16 July 1958, Reynolds 8875 (K, EA, PRE). *Western Prov.,* 7 miles S. of Uvinza, 19 July 1958, Reynolds 8929 (K, PRE, EA).

NATIVE NAME: "*Nkaka*" in the Kihaya tongue of the Bahaya tribe of Bukoba, Tanzania.

A. bukobana is nearest allied to *A. milne-redheadii* Christian, but the latter differs in having shorter denser racemes, longer pedicels, while leaves are much more spotted and plants are generally larger and form larger groups.

Certain plants further south in the Western Div., seen flowering on 19 July 1958, 76 miles S of Uvinza, Reynolds 8944 (K, PRE, EA), appear to be intermediates between *A. bukobana* and *A. milne-redheadii*.

40. **A. milne-redheadii** Christian in *Journ. S.A. Bot.* 6: 177, Plate 18 (1940).

DESCRIPTION based on many plants at Kalene, NW Zambia (N. Rhodesia).

Plants succulent, acaulescent or shortly caulescent, soboliferous and forming small to large groups.

Leaves about 16—20, densely rosulate, forming rather compact rosettes, ovate-lanceolate, up to 30cm. long, 7cm. broad gradually narrowing to an acute apex; *upper surface* brownish-green becoming slightly reddish in dry season, flat to very slightly concave, obscurely lineate, usually copiously spotted throughout, but sometimes scarcely spotted; *lower surface* similar to upper surface but greyer, and usually more profusely spotted, the spots or blotches sometimes arranged in wavy broken transverse bands; *margins* with cartilaginous edge armed with brownish teeth 3mm. long, 10—15mm. apart.

PLATE 24

ALOE MILNE-REDHEADII   Christian.

At Kalene, 50 miles N of Mwinilunga, N-W Province, Zambia. Height 80cm.

Inflorescence from 1—2-branched and 50cm. high in young plants to 5—7-branched and 80—90cm. high in old plants.
Peduncle basally flattened and 12—15mm. broad, branched about the middle, brown with a bloom, without sterile-bracts.
Racemes narrowly cylindric-acuminate, 20—25cm. long, 8cm. diam., subdensely flowered, the apical buds spreading to nutant, open flowers pendulous.
Bracts small, ovate acute, 6mm. long, 3mm. broad at base, thin, scarious, dirty-white, 3-nerved.
Pedicels the colour of the perianth, averaging 18mm. long.
Perianth scarlet, 30—35mm. long, basally flat to obtuse and shortly stipitate, 8mm. diam. across the ovary, trigonously indented above the ovary and very slightly narrowed, thence enlarging to the throat; *outer segments* free for 10mm., paler at the margins, 5—7-nerved, the apices subacute and slightly spreading; *inner segments* white shading to yellowish above, with 3 crowded nerves forming a scarlet keel, the apices more obtuse more spreading.
Filaments the 3 inner narrower and lengthening before the 3 outer with their *anthers* in turn exserted 0—1mm.; *stigma* at length exserted 1—2mm.; *ovary* pale green, 5mm. long, 3mm. diam. (Plate 24, Fig. 115).

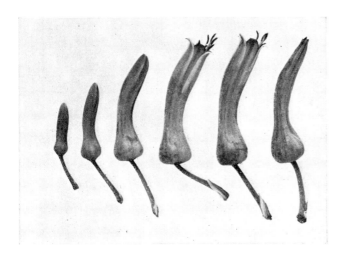

FIG. 115.

A. milne-redheadii Christian.   Flowers from a plant depicted on Plate 24.

ANGOLA. *Moxico Dist.*, on ridge of hills between River Zambezi and River Lusavo, E. Milne-Redhead 4253, cult. Ewanrigg, fl. July 1938, Christian 926, holotype (SRGH), isotype (K).

ZAMBIA (N. RHODESIA). *North-western Prov.:* Rocky ridge W side of Shintungu River, 105 miles W of Solwezi, 4,500 ft., 10 June 1959, Reynolds 9150 (PRE, K, SRGH)—a form; Kalene, 50 miles N of Mwinilunga, near Angola border, c. 10° 11′ S, 24° 11′ E, 4,400 ft., 12 June 1959, Reynolds 9181 (K, PRE, SRGH).

This charming species was named after Mr. E. Milne-Redhead of Kew, who discovered it on 20 June 1938, not flowering, across the border in Angola, about 12 miles walk NW of Matonchi, which is some 30 miles W of Mwinilunga in Zambia, close to the Angola border. Plants were sent to Mr. Basil Christian at Ewanrigg, near Salisbury in Rhodesia, and he described the species when plants flowered with him in July 1938.

A. *milne-redheadii* is nearest allied to *A. bukobana* Reynolds, but the latter differs in forming smaller groups, in having longer much laxer racemes, shorter pedicels, and usually less spotted leaves.

41. A. mzimbana Christian in *Fl. Pl. S. Afr.* 21: Plate 838 (1941); Reynolds in *Aloes of Nyasaland* 26 (1954).

DESCRIPTION based on many plants at type locality.
Plants acaulescent or with very short stem, in small to large dense groups, with rosettes sometimes 40cm. across.
Leaves about 20, densely rosulate, spreading-incurved, somewhat deltoid, averaging 20cm. long, 7cm. broad to 30cm. long, 8cm. broad in very robust specimens; *upper surface* grey obscurely striate, usually without spots, flat low down, slightly canaliculate near apex; *lower surface* convex, grey-green with reddish tinge usually unspotted, but sometimes with a few scattered spots; *margins* with reddish-pink edge armed with teeth the same colour, 2—3mm. long, 8—10mm. apart. *Sap* dries yellow.
Inflorescence simple and 30—40cm. high in young plants, 2—3-branched in older plants, 60—80cm. high and 5—8-branched in very robust forms.
Peduncle basally 15—20mm. broad, terete upwards, branched below the middle.
Racemes rather densely flowered, broadly cylindric, varying from 8cm. to 15cm. long (10—12cm. the average), the buds grey-green tipped spreading horizontally, open flowers pendulous.
Bracts somewhat fleshy, 8mm. long, 3mm. broad, 3—5-nerved.
Pedicels averaging 16mm. long.

Perianth coral-red to scarlet, 35mm. long, cylindric slightly curved, basally broadly obconic, 8mm. diam. across the ovary, trigonously indented and 6mm. diam. above the ovary, thence trigonously enlarging to the open mouth; *outer segments* free for 12mm., paler at margins, obscurely 5-nerved; *inner segments* broader than the outer, with 3 crowded nerves forming a keel, the apices more obtuse and more spreading.

Filaments pale lemon, with the 3 inner narrower and lengthening before the 3 outer with their *anthers* in turn exserted 0—1mm.; *stigma* at length exserted 1—2mm.; *ovary* green, 5mm. long, 2·5mm. diam. (Plate 25, Figs. 116–118).

FIG. 116.   FIG. 117.

A. mzimbana Christian.

FIG. 116. Plants 40 miles N of Sumbawanga, Western Prov., Tanzania (Tanganyika) alt. 6,100 ft. Height 45cm.

FIG. 117. Plants on mountain top 11 miles N of Mitwaba on the Jadotville – Manono road, Katanga Province, Congo (Leo) Alt. 5,800 ft. Height 50cm.

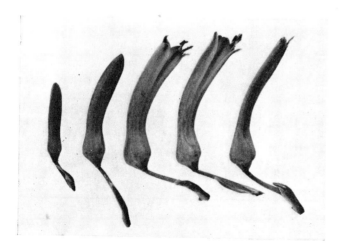

FIG. 118.

A. mzimbana Christian. Flowers 1/1 from a plant at the type locality – See Colour Plate 25.

PLATE 25

ALOE MZIMBANA   Christian.

A weak form at type locality, 19 miles NE of Mzimba, Northern Province,
Malawi (Nyasaland). Height 60cm.

MALAWI (NYASALAND). *Northern Prov.,* on hills about 18 miles NE of Mzimba, coll. 8 June 1938, fl. at Div. of Botany, Pretoria, in June 1940, I. B. Pole Evans et J. Erens 643! in Nat. Herb. No. 26486, holotype (PRE). *Vipya,* 18 miles NE of Mzimba, 5,000 ft., robust form fl. 16 June 1958, Reynolds 8622 (K, PRE, SRGH); 16 miles ENE of Mzimba, coll. W. H. J. Rangeley, cult. Blantyre, fl. 20 May 1956, Reynolds 8186 (PRE). *Nyika,* large numbers on rocks 61 miles from Rumpi, 2 miles SW of Chelinda Rest House, 7,000 ft., 18 June 1958, Reynolds 8643 (PRE, SRGH, K).

TANZANIA. *Western Prov.:* Ufipe Dist., on rocks 40 miles N of Sumbawanga (10 miles S of Chala Mission), 6,100 ft. 21 July 1958, Reynolds 8955 (K, PRE, EA); granite hills just north of the border, N of Abercorn, 17 June 1960, L. C. Leach 10080! (SRGH).

CONGO (LEO). *Katanga Prov.* Mountain top 11 miles N of Mitwaba on Jadotville-Manono Rd., 5,700 ft., 2 June 1954, Reynolds 7238 (PRE, K, SRGH)—a weak form.

ZAMBIA (N. RHODESIA): 5 miles N of Nchanga Mine, Chingola, 4,000 ft., 9 June 1959, Reynolds 9135 (PRE, K)—a form with taller inflorescence. *Central Prov.,* 35 miles E of Kapiri Mposhi, 4,000 ft., 14 June 1960, L. C. Leach 10020! (SRGH, PRE).

Material from Zambia is lacking, but forms of *A. mzimbana* occur abundantly in many parts of that country from Abercorn (near the southern end of Lake Tanganyika) southwards to Kasama, Mpika, and beyond; along the Mporokoso road at "The Gates of Hell", to Chipili, 35 miles N of Fort Rosebery.

Mr. Hugh Taylor has found plants at many places along the Copper Belt, i.e. Kamfinsa Hill near Kitwe, granite domes at Luano Siding, SE of Chingola, also hills SW of Chingola, 4—5 miles NE of Chingola, Kamenza Hill, Bancroft, and elsewhere.

A. mzimbana is an exceedingly variable species. Young plants will produce a simple inflorescence only 30cm. high. Older plants may have 2—3-branched inflorescences 50cm. high, while old specimens may have a 5—8-branched inflorescence 60—80cm. high. Racemes also vary from sub-capitate to broadly cylindric, and 12—15cm. long.

The nearest ally is *A. chabaudii* Schonl., but this is usually a larger plant with longer spreading leaves, a much more branched inflorescence with laxer, more acuminate, racemes.

NATURAL HYBRIDS

Mr. Hugh Taylor reports that crosses of *A. mzimbana* with *A. christianii* are common among both parents at Kamfinsa Hill, Bancroft, in the Copper Belt.

Mr. Taylor has also found crosses of *A. mzimbana* with *A. greatheadii* in some numbers along the Kafue River about 5 miles NE of Chingola.

42. **A. rivae** Bak. in Th. Dyer *Fl. Trop. Afr.* 7: 465 (1898); Berger in Engler's *Pflanzenr,* Liliac.– Aloin. 251 (1908); Reynolds in *Journ. S.A. Bot.* 20: 39 (1954) with Plate VI.

DESCRIPTION: Based on numbers of plants flowering on 7 Sept. 1953, near Mega, Borana, Southern Ethiopia, c. 4° 05′ N, 38° 20′ E, alt. 6,200 ft.

Plant succulent, solitary or in small groups.

Stem usually short, sometimes procumbent or ascending and up to 60cm. long.

Leaves leathery, about 20, densely rosulate, rather compact, arcuate-erectly spreading, somewhat deltoid, up to 50cm. long, up to 17cm. broad at base, 2—3cm. thick, gradually attenuate, the apex a spine; *upper surface* dull olive-green to brownish-green, flat low down, slightly canaliculate towards apex, of uniform colour throughout; *lower surface* rounded and of similar colour; *margins* reddish tinged, armed with firm semi-cartilaginous teeth which are reddish-brown and horny at apex, deltoid, more crowded near base, more distant upwards, about 4mm. long, 10—15mm. apart, the interspaces straight, obsolescent near apex. *Sap* dries deep purple.

Inflorescence a many-branched pyramidal panicle, about 60—70cm. high; usually 2, simultaneously or consecutively.

Peduncle plano-convex and 2cm. broad at base, divaricately about 12-branched, the lowest of which a panicle of 6—8 branches, producing a total of 45—50 racemes, the lowest branches subtended at base by a broadly and shortly ovate-acute bract 15mm. broad, 7mm. long, thin, scarious, 7—10-nerved.

Racemes laxly flowered, averaging 10cm. long, 7cm. diam., usually oblique with the flowers slightly subsecund, the buds dull scarlet, grey-tipped and with a bloom, open flowers spreading horizontally to nutant.

Bracts very small, ovate-acute, 2—4mm. long, 2—3mm. broad, dirty white, thin, scarious, 1—3-nerved.

Pedicels lowest averaging 12mm. long.

Perianth scarlet with a bloom, averaging 33mm. long, cylindric-trigonous, basally flat, 10mm. diam. across the ovary, thence trigonously indented and narrowing slightly to the throat with the mouth wide open; *outer segments* free for 13mm. with broad border, 3-nerved, the apices subacute and much spreading; *inner segments* themselves free but dorsally adnate to the outer to near the middle, the upper third broader than the outer, pale, with prominent median nerve, the apices more obtuse and more spreading than the outer, and markedly brown-edged.

Filaments filiform-flattened, the 3 inner narrower and lengthening before the 3 outer with their *anthers* in turn exserted 4mm.; *style* yellow, with *stigma* at length exserted 5mm.; *ovary* pale olive-green, 8mm. long, 3mm. diam. (Plate 26, Fig. 119).

PLATE 26

ALOE RIVAE Bak.

On the Consulate Hill at Mega, Borana, S. Ethiopia. Height 80cm.

Fig. 119.

A. rivae Bak. Flowers 1/1 from a plant at Mega, Borana, S. Ethiopia – See Plate 26.

S. Ethiopia. Sidamo, Borana: Gobbo Duaya, 16 October 1893, Riva 1766, presumably holotype (FI); Dry places in the NW Boran at Coromma, 7 Nov. 1893, Riva 1766 (FI); Mega, 15 Sept. 1952, Bally 9145! (EA); Same loc., 19 Nov. 1952, Gillett 14366! (EA); Mega Mountain, below the British Consulate, 6,200 ft., 8 Sept. 1952, Reynolds 7032! (K, PRE); Valley E of Amaro Mountains, 1320—1500m., c. 5° 35′ N, 38° 04′ E, 14 Dec. 1952, J. B. Gillett 14732! (EA, PRE).

Kenya. *Northern Prov.:* Furroli Mountain, near Ethiopian border, 3° 42′ N, 38° E, 5,000 ft., 15 Sept. 1952, J. B. Gillett 13877! (EA). *Note:* Mr. P. R. O. Bally has found *A. rivae* on the Huri Hills just south of Gebr Bori, at 3° 24′ N, 37° 45′ E in the N. Prov. of Kenya.

The type locality is "Somaliland: Gobbo Duaya, Riva n. 1509, 16 Oct. 1893". Also included under *A. rivae* is: "Dry places near Coromme, in the north-west Boran, Riva n. 1766, 7 Nov. 1893". Both sheets are at Florence.

Riva left Dolo, and travelled westwards up the valley of the Daua Parma River in April 1893, and arrived at Burgi. In September he was between the Jam Jam, and from there went up to Coromme and the source of the River Sagan in which region he remained until December. Coromme lies to the south-west of Agere Mariam (Alghe) at approx. 5° 30′ N, 38° 04′ E, while Burgi is further to the south-west at approx. 5° 23′ N, 37° 50′ E, northwards of Yavello in South-western Ethiopia. Gobbo Duaya (type locality) could not be traced on any map, but from the date, 16 Oct. 1893, it appears to be somewhere in or near the Burgi–Coromme area.

In Sept. 1953 (with Mr. P. R. O. Bally, Coryndon Museum, Nairobi) the author visited Southern Ethiopia for the express purpose of investigating *A. rivae* and other Aloe species.

He reached Agere Mariam north of Yavello and set off for Coromme, but was compelled to turn back owing to the indescribably bad condition of the track. Neither missionaries nor Ethiopian police had ever heard of Gobbo Duaya, the type locality. Fortunately he found numbers of flowering plants further south, which fitted the description and compared favourably with photographs of the type material. The largest numbers were found at Mega, flowering in early September, on lower slopes of the British Consulate hill to the east of the old Italian Fort; also 3—5 miles N of Mega, and in lower country 10 miles SE of Mega. Also occurs at and near Yavello, about 66 miles N of Mega, and in northern Kenya.

In *A. rivae* the stem is usually short, or procumbent and up to 60cm. long. When planted closely in hedges demarcating fields, stems may reach 1m. in height. The leaves are tough and leathery, even the pulp being difficult to cut. At Mega, numbers of plants were observed on graves.

A. rivae appears to be nearest allied to *A. chabaudii* Schonl. from which it differs in being a larger plant with a thick stem up to 60cm., and in having thick, leathery leaves that are 50cm. long and 17cm. broad, and thick fleshy flowers that average 33mm. long, and 10mm. diam. across the ovary.

43. **A. grata** Reynolds in *Journ. S.A. Bot.* 26: 87 (1960).

Description: *Plant* acaulescent or with short stem, forming dense groups of rather compact rosettes, mostly on rocks.

Leaves 16—20, densely rosulate, lanceolate-attenuate about 20—25 cm. long, 7—8cm. broad; *upper surface* green with reddish-brown tinge, without spots or markings, flat low down, very slightly canaliculate upwards; *lower surface* convex, paler glaucous-green with numerous crowded spots in lower quarter, the spots very pale green (almost white), circular and about 1mm. diam.; *margins* sinuate-dentate, sometimes almost serrate, the teeth varying from 2—3mm. long, 5—8mm. apart; *sap* dries pale yellow.

Inflorescence 2—3-branched, 70—90cm. high.

Peduncle brown, basally flattened and 10—12mm. broad, simple in young plants, forked in older, 3-branched in old plants, usually branched above the middle.

PLATE 27

ALOE GRATA   Reynolds.

On Chimbango Hill, 3 miles S of Chinguar, between Silva Porto and
Nova Lisboa, Angola. Flowers in June. Height 70—90cm.

Racemes capitate or subcapitate, 8—10cm. long, 8cm. diam., the axis pedicels and perianths scarlet, the buds grey-green-tipped and spreading horizontally or slightly nutant, open flowers cernuous to sub-pendulous.

Bracts very small, ovate-acute, 2mm. long, 1·5mm. broad, thin, scarious, 1-nerved.

Pedicels scarlet, averaging 20mm. long, suberectly spreading, the apices nutant.

Perianth scarlet, 25—28mm. long, shortly stipitate, 6mm. diam. across the ovary, narrowed to 5mm. above the ovary, thence trigonously enlarging to the throat and slightly contracted at the mouth; *outer segments* free for 7mm., obscurely nerved, the apices slightly spreading; *inner segments* broader than the outer, with broad pale marginal border and scarlet keel, the apices more obtuse.

Filaments pale lemon, filiform-flattened, the 3 inner narrower and lengthening before the 3 outer with their *anthers* in turn exserted 1—2mm.; *stigma* at length exserted 2—3mm.; *ovary* green, 4mm. long, 2mm. diam. (Plate 27, Fig. 120).

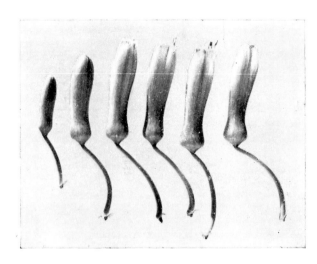

Fig. 120.

A. grata Reynolds. Flowers 1/1 from a plant at the type locality, Chimbango Hill, 3 miles south of Chinguar, Angola – see Plate 26.

ANGOLA. *Bié Dist.*, 3 miles south of Chinguar, on Chimbango Hill, c. 12° 35′ S, 16° 20′E, alt. 5,800 ft., 19 June 1959, Reynolds 9246 holotype (PRE), isotypes (K, LUA); Coll. Chimbango Hill cult. Mbabane, fl. 10 July 1964, Reynolds 11669 (K, LISC).

Note: Chinguar is on the main railway line, midway between Silva Porto and Nova Lisboa. Large numbers of plants occur on Morro (hill) Chimbango, 3 miles to the south, mostly on rocks, in dense groups of compact rosettes, with *A. rupicola* Reynolds nearby.

A. grata is characterized by having leaves with small crowded marginal teeth that are sometimes almost serrate; lower surface of leaves, copiously white-spotted near base, the spots being very small, circular (not elliptical or elongated) and 1mm. in diameter. The inflorescence is simple in young plants, forked in older, and 2—3-branched in the largest specimens. Racemes are capitate or almost so, and the perianth is scarcely trigonously indented above the ovary. The 2mm. long bracts are 1-nerved.

A. mzimbana Christian appears to be the nearest ally, but this species has marginal teeth more spaced, a shorter inflorescence, longer racemes, and perianths that are markedly trigonously indented above the ovary. The shape of the flowers is also different.

GROUP 9

(Mostly Series *Verae* Berger emended)

Principal distinguishing characters of species in this group are:

Pedicels averaging 5—8mm. long. *Bracts* reflexed, often twice as long as the pedicels. *Perianth* mostly cylindric-trigonous, 25—30mm. long, mouth slightly upturned, red, orange or yellow, varying from glabrous to pubescent and tomentose-villose; *outer segments* connate to the middle or higher.

Inflorescence short or tall, mostly simple or few-branched, branches erect, rarely many-branched. *Racemes* mostly narowly cylindric, sublax to subdense, elongated, apical buds sometimes hidden by large densely imbricate bracts.

Plants mostly acaulous, solitary or forming groups, rarely caulescent. *Leaves* densely rosulate, ensiform long-attenuate, fleshy, glaucous, sometimes spotted.

Type species: *A. barbadensis* Mill.

Tropical species: 17, mostly from North Africa and Arabia; none in Madagascar and South Africa.

Note: A. pubescens with 15mm. pedicels and 42mm. perianths does not fit here, but is included because the perianths are pubescent. For *A. venusta*, with pubescent perianths, see Group 11.

KEY TO THE SPECIES

1. PERIANTH PUBESCENT TO TOMENTOSE

A. Inflorescence simple or up to 1—3-branched, pedicels 5—6mm. long:

(a) *Inflorescence under 1m. tall:*

1. Leaves 45 × 10cm., inflorescence simple or 1—2-branched, racemes dense, 20cm. long, perianth scarlet, 28—31mm. long, pubescent .. ..   44 *A. niebuhriana*

2. Leaves 45 × 11cm., inflorescence 3—4-branched, racemes 25cm., perianth 32mm. long, minutely pubescent .. .. ..   45ᴀ *A. rigens* var. *glabrescens*

3. Leaves 35 × 9cm., inflorescence 3—4-branched, racemes 15cm., perianth 25—28mm. long, tomentose-shaggy.. .. ..   46 *A. tomentosa*

4. All buds spreading horizontally. Perianth 25mm. long, yellow, sparsely covered with white hairs, 8—9mm. long .. ..   47 *A. doei*

(b) *Inflorescence 1—2m. tall:*

1. Leaves 60—80cm. × 12—15cm., racemes narrowly cylindric, 20—30cm. long, perianth rose-pink, puberulent, 30—34mm. long .. ..   45 *A. rigens*

2. Leaves 45 × 10cm., racemes narrowly cylindric, 30cm. long, perianth pink, albo-tomentose, averaging 30mm. long.. .. ..   48 *A. trichosantha*

B. Inflorescence many-branched; pedicels 6mm. long, bracts twice as long:

1. Stem 50cm., leaves 40 × 16cm., inflorescence "elatus", many-branched, racemes subdense, 15—20cm. long, perianth scarlet, 30mm. long, albo-tomentose .. ..   49 *A. menachensis*

C. Pedicels 15mm. long, perianth 42mm. long:

1. Inflorescence simple or 1-branched, racemes 15cm. long .. ..   50 *A. pubescens*

2. PERIANTH GLABROUS

A. Inflorescence under 1m. tall:

(a) *Perianth cylindric-trigonous, 30mm. long:*

1. Leaves 35 × 10cm., inflorescence 3—5-branched, 40—75cm. high, racemes 20cm. long, densely flowered, pedicels 7—8mm., perianth rich scarlet .. ..   51 *A. eremophila*

2. Plant smaller, inflorescence less branched, racemes laxer, perianth scarlet-pink with powdery bloom, markedly stipitate ..   52 *A. serriyensis*

3. Leaves 40 × 8cm., inflorescence 2—4-branched, 80cm. high, raceme sub-dense, 20cm., pedicels 5mm. long, perianth lemon-yellow .. ..   53 *A. dhalensis*

4. Leaves 45 × 15cm., inflorescence 3—4-branched, 80—100cm. tall, raceme 20cm., pedicels 10mm., perianth scarlet .. .. ..   54 *A. audhalica*

(b) *Perianth cylindric, slightly ventricose:*

1. Suckers freely forming dense groups, leaves 50 × 7cm., inflorescence simple or 1—2-branched, racemes 30—40cm., pedicels 5mm.; perianth yellow, 28—30mm. long .. ..   55 *A. barbadensis*

B. Inflorescence over 1m. tall:

(a) *Inflorescence simple or few-branched:*

1. Leaves 30 × 8cm., racemes 35mm. long, bracts large, twice

as long as their 8mm. pedicels, perianth reddish-pink, 32mm. long   56 *A. metallica*
2. Suckers freely, leaves 50 × 10cm., inflorescence usually 3-branched, raceme sublax, 15—20cm. long, pedicels 6mm., perianth pale scarlet, 30—32mm. long   .. ..   57 *A. massawana*
3. Leaves averaging 50 × 12cm., inflorescence mostly 3-branched to 2m. high, racemes 35—40cm. long, sublax, pedicels 6mm. long, perianth 30mm., red   .. ..   58 *A. vacillans*
4. Leaves 70 × 12cm., inflorescence simple or 1—2-branched, racemes 15—20cm. long, rhachis pruinose, pedicels 6—8mm., perianth 28—30mm., scarlet, orange, or yellow   .. .. ..   59 *A. officinalis*
5. Leaves considerably narrower .. ..   59ᴀ var. *angustifolia*
  (*b*) *Inflorescence many-branched*:
    1. Leaves 30 × 5cm., inflorescence paniculate, racemes dense, 4—7cm. long, apical bracts densely imbricate, perianth yellowish-red, 27mm. long (*imperfectly known*) .. ..   60 *A. otallensis*
    2. Leaves 40 × 8cm., inflorescence 8—10-branched, racemes 15—20cm. long, pedicels 6—7mm., perianth cylindric, slightly clavate, 28mm. long, rose-pink   .. ..   60ᴀ *A. otallensis* var. *elongata*

    3. Leaves 60 × 15cm., inflorescence a many-branched and re-branched panicle, racemes 30—35cm. long, pedicels 8mm. long, perianth bright scarlet, 30—33mm. long .. ..   61 *A. splendens*
C. Stem 2—3m. tall, inflorescence a many-branched panicle:
  Leaves 60 × 12cm., racemes 30cm. long, pedicels 6mm. long, perianth deep-pink, 30—34mm. long – see Group 18, caulescent species   122 *A. littoralis*

44. **A. niebuhriana** Lavranos in *Journ. S.A. Bot.* 31: 68 (1965).

Dᴇsᴄʀɪᴘᴛɪᴏɴ: *Plant* usually, when growing in soft, sandy soil, suckering freely and forming dense groups; when growing on rocky ground, usually solitary, acaulous or with a short procumbent stem.
Leaves 15—25 rosulate, spreading or ascending-spreading, lanceolate-attenuate, tapering to an acute, dentate apex, up to 45 cm. long, 10cm. broad at base, 5—8mm. thick; *upper surface* uniformly grey-green with a purplish tinge, broadly canaliculate throughout; *lower surface* the same colour as the upper, convex; *margins* armed with dark brown, blunt or acute teeth, 1·5—2mm. long, 12—15mm. distant.
Inflorescence 50—100 cm. high, usually simple, sometimes 1—2-branched from its upper third, the branches short, arcuate-ascending.
Peduncle flattened and about 15mm. broad at base, terete upward, purplish-green with a bloom, minutely pubescent in its terminal portion, less often glabrous throughout; sterile bracts below the racemes whitish, many-nerved, deltoid, 8mm. long, 6mm. broad at base.
Racemes rather broadly conical, 12—30cm. long, 5—6cm. diameter, densely flowered, youngest buds suberect, older buds horizontally spreading, open flowers nutant.
Bracts narrowly deltoid, acute, 8mm. long, 3—4mm. broad at base, whitish, scarious, 5—7-nerved.
Pedicels red or greenish-yellow, terete, usually minutely pubescent, less often glabrous, 4—6mm. long.
Perianth scarlet (or rarely greenish-yellow), with greenish-yellow segment apices, usually shortly pubescent throughout, less frequently glabrous or papillose-tomentose on the free part of the outer perianth segments, cylindric-campanulate, shortly stipitate, 28—31mm. long, 6—7mm. diameter throughout their entire length, the mouth slightly constricted; *outer segments* free for 19—21mm., with 3 nerves which are red (or rarely yellow) low down, becoming bright green and confluent towards the recurved segment-apices; *inner segments* broader and more recurved than the outer, free but dorsally adnate to the outer, yellow with 3 nerves which are red (or rarely yellow) low down becoming bright green upward.
Filaments yellow, filiform-flattened, the three inner narrower and lengthening before the outer, with their *anthers* in turn exserted 3—4mm.; *style* yellow, the *stigma* at length exserted 4mm.; *ovary* 6mm. long, 2·5mm. diam. (Plate 28, Figs. 121–123).

Soᴜᴛʜ Wᴇsᴛᴇʀɴ Aʀᴀʙɪᴀ. Am Rija (Da'ar al Kudeimi) in the Subaihi country, 1952, Gilliland in Reynolds 6362, fl. Johannesburg, January 1960; Haushabi country, 5 miles S of Al Milah, 1,200 ft. (350m.), 13° 45′ N, 44° 50′ E, 24 Aug. 1962, Lavranos 1863; Subaihi country, on rocky slope near Tor al Baha, alt. approx. 1,200 ft. (350m.), lat. 13° 10′ N, long. 44° 19′ E, 31 March 1964, Rauh et Lavranos 3159 holotype (PRE), isotype (K); Da'ar al Kudeimi, 800 ft. (250m.), 31 March 1964, Rauh et Lavranos 3156, perianths scarlet, glabrous; 3 miles south of Tor al Baha, 31 March 1964, Rauh et Lavranos 3168, perianths yellow, glabrous (PRE, K) and Rauh et Lavranos 3169, perianths scarlet, pubescent; 4 miles S of Tor al Baha, 31 March 1964, Rauh et Lavranos 3170, perianths papillose-tomentose.

A. niebuhriana grows in the hot, arid foothills which lie between the mountain ranges of the interior and the wide coastal plain in the western part of the Aden hinterland. It also occurs in the low-lying valleys which dissect the seaward ranges of the mountains. It is a dominant component of a semi-desert vegetation in which its chief associates are *Salvadora* cf. *persica* Garcin, *Euphorbia qarad* Defl. *Tamarix articulata* Vahl, *Zizyphus spina-christi*. (L) Willd., various species of *Commi-*

PLATE 28

ALOE NIEBUHRIANA   Lavranos.

On sandy banks of Wadi Ma'adin, 4 miles S of Tor al Baha, Subaihi
country, S-W Arabia. Height 90cm.
From a Kodachrome by Prof. W. Rauh.

Fig. 121.   Fig. 122.

A. niebuhriana Lavranos.

Fig. 121. Plants in large numbers on rocky hill south of Tor al Baha, Subaihi country, S-W Arabia.
Height 1·20 m.

Photo: *J. Lavranos.*   Fig. 122. Red flowers 1/1.

phora etc. It was not observed above 1,500 ft. (500m.). In contrast to all other species of Aloe native to the southern fringe of Arabia (with the possible exception of *A. inermis* Forsk.) *A. niebuhriana* is most prolific in its natural habitat, forming large and dense colonies.

The closest ally of this species appears to be *A. trichosantha* Berger, from Eritrea and Ethiopia which, however, differs in having less numerous, usually spotted, leaves with much larger marginal teeth and much taller and usually 3-branched inflorescences.

In *A. niebuhriana* the racemes are usually broadly conical and average only 20cm. long, while the young buds are not hidden by the bracts which are 8mm. long. Finally, the perianths in *A. niebuhriana* are more campanulate and less slender than its ally, being rather constricted at the mouth; the outer segments are free for two-thirds of their length, while in *A. trichosantha* their free portion represents less than one-half of their length.

While in *A. niebuhriana* the flowers open, as in most other species of Aloe, from the bottom upwards, there are usually a few isolated buds at the very base of the raceme which open long after the lower portion of the raceme has finished flowering. The inflorescences are usually simple but, when they branch, they do so from their upper one-third only, in a manner which may be described as dichotomous.

While many plants have been named after Peter Forskal, the botanist of the expedition sent to Arabia by King Frederick V of Denmark in 1762, none, it appears, were dedicated to the memory of the intrepid Carsten Niebuhr, the only member of this expedition to return to Europe. Apart from his invaluable contribution to Europe's knowledge of Arabia, Niebuhr saved for posterity

FIG. 123.

A. niebuhriana Lavranos. Near Da'ar al Ku deimi, Subaihi country, S-W Arabia. Showing characteristic branching of inflorescence. Height 90 cm.
Photo: Prof. W. Rauh.

a considerable part of Forskal's collections and papers and published, at his own expense, Forskals *Flora Aegyptiaco-Arabica*. This species was named after Carsten Niebuhr as a very small tribute to his memory. – J. Lavranos.

45. **A. rigens** Reynolds et Bally in *Journ. S.A. Bot.* 24: 177, Pl. 20, 21 (1958).

DESCRIPTION: *Plant* succulent, acaulous or with short stem, mostly solitary, sometimes in small groups.

Leaves about 24, densely rosulate, varying from arcuate-ascending to suberectly spreading, very rigid, 60—80cm. long, 12—15cm. broad at base, gradually narrowing to the apex, 15—25mm. thick at base; *upper surface* unicoloured pale to darker grey-green, sometimes with reddish tinge, slightly canaliculate; *lower surface* convex, similar in colour; *margins* armed with isolated pungent deltoid teeth that are 4—6mm. long, 20—35mm. apart, paler at base, reddish-brown in upper half; *sap* dries yellow to orange.

Inflorescence branched, 1·25—1·75m. high.

Peduncle basally plano-convex and 3cm. broad, terete upwards, brown with a bloom, 3—4-branched from the middle or lower.

Racemes narrowly cylindric-acuminate, 20—30cm. long, 6cm. diam., youngest buds sometimes covered by densely imbricate bracts, older buds spreading horizontally, open flowers nutant to subpendulous.

Bracts up to 15mm. long, 6mm. broad, thin, scarious, white, rather brittle, 7—9-nerved.

Pedicels 5—6mm. long, minutely puberulent.

Perianth rose-pink to dull scarlet, very shortly puberulent, cylindric-trigonous, 30—34mm. long, basally obtuse, 7mm. diam. across the ovary, very slightly curved, the mouth open; *outer segments* free for 10—12mm. obscurely 3-nerved, the nerves greenish at apex, the apices subacute, slightly spreading; *inner segments* broader than the outer, and with more obtuse, more spreading apices.

Filaments pale lemon, the 3 inner narrower and lengthening before the 3 outer with their *anthers* in turn exserted 2—3mm.; *stigma* at length exserted 4mm.; *ovary* pale olive, 6mm. long, 3mm. diam. (Plate 29, Figs. 124—125).

Somali name: Daar merodi (elephant aloe).

SOMALIA NORTH. Foot of Sheikh Pass, cult. Nairobi, fl. 1943 Bally B. 9661 (EA); 4 miles NE of Darburruk, 15 Jan. 1954, Bally B. 10383 (K, EA); Ged Debti, 20 miles north of Hargeisa, 27 Sept. 1957, Bally B. 11769 (K, EA); 4 miles NW of Bawn on Zeila road, 23 Oct. 1957, Bally B. 11920 (G, EA); 5 miles NW of Bawn, 36 miles NW of Borama, 3,900 ft., c. 10° 13' N, 43° 03' E, 31 Aug. 1957, Reynolds 8369 holotype (PRE), isotype (K, EA).

PLATE 29

ALOE RIGENS   Reynolds et Bally.
4 miles NW of Bawn, Borama Dist., Somalia North (Type locality).
Height 5 ft.

FIG. 124.

A. rigens Reynolds et Bally, 55 miles NE of Hargeisa, 4 miles beyond Darburruk, on road to Berbera, Somalia North.   Height 1·50m.

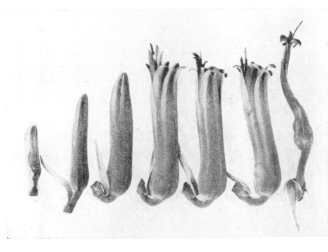

FIG. 125.

A. rigens Reynolds et Bally. Flowers 1/1 from a plant 5 miles NW of Bawn, 36 miles NW of Borama, Somalia North.

Mr. P. R. O. Bally collected plants (without flowers) and seeds of this species in 1943 and 1949, about 4 miles beyond Darburruk on the Hargeisa–Berbera road, at 3,400 ft. In 1954 and in 1956 he found plants in flower.

On 31 August 1957, the present author found large numbers of plants, many in flower, 5 miles NW of Bawn, 36 miles beyond Borama, and 112 miles westwards from Hargeisa on the road to Zeila, at 3,900 ft. altitude. This species continues for about 20 miles along the Zeila road down to 2,750 ft.

A. rigens, and the var. *glabrescens*, is the most widespread species in Somalia North and extends from the Bawn area eastwards to Ged Debti, 20 miles N of Hargeisa, eastwards to near Darburruk (55 miles from Hargeisa), also S of Berbera, between Bihendula and Hudiso (at 2,300 ft.), near the foot of Sheikh Pass and for a few miles up the pass to 3,900 ft.

On the flats of Gaan Libah, 9 miles NW of Ghor, a very robust form was seen at 5,100 ft. A cross with *A. megalacantha* was also noticed.

The western typical form of *A. rigens* is characterized by having very large rosettes of rather bright green, very rigid leaves up to 80cm. long and 12—15cm. broad, an inflorescence of up to 1·75m. high, short 5—6mm. pedicels, and perianths that are very shortly puberulent.

A. rigens seems to be nearest allied to *A. trichosantha* Berger, which the author has seen in large numbers at Ghinda (type locality) between Asmara and Massawa in Eritrea. *A. trichosantha* is, however, a smaller plant with shorter leaves, and has perianths that are conspicuously albo-tomentose.

45A. **A. rigens** Reynolds et Bally var. **glabrescens** Reynolds et Bally *l.c.* 179.

DESCRIPTION: *Plants* in small to large groups. *Stem* none, short, or sometimes decumbent and up to 50cm. long.
   Leaves 18—24, densely rosulate, ascending-spreading to recurved, 40—50cm. long, 10—12cm. broad; *upper surface* uniformly grey-green with reddish tinge, slightly canaliculate; *lower surface* convex; *margins* armed with reddish brown pungent deltoid teeth that are 3mm. long, 10mm. apart low down, 15—20mm. apart upwards.
   Inflorescence 3—4-branched, 75—100cm. high.
   Racemes cylindric-acuminate, 25cm. long, 5—6cm. diam., youngest buds usually not hidden by imbricate bracts.
   Bracts broadly ovate-acute, 9mm. long, 4mm. broad, thin, scarious, dirty white, 7—9-nerved.
   Pedicels 5mm. long.
   Perianth strawberry pink, paler to greenish at mouth, cylindric-trigonous, 32mm. long, glabrous or minutely pubescent under a lens; *outer segments* free for 9mm.
   Anthers in turn exserted 3—4mm.; *stigma* at length exserted 5mm.; *ovary* 7mm. long, 3mm. diam. (Figs 126–127).

FIG. 126.

A. rigens Reynolds et Bally var. *glabrescens* Reynolds et Bally. Plants on the Baaroh Plain, 16 miles north of Adad. Kularle, 28 miles south of El Afwein, on road to Erigavo, Somalia North. Height 1m.

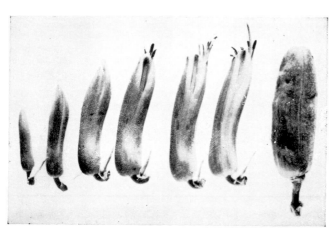

FIG. 127.

A. rigens Reynolds et Bally var. *glabrescens* Reynolds et Bally. Flowers 1/1 from bud to fruit stages.

SOMALIA NORTH. On the Baaroh Plains, 16 miles N of Adad Kularle (28 miles S of El Afwein) on the road to Erigavo, 2,700 ft., c. 9° 27′ N, 46° 55′ E, a few in flower on 6 Sept. 1957, Reynolds 8390 holotype (PRE), isotype (K, EA); Kirit, 15 Oct. 1957, Bally 11877 (EA); Adad Kularle, Burao-Erigavo road, 11 Nov. 1954, Bally 10296 (G).

The eastern form is well worth varietal rank and differs from the typical in having thinner, shorter, more triangular greyish-brown leaves that are more spreading to recurved and only 50cm. long. The inflorescence is 3—4-branched from below the middle and only 75—100cm. tall, with the apical buds of racemes usually not hidden by densely imbricate bracts. The perianth is usually glabrous although sometimes under a lens it is minutely pubescent. The variety occurs along the Burao-Erigavo road where it is first seen at Adad Kularle. Mr. Bally photographed a flowering plant there in November 1954. It occurs in considerable numbers on the Baaror Plain, 16 miles N of Adad Kularle (c. 9° 27′ N, 46° 55′ E), and for 28 miles northwards to El Afwein. The northern limit is Kal Sheikh, a few miles N of El Afwein. North of Kal Sheikh a totally different species, *A. tomentosa* Deflers, comes in, and the two do not appear to overlap.

Numbers occur to the E of Burao, near Kirit, and between Kirit and Ainabo on the road to Las Anod. The weakest form seen was on low gypsum hills a few miles S of Las Anod.

46. **A. tomentosa** Deflers in *Voyage au Yemen* 211 (1889); Berger in Engler's *Pflanzenr*. Liliac.–Aloin. 232 (1908); Reynolds in *Journ. S.A. Bot.* 24: 166, pl. 13–15 (1958); Blatter in *Fl. Arab., Rec. Bot. Surv. India* 464 (1936); O. Schwartz in *Fl. Trop. Arab.* 350 (1939).

DESCRIPTION based on certain plants at Moledera, 36—40 miles SSW of Erigavo, Somalia North (formerly Somaliland Protectorate) which appear to be conspecific with the type in the Yemen. See notes below.

Plant succulent, with short decumbent stems and upturned rosettes, forming small to large dense groups.

Leaves 16—20, densely rosulate, lanceolate-deltoid, averaging 35cm. long, 9cm. broad at base, narrowing to an acute dentate apex, spreading, the lowest usually falcately up-curved; *upper surface* grey-green with reddish tinge, flat low down, slightly channelled upwards, unicoloured, not spotted; *lower surface* convex, greener than upper surface; *margins* with narrow pinkish brown cartilaginous border armed with blunt teeth ·5—1mm. long, 20—40mm. apart, the teeth sometimes obsolete and margins entire; *sap* dries pale yellow.

Inflorescence branched, averaging 60—70cm. tall

Peduncle basally plano-convex and 14mm. broad, terete upwards, averaging 3—4-branched from about the middle, the lowest branch subtended at base by an ovate-acute, thin, scarious, 5—7-nerved bract, 10mm. long, 8mm. broad.

Racemes cylindric-conical, the terminal averaging 15cm. long, 5—6cm. diam., the lateral shorter, subdensely flowered, the apical buds erect, adpressed to the axis, and sometimes hidden by densely imbricate bracts, open flowers nutant.

Bracts ovate-deltoid, 7mm. long, 4mm. broad, thin, scarious, dirty white, 5-nerved.

Pedicels averaging 6mm. long, sometimes up to 9mm. long.

Perianth cylindric-trigonous, rose-pink, conspicuously tomentose-shaggy; 24—28mm. long, slightly rounded at base, 7—8mm. diam. across the ovary, thence slightly narrowed on underside only, and trigonous to a wide open mouth; *outer segments* free for 9mm. (tube 17mm.), paler at margins, obscurely 3-nerved, the apices subacute, spreading; *inner segments* free but dorsally adnate to the outer for 16mm., broader than the outer and with more obtuse more spreading apices.

Filaments lemon, the 3 inner narrower and lengthening before the 3 outer with their *anthers* in turn exserted 3—4mm.; *stigma* at length exserted 4—5mm.; *ovary* pale olive, 6mm. long, 3mm. diam.; *capsule* 18mm. long, 9—10mm. diam. at the middle. (Plate 30, Figs. 128–130).

YEMEN. Ad fauces montis Hadhur, prope Bauan, 2700m., 30 Juin 1887, Deflers 616! holotype (P).

SAUDI ARABIA. *Asir Prov.*, Suda, alt. 10,000 ft., 1 July 1946, D. Vesey Fitzgerald 16076/6! (BM).

SOMALIA NORTH (formerly Somaliland Prot.): Moledera, 36 miles SSW of Erigavo, 24 Jan. 1945, Glover et Gilliland, 643! (K, EA); Same loc., 19 Oct. 1960, Hemming 2037! (EA); Same loc. 2 Nov. 1956, Bally 11298! (K, EA); Moledera 40 miles SSW of Erigavo, c. 10° 09′ N, 47° 13′E, 4,700 ft., 12 Sept. 1957, Reynolds 8445 (K, PRE).

No figure accompanied Deflers's original description. His plant was described as fruticose, with short thick stem, while the leaves pose a problem. There is no leaf or portion of a leaf included in the type specimen of *A. tomentosa*. Deflers merely states (from the Latin): "leaves radical, ensiform, fleshy, thick, shorter than the scape". He gives no measurements, and makes no mention of the leaf margins; whether margins are entire or dentate is not known.

The type material consists of the terminal 40cm. of an inflorescence and includes the terminal raceme and a shorter branch-raceme. The terminal raceme is densely flowered, conical, 11cm. long, 5·5cm. diam., with the apical buds crowded and hidden by imbricate bracts. Perianths are remarkably tomentose, while the axis below the raceme is also tomentose.

Allowing for geographical variations, and for racemes usually varying from shorter and denser to longer and laxer, the Moledera plants are regarded as belonging to *A. tomentosa*.

Compared with the type, the Moledera form differs in having slightly longer, less dense racemes, with the apical buds less crowded and less hidden by their bracts.

There are no manuscripts or notebooks of Deflers in the Library of the Museum in Paris, hence the leaves, and the identity of true *A. tomentosa* will remain unknown until the type locality in the Yemen can be re-visited.

PLATE 30

ALOE TOMENTOSA Deflers.
At Moledera, 40 miles SSW of Erigavo, Somalia North. Height 3 ft.

Fig. 128.   Fig. 129.

A. tomentosa Deflers. Forms at Moledera, 40 miles south of Erigavo, North Somalia; alt. 4,800 ft. Height 65cm.

Fig. 130.

A. tomentosa Deflers. Flowers natural size.

Since the height and branching of the inflorescence, also the pedicels, bracts and very tomentose perianths agree with *A. tomentosa*, it seems that the Moledera plants are conspecific with *A. tomentosa*.

A. tomentosa is nearest allied to *A. trichosantha* Berger (which the author has seen in considerable numbers at the type locality Ghinda, between Massawa on the Red Sea coast and Asmara, in Eritrea,) but in *A. trichosantha* the leaf margins are markedly dentate, the racemes are much longer and laxer and the perianths are less tomentose.

The Moledera form of *A. tomentosa* usually has little or no stem, and sometimes forms small to large groups. The leaves average 35cm. long, 9cm. broad, while margins vary from entire to minutely dentate, with teeth ·5—1mm. long, and 20—40mm. apart.

47. A. doei Lavranos in *Journ. S.A. Bot.* 31: 163 (1965).

DESCRIPTION: *Plants* usually solitary, occasionally forming small groups.

Leaves 12—14, the young ones ascending, the older ones spreading with slightly recurved apices, 30—35cm. long, 8—10cm. broad at base; *upper surface* dull green, sometimes bearing a sparse scattering of white, roundish spots, flat at base but slightly canaliculate towards the apex; *lower surface* broadly convex, unicoloured; *margins* markedly sinuous with a purplish-brown, cartilaginous border and armed with hard, sharp, red-brown, deltoid teeth which are up to 3mm. long and 8—12mm. distant.

Inflorescence 2 or 3-branched, to 70cm. tall, the branches arcuate-erect.

Peduncle plano-convex at base and in its lower portion, terete thereafter, greyish-brown with a bloom, 10mm. broad at base, 5mm. diam. below the first branch, the branches produced from its upper third.

Racemes 15—20cm. long, 5cm. broad, conical, all buds spreading almost horizontally, open flowers pendulous;

Bracts rather small, deltoid, whitish, 5—7-nerved, 3—6mm. long, 2—3mm. broad.

Pedicels green, glabrous, 5—7mm. long.

Perianths yellow, cylindric-trigonous, covered rather sparsely with very long (up to 8—9mm.), white hairs over the entire outer surface, 25—26mm. long, 7mm. diam. over the ovary, the mouth much compressed laterally; *outer segments* free for 10—14mm., with 3 prominent bright green nerves which become confluent towards the slightly recurved apices; *inner segments* pale yellow, broader than the outer.

Filaments much flattened and whitish at base becoming filiform and red-brown in their upper part, the 3 inner narrower and lengthening before the 3 outer, the *anthers* dark brown on back and exserted in turn by 4 mm.; *style* yellow, the *stigma* at length exserted by 5mm.; *ovary* bright green, 5mm. long, 2mm. diam., the apex truncate.—J. J. Lavranos (Figs. 131–132).

SOUTHERN ARABIA. Edge of Audhali Escarpment, 10 miles E of Ras Thina on the track leading to Marwaha, alt. c. 7,400 ft. (2250m.), lat. 13° 59′ N, long. 45° 56′ E, coll. 17 Aug. 1962, fl. Bryanston, Johannesburg, Dec. 1964–Jan. 1965, Lavranos et Doe 2264, holotype (PRE).

A. *doei* was named after Mr. Brian Doe, Director of Antiquities, at Aden, who discovered it with Mr. J. J. Lavranos along the Marwaha track in the magnificent country along the edge of the Audhali Escarpment, at approximately 7,400 ft. This fascinating species is nearest allied to *A. niebuhriana* Lavranos which occurs in large numbers at about 500—1,500 ft. near Tor al Baba in the hot arid foothills of the Subhaihi country of S. Arabia. *A. niebuhriana* however, differs in forming large dense groups, and in having robust, mostly simple inflorescences, larger bracts, longer, somewhat curved perianths which are usually pubescent, or rarely hairy on the free part of the perianth segments only. In *A. niebuhriana* the perianth outer segments are free for 20mm.,

FIG. 131.

A. doei Lavranos. Plant collected 10 miles east of Ras Thina, on track leading to Marwaha on the edge of the Audhali Escarpment, Southern Arabia, flowering at Johannesburg.

Fig. 132.

A. doei Lavranos. Flowers natural size.

against 10—14mm., the pedicels and terminal portion of the inflorescence usually being pubescent. In *A. doei* the pedicels and peduncle are glabrous.

A. doei is closely related to the form of *A. tomentoa* Deflers which occurs in considerable numbers at Moledera, 36 miles SSW of Erigavo in Somalia North. This form, apart from having leaves with margins entire, or with very short blunt teeth that are far apart, has pink densely tomentose-shaggy perianths, 28—30mm. long, with outer segments free for 10mm.

A. doei is distinguished by having shorter, straighter, yellow perianths, 25mm. long, sparsely covered with remarkably long white hairs up to 8—9mm. long over the whole outer surface.

48. **A. trichosantha** Berger in Engler's *Bot. Jahrb.* 36: 62 (1905), in Engler's *Pflanzenr.* Liliac.–Aloin. 231 (1908); Verdoorn et Christian in *Fl. Pl. Afr.*, Plate 1014 (1947).

—— *A. percrassa* Schweinfurth in *Bull. Herb. Boiss.* 2, App. 2, 62 (1894), *non* Todaro; Baker in *Fl. Trop. Afr.* 7: 465 (1898), *non* Baker in *Journ. Linn. Soc.* 18: 175 (1880).

—— *A. percrassa* Schweinf. (*non* Tod.) var. *albo-picta* Schweinf. in *Bull. Herb. Boiss.* 2, App. 2, 64 (1894).

Note: *A. percrassa* Schweinf. (*non* Todaro) is *A. trichosantha* Berger in the Ghinda Valley, Eritrea, while Schweinfurth's var. *albo-picta* also comes from the same locality. At that locality, *A. trichosantha* grows in considerable numbers. Leaves vary from unspotted to spotted both sides, and spotted leaves without other distinguishing characters are not worth varietal rank.

DESCRIPTION based on thousands of plants at the type locality Ghinda, 41 miles WSW of Massawa, Eritrea.

Plants solitary or in small groups, acaulescent or with very short stem.

Leaves 12—16, densely rosulate, lanceolate-attenuate, suberectly spreading, 40—50cm. long, 10cm. broad at base; *upper surface* lighter to darker dull green, flat low down, slightly canaliculate upwards, usually not spotted, sometimes with a few scattered spots and rarely copiously spotted throughout; *lower surface* convex, similar to upper surface in colour and markings; *margins* armed with pungent reddish-brown deltoid teeth about 4—5mm. long, 12—15mm. apart low down, more distant upwards, the interspaces usually straight and the colour of the leaf, not joined by a horny edge. *Sap* dries yellow.

Inflorescence 2—3-branched, 1—1·5m. high.

Peduncle basally flattened and 25mm. broad, terete upwards, glabrous low down becoming pubescent towards the racemes, the lowest branch subtended at base by an ovate-acute thin, dry-brittle, white many-nerved bract 20—25mm. long, 18—20mm. broad, the rachis minutely tomentose.

Racemes narrowly cylindric-acuminate, averaging 30cm. long, reaching 50cm. long when apical buds open and lowest fruit begin to develop, the apical buds hidden by imbricate bracts, older buds spreading, open flowers nutant to subpendulous, all prominently albo-tomentose.

Bracts ovate-lanceolate, acute, 14mm. long, 6mm. broad, thin, scarious, white, many-nerved, about twice as long as the pedicel.

Pedicels 5—6mm. long, minutely pubescent.

Perianth strawberry-pink (RCS) or coral pink, markedly albo-tomentose, cylindric-trigonous 28—32mm. long, basally rounded and not stipitate, 7—8mm. diam. across the ovary, thence cylindric-trigonous with the mouth very slightly upturned; *outer segments* free for 10—12mm., whiter and thinner at the edges, with 3 dull obscure olive-green nerves confluent at apex, the apices subacute, spreading; *inner segments* free, but dorsally adnate to the outer to beyond the middle with 3 crowded nerves forming a greenish keel, the apices more obtuse and more spreading.

Filaments filiform-flattened, the 3 inner narrower and lengthening before the 3 outer with their *anthers* in turn exserted 2—3mm.; *stigma* at length exserted 3—4mm.; *ovary* pale brown, 5mm. long, 2·5mm. diam. (Plate 31, Figs. 133-134).

PLATE 31

ALOE TRICHOSANTHA   Berger.

In valley 10km. S of Nefasit, Eritrea, c. 15° 21′ N, 39° 04′ E, alt.
5,100 ft. Flowering in April. Height 1·60m.

Fig. 133.

A. trichosantha Berger. Plants at the type locality near Ghinda, between Massawa and Asmara, Eritrea; alt. 3,000 ft. Height 1·60m.

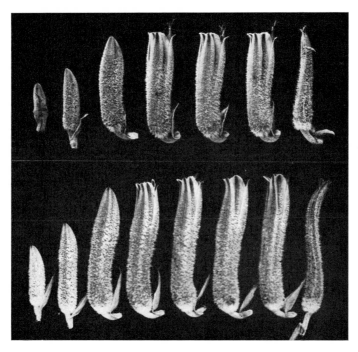

Fig. 134.
A. trichosantha Berger.
Above: Flowers 1/1 from a plant at Ghinda, type locality.
Below: Flowers 1/1 from a plant 39 km. north of Dessie, Wollo Prov. Ethiopia.

ERITREA. Great Valley of Ghinda, 950m., 16 May 1892, Schweinfurth et Riva 2291! (K) (it seems this should be regarded as the lectotype.) Selet Valley below Saganeitti, 1700m., 11 April 1892, Schweinfurth et Riva 1664! (K, G); abundant on rocky slopes near Chinda, 3,000 ft., 12 April 1956, Reynolds 8045! (K, PRE); North side of Meschillit Pass, 4,100 ft., 21 March 1949, Bally 6696! (K, EA).

ETHIOPIA. *Tigre Prov.:* Abundant on broad valley floor near Cobbo, 170km. N of Dessie, 4,700 ft., Reynolds 8119! (PRE, EA). *Shoa Prov.:* Moggio (Modjo), 70km. SE of Addis Ababa, 5,600 ft., cult. Pretoria, fl. 4 Nov. 1942, A. G. McLoughlin 833 (K, PRE), fl. Feb. 1943 (K, PRE), cult. Ewanrigg, fl. 21 May 1952, McLoughlin 833 (SRGH), fl. June 1943, Christian 1173 (PRE). *Harar Prov.* near Diredawa, 11 Sept. 1957, Bally 11648! (EA); Mt. Achim near Harar, 4 Sept. 1957, Bally 11647! (EA); 31 miles E of Harar, 4,700 ft., 11 Sept. 1957, Reynolds 8386! (K, PRE).

TYPE LOCALITY: The Great Valley of Ghinda is on the main road from Massawa on the Red Sea coast, to Asmara up in the mountains, 41 miles WSW of Massawa, 30 miles NE of Asmara at 3,000 ft., approx. 15° 27′ N, 29° 03′ E. Large numbers are found there. Plants grow singly or in small groups, and leaves vary from unspotted to copiously spotted both sides.

Inflorescences average 1·5m. in height and are mostly 2—3-branched from about the middle, racemes averaging 30cm. in length. In the Rift Valley of Ethiopa the inflorescence sometimes reaches 2—3m. A striking character of *A. trichosantha* is the albo-tomentose perianths, also found in *A. tomentosa* Deflers which occurs at Moledera in Somalia North (formerly Somaliland Prot.) and in the mountains of the Yemen, in Arabia. Both species have very shaggy perianths, but *A. tomentosa* forms much larger groups, has a lower, more robust inflorescence, has shorter, broader racemes, shorter bracts, and slightly longer pedicels.

DISTRIBUTION: From the Ghinda Valley and S of Nelfasit, southwards along the broad Rift Valley from the Tigre Province of Northern Ethiopia, Wollo Prov. (Jarie River Valley, 40—65km. N of Dessie at 5,400—6,200 ft.), Shoa Prov. from Sambeti Village, 134km. S of Dessie for 45 miles (3,800—4,600 ft.), to near Debre Sina at 6,000 ft. Also in Shoa Province near Moggio, 5,600 ft., 70km. SE of Addis Ababa, Nazreth, 5,000 ft., 100km., and Wolenchit, 123km. from Addis Ababa at 4,700 ft.

In Arussi Province along the Awash River Valley, 30—40km. S of Moggio, and further south between Shashamanua and Neghelli, and around Lake Shala. In Harar Province, W of Diredawa, near the Awash River; also on Mt. Achim near Harar, and E of Harar.

KENYA: Certain plants with yellow flowers between Isiolo and Archers Post, and with greenish flowers, 30 miles S of Garissa, need further investigation.

SOUTHERN ETHIOPIA: Plants 85 miles E of Yavello, 32 miles W of the Dawa Parma River, also seen 5—21 miles E of that river at 3,000 ft., with quite different large-spotted, thicker leaves, a lower, more robust 5—6-branched inflorescence (flowers not seen) belong to a new species awaiting description when material becomes available.

SOMALIA SOUTH: The same species was seen by the author, 30 miles SE of Lugh Ferrandi (900 ft.); on road northwards from Mogadishu to Bulo Burti at miles 68 (300 ft.), 91 and 106, abundant from 1—5 miles S of Bulo Burti which is 132—136 miles north of Mogadishu at 400 ft. on light grey soils. These plants do not belong to *A. trichosantha* var. *albo-picta* as was at first thought, but are an undescribed species.

49. **A. menachensis** (Schweinf.) Blatter in *Fl. Arabia, Rec. Bot. Surv. Ind.* 8: 463 (1936); Lavranos in *Journ. S.A. Bot.* 30: 83 (1964).

—— *A. percrassa* Schweinf. (*non* Todaro) var. *menachensis* Schweinf. in *Bull. Herb. Boiss.* 2: App. 2, 64 (1894).

—— *A. trichosantha* Berger var. *menachensis* Schweinf. in Engler's *Pflanzenr.* Liliac.–Aloin. 232 (1908); O. Schwartz in *Fl. Trop. Arab.* 351 (1939).

DESCRIPTION based on Schweinfurth's and Berger's accounts.

Plants whether solitary or forming groups unknown. *Stem* up to 50cm. long, erect (? sometimes decumbent).

Leaves compactly rosulate, incurved, very thick, triangular-lanceolate, 40cm. long, 16cm. broad, 2cm. thick, attenuate; *upper surface* basally flat, caniculate upwards, greenish-purple, purple at the margins, the epidermis subcoriaceous; *lower surface* with a keel near apex armed with 1—3 teeth, or without teeth; *margins* purplish, with 30—35 teeth along each side, the teeth broadly deltoid, brown at apex, blunt, 2mm. long, 15—20mm. apart.

Inflorescence "tall" (say 1·5m.?), much-branched.

Peduncle basally compressed and 35mm. broad, the many branches angular, puberulous.

Racemes cylindric, densely flowered, 15—20cm. long, 5—6cm. broad, the apex imbricate-bracteate.

Bracts 10—15mm. long, about twice as long as the pedicel, about 8-nerved, reflexed.
Pedicels 5—7mm. long.
Perianth pale or reddish-scarlet, very shortly albo-tomentose, cylindric-trigonous, 30mm. long, very slightly curved, nutant at anthesis; *outer segments* free for 12mm.
Anthers exserted after anthesis. (Fig. 135).

YEMEN. On rocky, sunny, slopes near Menacha (Haraz Mountains), 2200m., near Muthmar, 4 March 1889, Schweinfurth 1685! (K).

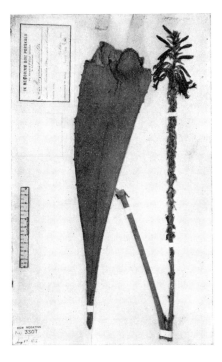

FIG. 135.

A. menachensis (Schwein.) Blatter. Much reduced photo of Schweinfurth 1685 at Kew – from Menakha in the Yemen, at alt. 2,200m. *Note.* Menakha is in the Haraz mountains which jut out from the western escarpment of the Yemen.

A. menachensis is another Yemeni species of Aloe which remains partly imperfectly known, and there appear to be no figures.

The original description does not state whether plants grow singly, or sucker and form groups. A 50cm. stem suggests the former. The inflorescence is stated to be tall. How tall, 2m. perhaps? It seems that the precise identity of this and some other Yemeni species will remain uncertain until plants can be studied again at their type localities. Mr. Lavranos (*l.c.*) points out that the type locality Menakha is in the Haraz Mountains which jut out from the western escarpment of the Yemen. In the meantime it seems that *A. menachensis* is nearest allied to *A. trichosantha* Berger from Eritrea and Ethiopa, the differences being chiefly that *A. trichosantha* has little or no stem, often has spotted leaves with possibly larger marginal teeth, an inflorescence which is only 2—3-branched, longer racemes, and flowers that are possibly a little more tomentose.

A. vacillans Forsk. which also comes from near Menakha in the Haraz Mountains, is a near ally, but differs in having longer, narrower leaves with more crowded marginal teeth, a 2—3-branched inflorescence, racemes twice as long, and smooth red flowers.

50. **A. pubescens** Reynolds in *Journ. S.A. Bot.* 23: 10, Plates X, XI (1957).

DESCRIPTION: *Plants* singly, or more frequently suckering and forming groups, acaulescent, or with short stems.
Leaves about 16, rosulate, lanceolate-attenuate, suberectly spreading, averaging 45cm. long, 8cm. broad at base; *upper surface* grey-green, without spots or markings except when young, flat low down, slighly concave upwards; *lower surface* convex, similar to upper surface; *margins* armed with deltoid pungent teeth that are white at base, reddish-brown in upper half, 2—3mm. long, smaller and more crowded low down, 15—20mm. distant in upper half of leaf.
Inflorescence simple or 1-branched, 70—100 cm. tall.
Peduncle plano-convex and 15mm. broad at base, terete and somewhat sulcate upwards.
Racemes cylindric-acuminate, about 20cm. long, the apical buds covered by large densely imbricate bracts, older buds grey-green tipped, spreading, open flowers subpendulous.
Bracts ovate-deltoid, 20mm. long, 6mm. broad, white, thin, scarious, 7—9-nerved.
Pedicels 15mm. long, the pink colour of the perianth.

Perianth coral-pink, cylindric-trigonous, 42mm. long, 8mm. diam. across the ovary, slightly narrowed above the ovary, thence enlarging a little and narrowing to the mouth, the whole perianth shortly pubescent; *outer segments* free for 16mm., 3-nerved with white border and subacute slightly spreading apices; *inner segments* broader than the outer, with 3 crowded nerves forming a pink keel, the apices more obtuse and more spreading than the outer.

Filaments lemon, the 3 inner narrower and lengthening before the 3 outer with their *anthers* in turn exserted 3—4mm.; *stigma* at length exserted 5mm.; *ovary* pale brown, 7mm. long, 3mm. diam. (Figs. 136—138).

ETHIOPIA. *Arussi Prov.*: on rocky banks of a stream 16km. NE of Shashemenne (Shashamanna), 234 km. south of Addis Ababa, c. 7° 16′ N, 38° 38′ E, c. 1,800m., 3 May 1956, Reynolds 8144 holotype (PRE), isotype (K); Plant from type loc. cult. Mbabane, Swaziland, fl. 15 July 1964, Reynolds 8144A (PRE, K).

FIG. 136.   FIG. 137.

A. pubescens Reynolds.

FIG. 136. Plant × 1/10 approx., 16km. (10 miles) north east of Shashamanna (234km. south of Addis Ababa), Arussi Prov., Ethiopia.

FIG. 137. Plants collected at type locality flowering at Mbabane, Swaziland.

This distinctive species grows in the Arussi Province of Ethiopia at a point 234km. (152 miles) S of Addis Ababa, 164km. (102 miles) S of Modjo, and 16km. (10 miles) N of Shashemenne (also spelt Shashamanna) on the road to Yrgalem and Neghelli in the far south. Many plants were growing on rocky banks of a stream at 1800m. (6,000 ft.) and were mostly in groups, with little or no stems, although sometimes stems reach 20—30cm.

A. pubescens is characterized by having cylindric-acuminate racemes about 15cm. long, the youngest buds hidden by large densely imbricate bracts, 15mm. pedicels, and strawberry-pink, 42mm. cylindric-trigonous flowers which are pubescent. The pubescence indicates an affinity with *A. trichosantha* Berger (which occurs further north, near Modjo) but the latter has longer (30cm.), narrower racemes, much shorter (5mm.) pedicels, smaller flowers that are strikingly albo-tomentose, and different leaves.

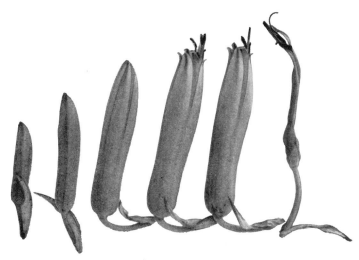

Fig. 138.

A. pubescens Reynolds. Flowers natural size.

51. **A. eremophila** Lavranos in *Journ. S.A. Bot.* 31: 71 (1965).

DESCRIPTION: *Plant* usually solitary, sometimes forming groups of 2—6 rosettes, acaulous or with a short, procumbent stem.

Leaves 10–22 arcuate-ascending to ascending-erect, deltoid, acute, very rigid, 35cm. long, 10cm. broad at base, 15–25mm. thick; *upper surface* uniformly grey-green with a brownish tinge, flat low down, broadly canaliculate upward; *lower surface* convex, the same colour as the upper surface; *margins* armed with dark-brown, pungent, deltoid teeth up to 4mm. long, 10—15mm. distant, more crowded and smaller near base.

Inflorescence 40—75cm. high, 3—5-branched from about the middle.

Peduncle biconvex and 15mm. broad at base, terete upward, striated, the branches terete, subtended by ovate-deltoid, many-nerved bracts, 14mm. long, 18mm. broad; sterile bracts below the racemes narrowly deltoid-acute, 12mm. long, 5mm. broad, 8—12-nerved.

Racemes conico-cylindric up to 22cm. long, 5cm. diam., rather densely flowered, terminating in a dense tuft or spike of wilted scarious bracts, the lateral racemes often shorter, young buds sub-erect, old buds spreading, open flowers pendulous.

Bracts narrowly deltoid, 8—12-nerved, 12mm. long, 5mm. broad, white.

Pedicels red, terete, 7—8mm. long.

Perianth rich scarlet, glabrous, cylindric-trigonous, almost straight, very shortly stipitate, 30mm. long, 8mm. diam. across the ovary, slightly constricted above, somewhat compressed laterally, the mouth wide open; *outer segments* free for 14mm. with three prominent red nerves throughout their entire length, the nerves becoming confluent and brownish towards the yellowish and slightly recurved apices of the segments; *inner segments* free but dorsally adnate to and broader than the outer, creamy-yellow with 3 red nerves which become confluent and brownish toward the segment-apices.

Filaments yellow, somewhat flattened in their lower part, the 3 inner narrower and lengthening before the 3 outer, the *anthers* in turn exserted 4mm.; *style* pale yellow, the *stigma* at length exserted 5mm.; *ovary* yellowish-green, 5mm. long, 2mm. diam., the apex truncate. (Plate 32, Fig. 139).

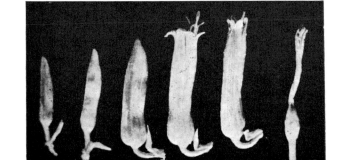

Fig. 139.

A. eremophila Lavranos. Flowers natural size
from the plant depicted on Plate 32.
Photo: Mr. J. Lavranos.

PLATE 32

ALOE EREMOPHILA   Lavranos.

On the limestone plateau (Jol.) of the Hadhramaut, E of Khureiba
(Wadi Duan), Southern Arabia. Height 75cm.
From a Kodachrome by Prof. W. Rauh.

SOUTHERN ARABIA. *Hadhramaut*, on limestone plateau (Jol); 8 miles N of Mola Matr (which is 54 miles NW of the port of Mukalla) 6,400 ft. (1900m.), 20 March 1964, Rauh et Lavranos 3100; near village of Fardha, approx. 20 miles NW of Mola Matr, 5,500 ft. (1674m.), 20 March 1964, Rauh et Lavranos 3103, both collected on 20 March 1964; E of Khureiba (Wadi Duan) approx. 4,500 ft. (1375m.), lat. 15° 02′ N, long. 48° 28′ E, 20 March 1964, Rauh et Lavranos 13348 (HEID) holotype, (K, PRE) isotype.

A. eremophila was first collected on 20 March 1964 on the Hadhrami Jol during a botanical journey from Mukalla on the coast of the Arabian Sea to the Wadi Hadhramaut. It is a plateau species and occurs as isolated individuals or in small colonies at intervals of many miles, from just north of the seaward escarpment at 6,500—7,000 ft. for 100 miles to the cliffs overlooking the Great Wadi, at 3,500 feet.

In the high, southern part of its habitat it is associated chiefly with *A. inermis* Forsk., *Euphorbia balsamifera* Ait., *Kalanchoe teretifolia* Defl., with scrub-forest remnants consisting chiefly of *Dodonaea viscosa* L. and *Acacia tortillis* (Forsk.) Hayne. Further north, at lower altitudes, its chief associates are *A. tortilis*, *Sarcostemma* cf. *stipitaceum* Forsk. and *Anisotes trisulcus* (Forsk.) Nees. Hot in summer, very cold in winter, this windswept plateau is now, for its greater part, a complete desert, although there is much evidence that this has not always been so, and that the present lack of vegetation is due to the destructive influence of man and goat.

A. eremophila is a close ally of the Somali species *A. rigens* Reynolds et Bally, from the typical form of which it differs by being a smaller plant with fewer, broader, shorter, deltoid leaves, shorter inflorescences, shorter, more cylindric racemes, longer pedicels and totally glabrous, almost straight perianths. It differs from the variety *glabrescens* Reynolds et Bally by its shorter, less numerous, much more rigid and thick leaves, its shorter, usually 4—5-branched inflorescences, its more cylindric racemes which are invariably terminated by a tuft of white sterile bracts, its longer pedicels and bracts and its glabrous, almost straight, perianths the outer segments of which are free for 14mm. – J. Lavranos.

52. **A. serriyensis** Lavranos in *Journ. S.A. Bot.* 31: 76 (1965).

DESCRIPTION: *Plants* usually forming small groups.

Leaves 30—35cm. long, 6—7cm. broad at base, gradually tapering to an acute apex, 5—8mm. thick, rather soft; *upper surface* green, sometimes with a brownish tinge, obscurely lineate-striate, flat or broadly canaliculate; *lower surface* flat to slightly convex, the same colour and texture as the upper surface; *margins* armed with short, rather blunt, horny, dark brown teeth, 20—40mm. distant.

Inflorescence 40cm. high, 2—3-branched.

Peduncle rather brittle, biconvex and 10mm. broad at base, terete upwards, brown with a bloom; sterile bracts deltoid, acute, 10mm. long, 6mm. broad at base.

Racemes conical 20—25cm. long, approx. 5cm. diam., rather laxly flowered, usually with a long sterile-bracteate apex, young buds sub-erect, old buds spreading, open flowers pendulous.

Bracts narrowly deltoid, 8—10mm. long, 3mm. broad at base, 5-nerved, whitish, scarious.

Pedicels brownish, terete, 10mm. long.

Perianth cylindric-campanulate, markedly stipitate and tapering into the pedicel, powdery scarlet-pink with a bloom, 27mm. long, 6mm. diam. over the ovary, thence scarcely constricted, the mouth wide open; *outer segments* free for 7—9mm., with 3 red nerves which become brown and confluent towards the slightly recurved apices; *inner segments* broader than the outer, cream with strongly recurved apices.

Filaments whitish and much flattened at base, filiform and bright yellow in their upper portion, the *anthers* in turn exserted by 2mm.; *style* filiform, yellow, the *stigma* at length exserted 3mm.; *ovary* bright green, 4mm. long, 2mm. diam. (Figs. 140–141).

SOUTHERN ARABIA. Fadhli country, in wooded valleys on the southern slopes of Jebel Arays around the derelict village of Serriya, alt. 1,000 ft. (300m.), lat. 13° 29′ N, long. 45° 58′ E, 19 Aug. 1962, fl. Johannesburg 20 July 1964, Lavranos 2101 (PRE) holotype.

A. serriyensis differs from *A. eremophila*, its closest ally, in being a much less robust plant. The leaves are narrower, softer, thinner and obscurely lineate-striate, while the marginal teeth are far less developed and more distant than in *A. eremophila*. The pedicels are longer and the perianths shorter, somewhat funnel-shaped and markedly stipitate while in *A. eremophila* the stipe is almost absent. The perianth outer segments are free for 8mm., (as against 14mm. in *A. eremophila*).

"The plant described as *A. serriyensis* was collected at my request by an Arab from Shuqra when, in the company of Mr. C. Meintjes, I was passing through that village on the way to and from the Audhali country. Due to lack of time we were unable to collect in the Jebel Arays but, in March 1964, I visited this fascinating mountain country together with Professor Dr. W. Rauh.

"The Jebel Arays rises steeply to some 4,500 ft., immediately behind the coast, some 75 miles east of Aden. Its slopes appear to catch the moisture-laden winds blowing off the Arabian Sea throughout the year, and the valleys and ridges are covered with a luxuriant vegetation, quite unexpected along the arid coastline of S.W. Arabia. Near the ruined village of Serriya we saw several plants which appeared to belong to *A. serriyensis*."—J. Lavranos.

7

FIG. 140.

A. serriyensis Lavranos. Plant from wooded valleys of southern slopes of Jebel Arays, near Serriya, Fadhli Country, Southern Arabia; flowering at Bryanston, Johannesburg. Height 50cm.

Photo: Mr. J. Lavranos.

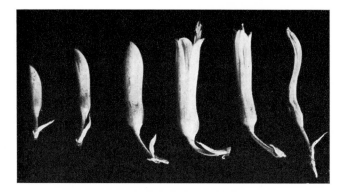

FIG. 141.

A. serriyensis Lavranos. Flowers 1/1.
Photo: Mr. J. Lavranos.

53. **A. dhalensis** Lavranos in *Journ. S.A. Bot.* 31: 62 (1965).

DESCRIPTION: *Plant* solitary, or producing off-shoots, acaulous or with a short, usually erect stem.

Leaves about 18, erect to ascending-erect, densely rosulate, lanceolate, tapering to a rather acute apex, about 40cm. long, 8cm. broad at base, 5—8mm. thick; *upper surface* glaucous-green, sometimes with a light brown tinge, unicoloured, flat or slightly canaliculate; *lower surface* the same colour as the upper, convex; *margins* armed with brown, pungent, deltoid teeth 2—3mm. long, 5mm. distant but more so towards the apex; *leaf-sap* dries dark purple.

Inflorescence simple or, more often, up to 4-branched, up to 70cm. high.

Peduncle plano-convex and approx. 12mm. broad at base, thereafter terete; *sterile bracts* white, lanceolate-deltoid, very scarious, many-nerved.

Racemes narrowly conico-cylindric, 20cm. long, 7cm. diam., subdensely flowered, terminating in a tuft of wilted bracts, the youngest buds sub-erect, older buds spreading, open flowers pendulous.

PLATE 33

Aloe dhalensis   Lavranos.

Young plant from near Dhala, 85 miles N of Aden, S. Arabia. Flowering
in the author's garden. Height 60cm.

Bracts lanceolate, acute, 12mm. long, 5mm. broad, papery, white, 7—9-nerved.

Pedicels lemon, 5mm. long.

Perianth lemon-yellow, smooth, 30mm. long, sub-cylindric, obtusely tapering into the pedicel at base, 6mm. diam. over the ovary, then constricted on underside to 5mm. diam., thereafter laterally compressed and enlarged towards the throat, the mouth wide open; *outer segments* free for 10mm., obscurely 3-nerved, the nerves greenish near apex, the apices sub-acute, slightly spreading; *inner segments* free but dorsally adnate to the outer to beyond the middle, broader than the outer, with 3 congested greenish nerves forming a keel throughout their length, and with broader, more obtuse, more spreading apices.

Filaments almost white, filiform flattened, the 3 inner narrower and lengthening before the 3 outer; the *anthers* in turn exserted 2—3mm.; *style* lemon, the *stigma* at length exserted 3mm.; *ovary* pale olive-green, 6mm. long, 2·5mm. diam. (Plate 33, Figs. 142–143).

SOUTH WESTERN ARABIA. Amiri Highlands near Dhala, alt. approx. 4,800 ft. (1460m.), lat. 13° 42′ N, long. 44° 44′ E, coll. Ken Guichard, 1949, fl. Johannesburg 26 April 1953, Reynolds 6227 holotype (PRE); foot of castle hill at Dhala, 4,950 ft., 24 August 1962, Lavranos 1885; on Jebel Jihaf, 6,500 ft., 25 August 1962, Lavranos 1884; near Dhala air-strip, 4,800 ft., 10 July 1964, J. H. Gross in Lavranos 3393.

Fig. 142.

A. dhalensis Lavranos. Plant from the Amiri highlands, near Dhala, about 85 miles north of Aden, S-W Arabia, flowering in the author's gardens in Johannesburg. Height 80 cm.

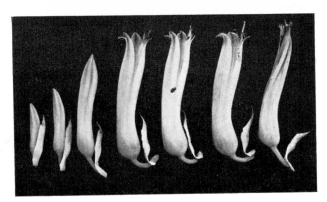

Fig. 143.

A. dhalensis Lavranos. Flowers natura size.

Von Wissmann's collections listed by O. Schwarts (*Fl. Trop. Arab.*, 350 (1939)) under numbers W827 and W2397 as belonging to *A. officinalis* Forsk. most probably represent *A. dhalensis*.

A. dhalensis was collected in 1949 by Mr. Ken Guichard near Dhala, which lies some 90 miles N of Aden, in the Amiri highlands. It seems to be widespread on the Amiri highlands where it occurs in scattered colonies between approx. 4,000 feet at the top of the Khureiba Pass, E of Dhala, to 6.500 feet on the slopes of Jebel Jihaf.

These high plateaux enjoy a mild climate and an annual rainfall averaging some 350mm. (14 in.), which falls mainly between April and September.

A. dhalensis appears to be nearest allied to *A. vacillans* Forsk., from which it differs in being a much smaller plant with 3-branched inflorescences reaching 70cm. in height, compared with those of *A. vacillans* which are stated to be up to 2m. tall. *A. dhalensis* is usually stemless or has a very short, erect stem, while *A. vacillans* often has a decumbent stem.

54. **A. audhalica** Lavranos et Hardy in *Journ. S.A. Bot.* 31: 65 (1964).

DESCRIPTION: *Plant* usually solitary, occasionally forming groups of several rosettes.

Leaves up to 30, deltoid-acute, densely rosulate, ascending-erect, to 45cm. long, 15cm. broad at base; *upper surface* flat but somewhat canaliculate towards the apex, somewhat rough, uniformly glaucous-green when in complete shade, otherwise pinkish-brown; *lower surface* convex, the colour of the upper surface; *margins* with a continuous, pink, cartilaginous border armed with pungent, straight, dark-brown teeth, up to 4mm. long, 4—6mm. distant.

Inflorescence 80—100cm. high, up to 4-branched from about the middle.

Peduncle at base plano-convex, terete upwards, grey-brown with a bloom; *sterile bracts* deltoid, acute, to 15mm. long, 5mm. broad at base, 7-nerved, white, scarious.

Racemes 18—22 cm. long, about 5cm. diam., cylindric-acuminate, rather densely flowered.

Bracts ovate-deltoid, acute, 15mm. long, 5mm. broad at base, pinkish-white, 7-nerved, the nerves red.

Pedicels red, terete, 10mm. long.

Perianth glabrous, straight, cylindric-trigonous, very slightly constricted above the ovary, scarlet, 30mm. long, 6mm. diameter over the ovary; *outer segments* free for 8mm., 3-nerved with creamish margins; *inner segments* broader than the outer, cream with 3 contiguous nerves which become confluent and brown at the segment-apices.

Filaments cream, the 3 inner narrower and lengthening before the 3 outer with their *anthers* in turn exserted 3—4mm.; *style* cream, the *stigma* at length exserted 4mm.; *ovary* truncate, yellowish-green, 6mm. long, 3mm. broad at base; *sap* clear, drying reddish-brown. (Figs. 144, 145A).

FIG. 144.

A. audhalica Lavranos et Hardy. Young plant from Wadi Salui, Audhali Plateau, South-Western Arabia, flowering in Mr. Lavranos's garden at Bryanston, Johannesburg. Height 50cm.

Photo: Mr. J. Lavranos.

144 *Aloe barbadensis*

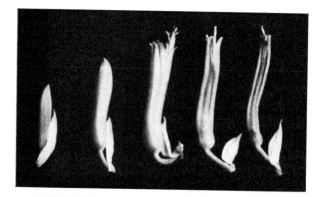

FIG. 145.

A. audhalica Lavranos et Hardy. Flowers
natural size.
Photo: Mr. J. Lavranos.

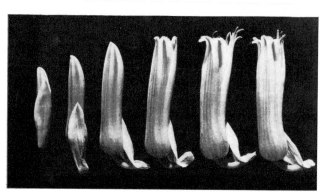

FIG. 145A.

A. audhalica Lavranos et Hardy. Flowers
1/1 from a plant flowering at Mbabane
Swaziland originally collected by Mr. J.
Lavranos on the Audhali Plateau, SW
Arabia.

SOUTH-WESTERN ARABIA: Audhali Plateau, near Mukeiras, 6,900 ft. (2100m.), lat. 45° 41' N, long. 13° 56' E, coll. 25 Dec. 1961, fl. Johannesburg April 1964, Meintjies in Lavranos 1652 (PRE) holotype; Mukeiras, 16 Aug. 1962, Lavranos 1817; Karish, 7,100 ft. (2160m.), 18 Aug. 1962, Lavranos 1896; Wadi Idhi, 6,800 ft. (2070m.), 4 March, 1964, Rauh et Lavranos 2789; Wadi Salul, 6,800ft. (2070m.), 5 March 1964, Rauh et Lavranos 2800.

A. audhalica is widespread in rocky, sunny places throughout the Audhali plateau at altitudes exceeding 6,650 ft. (2000m.). Its distribution probably extends into the adjacent district of Beidha. This species, while widely distributed on the plateau itself was nowhere found within less than a half-mile from the edge of the escarpment which, in turn, is the habitat of another species as yet unidentified. In its habitat, which enjoys an average annual rainfall of some 12 inches, and is subject to occasional frosts during the winter months, *A. audhalica* grows in exposed positions in association with various low Acanthaceae and Labiatae, *Dracaena serrulata* Bak., *Euphorbia balsamifera* Ait., *Caralluma quadrangula* (Forsk.), N.E. Br., *C. plicatiloba* Lavranos, etc. It is nowhere common but is found in isolated individuals or small groups.

A. audhalica seems to be rather closely allied to *A. vacillans* Forsk., which was collected at various places in the central region of the Western Yemeni escarpment. *A. vacillans* however, differs in the shape of its leaves, which are longer and narrower, in having inflorescences 1·5—2m. tall, while its racemes are said to be 35—40cm. long and more laxly flowered and finally by the fact that its flowers are described by Forskal as subsessile, whereas Berger states the pedicels are 5—7mm. long.

55. **A. barbadensis** Mill. *Gard. Dict.* ed. 8, No. 2 (1768); Haw. in *Trans. Linn. Soc.* 7: 19 (1804), in *Synops.* 79 (1812); R & S *Syst. veg.* 7: 693 (1892), Kunth *Enum.* 4: 521 (1843).
—— *Aloe perfoliata* (var.) π *vera* L. *Spec. Pl.* 1: 320 (1753).
—— *A. perfoliata* L. (var.) γ *barbadensis* Ait. *Hort. Kew.* 1: 466 (1789).
—— *A. perfoliata* L. (var.) λ *vera* Willdenow *Sp. Pl.* 2: 186 (1799).
—— *A. vera* "L" of many authors, *not* of Miller (1768); Webb et Berth, *Hist Nat. II Canar.* iii, 2, 3, 348 (1848); Baker in *Journ. Linn. Soc.* 18: 176 (1880); *Non* Schweinfurth in *Bull. Herb. Boiss.* App. 2, 59 (1894); Berger in Engler's *Pflanzenr.* Liliac.–Aloin. 229 (1908).
—— *A. vera* "L" var. *littoralis* Koenig ex Baker in *Journ. Linn. Soc.* 176 (1880) – *fide* Berger.
—— *A. vera* "L" var. *chinensis* Berger *l.c.* 230.
—— *A. vera* "L" var. *lanzae* Berger *l.c.* 230.

—— *A. lanzae* Todaro *Hort. Bot. Panorm.* 55, *t.* 39 (1891) – *fide* Berger.

—— *A. chinensis* Bak. in *Bot. Mag. t.* 6301 (1877). *Note:* Received at Kew in 1817 from China (where it had in all probability been introduced from the West previously), also received from other sources but never with any definite information as to its native country; not worth upholding. – G.W.R.

—— *A. barbadensis* Mill. var. *chinensis* Haw. *Supp. pl. succ.* 45 (1819); Kunth *Enum. pl.* 4: 522 (1843).

—— *A. indica* Royle *Ill. Pl. Himal.* 1: 390 (1839) – a reddish-flowered form from the northwestern Provinces of India, *fide* Bentley et Trimen *Medic. Plants* 4: 282 (1805) – Royle did not publish any full description or figure of his *A. indica*; he merely mentions it had red flowers.

—— *A. elongata* Murray in *Comm. Goett.* 9: 191, *t.* 2 (1789).

—— *A. vulgaris* Lam. *Encycl.* 1: 86 (1783) – excl. syn. *A. officinalis* Forsk.; Sibth. et Smith *Fl. Graec.* 1: 238, *t.* 341 (1806); Aiton *Hort. Kew* 2: 292 (1811); Salm Dyck *Cat. rais.* 25, 58 (1817), *Monogr. gen. Al.* sect. 18, fig. 2 (1849); Stephenson et Churchill *Medic. Bot.* 2: *t.* 109 (1835); Bentley et Trimen *Medic. Pl.* 4; *t.* 282 (1805).

—— *A. rubescens* D.C. *Plant. grass* p. 15 (1799) – appears to be a red-flowered form of *A. barbadensis* Mill.

—— *A. flava* Persoon *Synops.* 1: 378 (1805).

PRE-LINNEAN CITATIONS

—— *Aloe foliis spinosis confertis dentatis, vaginantibus planis maculatis* – *Hort. Cliff.* 130 (1736); *Hort. Upsal.* 86 (1748). *Hort. Cliff.* cites the Aloe figure on p. 335 of Dodonaeus's *Stirpium Historiae* (1583).

—— *Aloe vulgaris sive Sempervivum marinum*, Common Aloe or Sea Houseleeke – under this name Dodonaeus's figure is exactly reproduced in *The Herball*, first published by John Gerard, in 1597, amended by Thos. Johnson in 1633, London.

—— *A. vulgaris* in Caspar Bauhinus's *Pinax* to his *Theatre of Plants* 386 (1671) – cited by Linnaeus in *Hort. Cliff.* (1736), *Spec. pl.* 1: 321 (1753), Miller, Lamarck and others.

—— *Aloe vera vulgaris* Muntingius *Adoidarium t.* 19 (1680), cited by Lamarck, Haworth and others.

—— *Aloe Vulgaris* B.P.H.L.H.A. etc., *Aloe Hispanica* & *Aloe vera vulgo* listed in *Hort. Beaumont.* 6, no. 17 (1690) appear to belong here.

NOTE ON NOMENCLATURE

Many authors have incorrectly assumed that this species was published under the name *Aloe vera* Linnaeus. In his *Spec. pl.* 1: 320 (1753), Linnaeus originally described it as a variety, i.e. *A. perfoliata* (var.) *vera*, not as a numbered species. In Ed. 2 (1762), and again in Ed. 3 (1764), Linnaeus lists it as *A. perfoliata* (var.) π *vera*.

The International Code of Botanical Nomenclature lays down "When the rank of a genus or infrageneric taxon is changed, the correct name or epithet is the earliest legitimate one *in the new rank*. In no case does an epithet have priority outside its own rank".

The earliest legitimate name in the new rank (of species) is *A. barbadensis* Mill. and that is the name that must be used. *Note: A. vera* Mill. (*non* L) is a very different species, in all ways distinct from *A. barbadensis* Mill.

DESCRIPTION: Based mostly on plants from Masca, Tenerife, Canary Islands.

Plants with fibrous fleshy roots, acaulescent, or with short stems, freely suckering and forming dense groups.

Leaves about 16, densely rosulate, erectly spreading and forming rather compact rosettes, averaging 40—50cm. long, 6—7cm. broad at base, gradually narrowing to the apex, rather thick and fleshy; *upper surface* grey-green with reddish tinge, without spots or markings but sometimes at first spotted in young plants, rather flat low down, slightly canaliculate towards apex; *lower surface* convex, otherwise as in upper surface; *margins* with slightly pinkish edge armed with firm deltoid pale teeth about 2mm. long, more crowded and 10mm. apart low down, wider apart (15—20mm.) upwards. *Sap* dries yellow.

Inflorescence simple or 1—2-branched, 60—90cm. high.

Peduncle basally plano-convex and 20mm. broad, terete upwards, simple or compactly 2—3-branched from about the middle.

Racemes narrowly cylindric-acuminate, the terminal averaging 30—40cm. long, 5—6cm. diam., the lateral a little shorter, rather densely flowered, the apex a tuft of dried bracts, youngest buds suberect, older buds spreading, greenish-nerved, open flowers stiffly pendulous, almost as if appressed to the axis.

Bracts ovate-acute, deflexed, thin, dry, rather white, 10mm. long, 5—6mm. broad, 5—7-nerved, twice as long as the pedicels.

Pedicels averaging 5mm. long.

Perianth yellow, cylindric, slightly ventricose, averaging 28—30mm. long, basally obconic, 7mm. diam. across the ovary, enlarging at the middle, narrowing to the throat, with the mouth somewhat closed and slightly up-turned; *outer segments* free for 18mm., thinner at the edges, with 3 greenish nerves to base; *inner segments* themselves free but dorsally adnate to the outer for one-third their length, broader than the outer, with 3 crowded yellowish nerves forming a keel in upper two-thirds, the apices more obtuse than the outer.

Anthers in turn exserted 3—4mm.; *stigma* at length exserted 5mm.; *ovary* pale green, 5—6mm. long, 3mm. diam. (Figs. 146–151).

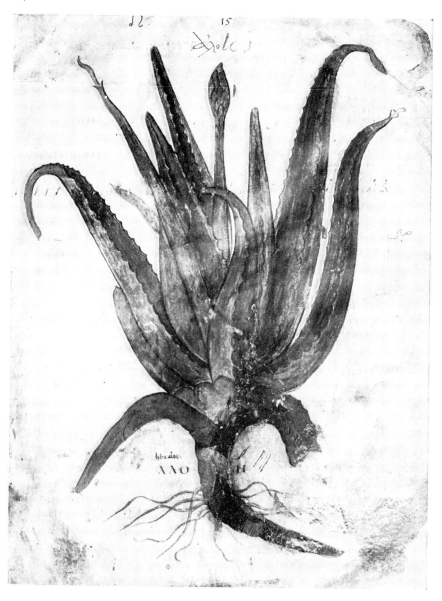

Fig. 146.

A. barbadensis Mill. (= "*A. vera* L."). The earliest known illustration of any species of Aloe. This is a photographic reproduction (reduced) of the original coloured figure of "Aloe" included in the *Codex Aniciae Julianae* – the earliest illustrated Herbal, made at Constantinople about the year 512 AD. The original parchment Codex which includes the Greek text of Dioscorides's Herbal (1st cent. AD.) is in the Osterreichische Nationalbibliothek, Vienna.

Photo by courtesy The General Director.

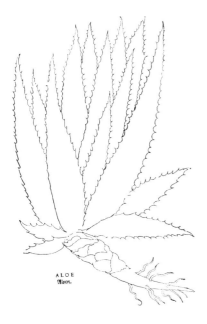

ALOE
Aloen.

FIG. 147.

A. barbadensis Mill. *Aloe sempervivum marinum* from Leonard Fuchs
De Historia Stirpium p. 138 (1542) – this appears to be founded on the
Codex Aniciae Julianae figure of 512 AD.
Photo: By courtesy The Director, Kew.

FIG. 148.

From Dodonaeus *Stirpium Historiae* Pemptades Sex, p. 355, published
at Antwerp in 1583. The figure on the left was named "Aloe" and is obviously
based on Fuchs's figure (1542) – with flowers added. (The figure on right is *Agave
sp.*). – *Reproduction by courtesy The Chief, Botanical Research Institute, Pretoria.*

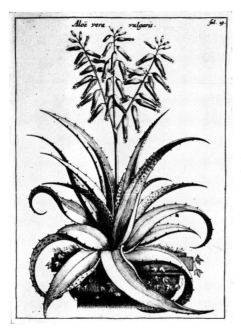

FIG. 149.

A. barbadensis Mill.   *Aloe vera vulgaris* in Muntingius
Aloidarium t. 19 (1680). – *Photo: By courtesy, The Chief,
Botanical Research Inst. Pretoria.*

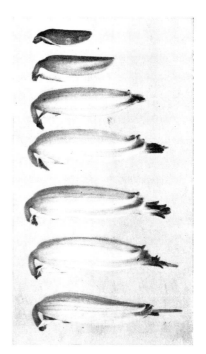

FIG. 150.   FIG. 151.

A. barbadensis Mill.

FIG. 150. Plant from Masca, Tenerife, Canary Islands flowering in the author's garden.
Height 1m.

FIG. 151. Flowers (Yellow) natural size.

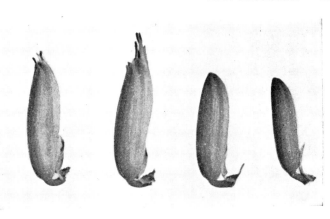

FIG. 151B.

A. barbadensis Mill.

FIG. 151A. Plant collected by Dr. E. J. Mendes on the escarpment at Sines, south of Lisbon, Alentejo Prov., Portugal; fl. May 1965.

FIG. 151B. Flowers 1/1.

Photos: Dr. E. J. Mendes

FIG. 151A.

CANARY ISLANDS. Tenerife, April 1846, E. Bourgeau 358! (K); Garachio, maritime bush, 19 June 1855, E. Bourgeau 1533! (K); El Campo, above Sta. Cruz, 22 Feb. 1859, Rev. R. T. Lowe s.n.! (K); Road to Realijo, 500m., flowers yellow, 8 June 1903, Th. J. Dinn 265! (K).

The following are considered to have been introduced to the New World, and subsequently naturalised:
CUBA. Oil fields near Havana, 13 March 1905, A. R. Curtis 664! (K).

BARBADOS. Bel Air, St. Philip, March 1940, H. B. Gooding 558! (BM).

BERMUDA. Castle Harbour, Walsingham Bay, 22 March 1933, A. B. Rendle 377! (BM).

JAMAICA. Fort Clarence, Port Henderson Hill, 200 ft., 3 May 1956, W. T. Stearn 812! (BM).

EARLY HISTORY

Plants of the species of Aloe now to be known as *Aloe barbadensis* Mill. (formerly known as *A. vera* "L" for nearly 200 years) were known in the 1st century A.D. In his Greek Herbal (which describes plants then reputed to have healing virtues), Dioscorides gives the medicinal qualities of the dried juices of *A. barbadensis*, while a coloured illustration of a plant in bud was included in 512 A.D.

Pedianos Dioscorides, from Anazarba in Asia Minor, travelled widely in the 1st century A.D. The illustrations included with his Herbal, are the oldest surviving representatives of many Eastern Mediterranean plants, and these include a coloured plate of *A. barbadensis*, which presumably then came from the Eastern Mediterranean.

Of the early illustrated botanical manuscripts the most important is the *Codex Aniciae Julianae*, made at Constantinople (Istanbul) about the year 512 A.D. The original parchment Codex, consisting of 491 yellowish-white sheets, roughly a foot square, and containing the Greek text of Dioscorides' Herbal is in the Osterreichische Nationalbibliothek at Vienna. It seems that at least seven books originally went into the making of the text and illustrations, the most important being the original Greek text of Dioscorides. (*Note:* The foregoing is culled from an article dealing with the *Codex Aniciae Julianae*, the earliest illustrated herbal, by Dr. Wm. T. Stearn, published in Zurich in *Graphia* Vol. 10, No. 34, 1954. I am grateful to Dr. Stearn for providing me with a photostat copy of his article. – G.W.R.)

The *Flora of Egypt* 3: 249 (1954) states that the Egyptian name for *A. barbadensis* (= *A. vera* "L") is *Saber, Sabr*, also *Sabbara*, literally meaning "endurance" and "bitter medicine".

A. barbadensis has been cultivated in Egypt since remote times, especially as a cemetery plant, and sometimes as boundry marks demarcating fields. Aloe plants planted on graves is a fairly common practice in parts of Somalia, Ethiopia and Eritrea today, where the present author has seen it repeatedly.

In Egypt the plant has always been connected with superstitions. It is stated to be a common custom in Cairo, also among the fallahin in the country to hang an aloe plant over the door of a house, particularly that of a new house. This is regarded as a charm to ensure long and flourishing lives for the inmates. The Aloe plant thus hung will live for some years and even flower. Hence the name *Sabr*, signifying patience. The same authority records that R. Campbell Thompson in *A Dictionary of Assyrian Botany*, p. 192, London (1949), states "the custom of hanging Aloe plants over house doors is apparently of very ancient origin. 'Aloe vera' is spoken of in Akkadian texts of Ancient Assyria-Babylonia as the 'plant for the adornment of a door.' Its Akkadian name was *Si-ba-ru* from which originated the Syriac *sabhra* and the Arabic *sabr*.". If this is actually the case, then the history of *A. barbadensis* goes back 2000 years B.C.

The Aloes of commerce must not be confused with "Aloes" of the Old Testament of the Bible. The references to Aloes in *Psalms* 45: 8, *Proverbs* 7: 17, and *Solomon* 4: 14, are to a perfume, the produce of some Judean gum-tree, generally supposed to be *Aquilaria agallocha,* Roxb., which gave off a fragrant odour when decaying.

In the New Testament, *John* 19: 39 refers to Nicodemus coming by night and bringing "a mixture of myrrh and aloes about an hundred pound weight" for the embalming of the body of Jesus. The aloes mentioned here might possibly have been derived from either *A. barbadensis* or *A. perryi* from Socotra.

MODERN HISTORY

After Dioscorides (c. 78 A.D.) and the Aloe plant figured in the *Codex Aniciae Julianae* (c. 512 A.D.), 1,000 years were to pass before the next figure of an Aloe plant representing *A. barbadensis* saw the light of day. This is found on page 138 of Leonard Fuchs's *De Historia Stirpium,* Basle, 1542. The figure was founded on a plant without flowers, and was named *Aloe Sempervivum marinum*. Fuchs followed Dioscorides rather closely in his description of the species and its locality of origin, for example "Plentiful in India also in Arabia, Asia, and maritime places and Islands, as in (the Greek island) Andros."

The next figure was on p. 355 of Dodonaeus *Stirpium Historiae* Pemptades Sex, published in Antwerp in 1583. This is obviously based on Fuchs's figure of the plant, but has the flowers added. This figure is cited by Linnaeus in *Hort. Cliff*. 130 (1736).

In *The Herball* or *Generall Historie of Plantes*, first published by John Gerard in 1597, amended by Thos. Johnson in 1633, London, the Aloe figure on p. 507 is an exact copy of Dodonaeus's figure, but he calls it "*Aloe vulgaris, sive Sempervivum Marinum,* Common Aloe or Sea Houseleeke." It seems that Gerard took over much of Dodonaeus's work and passed it off as his own.

Abraham Munting or Muntingius, figured three aloes in his *Aloidarium* (1680), one of them being *Aloe vera vulgaris* on fol. 19. This is generally accepted by Lamarck, Haworth and others as representing *A. barbadensis*.

TYPE LOCALITY AND DISTRIBUTION

In his original listing of *Aloe perfoliata* (var. π) *vera*, in *Spec. pl.* 1: 321 (1753), Linnaeus gives "*Habitat in Indiis*" which is almost certainly India. Whether his plant grew wild in India, or whether it originated elsewhere and was merely shipped from India (Bombay) is not known. In ed. 3: 458 (1764) Linnaeus states: "In Indiis, Africa, and π in Italy and Sicily."

Against this, *A. indica* Royle (which might or might not be a form of *A. barbadensis*) is stated by Royle to be common in the North-Western Provinces of India, and also frequently cultivated in gardens. Miller, in *Gard. Dict.* no. 2 (1768) says: "The second sort (*A. barbadensis*) is very common in the Islands of America where the plants are propagated to obtain the Hepatic Aloes which are brought to England and used chiefly for horses, being too coarse for medicine."

In *Trans. Linn. Soc.* 18: 176 (1880) Baker records that "*A. vera*" was introduced into English gardens in 1596 from the Island of Barbados (where it had doubtless been taken by earlier travellers).

DISTRIBUTION: *A barbadensis* has been cultivated all round the Mediterranean since remote times, and naturalized. Bentley and Trimen *Medic. Plants* 4: 282 (1805) state that this species grows wild in North Africa from Morocco eastwards e.g. Algeria, Tunisia, Tripolitania, Libya, Cyrenaica, Egypt (i.e. the Barbary Coast, the inhabitants being referred to as Barbarians), Palestine, Syria, Aegean Archipelago, Greece, Cyprus, Malta, Sicily, S. Italy, and also probably in Peninsula India,

It seems that *A. barbadensis* occurred wild on the Cape Verde Islands, The Canaries (Tenerife, etc.) and possibly Madeira. It seems very probable that plants were introduced by early Spaniards from the Canaries to the New World where they have become widely naturalized, e.g. the Barbados, Jamaica, Antigua, Mexico, Porto Rico, Venezuela, New Granada, Peru, Bolivia, etc.

EARLY MEDICINAL USES

It might be of interest to reproduce in full the account of Aloe given in "THE GREEK HERBAL OF DIOSCORIDES – ILLUSTRATED BY A BYZANTINE A.D. 512, ENGLISHED BY JOHN GOODYER A.D. 1655", by Robert T. Gunther, M.A., Hon. LL.D. (Oxford University Press, 1934). At page 258, Book III, there is a line-drawing of "25 Aloe" based on the original coloured illustration which is included in the *Codex Aniciae Julianae* (512 A.D.), preserved in the Osterreichische National-bibliothek, Vienna – see accompanying figure. The text of Dioscorides (c. 78 A.D.) reads:

"Aloe (but some call it Amphibion, some Eryngium, some Herminum, some Tragoceros, ye Romans Aloa, by ye Barbarians Aloe) hath a leaf near like Squill, thick, gross, somewhat broad in ye compass, broken or bowbacked behind, but on either part it hath ye leaves prickly by ye sides, appearing thinly, short. But it sends out a stalk like to Anthericum, but a white flower, & a seed like unto Asphodelus. All of it, is of a strong scent, & very bitter to ye taster, but it is but of one root having a root as a stake. It grows in India very much, gross, from whence also ye extracted juice is brought. It grows also in Arabia and Asia, & in certain sea-bordering places and Islands, as in Andros, not good for extracting juice but fitting for ye conglutinating of wounds, being laid on when it is beaten small. But there is a double kind of the juice, this indeed sandie, which seemeth to be ye subsistence of the purest, ye other like a liver. But chuse thou the pure & undeceitful, & unstonie, glittering, yellowish, brittle, liver-like easily melted, excelling in bitterness. But the black and hard to be broken, refuse. But they counterfeit it with gum, which is convinced by ye taste, & ye bitterness, & ye strongness of ye smell, and by not falling in pieces even to the smallest crumb when squeezed by the fingers. Some also mix Acacia with it. But it hath a power of binding, of procuring sleep, of drying, of thickening of bodies, & of loosening of ye belly, & of cleansing of ye stomach being drank ye quantity of 2 spoonfulls with water cold, or warm milk; & with 3 oboli of water or ye quantity of 1 dragm in drink, it stops ye spitting of blood; & it cleanseth ye Icterus. And it being swallowed also with Rosin, or taken either with water, or sod honey it looseth ye belly, but ye quantity of 3 dragms doth fully purge. But being mixed with other purging medicines it makes them less hurtfull to ye stomach. By being sprinkled on drie it conglutinates wounds, & brings to a cicatrix boils, & represseth them; but it properly healeth exulcerated geni-talls, and conglutinates ye broken preputia of boys. It cures also the Condylomata, & ye chaps of ye seate being mixed with sweet wine. And it stops ye fluxes of blood that come from Haemorrhoids, & it brings to a cicatrix ye Pterygia, takes away blacks & blues, and ye Hypopia with Honey. And it assuageth Scabritias and the itchings of ye eye corners, and ye headache being anointed with acetum & Rosaceum, on ye forehead & the temples, & with wine it stays ye hair falling off, & with honey and wine it is good for ye tonsillae, as also the gums and all griefs in ye mouth. But it is roasted also for eye medicines in a cleane and red hot earthern vessell, being kept turned with a splatter until that it is roasted equally. It is washed also, ye sandy part of it being severed as un-profitable, & the fattest and smooth being taken."

56. **A. metallica** Engler et Gilg. in Baum et Warburg *Kunene-Sambesi Exped.* 191 (1903); Berger in Engler's *Pflanzenr.* Liliac.–Aloin. 225 (1908).

DESCRIPTION based partly on a plant from type locality collected by Dr. E. J. Mendes that flowered in the author's gardens, and partly on the original description.

Plants acaulous or almost so, growing singly it seems.

Leaves about 15, densely rosulate, broadly lanceolate, 25—40cm. long, 7—9cm. broad at base, gradually attenuate, forming a somewhat compact rosette; *upper surface* bluish-grey with greenish tinge in cultivation, but described as having a metallic sheen in wild plants, without spots or markings, rather flat low down, slightly canaliculate in upper half; *lower surface* convex, otherwise as the upper surface; *margins* with slight reddish-brown horny edge armed with reddish-brown, deltoid pungent teeth 2—3mm. long, 10mm. apart near base, becoming 15—20mm. apart towards apex.

Inflorescence paniculate sparingly branched, up to 1·20m. high, branches compact, erect.

Racemes narrowly cylindric-acuminate, subdensely flowered, the terminal 35cm. long, 6cm. diam., the apical buds at first hidden by large densely imbricate white prominently nerved bracts.

Bracts large, lanceolate-acute, thin white scarious, brittle, 18—20mm. long, 8mm. broad, 7-nerved.

Pedicels 8mm. long.

Perianth reddish-pink, 32mm. long, cylindric and 7mm. diam. across the ovary, thence very slightly compressed-trigonous and slightly enlarging to the throat; *outer segments* free for 13mm., paler at the edges, obscurely 3-nerved; *inner segments* broader than the outer, with broad white border and 3 crowded nerves forming a reddish keel, the apices more obtuse and more spreading.

Filaments filiform-flattened, the 3 inner narrower and lengthening before the 3 outer with their *anthers* in turn exserted 2mm.; *stigma* at length exserted 3mm.; *ovary* pale green, 6mm. long, 3mm. diam. (Figs. 152–153).

ANGOLA. *Bié Dist.:* River Kutsi (Cuchi) just above Kapulo at 1300m. alt., fl. 4 May 1900, Baum 891 (B). *Bié Dist.,* Menongue, Cuchi River, Caquima Gorge, about 12km. N of Cuchi, alt. c. 1430m., coll. Dr. E. J. Mendes, 3 April 1960 (Mendes 3444), cult. Mbabane, Swaziland, fl. 15 July 1964, Mendes in Reynolds 10104 (LISC,PRE).

In May 1900 Baum discovered *A. metallica* which he saw only between high sandstone rocks near Kutsi (Cuchi), a village near the Cuchi River between Serpa Pinto and Vila da Ponte in Bié Div., Angola, at approx. 14° 40″ S, 17° E. No figures were published with the description.

In April 1960, Dr. E. J. Mendes (LISC) found plants along the top of a rocky gorge of the Cuchi River called Caquima, about 12km. north of Cuchi Village, and this could well be where Baum originally found it. When one of the plants collected by Dr. Mendes flowered in the present

FIG. 152.

A. metallica Engler et Gilg. Plant collected by Dr. E. J. Mendes (LISC.) on top of Caquima Gorge, Cuchi River, 12km. north of Cuchi village, Bié Dist., Angola; flowering at Mbabane, Swaziland. Height 1·25m.

FIG. 153.

A. metallica Engler et Gilg. Flowers natural size.

author's gardens at Mbabane, Swaziland, photographs were secured and a fuller description was drawn up.

A. metallica was originally described as having leaves with a metallic sheen, but Dr. Mendes saw no metallic sheen at Caquima gorge, while plants grown at Sintra (near Lisbon) and at Mbabane produced leaves that were of a dull bluish-green colour, with no trace of a sheen.

A striking character of *A. metallica* is the long bracts which are white, and prominently nerved. The apical buds of racemes are at first covered by densely imbricate bracts.

57. **A. massawana** Reynolds in *Journ. S.A. Bot.* 25: 207, pl. 18, 19 (1959).

DESCRIPTION: *Plants* acaulous or with short stems, with numerous shoots at random forming large dense groups sometimes 2—3m. across.

Leaves about 16, densely rosulate suberectly. spreading, about 50cm. long, 10cm. broad and 2cm. thick at base, gradually narrowing to the apex; *upper surface* dull grey-green, flat low down, slightly canaliculate upwards, with or without a few dull white spots low down; *lower surface* convex, dull grey-green, with or without a few white spots low down; *margins* armed with soft to firm almost white teeth that are reddish-brown at apex only, smaller and 10mm. apart low down, longer (2—3mm.) and more distant (15—25mm.) upwards; *sap* dries yellow.

Inflorescence usually 3-branched and 120–150 cm. high.

Peduncle plano-convex and 20mm. broad at base, terete upwards, 2—3-branched from about the middle.

Racemes narrowly cylindric-acuminate, the terminal the highest and 15—20cm. long, 5cm. diam., sublaxly flowered, youngest buds suberect and denser, open flowers laxer and nutant.

Bracts narrowly ovate-deltoid, 7mm. long, 3mm. broad, thin, scarious, white, 5-nerved.

Pedicels 6mm. long, obliquely spreading, decurved at apex.

Perianth pale scarlet, glabrous, 30—32mm. long, cylindric, trigonous, 7mm. diam. across the ovary, thence slightly narrowed on underside and enlarging slightly towards the throat with mouth slightly upturned; *outer segments* free for 12mm. (sometimes 15mm.) with white margins, obscurely 3-nerved, the apices subacute, slightly spreading; *inner segments* broader than the outer, with broad almost white border, with 3 crowded orange nerves forming a keel, the apices more obtuse and more spreading than the outer.

Filaments lemon, filiform-flattened, the 3 inner narrower and lengthening before the 3 outer with their *anthers* in turn exserted 2mm.; *stigma* at length exserted 3mm.; *ovary* pale green, 4—5mm. long, 2mm. diam. (Figs. 154–156).

FIG. 154.

A. massawana Reynolds. Plants at Arkiko, 8 miles S of Massawa, Eritrea.
Height 1·40m.
Photo: Professor H. B. Gilliland.

Fig. 155.

A. massawana Reynolds. Plants cultivated near Dar es Salaam, Tanzania (Tanganyika) Height 1·50m.

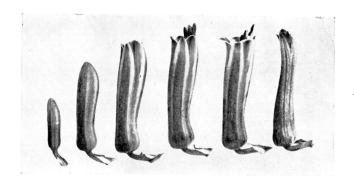

Fig. 156.

A. massawana Reynolds. Flowers natural size.

ERITREA. *Massawa Dist.*: Arkiko, 8 miles S of Massawa, 13 April 1956, leaf only, Reynolds 8047 (PRE); plant ex Arkiko cult. Johannesburg, fl. 4 May 1958, Reynolds 8047 (PRE); plants cult. hort. Mr. A. J. Bell, N of Dar-es-Salaam, fl. 30 June 1958, Reynolds 8733 holotype (PRE), isotypes (K, EA).

TANZANIA. 17 miles N of Dar-es-Salaam, 2 July 1960, Leach et Brunton 10170! (SRGH)—almost certainly introduced.

This species was first brought to the author's notice by Professor H. B. Gilliland who, in January 1952, photographed flowering plants at Arkiko, 8 miles S of Massawa, in Eritrea. This locality is about 50—100 ft. above sea-level, at 15° 31″ N, 39° 26″ E, near the shore of the Red Sea.

Subsequently Mr. P. R. O. Bally informed the author that he had found this species at Arkiko in April 1949, and also at the southern end of Zula Bay, further to the south, but none was then flowering.

When the author investigated the Aloes of Eritrea in May 1956, he found many plants at Arkiko, and also in a dry sandy depression at Tumalo about 5 miles W of Massawa. No plants were then in flower, and the description could not be completed, but plants from Arkiko subsequently flowered in Johannesburg.

In July 1957 Mr. J. A. Whellan of Salisbury, Southern Rhodesia, and Mr. L. D. E. F. Vesey FitzGerald of Abercorn, Zambia, found some Aloe plants "closely resembling *A. vera*" near the Inn-by-the-Sea, 16 miles N of Dar-es-Salaam in Tanzania. On 30 June 1958 the author visited that locality and found the plants.

He also met Mr. A. J. Bell, and saw large numbers of this species flowering in his gardens at Ukutani, 21 miles N of Dar-es-Salaam. Many years ago, Mr. Bell had found a group of these plants growing on an old Arab grave on his estate. He divided them up and cultivated the increases. It seems that all the plants now cultivated in the neighbourhood derived from the original plants on that grave. This species is not known anywhere else along the Tanzanian coast, but Mr. L. C. Leach has collected it much further south, near Lumbo, on the Moçambique coast.

These cultivated plants are, without any doubt whatever, conspecific with those at Arkiko in Eritrea.

A. massawana is named after the district of Massawa in Eritrea, which appears to be the specific centre, and where considerable numbers are found wild.

In habit of growth and in leaf and rosette characters, *A. massawana* bears a striking resemblance to *A. barbadensis* Mill. (= *A. vera* "L" non Mill.) but the latter differs in having a shorter, thicker peduncle, shorter pedicels, and longer, denser racemes of yellow flowers.

In inflorescence characters, *A. massawana* is closely allied to *A. trichosantha* Berger, but the latter (which the author has studied in the Ghinda valley, about 44 miles W of Massawa) has longer racemes and tomentose perianths apart from very different leaves.

58. **A. vacillans** Forskal in *Fl. Aegypt. Arab.* 74 (1775); Schweinfurth (*errore vaccillans*) in *Bull. Herb. Boiss.* 2: App. 2, 65 et 109 (1894); Berger in Engler's *Pflanzenr.* Liliac.-Aloin. 227 (1908); Christensen in *Dansk. Bot. Ark.* 4, No. 3, 18 (1922); Blatter in *Rec. Bot. Surv. India, Fl. Arab.* 8: 6, 436 (1936); O. Schwartz in *Fl. Trop. Arab.* 350 (1939); Lavranos in *Journ. S.A. Bot.* 31: 58 (1965).

DESCRIPTION: Based on Schweinfurth's and Berger's accounts: *Stem* stout, 30—50cm. long, at length decumbent.

Leaves rosulate (15—20) ensiform, long-attenuate, dull green-glaucous, somewhat leathery, 45—60cm. long, 10—13cm. broad, 15—18mm. thick; *upper surface* rather flat, concave towards apex, young leaves greyish and somewhat rough to the touch; *lower surface* convex, with or without a few small teeth in median line towards apex; *margins* with reddish-brown edge armed with deltoid, spreading or incurved teeth of the same colour, 2—3mm. long, 6—10mm. apart, smaller and more crowded towards base of leaf.

Inflorescence 1·50—2m. high, paniculate, twice three-branched.

Racemes cylindric, 35—40cm. long, sublaxly many-flowered, the rhachis smooth, sulcate.

Bracts ovate-acute, scarious, 10—15mm. long, 5—7-nerved, reflexed (twice as long as pedicels).

Pedicels 5—7mm. long.

Perianth cylindric-trigonous, red, glabrous (not pubescent) at first spreading, later nutant, 30mm. long, 8mm. diam., very slightly decurved; *outer segments* free for 6mm., 3-nerved, acute.

Anthers and *style* shortly exserted. (Figs. 157, 158).

TYPE LOCALITY: Kurma (in the mountains of the S. Yemeni escarpment)—Forskal.

S. ARABIA, YEMEN. Jebel Bura above Hille, 700—800m., Schweinfurth 377; Ussil (Haras Mountains) 1400m., in fruit only, 14 Feb. 1889, Schweinfurth 1350! (K); around Menacha (Haraz Mountains) 2200—2300m., Schweinfurth 1497, 1623.

Schweinfurth 1350! at Kew comprises one leaf which is 40cm. long and 5·5cm. broad with small, rather crowded, marginal teeth, and one raceme with dehisced dried capsules 15—20cm. long. (See photograph of Kew sheet.)

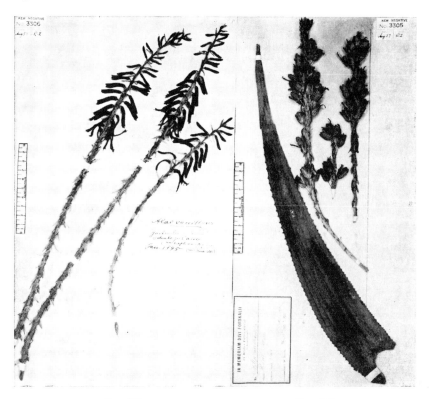

FIG. 157.   FIG. 158.

A. vacillans Forskal.

FIG. 157. Schweinfurth's material at Kew collected in the Yemen in 1889, and flowered at Cairo in Jan. 1895 – "Brought by me from Menacha to Cairo".

FIG. 158. Schweinfurth 1350 (K) from Uossil (Ussil, Haraz Mtns., Yemen) 1,400m., in fruit 14 Feb. 1889.

Judging from description it seems that *A. vacillans* and *A. menachensis* are very closely allied, and both come from the Haraz Mountains, around Menakha, at 2,200—2,300 ft.

A. vacillans is described as having leaves to 60cm. long, 10—13cm. broad, with rather crowded marginal teeth only 6—10mm. apart; the inflorescence is 2—3-branched, racemes 35—40cm. long, and smooth red flowers, 30mm. long.

In *A. menachensis* leaves are shorter and broader (40cm. long, 16cm. broad), purplish at margins, with more spaced marginal teeth; the inflorescence is many-branched with shorter (15—20cm. long) racemes; perianth is paler scarlet or pale red and slightly albo-tomentose.

A. audhalica Lavranos et Hardy is a near affinity but differs in having shorter, broader leaves, a much lower inflorescence (80—100cm.), shorter, denser racemes (20cm.) and longer (10mm.) pedicels.

A. dhalensis Lavranos is a smaller plant with little or no stem and with a 2–3-branched inflorescence 70cm. high.

59. **A. officinalis** Forskal, *Fl. Arab. Aegypt.* 73–74 (1775); Deflers in *Voyage au Yemen* 211 (1889).
—— *A. vera* "L" var. *officinalis* (Forsk.) Bak. in *Journ. Linn. Soc.* 18: 176 (1880); Schweinfurth in *Bull. Herb. Boiss.* 2: App. 2, 59 (1894); Berger in Engler's *Pflanzenr.* Liliac.–Aloin. 229 (1908); Blatter in *Fl. Arab., Rec. Bot. Surv. Ind.* 8: 6, 464 (1936); O. Schwartz in *Fl. Trop. Arabia* 350 (1939).
—— *A. rubescens* D.C. *Plant. grass t.* 15 (1799) – *fide* Berger, but this is doubtful.

DESCRIPTION based on Forskal's and Schweinfurth's accounts.

Plants with short decumbent stems (usually suckering and forming dense groups of many rosettes).

Leaves compactly rosulate, erectly spreading, ensiform, long-attenuate, 70cm. long, 12cm. broad, 10—18mm. thick, rigid, very fleshy; *upper surface* canaliculate towards apex, grey-green, often white-spotted; *lower surface* convex, sometimes with 8—9 teeth dorsally in median line; *marginal teeth* stout, crowded, subuncinate, incurved or rarely horizontally spreading, compressed subdeltoid.

Inflorescence Forskal states *bicubitalis*, say 90—100cm. (Schweinfurth states 2m. high, simple, or few-branched, often 3-branched)—perhaps Forskal should be followed.

Peduncle basally plano-convex, 2cm. thick.

Racemes elongate, densely flowered, 15—20cm. long, the apex comose-attenuate, the rhachis often pruinose as if very minutely pubescent.

Bracts broadly ovate-acute or lanceolate, 10mm. long, membranous, 9—11-nerved, with 3 prominent median nerves, imbricate at apex of racemes.

Pedicels 6—8mm. long, sometimes asperulous-pruinose.

Perianth 28—30mm. long, cylindric-trigonous, red (Forskal) yellow to orange (Schweinfurth); *outer segments* connate to the middle—say free for 15mm., prominently 3-nerved.

Anthers and *style* scarcely exserted. (Fig. 159).

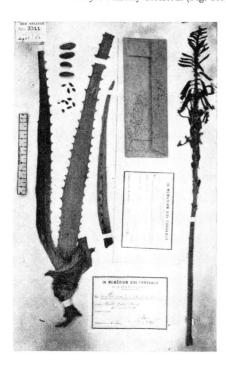

FIG. 159

Material on left Schweinfurth 360 (K) at foot of Jebel Bura, near Hille, Yemen is probably *A. officinalis* Forsk. var. *angustifolia* (Schweinf.) Lavranos. Material on right is Schweinfurth 182 (K) *A. officinalis* Forsk.

TYPE LOCALITY: Wadi Mor, near Lohayya (Lohaja)—Forskal.

Schweinfurth cites the following material for his *A. vera* var. *officinalis*:

YEMEN. Badjil foothills, 200m., Schweinf. 531, fl. Jan. 1889; Foot of Jebel Bura at Hille, 600m., Schweinf. 360! (K); near Chalife to E of Merrana (Marawa), 300m., Schweinf. No. 182! (K); at foot of Jebel Melhan at Wolledje, 600m., Schweinf. 658! (K).

Notes: Schweinfurth 360 and 182 are mounted on one sheet at Kew. No. 360 comprises 2 leaves only, measuring 47cm. long, and only 2·6cm. broad, notwithstanding his description of a leaf being 75cm. long, 9—12cm. broad. No. 182 is a raceme with peduncle measuring 40cm. overall, the raceme only being about 15cm. long.

Schweinf. 360 should be cited under the var. *angustifolia* not *A. officinalis*.

Forskal gives the inflorescence as "*bicubitalis* (say 1m. at most) *interdum bifidus Flores rubri*", while Schweinfurth states 2m. high, flowers yellow to orange. It is a pity that habitat photographs of flowering plants at the type locality are not available.

59A. **A. officinalis** Forsk. var. **angustifolia** (Schweinf.) Lavranos. Comb. nov. in *Journ. S.A. Bot.* 31: 59 (1965).

—— *A. vera* L. var. *angustifolia* Schweinf. in *Bull. Herb. Boiss.* 2: App. 2, 62 (1894); Blatter in *Rec. Bot. Surv. India* 8: 464 (1936); O. Schwartz in *Fl. Trop. Arab.* 350 (1939).

Differs in having leaves exceedingly narrow, 2·4cm. broad, 35cm. long, 1·7cm. thick "in fresh condition 5·7cm. broad," upper surface flat, lower surface convex, with large oblong spots near base, marginal teeth crowded, white, straight, spreading. YEMEN: Gebel Bura, at Hille 600m., coll. Jan. 1889, Schweinfurth 305.

Note: Schweinfurth 360 (K) from the same locality, with leaf 47cm. long, 2·6cm. broad, should be cited here. (Fig. 159).

60. A. otallensis Bak. in Th. Dyer *Fl. Trop. Afr.* 7: 458 (1898); Berger in Engler's *Pflanzenr.* Liliac.–Aloin 225 (1908).

DESCRIPTION based on Baker and Berger (*l.c.*).

Stem if any not stated.

Leaves about 12, triangular-lanceolate, 4—5cm. broad at base, gradually attenuate, about 30cm. long, rigid, fleshy, glaucous-green; *upper surface* with round-oblong white spots in series lengthways; *lower surface* more copiously spotted; *margins* with narrow cartilaginous edge armed with brown-tipped uncinate-deltoid teeth about 2mm. long, 8—10mm. apart.

Inflorescence paniculate, with arcuate-ascending branches.

Racemes dense, oblong, 4—7cm. long, with densely imbricate bracts at apex.

Bracts erect, broadly ovate, obtuse, shortly cuspidate, white, scarious, about 12mm. long, 5—7-nerved.

Pedicels as long as or shorter than the bracts, longer in fruit.

Perianth yellowish-red (?) 27mm. long, narrowly stipitate at base, oblong around the ovary (in dried specimens), slightly constricted at the middle and decurved; *outer segments* linear-oblong, obtuse 3—5-nerved, longer than the tube; *inner segments* pale, more obtuse.

Filaments scarcely exserted; *style* at length distinctly exserted.

SOUTHERN ETHIOPIA, SIDAMO, BORANA. Ahele Bekaka, between Coromme and Otallo, 11 Oct. 1893, Riva 1711 (FI).

The present author was unable to trace Ahele Bekaka when he visited Southern Ethiopia in September 1953. Neither the Ethiopian Police nor Missionaries in Yavello had heard of such a place. Otallo is about 12 miles S of Yavello, while Coromme is shown about 25 miles SW of Agere Mariam (Alghe). Otallo and Coromme are about 50 miles apart as the crow flies. Ahele Bekaka is therefore, presumably, somewhere NW of Yavello, towards the Sugan River Valley.

The author did not find any plants fitting the description of *A. otallensis* in the neighbourhood of Yavello or north and west of that village, or at Otallo, 12 miles S of Yavello. At and near Otallo no less than four species occur, namely *A. rivae* Bak., *A. secundiflora* Engler, *A. calidophila* Reynolds and *A. wrefordii* Reynolds occur in abundance and hybrids are not rare.

60A. A. otallensis Bak. var. elongata Berger in Engler's *Pflanzenr.* Liliac.–Aloin. 226 (1908.)

According to Berger the var. *elongata* differs from the typical in having:

Leaves 6cm. broad at base, asperulous, gradually attenuate, *margins* sinuate-dentate, marginal teeth 3—4mm. long, 9—10mm. apart. *Racemes* elongate, 13—20cm. long with basal flowers wide apart. *Bracts* narrower than in the type, spreading or reflexed, twice as long as the pedicels.

Judging from a photograph of Riva 476, it seems that certain plants seen near Yavello, Otallo, northwards to Dubuluch and Mega (all in Southern Ethiopia), to Moyale and beyond in Northern Kenya, belong to the var. *elongata* which can now be more fully described:

Plants sometimes solitary, usually in small groups of 6 or more, with *stem* short or procumbent and up to 50cm. long.

Leaves 16—20, densely rosulate, fairly compact, lanceolate-attenuate, 35—40cm. long, 7—8cm. broad at base; attenuate-acute, arcuate-erectly spreading; *upper surface* flat near base, slightly canaliculate towards apex, deep green to brownish-green with numerous clear to dull white lenticular-oval spots irregularly scattered throughout; *lower surface* convex, similar in colour and markings; *margins* sinuate-dentate, armed with deltoid pungent rigid teeth which are reddish-brown from a paler base, 3—5mm. long, 10—15mm. apart, isolated and not joined by a horny line, the interspaces mostly rounded. *Sap* dries yellow.

Inflorescence paniculate, 1·5—1·75m. high.

Peduncle basally flattened and 2—3cm. broad, compactly 8—10-branched from the middle or higher, the branches slender.

Racemes cylindric-acuminate, erect, the terminal 15—20cm. long, 15cm. in the lowest branch, 10cm. in the others.

Bracts large, ovate-acute, 13mm. long, 7—8mm. broad when pressed flat, very dry, brittle, white, 7—9-nerved, deflexed, twice as long as the pedicels.

Pedicels 6—7mm. long.

Perianth rose-pink, cylindric, very slightly clavate, 28mm. long, 5—6mm. diam. across the ovary, thence slightly enlarging to 8mm. with open mouth; *outer segments* free for 15mm., paler at the margins, obscurely 3-nerved, apices subacute; *inner segments* broader than the outer, with broad white border and 3 crowded nerves forming a pinkish keel turning greenish at apex, the apices more obtuse.

Filaments filiform-flattened, pale lemon, the 3 inner narrower and lengthening before the 3 outer with their *anthers* in turn exserted 1—2mm.; *stigma* at length exserted 2—3mm.; *ovary* green, 6mm. long, 2·5mm. diam. (Figs. 160–162).

FIG. 160.   FIG. 161.

A. otallensis Bak. var. *elongata* Berger.

FIG. 160. Plant collected between Mega and Otallo, near Dubuluck, Sidamo Prov., Borana, S. Ethiopia, flowering at Mbabane, Swaziland. Height 5 feet.

FIG. 161. Plant near Moyale, Northern Prov., Kenya, alt. 3,000 ft. Height 6 feet.

Photo: Mr. J. B. Gillett.

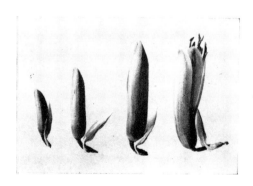

FIG. 162.

A. otallensis Bak. var. *elongata* Berger. Flowers 1/1 from the Fig. 160 plant.

"Somaliland. Bei der Station Banis (Banisi?)", 21 July 1893, Riva 476 (FI).
   Note: The type locality is Banissa in the remote Northern Frontier District of Kenya at approx. 3° 56′ N, 40° 20′ E. This lies due W of Mandera, and ENE of Moyale, about halfway between the two places.

S. Ethiopia, Sidamo, Borana, coll. near Otallo, 20 miles S of Yavello, cult. Mbabane Swaziland, fl. 17 July 1964, Reynolds 7049 (PRE); coll. 12 miles N of Dubuluch between Mega and Yavello, cult. Johannesburg, fl. 18 Aug. 1958, Reynolds 7046 (PRE); 6 miles N of Yavello, in fruit 17 Sept. 1953, Reynolds 7054 (K); in valley E of Amara Mountains, SE of Yavello, 4° 50′ N, 38° 10′ E., cult. Nairobi, fl. Dec. 1956, J. B. Gillett 14472 (Bally 11343) (G, EA).

A. otallensis var. *elongata* is nearest allied to *A. deserti*, but the latter differs in being of low, shrubby growth with 20—30cm. of the apical part of stems sublaxly foliate. The leaves of *A. otallensis* are more lanceolate and copiously spotted, while rosettes are more compact.
   A most striking difference is that in *A. deserti* the young racemes are at first limp and drooping and only become stiff and erect when the lowest buds commence opening. In *A. otallensis* the racemes are erect at all stages. Both species have large very white bracts that are deflexed and twice as long as the pedicels.

61. A. splendens Lavranos in *Journ. S.A. Bot.* 31: 77 (1965).

Description. *Plant* solitary or forming groups of up to 8 rosettes, usually acaulous, but frequently with a prostrate stem up to 40cm. long.
   Leaves 20—24 ascending-spreading, deltoid-attenuate, acute, up to 60cm. long, 15cm. broad at base, 10mm. thick; *upper surface* uniformly dull green, often with a purplish-brown tinge, flat, but canaliculate towards the apex; *lower surface* flat or broadly convex, the same colour as the upper surface; *margins* with dark-brown cartilaginous border, armed with dark-brown, hard, rather blunt, deltoid teeth, 2mm. long, 15—30mm. distant but more so towards the apex.
   Inflorescence a much-branched and rebranched panicle, 2—3 simultaneously, 140cm. high, each with up to 15 racemes, making a total of over 40 racemes to some plants.
   Peduncle plano-convex and 30mm. broad at base, terete upwards, somewhat elliptical in section, brown with a bloom, branched from below the middle, sterile bracts ovate-deltoid, 8—10mm. long, scarious, white, 11-nerved.
   Racemes conico-cylindric with a long sterile, bracteate apex, sub-densely flowered, 30—35cm. long, 6cm. diam., the lateral racemes somewhat shorter, only the youngest buds sub-erect, all other buds spreading horizontally, open flowers nutant.
   Bracts narrowly deltoid, 10mm. long, 6mm. broad at base, scarious, white, 7-nerved.
   Pedicels red-brown, terete, 8mm. long.

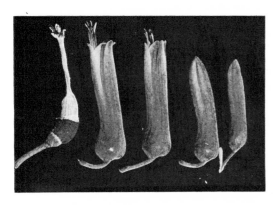

Fig. 163.

A. splendens Lavranos. Flowers 1/1 from the Colour Plate No. 61 plant – on the sandy Dathina Plain, 6 miles E of Mudiya, South-Western Arabia.
Photo: Professor W. Rauh.

Perianth bright-scarlet with a bloom, 30—33mm. long, shortly stipitate, cylindric-trigonous, 8mm. diam. over the ovary, thereafter constricted to 6mm., widening to 7mm. towards the laterally compressed mouth; *outer segments* free for 13mm. with 3 dark-brownish nerves which become confluent towards the cream segment-apices; *inner segments* free, but dorsally adnate to the outer to beyond the middle, broader but equal in length to the outer segments, with three rather congested, brown nerves throughout, broad cream margins and apices which are broader, more obtuse and more reflexed than in the outer segments.
   Filaments much flattened and white at base, filiform and yellow upwards, the 3 inner narrower and lengthening before the 3 outer, their *anthers* in turn exserted 3mm.
   Style yellow, with *stigma* at length exserted 4mm.; *ovary* bright green, 7mm. long, the apex truncate (Plate 34, Fig. 163).

South Western Arabia. Dathina plain, 6 miles E of Mudiya, approx. 2,500 ft. (760m.), lat. 13° 50′ N, long. 46° 10′ E, coll. 3 March 1964, Rauh et Lavranos 13008 (HEID) holotype, (K, PRE) isotype; 1 mile W of Mudiya, 3 March 1964, Rauh et Lavranos 2767; 2 miles E of Mudiya, 3 March 1964, Rauh et Lavranos 2768.

When describing this outstanding species, Mr. Lavranos wrote:
   "This magnificent species was first observed in flower by Mr. T. W. Hague, Agricultural Officer at Lodar in the Audhali Sultanate. When Professor Rauh and I visited this area and the adjacent

PLATE 34

ALOE SPLENDENS Lavranos.

On the sandy Dathina Plain 6 miles E of Mudiya, SW. Arabia.
Height 1·55m.
From a Kodachrome by Mr. J. Lavranos.

Dathina country in March 1964, Mr. Hague directed us to the locality, some 6 miles E of the village of Mudiya where numerous plants were found growing in sparse scrub consisting mainly of 2 species of *Acacia* and one or two of *Commiphora*. Only one plant was found in full flower and it is from this that the type material was obtained.

"Plants which may belong to this species were found a few miles further west near Lodar. Some very large plants which are conspicuous in the southern part of the Jahhayn flats at the edge of the desolate lava country of the Arqub, halfway between Lodar and the coastal village of Shuqra, may also belong here.

"*A. splendens* is a beautiful plant, its beauty being in contrast to the austerity of its surroundings which is accentuated by the fact that the species seems to flower in March and early April, at the end of the long, dry season, when the country is covered in dust and the trees are devoid of foliage.

"*A. splendens* does not seem to have close relatives, either in Arabia or in Africa. It appears to be rather distantly related to *A. megalacantha* Bak., which, however, has an erect stem 1—2 ft. high, narrower, strongly recurved leaves, considerably larger marginal teeth, shorter inflorescences, racemes and flowers and much longer pedicels".

GROUP 10

PLANTS PENDENT, OR SEMI-PENDENT

Stems mostly slender, simple or branched; in some the apical 20—30cm. of stems laxly foliate, the leaf basal sheaths 10—20mm. apart, in others densely rosulate. *Inflorescence* simple or 3—4-branched, pendent with only the racemes ascending, or arcuate-ascending.

Type species: *A. veseyi* Reynolds.

KEY TO THE SPECIES

A.—STEMS 10—15MM THICK, THE APICAL 20—30CM LAXLY FOLIATE

(*a*) *Leaves* basally sheathing, the sheaths 10—20mm. apart, *pedicels* 15mm. long, *inflorescence* 2—4-branched, *racemes* 15—20cm. long:
    1. *Stems* 30—50cm. long, *leaves* 30—40cm. long, 4—5cm. broad, *perianth* 22mm. long, yellow or red, pubescent .. ..   63 *A. pendens*
    2. *Stems* 1m. or more, *leaves* 3cm. broad, *inflorescence* 45cm. long, *perianth* 30mm. long, yellow or red, glabrous .. ..   64 *A. confusa*

B.—LEAVES DENSELY ROSULATE, (NOT SPACED AT APEX OF STEMS):

(*a*) Small plants, with *stems* 10—25cm. long, 8—10mm. thick:
    1. *Leaves* 10cm. long, 2cm. broad, *inflorescence* simple, 25—30cm. long, *pedicels* 10—12mm., *perianth* scarlet, 25mm. long .. ..   62 *A. cremnophila*
(*b*) Larger plants, entirely pendent, *leaves* falcately decurved; *inflorescence* 2—3—4-branched, 60cm. long:
    1. *Stems* 40cm. long, 2cm. thick, *leaves* 40—50cm. long, 3cm. broad, *raceme* lax, 12cm. long, *perianth* narrowly cylindric, 25mm., yellow .. ..   65 *A. veseyi*
    2. *Stem* to 1m. long, simple or few-branched, *leaves* 50cm. long, 7—8cm. broad, *pedicels* 14mm. long, *raceme* dense, 10cm. long, *perianth* 25—28mm., scarlet, cylindric, slightly ventricose .. ..   66 *A. mendesii*
(*c*) Plant with 2—3m. erect stem, cultivated at Kew:
    1. *Leaves* 40cm. long, 3cm. broad, only the *inflorescence* hanging downwards with the raceme up-turned, *raceme* dense, 4cm. long, *pedicels* 15—20mm. long, *perianth* 30mm. long, yellow.. .. ..   67 *A. penduliflora*

62. **A. cremnophila** Reynolds et Bally in *Journ. S.A. Bot.* 27: 77, pl. 13, 14 (1961).

DESCRIPTION: *Plant* of low shrubby growth, pendent on precipice faces, with *stems* 10—20cm. long, 8—10mm. diam., many-branched from base.

   Leaves 6—8, rosulate, usually crowded at apex of stems, basally sheathing, narrowly lanceolate-attenuate, averaging 10cm. long, 2cm. broad at base, spreading, recurved; *upper surface* grey-green, without spots or markings, flat low down, slightly canaliculate upwards; *lower surface* rounded, grey-green, without spots or markings; *margins* armed with deltoid rather pungent pale-brown teeth that are 2mm. long, 3—5mm. apart.

   Inflorescence simple, 25—30cm. long, at first pendent, then arcuate-ascending.

   Peduncle slender, 6mm. diam., with a few sterile bracts below the raceme.

   Raceme cylindric-conic, 10—12cm. long, 5·5cm. diam., the buds grey-green tipped, denser, sub-erect, the open flowers scarlet, laxer, sub-pendulous.

   Bracts ovate-acute, 10mm. long, 5mm. broad at the middle, dirty-white, rather brittle, 5-nerved.

   Pedicels 10—12mm. long.

   Perianth scarlet, turning yellowish-green at mouth, 25mm. long, cylindric, slightly clavate, basally obtuse, 5mm. diam. across the ovary, thence trigonous upwards, the mouth wide open; *outer segments* free for 5mm., the apices acute, slightly spreading; *inner segments* with a greenish keel in apical 5mm., the apices more obtuse and more spreading than the outer.

   Filaments pale-lemon, filiform-flattened, the 3 inner narrower and lengthening before the 3 outer, with their *anther* in turn exserted 0—1mm.; *stigma* at length exserted 1—2mm.; *ovary* green, 5mm. long, 2·5mm. diam. (Figs. 164–165)·

SOMALIA NORTH (formerly Somaliland Prot.), on precipice faces near Daloh, 13 miles N of Erigavo, c. 10° 46′ N, 47° 15′ E, alt. 6,500 ft., cult. Bryanston, Johannesburg, fl. 7 Oct. 1960, Reynolds 8450B, holotype (PRE).

A. cremnophila was discovered by Mr. P. R. O. Bally in October 1956 on cliff faces of the Daloh Escarpment, about 13 miles north of Erigavo at an altitude of 7,000 ft. Mr. Bally also found plants on rocks at Mait Escarpment, at 5,400 ft., but none was then in flower.

Subsequently, on 12th September 1957, the present author also found plants on the precipice face at Mr. Bally's locality, but again, no flowers were available.

Of several plants cultivated in his gardens at Bryanston, Johannesburg, only one stem produced an inflorescence in October 1960, and this enabled the description to be completed, and a specimen made.

FIG. 164.   FIG. 165.

A. cremnophila Reynolds et Bally.

FIG. 164. Plants on Daloh Precipice, 13 miles N of Erigavo, Somalia North. Alt. 6,500 ft.
FIG. 165. Raceme × 6/10 approx., from a plant flowering in Johannesburg.

Aloe pendens, Forsk.

Fig. 166.

A. pendens Forsk. from an uncoloured plate of *Bot.
Mag. t.* 7837 (1902).
By courtesy The Director, Royal Botanic Gardens, Kew.

Fig. 167.

A. pendens Forsk. Plant in the garden of M. J. Gatafosse
at Ain-es-Sebaa, Marocco, from *Cactus* No. 58 p. 2, Paris
(March 1958).
By courtesy Professor A. Guillaumin.

A. cremnophila appears to be nearest allied to *A. tororoana* Reynolds (from Tororo Rock in Uganda near the Kenya border) but differs in having slenderer stems, unspotted leaves, larger racemes, larger bracts as long as the 10—12mm. pedicels, while the whole plant is pendent on cliff faces.

The simple inflorescence is produced downwards with the raceme ascending, while it seems that the flowers open one at a time. Leaves are mostly rosulate, but sometimes the apical 5—10cm. of stems is sublaxly foliate.

Plants do not like acid soils; much lime should be added for cultivated plants.

63. **A. pendens** Forskal in *Fl. Aeg.-Arab.* 74 (1775); Baker in *Journ. Linn. Soc.* 18: 181 (1880); Schweinfurth in *Bull. Herb. Boiss.* 2: App. 2, 72 (1894); Engler in *Notizbl. Berl. Bot. Gart.* 1: 5 (1897); Berger in *Bot. Mag. t.* 7837 (1902), in Engler's *Pflanzenr.* Liliac.–Aloin., 272 (1908); Christensen in *Dansk. Bot. Ark.* 4: No. 3, 18 (1922); Blatter in *Fl. Arab., Rec. Bot. Surv. India* 8: 6, 464 (1936); O. Schwartz in *Fl. Trop. Arab.* 351 (1939); Guillaumin in *Cactus*, No. 58, p. 2, Paris (March 1958).
—— *A. dependens* Steud., *Nomencl.* 1: 30 (1840).

DESCRIPTION based on Schweinfurth's and Berger's accounts.
   Plant of shrubby growth, suckering from base, the stems quickly becoming pendent, 30—40cm. long, 10—15mm. thick, leaves subdistichous when young and basally sheathing, and spotted near base, older leaves spirally twisted to rosulate, the internodes 1—2cm. apart and white-striped and spotted.
   Leaves narrowly ensiform, gradually narrowing to the apex, deflexed and recurved, about 30—40cm. long, 4—5cm. broad; *upper surface* bright or pale green, slightly swollen; *lower surface* rounded; *margins* with narrow reddish horny edge with very small deltoid remote teeth 1mm. long.
   Inflorescence ascending, 80—90cm. high, slender, with 2—3 lateral branches which have a few deltoid sterile bracts.
   Racemes somewhat erect cylindric, slightly acuminate, many-flowered, the terminal up to 30cm. long, the lateral 15—20cm. long.
   Bracts ovate-deltoid, 8—10mm. long, many-nerved; pubescent according to Schweinfurth.
   Pedicels 15—17mm. long.
   Perianth red, or yellowish-red, pubescent (Schweinfurth), glabrous (Berger), 22mm. long, cylindric-trigonous, not at all constricted above the ovary; *outer segments* connate for one-third their length, i.e. free for 14mm., with dark central nerves, spreading at apex.
   Anthers and *stigma* shortly exserted. (Figs. 166–167).

TYPE LOCALITY: Hadie, in the Southern Yemen mountainous country—Forskal.

S. ARABIA, YEMEN. Above Ussil (Uossil), 1500m., 7 Feb. 1889, Schweinfurth 1222! (K)—this comprises 2 very small plants without flowers, and is useless for purposes of identification. (Berger also cites: Jebel Buru 900m., Schweinfurth 363 (Aquarell), 1845; Wadi Nahemi above Attara, 2000m., Schweinfurth 1751).
   Plant cult. La Mortola, fl. March 1902, type of *Bot. Mag. t* 7837, *leg.* Sir Thomas Hanbury (K!).—*Note:* Berger states that the type of *Bot. Mag. t* 7837 is exactly the same as a plant in Naples, then with A. Sprenger, who was a friend of Schweinfurth and obtained his plant direct from him.

Forskal discovered his *A. pendens* in 1773 or 1774 growing on rocks at Hadjeh in the Yemen. Schweinfurth collected plants at altitudes ranging from 900m. to 2000m. He stated that wild plants form large masses on rocky slopes, and take root in rock crevices. He describes the stems as sarmentose, and compares the species with *A. ciliaris* Haw (a scandent species found in the Cape Province of S. Africa). Schweinfurth also described the bracts and perianths as pubescent in the wild state, but Berger states he has seen only glabrous perianths in cultivation.

Colour of perianth, it seems, varies from pale yellow to reddish.

It seems that *A. pendens* is a somewhat shrubby species of pendent growth, with very slender stems much branched from base, the apical 20—30cm. being laxly foliate, with striped and white-spotted sheathing internodes 10—20mm. apart.

It also seems that *A. pendens* is allied to *A. confusa* Engler, but the latter, which also forms dense tangled masses in nature, differs in having shorter leaves with larger marginal teeth, shorter, much laxer racemes, smaller bracts, and larger flowers.

64. **A. confusa** Engler in *Pflanzenwelt Ost-Afrikas* 141 (1895); Baker in Th. Dyer, *Fl. Trop. Afr.* 7: 464 (1898); Berger in Engler's *Pflanzenr.* Liliac.–Aloin. 272 (1908).

DESCRIPTION based on many plants at the type locality, L. Chala.
   Plants pendent on sheer rock faces, or sprawling, creeping and rooting and forming dense tangled masses 2—4m. across.
   Stem up to 1m. or more long, 18mm. thick, pendent or procumbent, with numerous shoots mostly from near base, the apical 20—30cm. sublaxly foliate.

166   *Aloe confusa*

Leaves up to 30cm. long, 3—4cm. broad at base, gradually tapering to an acute apex, mostly falcately decurved, basally sheathing-amplexicaul, the sheath bases (internodes) about 15mm. distant, the oldest leaves mostly grey-green, without spots, but sometimes with a few small white spots especially dorsally near base, the sheathing portion usually green-striate and sometimes spotted; *upper surface* flat low down, slightly canaliculate upwards, mostly grey-green, unspotted; *lower surface* rounded, usually with several white spots near base; *margins* with a narrow white cartilaginous edge armed with firm whitish teeth 2mm. long, about 10mm. apart.

Inflorescence produced laterally, simple or 2—3-branched, about 45cm. long, usually oblique with racemes ascending.

Peduncle plano-convex and 13mm. broad at base.

Racemes cylindric-acuminate, averaging 15cm. long, 7cm. diam., laxly about 25-flowered, the pedicels spreading to almost horizontally disposed, and about 5—10mm. apart, the open flowers cernuous to pendulous.

Bracts deltoid-acuminate, 7mm. long, 3mm. broad at base, thin, scarious, pale brownish, about 5-nerved.

Pedicels the lowest 15mm. long.

Perianth mostly yellow, sometimes red, cylindric-trigonous, averaging 30mm. long, basally obtuse and shortly stipitae, very slightly narrowed above the ovary, thence slightly compressed laterally and with an open trigonal mouth; *outer segments* free for 11mm., 3-nerved, the apices subacute, slightly spreading, turning brownish; *inner segments* dorsally adnate to the outer for two-thirds their length, broader than the outer, and with more obtuse more spreading apices.

Filaments pale-lemon, filiform-flattened, the 3 inner narrower and lengthening before the 3 outer with their *anthers* in turn exserted 2—3mm.; *stigma* at length exserted 4mm.; *ovary* pale green, 5mm. long, 3mm. at base. (Plate 35, Figs. 168—169).

TANZANIA (TANGANYIKA). *Northern Prov.:* Moshi Dist., Lake Chala (7 miles N of Taveta): Dschallasee, 1000m., 15 June 1893, Volkens 410, holotype (B), isotype (BM); cult. Amani, 2 July 1936, Greenway 2252! (PRE); L. Chala, cult. Ewanrigg, fl. 18 June 1943, Christian 1902! (PRE); L. Chala, on western rim, 30 March 1952, Reynolds 6371! (PRE); Same loc., 3,200 ft., 5 July 1958, Reynolds 8784 (K, PRE).

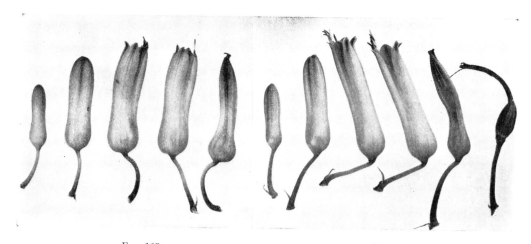

FIG. 168.   FIG. 169.

A. confusa Engler. Flowers from two different plants, showing variation.

Lake Chala is a water-filled volcanic crater (or blow-hole), 2 or 3 miles across, lying 7 miles N of Taveta, Taveta being 9 miles E of Himo, and 26 miles E of Moshi, on the Kenya–Tanzania border, just inside Tanzania. This is SE of Kilimanjaro, at approx. 3° 18′ S, 37° 42′ E. It is an enchanting place of exquisite beauty, with considerable numbers of *Euphorbia quinquecostata* Volk. lining the crater walls. The western wall is much higher than the eastern.

A. confusa forms large, densely tangled masses either sprawling on slopes, or hanging down sheer rock faces. There appear to be more yellow-flowered forms than reds.

A. confusa appears to be nearest allied to *A. pendens* Forsk. in the Yemen. Both have very slender stems with the apical 20—30cm. laxly foliate, but *A. pendens* differs in having slightly larger leaves with much smaller marginal teeth, a much taller inflorescence with longer, denser racemes, larger bracts, smaller flowers which Schweinfurth states are pubescent.

A noteworthy character of *A. confusa* is the leaf sap which turns deep purple, almost black, and stains clothing badly. Local natives are reported to use this for making ink.

PLATE 35

ALOE CONFUSA   Engler.

On sheer volcanic rock face at Lake Chala, 7 miles N of Taveta,
Moshi Dist., Northern Province, Tanzania (Tanganyika). Alt. 3,200 ft.
Flowering in July. $\times \frac{1}{8}$ approx.

168 *Aloe veseyi*

65. **A. veseyi** Reynolds in *Journ. S.A. Bot.* 25: 315 (1959).

DESCRIPTION: *Plant* with stems, leaves and inflorescence all hanging downwards on precipice faces.

Stem about 30—40cm. long, 2cm. thick, with offshoots from base forming 5 or more rosettes of leaves per plant.

Leaves about 12, rosulate, 40—50cm. long, 3cm. broad at base, gradually narrowing to a long-pointed apex, all falcately decurved and pointing downwards; *upper surface* dull grey-green with reddish tinge, flat to slightly canaliculate with numerous spots throughout, the spots dull white, lenticular to narrowly elliptical; *lower surface* rounded, similar to upper surface; *margins* armed with firm cartilaginous deltoid teeth 1—2mm. long, up to 20mm. apart, larger near base, gradually smaller to obsolescent upwards.

Inflorescence a slender 2—4-branched panicle about 60cm. long, pendent, with only the racemes arcuate-ascending.

Peduncle slender, basally flattened and 6mm. broad, 2—4-branched from about the middle, the branches arcuate-spreading slightly downwards, with the racemes arcuate-ascending, lowest branch subtended at base by a thin, scarious, 3—5-nerved bract which is long-pointed, 15mm. long, 6mm. broad at base.

Racemes cylindric-conical, rather laxly flowered, the terminal 12cm. long, 7cm. diam., about 30-flowered, the lateral a little shorter, the buds and flowers nutant.

Bracts narrowly lanceolate, long-pointed, 6mm. long, 3mm. broad, thin, scarious, white, 3-nerved.

Pedicels 14mm. long, spreading horizontally to curved slightly downwards.

Perianth narrowly cylindric-trigonous, 25mm. long, pale yellow, obtuse at base, 5mm. diam. and greenish-yellow across the ovary, thence slightly trigonous and enlarging to the throat with the mouth wide open and 10mm. across; *outer segments* free for 5—6mm., with 3 orange nerves, the apices orange-brown tipped, spreading to recurved; *inner segments* themselves free but dorsally adnate to the outer for 18mm., broader than the outer, and with more obtuse, more spreading apices.

Filaments filiform-flattened, white within the perianth, the exserted part lemon, the 3 inner narrower and lengthening before the 3 outer with their *anthers* in turn exserted 3—4mm.; *stigma* at length exserted 4—5mm.; *ovary* green, 4mm. long, 2mm. diam. (Figs. 170–172).

ZAMBIA (NORTHERN RHODESIA). *Abercorn Dist.*: Kalambo Falls, 15 May 1936, B. D. Burtt 5866! (K)—leaf only in BM; escarpment above Lunzua River overlooking Mpulungu, 4,000 ft., 9 May 1936, B. D. Burtt 5870!—leaves only (K, BM), 15 June 1936, inflorescence, B. D. Burtt 5868! (K, BM); Kalambo Falls, 22 miles N of Abercorn, cult. Johannesburg, fl. 29 March 1959, Reynolds 8659 holotype (PRE), isotype (K, SRGH); fl. again 10 April 1960, Reynolds 8659A (PRE, K).

FIG. 170.

A. veseyi Reynolds. Plant collected at Kalambo Falls, 22 miles N of Abercorn, Northern Zambia, flowering in the author's garden. × 1/8 approx.

Fig. 171.

A. veseyi Reynolds. Pendent inflorescence × 1/8 approx.

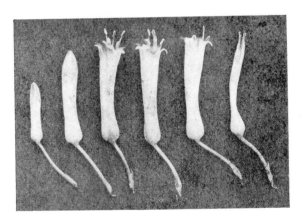

Fig. 172.

A. veseyi Reynolds. Flowers natural size.

The spectacular and breath-taking Kalambo Falls lie 22 miles N of Abercorn on the border of Tanzania. Mpulungu is a small port at the southern tip of Lake Tanganyika, W of Abercorn.

Mrs. H. M. Richards has found plants hanging on cliffs, Kambole Escarpment, E of Abercorn on the Lufubu River.

This distinctive species was named after Mr. L. D. E. F. Vesey-FitzGerald (Principal Scientific Officer, International Red Locust Control Services, Abercorn, Zambia), who discovered plants in July 1939 at Kalambo Falls, 22 miles N of Abercorn. When plants collected at Kalambo Falls by the present author flowered in Johannesburg in March–April 1959, the species was described.

A. veseyi grows on both sides of Kalambo Falls (703 ft. in one unbroken drop), the largest number being found on the southern side, facing west on a perpendicular rock face about half a mile broad and 400—500 ft. deep – impossible to reach without block and tackle.

Plants cling to this precipice face, with their stems hanging downwards. The leaves are falcately decurved with their apices pointing downwards, while the slender 3—4-branched inflorescence is also pendent with only the racemes upturned.

It was subsequently ascertained that that born naturalist and famous plant collector, B. D. Burtt, had collected material at Kalambo Falls in May 1936, by using a rope with a slip-knot.

A. veseyi appears to be nearest allied to *A. confusa* Engler which occurs at Lake Chala, a water-filled crater on the Tanzania–Kenya border, 7 miles N of Taveta. *A. veseyi* differs from *A. confusa* chiefly in having much shorter, thicker pendent stems, broader, more densely rosulate pendent leaves, and shorter, narrower flowers. Another noteworthy difference is that the leaf sap of *A. confusa* is deep purple and stains clothing, while in *A. veseyi* it is yellowish-orange.

Another species to be considered is *A. penduliflora* Baker, sent by Sir John Kirk to Kew from Zanzibar in 1884, and described when it flowered at Kew in August 1888. The precise locality of origin of this species is unknown, and there are (it seems) no published figures. According to description, *A. penduliflora* is a near ally in leaf characters, bracts, pedicels and hanging inflorescence with upturned racemes, but differs in having a much more densely flowered raceme that is only 5cm. long. Berger states that when he saw the plant at Kew in September 1905, it had a stem 2—3m. high and 3—4cm. diam.

Judging from the name, *A. pendens* Forsk. from the Yemen seemed a possible affinity, but the figure in *Bot. Mag. t.* 7837 (1902) depicts a plant in all ways distinct from *A. veseyi*.

66. **A. mendesii** Reynolds in *Journ. S.A. Bot.* 30: 31 (1964).

DESCRIPTION: *Plant* pendent, clinging to precipice faces, with stems up to 1m. long, 4cm. diam.

Leaves about 10, all hanging downwards, ensiform, falcately decurved, 50cm. long, 7—8cm. broad; *upper surface* green, obscurely lineate, without spots, flat to very slightly canaliculate; *lower surface* slightly convex, otherwise as in the upper surface; *margins* with narrow cartilaginous edge with cartilaginous blunt teeth 1—2mm. long, irregularly 10—15mm. distant.

Inflorescence pendent, up to 60cm. long, 3—4-branched, the racemes arcuate-ascending.

Racemes cylindric-acuminate, subdensely flowered, 10cm. long, 6cm. diam., the youngest buds at first hidden by imbricate bracts, the open flowers cernuous to subpendulous.

Bracts ovate-acute, 12mm. long, 5mm. broad, deep-pink, thinner and paler at the margins, 5-nerved.

Pedicels deep-pink, 18—20mm. long.

Perianth scarlet, cylindric slightly ventricose, slightly contracted at the mouth, 25mm. long, 4mm. diam. across the ovary, thence trigonally enlarging to the throat then narrowing to the mouth; *outer segments* free for 20mm. (tube 5mm.), very obscurely 5-nerved, the apices subacute, slightly spreading; *inner segments* broader than the outer, paler and thinner at the margins, with a prominent scarlet keel, the apices more obtuse, more spreading.

Filaments pale lemon, the 3 inner narrower and lengthening before the 3 outer with their *anthers* in turn exserted 2—3mm.; *stigma* at length exserted 3mm.; *ovary* very pale green, 6mm. long, 2·5mm. diam. (Figs. 173–175).

ANGOLA. *Huila Dist.:* Lubango, Humpata, Buraco do Bimbe, 2220m., in bud April 22 1960, E. J. Mendes 3815 (LISC); Bimbe, May 3 1963. R. Santos 1109 (LISC, LUAI)—leaf only with portion of undeveloped raceme; Humpata, Tundavala escarpment, alt. c. 2220m., July 4 1963, R. Santos et C. Henriques 1131 (LISC, holotype; LUAI, PRE, isotype).

FIG. 173.

A. mendesii Reynolds. Whole plant pendent on precipice face at Bimbe, 25km. W of Sá da Bandeira, Huila Dist., Angola. Length 1·5m. *Photo: Dr. E. J. Mendes.*

FIG. 174.

A. mendesii Reynolds. Young plant (from type locality) flowering for the first time at Mbabane, Swaziland × 1/6 approx.

FIG. 175.

A. mendesii Reynolds. Buds and flowers. 1/1.

This distinctive species was named after Dr. E. J. Mendes (Centro de Botânica, Lisboa) who discovered and photographed it in January 1956 on precipice faces of the Serra da Chela, on the western escarpment of Humpata plateau at Bimbe, which is approximately 25km. (15 miles) W of Sá da Bandeira, Huila District, at an altitude of 2220m. In April 1960, Dr. E. J. Mendes went to Angola again and tried to collect good material at the same locality, but at that time racemes were in young bud only, and open flowers were not available.

Subsequently, in May and in July 1963, Sr. R. Santos and Sr. C. Henriques (Instituto de Investigação Científica de Angola, Luanda) collected plants again on the Bimbe, and rediscovered and collected them also on the Tundavala escarpment which is about 18km. (11 miles) NE of Bimbe and 16km. (10 miles) NW of Sá da Bandeira, when plants were mostly in fruit with few flowers left. No spirit material was made, and it was not possible to figure flowers natural size. Subsequently, two plants flowered in the Author's gardens at Mbabane which enabled a fuller description of the flowers to be made, and flowers photographed 1/1.

It appears that *A. mendesii* is closely allied to *A. veseyi* Reynolds from Kalambo Falls, 22 miles N of Abercorn, Zambia. Both species hang downwards on precipice faces, mostly with western aspect, both have similar branched inflorescences with only the racemes arcuate-ascending, and both have 25mm. flowers.

A. mendesii differs from *A. veseyi* in having much broader unspotted leaves, much longer bracts, longer pedicels, and scarlet flowers.

Mr. W. Giess (Windhoek, S.-W. Africa) reports a form of *A. mendesii* near Okambambi Fountain, Baynes Mountains, S of the Kunene River in S.-W. Africa, near the Angola border.

67. **A. penduliflora** Baker in *Gard. Chron.* 4: ser. 3, 178 (1888), in *Fl. Trop. Afr.* 7: 464 (1898); Durand et Schinz in *Consp. Fl. Afr.* 5: 310 (1893); Berger in Engler's *Pflanzenr.* Liliac.–Aloin. 242 (1908).

DESCRIPTION based on the type material at Kew, also on Berger's account (l.c.).

Stem slender, simple or sparingly branched, ascending, 2—3m. high, 3—4cm. thick.

Leaves laxly disposed, the younger erectly incurved, the older spreading, ensiform, 30—40cm. long, 25—30mm. broad; *upper surface* flat or slightly concave, plain green; *lower surface* convex; *marginal teeth* small, deltoid, cuspidate, apices hooked forward, 1—2mm. long, 20—25mm. apart.

Inflorescence slender, sparingly branched, produced laterally, pendulous with the racemes ascending, ? length.

Racemes densely flowered, sub-capitate, 4cm. long in the type.

Bracts lanceolate-acuminate, 10mm. long, 3mm. broad, 5-nerved.

Pedicels 15—20mm. long.

Perianth probably 30mm. long (27mm. dry), pale yellow tipped with green; *outer segments* free for 9mm. *Anthers* exserted 3—4mm.; *stigma* at length exserted 5mm. (Figs. 176—177).

"ZANZIBAR". Sent from Zanzibar Sept. 1884 by Sir John Kirk, fl. Kew Gardens 8 Aug. 1888, type! (K).

FIG. 176.   FIG. 177.

A. penduliflora Bak.

FIG. 176. Photo of the type material at Kew, much reduced.   FIG. 177. Raceme of the type natural size.

Photos: By courtesy, The Director, Royal Botanic Gardens, Kew.

A pencilled note by Mr. E. Milne-Redhead on the sheet reads: "An inflorescence from the same plant, grown at Kew in 1903 has two lateral branches as well, all three turned up at the apex."

Berger says he saw the same plant flowering in September 1905 (7 years after Baker described it), and described it as having a stem 2—3m. high and 3—4cm. thick; such a slender stem would need supporting.

A. penduliflora is one of the several Aloe species sent by Sir John Kirk from Zanzibar, but where it grows wild is unknown. Nothing like it has been found on Zanzibar.

One species that is very near *A. penduliflora* on the mainland is *A. veseyi* from Kalambo Falls in the Abercorn district of Zambia (formerly Northern Rhodesia). This species closely resembles *A. penduliflora* in pendent stems, leaves pendent, branched inflorescences with upturned racemes and yellow flowers, but differs in having much laxer racemes that are three times as long, shorter bracts, and other differences.

Besides, had any botanist penetrated as far as Kalambo Falls in 1884?

Another species to be considered is *A. confusa* Engler from Lake Chala on the Kenya-Tanzania border N of Taveta. *A. confusa* differs in developing dense masses of slender sprawling tangled stems, with the apical 30cm. rather laxly foliate. The inflorescence, about 45cm. long, is produced obliquely – not pendent.

It is noteworthy that *A. penduliflora* has not been collected again since Kirk sent it to Kew in 1884.

What then is *A. penduliflora*? Where does it grow wild? Are there any authentic unpublished sketches or drawings in existence?

GROUP 11

(Series *Latebracteatae* Berger *pro parte*)

Bracts large, broadly ovate or suborbicular, shortly acute, sometimes clasping the pedicels.

Plants acaulescent, or shortly caulescent; *bracts* large, as long as or mostly longer than the pedicels; *perianth* cylindric-ventricose, 30—35mm. long, glabrous except in *A. venusta* which is minutely pubescent.

Type species: *A. cryptopoda* Baker.   Tropical species: 4.

KEY TO THE SPECIES

A. ACAULESCENT; LEAVES ENSIFORM; INFLORESCENCE BRANCHED, 1—1·50M. HIGH

Perianth cylindric-trigonous, 30—35mm. long, glabrous (except in *A. venusta*):

(*a*) *Leaves copiously spotted both sides:*
1. *Leaves* 50 × 9cm., racemes 15—20cm. long, *bracts* 11mm. long, 10mm. broad; *pedicels* 11mm., *perianth* pale scarlet, 32mm. long, minutely pubescent.. .. ..   68 *A. venusta*
2. *Leaves* 60 × 8cm.; *racemes* 20cm. long, *bracts* 15mm. long, 8mm. broad; *pedicels* 10mm.; *perianth* rose-pink, 33mm... ..   69 *A. macrosiphon*
(*b*) *Leaves sparingly spotted on underside:*
1. *Leaves* 30—45cm. long, 7—8cm. broad; *inflorescence* very compactly branched; *racemes* 30cm. long; *pedicels* 15mm.; *perianth* pale scarlet, 35mm. .. ..   70 *A. compacta*
(*c*) *Leaves unicoloured throughout:*
1. *Leaves* 60 × 8—9cm.; *inflorescence* 2—3-branched; *racemes* 30—35cm. long with prominent spreading bracts; *perianth* 30mm.   71 *A. cryptopoda*

68. A. venusta Reynolds in *Journ. S.A. Bot.* 25: 211 (1959).

DESCRIPTION: *Plants* acaulous, solitary or in small groups.

Leaves about 20, densely rosulate, compactly arcuate-ascending, about 50cm. long, 9cm. broad at base, gradually narrowing to an incurved apex with the apices rather closely grouped together; *upper surface* flat low down, somewhat canaliculate upwards, dull grey-green, copiously spotted throughout, the spots elliptical, pale green, more crowded low down, more scattered upwards; *lower surface* convex, reddish-brown where exposed to the sun, copiously spotted throughout, the spots smaller, more numerous and more crowded than in the upper surface; *margins* sinuate-dentate, with distinct continuous pinkish edge armed with teeth of the same colour, the teeth deltoid, forward-uncinate, 3mm. glon, 8—10mm. apart at middle of leaf, smaller and more crowded low down, longer and more distant upwards.

Inflorescence a many-branched panicle 1—1·20m. tall.

Peduncle basally flattened and 15mm. broad, terete upwards, about 10-branched from the middle upwards, the bracts subtending lowest branches, thin, white, papery brittle, 40mm. long, 30mm. broad, many-nerved.

Racemes rather densely flowered, cylindric-conical, up to 15—20cm. long, erect or suberect, the buds denser and hidden by thick fleshy densely imbricate bracts, the open flowers laxer and nutant.

Bracts broadly ovate-cuspidate, somewhat fleshy in the middle and thinner at the edges, about 11mm. long, 10mm. broad, 7—9-nerved.

Pedicels 13mm. long (up to 20mm. in the fruit).

Perianth pale scarlet, minutely pubescent, cylindric-trigonous, 32mm. long, cylindric and 7mm. diam. across the ovary, slightly narrowed on underside above the ovary, thence trigonous and slightly enlarging to an open mouth; *outer segments* free for 12mm., thinner and paler at the margins, the apices subacute and slightly spreading; *inner segments* broader than the outer, with broad pale marginal border and with three crowded nerves forming a slight keel, the apices more obtuse and more spreading than the outer.

Filaments pale lemon, the 3 inner narrower and lengthening before the 3 outer with their *anthers* in turn exserted 2—3-mm.; *stigma* at length exserted 3—4mm.; *ovary* green, 6mm. long, 3mm. diam.; *capsule* 20mm. long, 12mm. diam. at the middle. (Figs. 178—181).

Tanzania. *Western Prov.*, on rocks 71 miles S of Mpanda, 35 miles N of Namanyere, c. 7° 07′ S, 30° 58′ E, alt. 4,600 ft., fl. 20 July 1958, Reynolds 8948 holotype (PRE), isotype (K, EA).

A. venusta was discovered by the late Dr. N. R. Smuts and the author on a rocky outcrop sourrounded by woodland, half a mile E of the road at a point 71 miles S of Mpanda, 9 miles N of Chisi, and 35 miles N of Namanyere in the Western Province of Tanzania, at 4,600 ft.

It is nearest allied to *A. macrosiphon* Bak. which occurs in numbers in the Kagera Valley near the boundary between Tanzania and Uganda, also west and south of Lake Victoria. Both *A. macro-siphon* and *A. venusta* have leaves copiously spotted on both surfaces, a more or less 10-branched inflorescence 1—1·20m. high, racemes 15—20cm. long, and cylindric-trigonous perianths 32mm. long.

Fig. 178.

A. venusta Reynolds. Plants in natural habitat 71 miles S of Mpanda, Western Province, Tanzania (Tanganyika). Height 1·20m.

Fig. 179.

A. venusta Reynolds. Portion of leaf upper surface 1/1.

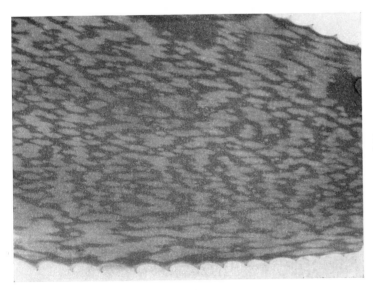

Fig. 180.

A. venusta Reynolds. Portion of leaf lower surface 1/1. (Compare *A. macrosiphon* Bak.)

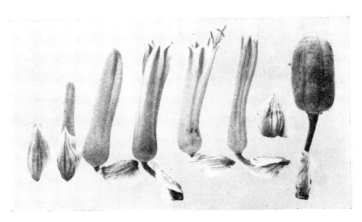

Fig. 181.

A. venusta Reynolds. Flowers 1/1 from bud to fruit stages.

A. venusta differs in having leaves that are not glossy, leaf margins with a rather pronounced continuous pink cartilaginous edge, racemes with the apical buds denser and hidden by large fleshy imbricate bracts, slightly longer pedicels, and perianths that are pale scarlet and minutely pubescent.

In *A. venusta* the leaves are arcuate-ascending, with the apices incurved and grouped rather closely together. The lower surface of leaves is thus more exposed to the sun than the upper.

In all inflorescences seen, the peduncle was erectly ascending until above the leaf apices, then curved somewhat suberectly with the upper portion again ascending.

A. macrosiphon grows almost invariably in shady thickets on termite mounds in bush or woodland, with the inflorescence usually entangled in bush, whereas *A. venusta* was found only in scanty soil on exposed rocks surrounded by Brachystegia-Isoberlinia woodland. Plants occur singly or in small groups and in an area infested with tsetse flies.

69. A. macrosiphon Baker in *Fl. Trop. Afr.* 7: 459 (1898); Berger in Engler's *Pflanzenr.* Liliac.–Aloin. 273 (1908).

—— *A. mwanzana* Christian in *Journ. S.A. Bot.* 6: 184, pl. 22 (1940).

DESCRIPTION: Based on plants along the Kagera River, and N and E of Biharamulu, Tanzania.

Plant acaulescent, soboliferous and forming large dense groups.

Leaves about 16, densely rosulate, averaging 60cm. long, 8cm. broad at base, gradually tapering to an acute apex, mostly suberect when densely grouped; *upper surface* flat low down, slightly canaliculate upwards, glossy deep green when in shade, more reddish-brown tinged out in the open, with numerous dull white to pale green lenticular markings that at 10—15mm. long, 1mm. broad, more crowded low down, fewer upwards; *lower surface* convex, paler green than the upper, rather mottled near base, the markings rather dull pale-greenish, larger and more defined upwards; *margins* armed with deltoid pungent teeth that are 10—15mm. apart, smaller and more crowded near base, larger and more distant upwards, 4—5mm. long in upper third; *sap* dries brownish-orange.

Inflorescence a branched panicle 1—1·50m. high, mostly entangled in bushes.

Peduncle basally flattened and 20mm. broad, compactly 8—10-branched from about the middle, the lowest branches subtended at base by a large ovate-acute thin, brittle, very white, dry bract, 25mm. broad and 30mm. long, many-nerved.

Racemes cylindric-acuminate, subdensely flowered, the terminal averaging 20cm. long, 6cm. diam., the lateral slightly shorter, the buds mostly grey-green tipped, suberect, denser, gradually slightly laxer downwards, with open flowers subpendulous.

Bracts ovate-acute, lowest 15mm. long, 8mm. broad, very dry and white, thin crisp brittle, about 7-nerved.

Pedicels 10mm. long, the colour of the perianth.

Perianth bright rosy-pink shading to pale yellowish at mouth, cylindric-trigonous, averaging 33mm. long, basally obtuse and slightly stipitate, 7mm. diam. across the ovary, very slightly narrowed above the ovary on the underside only, thence slightly enlarging to the throat; *outer segments* free for 10mm. paler at the margins, the apices subacute and slightly spreading; *inner segments* free, but dorsally adnate to the outer for two-thirds their length, broader than the outer, with broad pale border and more obtuse more spreading apices.

Filaments lemon, filiform-flattened, the 3 inner narrower and lengthening before the 3 outer with their *anthers* in turn exserted 2—3mm.; *stigma* at length exserted 3—5mm.; *ovary* pale greenish-yellow, 6mm. long, 3mm. diam. (Plate 36, Figs. 182–185).

URUNDI AND KARAGWE. 4,000—5,000 ft., Ruwenzori Expedition 1893–94, Scott-Elliot 8176! (K holotype, BM).

TANZANIA. *Lake Province,* Speke Gulf, near Mwanza, 31 May 1931, B. D. Burtt 2494! (K); Kahama, near Mkweni, 4 May 1937, B. D. Burtt 6554! (K, SRGH); Lake Victoria Coast, Mwanza, July 1937, B. D. Burtt 5186! (K, SRGH)— the type of *A. mwanzana* Christian—excellent material. *Bukoba Dist.,* N side of Kagera River, 3 miles E of Uganda border, 31 July 1954, Reynolds 7503 (K, PRE); S of Kagera River, 47 miles SE of Mbarara, 3,900 ft., 31 July 1954, Reynolds 7508 (K, PRE); in thickets on termitaria, 52 miles NW of Kahama, 3850 ft., 15 July 1958, Reynolds 8867 (PRE); abundant 24 miles ENE of Biharamulu, 11 miles WSW of Port Nyamirembe, 3,900 ft., 16 July 1958, Reynolds 8890 (K, PRE, EA). *Musoma Dist.,* S of Banagi, Muhomo Hills, 3 May 1961, Greenway 10349! (PRE, EA)—excellent material; 15 miles E of Musoma, 18 July 1960, Verdcourt 2909! (EA).

UGANDA. *Ankole,* 31 miles SE of Mbarara (4 miles N of Kagera River), 4,200 ft., 31 July 1954, Reynolds 7502 (K, PRE).

RUANDA. Dr. G. Troupin records the following: *Mutare Dist.,* near Kakitumba, Kayonza hill, 1350m., May 1957, Troupin 3245 (BR, LWO, YBI, EA, K); Parc National de la Kagera between Uruwita and Kamakaba, Jan. 1938, Lebrun (BR).

TYPE LOCALITY: The original label reads "Urundi and Karagwe" not *between* these two places as stated in *F.T.A.* At the back of his book *A Naturalist in Mid-Africa,* London (1896), Scott Elliot includes two maps, one of which clearly shows the Karagwe country as being in the Kagera River area SW of Bukoba, while Urundi territory is shown further SSW—which is ENE of the north end of Lake Tanganyika. It seems highly likely that Scott Elliot collected his specimen in the Kagera Valley somewhere SW of Bukoba.

DISTRIBUTION: In the lower eastern parts of Ruanda–Burundi, and generally in the Kagera Valley in Uganda, and more so in Tanzania. It occurs N of Biharamulu, and is particularly plentiful along the lower parts of the road from Biharamulu eastwards to Nyamirembe on Lake Victoria; along the southern shores of Lake Victoria, Uzinza, Mwanza, Musoma, that is the country to the west, south and east of Mwanza.

PLATE 36

ALOE MACROSIPHON Baker.

Growing in thickets between Biharamulu and Nyamirembe, Lake
Province, Tanzania (Tanganyika). Height 1·20m.

FIG. 182.

A. macrosiphon Bak. Plants between Biharamulu and Port Nyamirembe, Lake Province. Tanzania (Tanganyika), Height 5 ft.

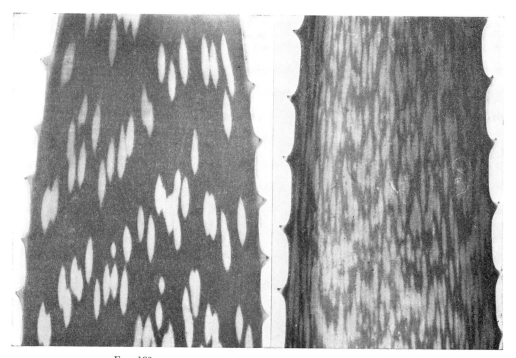

FIG. 183.   FIG. 184.

A. macrosiphon Bak.

FIG. 183. Portion of leaf upper surface 1/1.   FIG. 184. Portion of under surface 1/1.

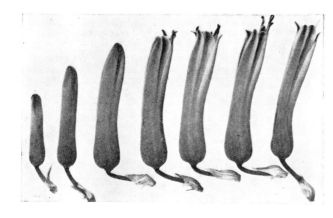

Fig. 185.

A. macrosiphon Bak. Flowers natural size.

Habitat. Plants sucker freely and form large colonies, often around the base of termitaria in partial shade, and often in thickets with the inflorescence (1—1·5m. high) entangled in bushes; rarely found out in the open.

A. macrosiphon has very striking polished-looking, deep-green leaves that are copiously "spotted" on both sides with numerous dull-white to pale-green lenticular markings or streaks that are 10—15mm. long and 1mm. broad. (*A. venusta* has similarly marked leaves.) The large bracts are conspicuously snow-white, thin and brittle. In this respect, racemes resemble those of *A. deserti* Engler. In cultivation, plants do best in partial shade.

NATURAL HYBRIDS

Crosses of *A. macrosiphon* with *A. bukobana* and with *A. secundiflora* are not rare from 17 to 19 miles N of Biharamulu. In the cross with *A. secundiflora*, all racemes seen were erect with flowers evenly distributed around the axis. This suggests that oblique racemes with second flowers are recessive in assumed F_1 crosses of *A. secundiflora*.

70. A compacta Reynolds in *Kirkia* 1: 162 (1961).

DESCRIPTION: *Plant* succulent, solitary or in small groups, on rocks. *Stem* none or short, sometimes up to 50cm. long decumbent.

Leaves about 20, densely rosulate, lanceolate-attenuate, 30—45cm. long, 7—8cm. broad at base, arcuate-ascending and slightly recurved; *upper surface* flat low down, slightly canaliculate upwards, dull green with reddish tinge, usually with a few small scattered white spots low down; *lower surface* of similar colour, usually with numerous dull white lenticular spots throughout; *margins* with a pinkish edge armed with teeth of the same colour and averaging 2—3mm. long, 10mm. apart. *Sap* dries yellow.

Inflorescence simple and 1m. ta'l in young plants only, mature specimens 4—5-branched and 120cm. tall.

Peduncle reddish-brown, plano-convex and 25mm. broad at base, very narrowly and compactly 4—5-branched from the middle or lower, the lowest branch subtended at base by a narrowly deltoid brittle, white, many-nerved bract, 10cm. long, 2·5cm. broad.

Racemes narrowly cylindric-acuminate, the terminal and those of the two lowest branches 30cm. long, 6cm. broad, the buds for some time hidden by large densely imbricate bracts.

Bracts broadly ovate-acute, 13mm. long, 8mm. broad at the middle, scarious, many-nerved.

Pedicels 15mm. long.

Perianth pale scarlet-red, 35mm. long, cylindric slightly decurved, basally obtuse and shortly stipitate, 6mm. diam. across the ovary, slightly enlarging to the throat; *outer segments* free for 10mm., paler at the margins, obscurely nerved, the apices slightly spreading; *inner segments* broader than the outer, with three crowded nerves forming a scarlet keel, the apices more obtuse and slightly more spreading than the outer.

Filaments pale orange, the 3 inner narrower and lengthening before the 3 outer with their *anthers* in turn exserted 2—3mm.; *stigma* at length exserted 3—4mm.; *ovary* pale green, 6mm. long, 2·5mm. diam. (Figs. 186–187).

TANZANIA. *Western Prov.*, 24 miles S of Uvinza, c. 5° 23′ S, 30° 25′ E, alt. 5,000 ft., cult. Bryanston, Johannesburg, fl. 10 July 1960, Reynolds 8936, holotype (PRE), isotype (K).

A. compacta was found by the late Dr. N. R. Smuts and the Author in July 1958, in the well-wooded highlands 24 miles S of Uvinza on the road to Mpanda, at an elevation of 5,000 ft., in an area utterly infested with Tsetse flies.

Uvinza is on the Malagarazi River E of Kigoma (port on Lake Tanganyika), 47 miles S of Kasula and 124 miles NW of Mpanda in the Western Province of Tanzania.

FIG. 186.

A. compacta Reynolds. Plant collected 24 miles S of Uvinza, Western Province, Tanzania (Tanganyika) alt. 5,000 ft. Flowering in Johannesburg. Height 4 feet.

FIG. 187.

A. compacta Reynolds. Flowers natural size.

A. compacta, found 24 miles to the south of Uvinza and nearly 2,000 ft. higher, appears to be a near ally of *A. trothai* as described, but differs in having much broader leaves with larger marginal teeth, bracts not clasping the pedicels, shorter pedicels and shorter flowers.

A striking character of *A. compacta* (which suggested the specific epithet) is the exceptionally compactly branched inflorescence. The two lowest branches produce racemes as long as the terminal and average 30cm. long, but the two higher branches are much shorter, with all racemes lying very close to the main axis.

Another near ally, found 170 miles away to the SE, is *A. venusta* Reynolds, but this species differs in having compact rosettes of leaves that are copiously spotted on both sides, a divaricately much more branched inflorescence, and slightly shorter perianths that are minutely pubescent.

71. **A. cryptopoda** Baker in *Journ. Bot.* 52 (1884), in Th. Dyer *Fl. Trop. Afr.* 7: 467 (1898); Durand et Schinz in *Conspec. Fl. Afr.* 5: 305 (1893); Berger in Engler's *Pflanzenr.* Liliac.–Aloin. 233 (1908); Christian *Journ. S.A. Bot.* 6: 117 (1940); Reynolds in *Aloes S. Afr.* 331 (1950), in *Aloes of Nyasaland* 31 (1954).

—— *A. pienaarii* Pole Evans in *Trans. Roy. Soc. S. Afr.* 5: 27, pl. 6—7 (1915), in *Fl. Pl. S. Afr.* 1: pl. 17 (1921); Reynolds in *Journ. S.A. Bot.* 3: 146 (1937).

DESCRIPTION based mostly on plants at Dona Ana, opposite Sena, Zambezi Valley, Moçambique (type loc.).

Plants acaulescent or with very short decumbent stem, growing singly or in small groups.

Leaves about 25, densely rosulate, compactly arcuate-ascending, up to 60cm. long, 8—9cm. broad at base and gradually narrowing to an acute apex; *upper surface* unicoloured dull to somewhat glossy deep green, without spots or markings, flat low down, slightly canaliculate upwards; *lower convex* convex, similar in colour; *margins* sinuate-dentate, armed with pinkish, pungent, deltoid teeth about 3mm. long, 5—8mm. distant. *Leaf sap* dries purplish.

Inflorescence furcate or dichotomously 2—3-branched from the middle or lower, 1—3 simultaneously, averaging 1·6m. high.

Peduncle basally flattened and 25mm. broad.

Racemes densely flowered, narrowly cylindric-acuminate, 30—35cm. long, 6—7cm. diam. low down, the buds crowded and covered by densely imbricate bracts which have conspicuously spreading apices, bright red to scarlet, greenish-tipped, open flowers subpendulous, dark reddish turning orange to greenish-yellow at mouth, the whole raceme more or less uniformly scarlet.

Bracts broadly ovate-cuspidate, about 15mm. long, 12mm. broad at base when pressed flat, thin, scarious, brownish, many-nerved.

Pedicels 15—20mm. long, erectly-spreading.

Perianth cylindric-trigonous, 30—35mm. long, 8—9mm. diam. across the ovary; *outer segments* free to base but somewhat cohering for the basal 10mm., obscurely nerved, the nerves confluent and turning greenish at apex, the segment apices brownish, subacute, slightly spreading; *inner segments* free, broader than the outer, with thin broad marginal border and 3 crowded nerves forming a keel which is reddish-orange in lower half turning orange to greenish at apex, the apices of segments more obtuse, more spreading than the outer.

Filaments lemon, filiform-flattened, the 3 inner narrower and lengthening before the 3 outer with their *anthers* in turn exserted 2—3mm.; *stigma* at length exserted 5mm.; *ovary* green, 8mm. long, 3·5mm. diam. (Plate 37, Fig. 188).

MOÇAMBIQUE. Banks of the Zambezi opposite Sena, 21 July 1859, Kirk No. 96!, holotype (K); Nhaondue, Zambezi Valley, Menyharth 1238! (K); *Manica and Sofala*, Baixo Mosawire, between Maringa (River Save) and Machaze, 29 July 1949, Pedro et Pedrogaõ 7849 (PRE). On rocks near Dona Ana, Zambezi Valley opposite Sena, 200 ft., fl. 12 July 1952, Reynolds 6674 (K, PRE, SRGH).

FIG. 188.

A. cryptopoda Bak. Flowers 1/1 from a plant at the type locality – see Plate 37.

PLATE 37

ALOE CRYPTOPODA   Baker.

On rocky rise at Dona Ana, opposite Sena, Zambezi Valley, Moçambique, alt. 45m. (Type locality). Height 1·60m. (*Euphorbia nyikae* Pax. at right).

RHODESIA. Twentydales Estate, 12 miles S of Salisbury, fls. July, R. N. Jack 7005! (K, SRGH); Granite hill, 6 miles NE of Mtoko, 24 July 1959, L. C. Leach 9246! (K, SRGH). *Bikita Dist.,* Moodie's Pass on Birchenough, Fort Victoria Rd., 27 June 1961, L. C. Leach 11143 (PRE, SRGH). *Umtali Dist.,* Inyamatshira Mountains, cliffs east face of Chipondiomwe Peak, 5,000 ft., 15 July 1956, N. C. Chase 6147 (PRE, SRGH). *Wankie Dist.,* Lukosi River, near Wankie, 27 July 1962, L. C. Leach 11388 (SRGH), also Leach 11513 (SRGH). *Mtoko Dist.,* 6 miles NE of Mtoko, 24 July 1959, L. C. Leach 9246 (SRGH). *Sebungwe* Ngondoma 3,200 ft., 15 Aug. 1956, J. H. Whellan 1119 (SRGH).

ZAMBIA. Eastern slopes of Palm Grove, Victoria Falls, Greenway et Brennan 8007! (K, EA); cliff edge N side of Victoria Falls, cult. Greendale, 9 Aug. 1962, L. C. Leach 11514 (SRGH).

MALAWI. Mountains between Katumbi and Mzimba on Great North Rd., 4,000—5,000 ft., 25 June 1936, B. D. Burtt 5860! (K, EA, SRGH); foothills of Kirk Range, 8 miles E of Mwanza, July 1956, L. C. Leach 381! (SRGH).

A. cryptopoda was discovered and collected by Kirk (Later Sir John) on 21 July 1859, on "banks of the Zambezi River, opposite Sena", in Moçambique, when he was accompanying David Livingstone on their Zambezi Expedition.

Today, a magnificent 2¼-mile-long bridge spans the Zambezi linking Sena on the west bank with Dona Ana on the eastern side. Near Dona Ana, there is a slight rocky rise, and here many plants of *A. cryptopoda* are still to be found.

A. cryptopoda is a very handsome and distinctive species. The epithet *cryptopoda,* meaning "hidden foot" was aptly chosen because a conspicuous character is the large bracts which clasp the pedicels and hide them from view.

DISTRIBUTION

A. cryptopoda is widely distributed from the southern parts of Moçambique (Namaache and Goba) and the Transvaal in the south, through Rhodesia and Zambia (N. Rhodesia) to as far north as the Mitanga River, near road between Fort Hill and Njakwa in northern Malawi—formerly Nyasaland—where Field Marshal J. C. Smuts has collected specimens.

RHODESIA: Twentydales Estate, 12 miles S of Salisbury; Wankie Dist.; Lomagundi Dist.; Umvukwes; Mazoe Dist.; mouth of Sabi River Gorge; Mtaradza River, near eastern border; between Ndanga and Zaka SE of Fort Victoria; at foot of Moodie's Pass on road to Birchenough Bridge; SE of Chirundu Bridge on road to Zambia.

Mr. E. J. Bullock gives some further localities: Hope Fountain Mission near Bulawayo; scattered colonies in the Matopos hills; Maitengue River area, Bechuanaland Border, NW of Plumtree with *A. globuligemma*; W. Urungwe Reserve; between Headlands and Mtoko etc.

ZAMBIA: Victoria Falls, Dales Kop, sheer rock faces of second gorge on N side; Mkushi Div., N of Choma; Fort Jameson.

MALAWI: 51 miles S of Blantyre on Tete road; Mpatamanga Gorge, 500 yards downstream from road bridge over Shire River on Blantyre–Tete road; foothills of Kirk Range between Mwanza Customs and Zobue in Moçambique; on Mikalongwe, and nearby hills in Cholo Dist.; near Fort Johnston.

VARIATION. Plants found in the Transvaal, Republic of South Africa, are mostly much larger than in Rhodesia northwards. This southern form has much larger bracts, longer pedicels and perianths sometimes 40—45mm. long. The inflorescence is also more branched – see *Aloes of South Africa* 331–4 (1950).

GROUP 12

Plants acaulescent or with short stem. *Leaves* densely rosulate, broadly to narrowly lanceolate, not spotted, obscurely lineate. *Inflorescence* a branched panicle under 1m. tall or up to 2—2·60m. high. *Racemes* cylindric-acuminate. *Pedicels* 8—25mm. long. *Segments* almost free, or connate to beyond the middle.

Type species: *A. christianii* Reynolds.

Although *A. crassipes* is a rather small inconspicuous species it is clearly closely allied to *A. christianii* and *A. pretoriensis.*

A. guerrai from Angola is also closely allied to *A. christianii* and *A. pretoriensis* in leaves, pedicels, bracts and flowers but its branched inflorescence has oblique racemes with secund flowers.

KEY TO THE SPECIES

A. SMALL PLANTS WITH BRANCHED INFLORESCENCE LESS THAN 1M. HIGH

1. Acaulescent, *inflorescence* branched, 50—60cm. high, *bracts* 10mm. long, *pedicels* 14mm., *perianth* 38mm. long, dull yellowish-green .. 72 *A. crassipes*

B. LARGE PLANTS WITH BRANCHED INFLORESCENCE, 2—2·75M. HIGH

1. Shortly caulescent, *pedicels* 25—30mm. long, *bracts* half as long, clasping the pedicel, *outer segments* free almost to base .. .. .. 74 *A. pretoriensis*

2. *Pedicels* 8—10mm. long, *bracts* 5—6mm. long, *outer segments* free 15mm. .. .. 73 *A. christianii*

72. **A. crassipes** Baker in *Journ. Linn. Soc.* 18: 162 (1880), in Th. Dyer *Fl. Trop. Afr.* 7: 468 (1898); Durand et Schinz *Consp. Fl. Afr.* 5: 305 (1893); Berger in Engler's *Pflanzenr.* Liliac.–Aloin. 240 (1908); Reynolds in *Journ. S.A. Bot.* 27: 7 (1961).

DESCRIPTION: *Plant* succulent, acaulous or very shortly caulescent.
Leaves c. 20—24, densely rosulate, spreading, about 40cm. long, 7cm. broad at base, gradually narrowing to the apex; *upper surface* dull glaucous-green, unspotted, flat low down, very slightly canaliculate upwards; *lower surface* slightly convex, glaucous-green, unspotted; *margins* armed with firm brown-tipped deltoid teeth that are 5mm. long, 15mm. apart at middle of leaf.
Inflorescence branched, 50—60cm. high.
Peduncle basally plano-convex and 12mm. broad, green, about 5-branched from below the middle.
Racemes rather densely flowered, cylindric-conic, the terminal 17cm. long (lengthening to 25cm.), 8cm. diam., the lateral a little shorter.
Bracts narrowly deltoid-acute, 10mm. long, 4mm. broad, thin, scarious, 5-nerved.
Pedicels the lowest 14mm. long.
Perianth dull yellowish green, cylindric-trigonous, 38mm. long, flat at base, cylindric and 10mm. diam. across the ovary, very slightly narrowed above the ovary, thence trigonously very slightly enlarging upwards, and slightly compressed laterally in upper half: *outer segments* free for 13mm., 5-nerved, the nerves dull green from base turning brownish to purplish-brown in apical 10mm., the apices subacute, slightly spreading; *inner segments* themselves free but dorsally adnate to the outer for 20mm., with broad marginal border and a brownish keel, the apices more obtuse and more spreading than the outer.
Filaments the 3 inner narrower and lengthening before the 3 outer, with their *anthers* in turn exserted 0—1mm.; *stigma* at length exserted 1—2mm.; *ovary* green, 7mm. long, 4mm. diam. (Figs. 189–190).

SUDAN REPUBLIC. *Equatoria Prov.:* Near the Kisi River about 10 miles W of Mt. Bangenze, fl. 22 May 1870, Schweinfurth 3765! holotype (K); between Mts. Bangenze and Duanvuru, on rock outcrops in grass-woodland, flowers stone-coloured, 17 May 1937, Myers 6657. (K)

ZAMBIA. *North-Western Prov.*, on slopes of Kalenda Dambo, half-mile W of Matonchi Farm, fl. 23 Jan. 1938, Milne-Redhead 2644A (K); half-mile W of Matonchi Farm (30 miles W of Mwinilunga), c. 11° 40′ S, 23° 58′ E, c. 4,200 ft., cult. Bryanston, Johannesburg, fl. 30 Jan. 1960, Reynolds 9174 (PRE), same plant fl. again 30 March 1960, Reynolds 9174A (K, SRGH).

Schweinfurth collected *A. crassipes* near the Kisi River on 22 May 1870, while Baker gave the locality as "Nubia, between Suakin and Berber, at Kishi". Suakin is on the Red Sea south of Port Sudan, while Berber is north of Atbara on the Nile. The present author could not trace this locality. Subsequently Mr. E. Milne-Redhead at Kew ascertained that someone at Berlin had originally written the locality Kishi on the wrong printed label, but fortunately there was a date – 22 May 1870 – on the label. Milne-Redhead checked this date in Schweinfurth's book *The Heart of Africa* (London, 1873), a task simplified by N. E. Brown having made an index by dates.

In Vol. 2, p. 203, Schweinfurth refers to "a brook fifteen feet in width called the Kishy", which "speeds swiftly along over the level steppe in the Babuckur country, and after receiving the Bodumoh, contributes materially to the volume of the Sway, which in that region has already assumed the dimensions of a considerable river."

Schweinfurth refers to a little spring beyond the "Kishy" called "Nambia, that went rippling between the bare gneiss flats." He continues, "Hidden deep amongst the long thick grass I here found an aloe, of which the blossoms were of a greenish cast; it was a plant that except to an eye keenly looking for botanical rarities would have been overlooked entirely."

FIG. 189.

A. crassipes Bak. Plant collected near Matonchi, 30 miles W of Mwinilunga, north-western Zambia, flowering in the author's garden at Johannesburg. Height 65cm.

FIG. 190.

A. crassipes Bak. Flowers natural size.

Milne-Redhead has investigated Schweinfurth's localities and states, "The Kisi is a tributary of the Hu, itself a tributary of the Sue and runs from 4° 28′ N, 28° 49′ E (about 11 miles due west of Mt. Bangenze) to a point 4° 50′ N, 28° 32′ E. Schweinfurth evidently did not realise that the Kisi joined the Hu before running into the Sue. It seems he may have crossed the Kisi going eastwards somewhere near where the Yambio—Juba road now appears to cross it, at 4° 43′ N, 28° 37′ E."

(In 1954 I had travelled along the Yambio–Juba road en route to Mt. Bangenze (where I found *A. schweinfurthii* Bak.), and it is maddening to realise that, because of a wrong label having been used, I never knew I was in the very area where Schweinfurth had found *A. crassipes*. – G.W.R.)

TYPE LOCALITY: The type locality of *A. crassipes*, therefore, appears to be about 30 miles WNW of Mt. Bangenze, Equatoria Province, in the south-western corner of the Sudan Republic.

On 17 May 1937, J. G. Myers collected *A. crassipes* "between Mts. Bangenze and Duanvuru, on rock outcrops in grass-woodland, flowers stone coloured". Mt. Duanvuru is about 3 miles N of Mt. Bangenze. Myers 6657 is an excellent specimen at Kew.

Plants of *A. crassipes* were found by Mr. Milne-Redhead in October 1937 (not flowering then), on a grassy slope above Kalenda Dambo, just W of Matonchi Farm, which is about 8 miles E of the Angola border, 30 miles W of Mwinilunga (over 300 miles W of Chingola in the Copper Belt) in the North-Western Province of Zambia.

On 23 January 1938, Milne-Redhead collected plants from the same locality, in flower, and made specimens under his No. 2644A. "The flowers of my plant were a dull yellowish-green with greenish nerves towards the base and dull purplish nerves towards the apex; the leaves were rather glaucous-green and unspotted. It was definitely an inconspicuous plant as Aloes go, when growing in grass".

In June 1959, the author specially visited Kalenda Dambo just west of Matonchi, to investigate this species. He collected a plant (not flowering) which appeared to belong to *A. christianii* but when this plant flowered in Bryanston, Johannesburg, in January 1960, it proved to be *A. crassipes* – the same species that had previously been collected by Milne-Redhead in January 1938.

Certain plants in the Katanga Province of the Congo, reported 135km. N of Jadotville on the Mitwaba road, flowering in January, appear to belong here.

A. crassipes is an inconspicuous plant growing in grassland, and produces a 4—6-branched inflorescence that is only about 50—60cm. in height. The flowers are dull yellowish-green, with the genitals not or very shortly exserted.

In general habit of growth, rosettes and leaves (and when not flowering), *A. crassipes* closely resembles *A. christianii* Reynolds (found in Zambia, Malawi, Rhodesia, Tanzania Territory and the south-eastern parts of the Congo) and *A. guerrai* Reynolds (Angola).

A. christianii differs in having a more-branched inflorescence 2m. and more high, while *A. guerrai* has a divaricately branched inflorescence about 1m. high, with oblique racemes and secund flowers. North of the Equator *A. crassipes* flowers in May, and south of it in January.

The leaf of the holotype of *A. crassipes* is probably a small immature inner one only 2cm. broad, whereas in adult plants the outer leaves are 30—40cm. long and 7cm. broad.

73. **A. christianii** Reynolds in *Aloes of S. Africa* 309 (1950).

DESCRIPTION: *Plants* growing singly, or in very small groups, with *stem* simple, erect or decumbent, short or sometimes reaching 1m. in length, 10—15cm. thick, the stem usually covered with the remains of the old dry leaf bases.

Leaves 30—40, densely rosulate, lanceolate-attenuate, erectly spreading, 30—50cm. long, 10cm. broad at base; *upper surface* slightly concave at base, gradually more canaliculate upwards, dull green, obscurely lineate, not spotted; *lower surface* dull bluish-green, very obscurely lineate, not spotted; *margins* sinuate-dentate, corneous, armed with teeth 3—5mm. long, 10—20mm. apart, the teeth deltoid, pungent, pinkish to pale brown in colour.

Peduncle basally flattened and 6—7cm. broad, brown, covered with a greyish powdery substance.

Inflorescence a branched panicle 2—3m. high, compactly 6—10-branched from above the middle, the 1—3 lowest sometimes with 1—2 branchlets, the lowest branches subtended at base by ovate-acute, scarious, many-nerved brownish bracts up to 6cm. long.

Racemes cylindric-acuminate, 25—30cm. long, subdensely 40—50-flowered, the terminal the highest, the lateral slightly shorter, unicoloured, the buds suberect, subdensely imbricate, gradually laxer downwards, with the lowest open flowers cernuous to pendulous.

Bracts ovate-acute, 5—6mm. long, 3mm. broad, white, scarious, 5—7-nerved.

Pedicels the lowest 8—10mm. long.

Perianth coral-red with a bloom, cylindric-trigonous, 40—45mm. long, straight, the base rounded, usually shortly stipitate, 9—10mm. diam. across the ovary, trigonous upwards; *outer segments* free for 15mm., very obscurely 5-nerved, apices subacute, brownish, slightly spreading; *inner segments* free but dorsally adnate to the outer for two-thirds their length, the upper third with a keel the colour of the perianth, the apices more obtuse more spreading.

Filaments filiform-flattened, the 3 inner narrower and lengthening before the 3 outer with their *anthers* exserted 3—4mm.; *stigma* at length exserted 4—5mm.; *ovary* green, 8mm. long, 4mm. diam. (Plate 38 Figs. 191–193).

PLATE 38

ALOE CHRISTIANII   Reynolds.

In woodland 19 miles SSE of Ncheu, Central Province, Malawi, 4,900 ft.
Height 9 feet. Flowering in July.

FIG. 191.   FIG. 192.

A. christianii Reynolds.

FIG. 191. Plant at the Mutanda River, 20 miles SW of Solwezi, between Chingola and Mwinilunga, North-Western Prov., Zambia, alt. 4,200 ft. Height 8 feet.

FIG. 192. An unusual form with 4—5 ft. inflorescence, 27 miles E of Mbeya on old Iringa Road, Southern Highlands Province, Tanzania (Tanganyika).

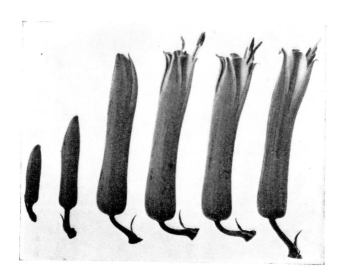

FIG. 193.

A. christianii Reynolds. Flowers natural size.

RHODESIA. Ewanrigg, 25 miles eastwards from Salisbury, fl. May–June 1936, Reynolds 1885, holotype (PRE), isotype (K, SRGH); Ewanrigg, 21 May 1952, H. Wild 3835 (PRE, SRGH). *Hartley Dist.*, near Hartley, June 1953, Leach 51 (PRE, SRGH). *Darwin Dist.*, Rusambo, 8 June 1960, Leach 9986 (SRGH).

ZAMBIA (formerly N. Rhodesia). *Southern Prov.*, 23 miles NE of Chomo, 11 July 1930, Hutchinson et Gillett 3550! (K). *Western Prov.* (Copper Belt), 2 miles NE of Mufulira, 25 May 1954, Reynolds 7222 (K, PRE). *North-Western Prov.*, at Mwinilunga (300 miles W of the Copper Belt), 4,400 ft., 11 June 1959, Reynolds 9159 (PRE, K); abundant each side of the Mutanda River, 20 miles SW of Solwezi (between Chingola and Mwinilunga), 4,200 ft., 10 June 1959, Reynolds 9146 (PRE, K). *Northern Prov.*, 2 miles N of Kasama, 4,100 ft., 23 July 1958, Reynolds 8968 (PRE, K, SRGH). *Abercorn Dist.*, near Mpulungu, 3,000 ft., 13 June 1936, B. D. Burtt 5876 (SRGH). *Eastern Prov.*, 30 miles SW of Petauke (Great East Road), 3,000 ft., 31 May 1961, Leach et Rutherford Smith 11090 (PRE, SRGH).

CONGO REPUBLIC. *Katanga Prov.:* 24 miles S of Elisabethville, 4,000 ft., 26 May 1954, Reynolds 7225 (K, BR, PRE); 27 miles N of Kiubo Falls (149 miles N of Jadotville), 30 May 1954, Reynolds 7235 (K, BR, PRE); large numbers near Kipaila, half-mile N of the Luvua River ferry (77 miles E of Manono), 2,300 ft., 4 June 1954, Reynolds 7240 (K, BR, PRE); Mulwani, 9 miles SW of Albertville, 3,100 ft., 6 June 1954, Reynolds 7243 (K, BR, PRE). *Kivu Prov.*, 3 miles N of Libondja Village (142 miles N of Albertville), 3,700 ft., 9 June 1954, Reynolds 7249 (K, BR, PRE). *Note:* This is the furthest north seen. The furthest west seen personally is 53 miles W of Kasaji, 32 miles E of Dilolo, on the Angola border.

ANGOLA. *Moxico Dist.:* Mr. E. Milne-Redhead reports having seen *A. christianii* in Angola, across the border W of Matonchi—which is about 30 miles W of Mwinilunga, North-Western Prov. of Zambia.

TANZANIA. *Lake Prov.:* Kahama, near Mkwemi, 15 March 1937, B. D. Burtt 6391 (SRGH); near Nyantakara (51 miles SE of Biharamulu), 15 July 1958, Reynolds 8870 (PRE)—the furthest north seen. *Western Prov.*, Ufipa Dist., 30 miles S of Sumbawanga, 5,600 ft., 21 July 1958, Reynolds 8959 (PRE, EA); Ugalla Flats, 29 Sept. 1956, Bally 10686 (G, EA). *Southern Highlands Prov.:* Mountains 22 miles N of Mbeya, 6,550 ft. (weak form, inflor. 4 ft.), June 1958 Reynolds 8760 (K, PRE); 27 miles E of Mbeya on old road to Iringa, 5,800 ft., 26 June 1958, Reynolds 8677 (PRE, K, EA). *Southern Prov.*, 24 miles N of Songea, 3,400 ft., 26 June 1958, Reynolds 8,700 (K, PRE, EA).

MALAWI (Nyasaland). *Central Prov.:* 18 miles SE of Dedza, 4,900 ft., 20 July 1952, Reynolds 6691 (K, PRE); 19 miles SSE of Ncheu (40 miles NW of the Shire River), 2,600 ft., 18 May 1956, Reynolds 8175 (K, PRE). *Northern Prov.*, River Mutanga, near road between Fort Hill and Jakwa, July 1933, Gen. J. C. Smuts 2027 (PRE); 62 miles N of Rumpi, 29 July 1960, Leach et Brunton 10354 (PRE, SRGH). *Southern Prov.*, 10 miles E of Mpatamanga Gorge, 1 May 1960, Leach et Brunton 9884 (SRGH)—excellent!

MOÇAMBIQUE. 10 miles S of the Malawi border, 3 June 1938, Pole Evans et Erens 528! (PRE, K). *Niassa:* 5 miles E of Nova Freixa (Cuamba), 15 May 1961, Leach et Rutherford Smith 10890! (PRE, SRGH)—a form with exceptionally narrow leaves; near Ribaue, c. 1800m., 24 July 1962, Leach et Schelpe 11442 (SRGH). *Moçambique Dist.*, Malema, Mutuali, Estaçaõ Experimental do CICA, 25 April 1961, A. Balsinhas et L. Marrime 446A (LM, PRE).

TYPE LOCALITY

The late Mr. H. B. Christian's farm Ewanrigg, about 25 miles eastwards from Salisbury, Rhodesia.
Note: Mr. Christian died in May 1951, and bequeathed his extensive gardens and Aloe collections to the Nation. It is now the Ewanrigg National Park, controlled by the Department of National Parks and Wild Life Management. Mr. H. F. Davies, the Curator, has done a magnificent piece of work extending and improving the layout and collections, and today a visit to Ewanrigg is a "must" for Aloe enthusiasts and plant lovers visiting Salisbury. The blaze of colour in June–July is breath-taking.

HABITAT AND DISTRIBUTION

A. christianii is found over a considerable area, mostly as single plants, sometimes in small groups, almost invariably in partial shade in Brachystegia-Isoberlinia woodland, or sometimes in medium to tall grasslands, never on rocks. It is essentially a plant of the flat bush soils.

The furthest south known for *A. christianii* is 30 miles NW of Bulawayo in Rhodesia (where Mr. E. J. Bullock has found it in association with numbers of *A. littoralis*). It is widely distributed in the Salisbury, Hartley, Mazoe, Darwin and Gwelo (Que Que) districts. It can be found almost throughout Zambia, and it occurs in a part of the Moxico district of Angola, W of Mwinilunga and Kalene and S of Luashi.

In the Congo it extends from Elisabethville and Jadotville westwards to beyond Kasaji, and northwards to Manono, Albertville (on Lake Tanganyika), and northwards for 145 miles on the west side of the lake. In Tanzania, *A. christianii* ranges from the Biharamulu district in the north, to Kabondo and Kasala down the eastern side of Lake Tanganyika to Abercorn; south-eastwards to the Mbeya district; and to Songea, E of Lake Nyasa, and southwards.

It grows almost throughout Malawi and all around Lake Nyasa into Moçambique where it occurs at Mandimba on the border, south-east to Nova Freixo and Ribaue where Mr. L. C. Leach has found plants with leaves considerably narrower than usual. It is also found between Tete and Zobue on the Malawi border, and towards the Rhodesian border beyond Changara; also along the road from Tete through Vila Gouveia to the south.

VARIATION AND AFFINITIES

In old specimens, rosettes of leaves sometimes reach 3 ft. across, the leaves often drying and turning reddish in winter.

A. christianii is closely related to *A. pretoriensis* in rosettes, leaves, height and branching of the inflorescence, but differs chiefly in having smaller, shorter bracts (6mm. against 15—20mm.), much shorter pedicels (8—10mm. against 15—20mm.), differently shaped flowers, the perianth being thicker and more fleshy with the outer segments free for only 15mm. against free to base in *A. pretoriensis*.

On mountains 22 miles N of Mbeya (6,550 ft.) a weak form occurs with inflorescence only 3—4 ft. high; 27 miles E of Mbeya, on old road to Iringa, plants bear inflorescences 4—5 ft. high. Elsewhere the usual height is 6—8 ft.

74. **A. pretoriensis** Pole Evans in *Gard. Chron.*, Ser. 3, 56: 106, Fig. 44 (8 August 1914), in *Trans. Roy. Soc. S. Afr.* 5: Part 1, 32, Plates 12—13 (1915), in *Fl. Pl. S. Afr.* 1: Plate 18 (1921); Reynolds in *Journ. S.A. Bot.* 6: 115 (1940), in *Aloes S. Afr.* 306 (1950).

DESCRIPTION based on plants in the Rusape, Umtali and Melsetter Districts of Rhodesia.

Plants solitary, with an ascending or decumbent stem up to 60cm. long.

Leaves about 40, densely rosulate, the youngest suberect, older ones arcuate-erect to spreading lanceolate-attenuate, 40—50cm. long, 12—15cm. broad, with an additional 10cm. of dried reddish apex; *upper surface* flat below, slightly canaliculate upwards, green, somewhat glaucous and obscurely lineate; *lower surface* convex, similar to upper surface; *margins* armed with reddish, deltoid, horny, pungent teeth about 3—4mm. long, 10—15mm. apart.

Inflorescence a branched panicle, 2—3m. high.

Peduncle stout, about 6cm. broad at base, 5—8-branched from about the middle or higher, the lowest 1—2 branches sometimes with 1—2 branchlets.

Racemes cylindric-acuminate, 20—30cm. long, 10cm. diam., mature open flowers rose-pink to rich peach-red with a bloom, sometimes paler to yellowish at mouth, youngest buds hidden by longer densely imbricate bracts.

Bracts the lowest about half as long as the pedicel, clasping and enfolding the pedicel, ovate-deltoid, thin, scarious, dry, many-nerved, about 15mm. long, 10mm. broad when pressed flat.

Pedicels averaging 30mm. long.

Perianth cylindric-trigonous, very slightly swollen near the middle, narrowing to the mouth, about 40mm. long; *outer segments* free, obscurely 3—5-nerved, the apices paler, slightly spreading; *inner segments* broader than the outer and with more obtuse, more spreading apices, with 3 crowded raised nerves forming a keel which is almost white near base, pink at the middle and green at the apex.

Filaments the 3 inner narrower and lengthening before the 3 outer with their *anthers* exserted about 1mm.; *stigma* at length exserted 2mm.; *ovary* green, 8mm. long, 3mm. diam. (Figs. 194—195).

RHODESIA. Matoni, 10 miles E of Headlands, June 1957, Leach 184 (K, SRGH), fl. July 1955 (PRE); same loc. 15 June 1962, D. C. H. Plowes 2250 (PRE, SRGH). *Melsetter Dist.*, Biriwiri, 29 May 1962, D. C. H. Plowes 2249 (PRE, SRGH). *Rusape Dist.*, "Mona", 8 miles N of Rusape, 15 July 1956, Reynolds 8202 (K, PRE). *Inyanga*, Inyangombie Falls, 17 June 1952, J. H. Whellan 674 (SRGH).

TYPE LOCALITY: Meintjes Kop, Pretoria, South Africa – the ridge on which the Union Buildings are situated.

DISTRIBUTION. Occurs in a restricted area in the eastern parts of Rhodesia; near Headlands and on the road to Rusape; Makoni Kop, about 16 miles E of Rusape on direct road to Inyangombi Falls near Inyanga village; large numbers on hills of the Odzani River 19 miles N of Umtali at 5,000 ft.; S of Umtali in the Biriwiri valley, 18 miles NW of Melsetter at 4,100 ft.; near Bridal Vale Falls, 3 miles NW of Melsetter.

Considerable numbers occur in the northern and eastern Transvaal, South Africa.

A. pretoriensis is closely allied to *A. christianii* Reynolds in habit of growth, rosettes, leaves, branched inflorescence 2m. and more high, but chiefly differs in having much longer pedicels and bracts and shorter flowers.

For colour plate and further data see *Aloes of South Africa* 306–9 (1950).

GROUP 13

PLANTS WITH CLAVATE PERIANTHS

Plants small to large, acaulescent and solitary to caulescent and of shrubby growth.

Leaves densely rosulate or amplexicaul and spaced at apical portion of stems; *margins* dentate (except in *A. scobinifolia*). *Inflorescence* a branched panicle. *Racemes* laxly to densely flowered. *Bracts* small. *Perianth* clavate, yellow orange or scarlet, 20—30mm. long; *outer segments* free for one-third to one-half their length.

Fig. 194.

A. pretoriensis Pole Evans. Plant on Mr. R. C. Munch's farm "Mona" 8 miles N of Rusape, Rhodesia. Height 8 feet.

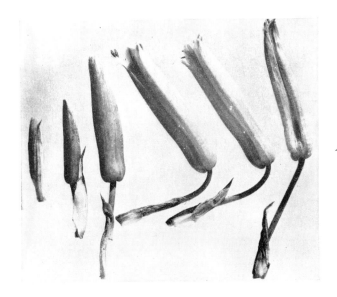

Fig. 195.

A. pretoriensis Pole Evans. Flowers natural size.

Typical species: *A. camperi* Schweinfurth.

The species in this group are characterized by having clavate (club-shaped) perianths.

Note: The Island of Socotra is one locality that the present author has found impossible to visit, and, consequently he does not know what *A. perryi* Bak. and *A. forbesii* Balf. *f.* look like in the wild state. In the absence of habitat photographs and more reliable data, these two species may be incompletely described, and their keying might not be reliable.

KEY TO THE SPECIES

ALL SPECIES WITH CLAVATE PERIANTHS

A. Stem None Or Short, Plants Solitary Or In Small Groups, Leaves Densely Rosulate

(a) *Pedicels 8mm. long:*

1. *Leaves* 35 × 7·5cm., *inflorescence* 2—3-branched, 60cm. high, *peduncle* purple-tinted, *racemes* sub-dense, 15—25cm. long, *perianth* bright red, 25mm. long *(fide Bot. Mag.)* ..   ..   ..   76 *A. perryi*

(b) *Pedicels 12mm. long?:*

1. *Stem* short? *Leaves* 25 × 6—7cm., marginal teeth ·5—1mm. long, *inflorescence* described as 1-branched, 50cm. high but probably 5-branched and higher; *racemes* laxly flowered, 15—25cm. long, *perianth* 21—24mm. long – imperfectly known   .. ..   75 *A. forbesii*

(c) *Inflorescence many-branched, racemes densely flowered, pedicels 15—18mm. long:*

1. *Leaves* rasp-like, with no marginal teeth, *racemes* corymbose-capitate, 3—4cm. long, *perianth* 22mm. long, scarlet or yellow ..   77 *A. scobinifolia*
2. *Leaves* leathery, 50—60 × 6—8cm., *racemes* subcapitate, 4—6cm. long, *pedicels* 18mm., *perianth* scarlet, orange or yellow, 22mm. long..   ..   ..   78 *A. sinkatana*
3. *Leaves* 60 × 15—18cm., slightly canaliculate, *inflorescence* many-branched, 1m. high, *racemes* sub-capitate, 8cm. long, *pedicels* 15mm. long, *perianth* yellow, orange or scarlet, 25—30mm. long..   79 *A. elegans*
4. *Plants* mostly solitary, *leaves* 60 × 15cm., *inflorescence* 120cm. high, much-branched, *racemes* subcapitate-conic, 5—8cm. long, *perianth* scarlet or orange, 22mm. long   ..   ..   80 *A. wrefordii*

B. Plants Caulescent, of Shrubby Growth, Forming Groups

Inflorescence a branched panicle:

(a) *Racemes sublax:*

1. Apical 20—30cm. of stems foliate, *leaves* 60—70cm. long, 10—13cm. broad, *raceme* broadly conical, 6—10cm. long, *pedicels* 18—20mm., *perianth* 28mm., scarlet   .. ..   81 *A. sinana*

(b) *Racemes densely flowered:*

1. *Leaves* basally sheathing, 50—60cm. long, 8—12cm. broad, *racemes* 6—9cm. long, *bracts* minute, *pedicels* 14mm., *perianth* orange to yellow, 20—22mm...   ..   ..   82 *A. camperi*
2. Apical 30cm. of stems foliate, *leaves* 60—80cm. long, 15cm. broad, spreading-canaliculate, marginal teeth up to 10mm. long, *racemes* 6—9cm. long, *pedicels* 18mm., *perianth* orange or yellow, 28—33mm. long   ..   ..   83 *A. adigratana*
3. *Leaves* recurved, deeply canaliculate, 80cm. long, 16cm. broad, *inflorescence* many-branched, 1—1·3m. high, *racemes* conic-cylindric, 10—13cm. long, *pedicels* 10mm., *perianth* scarlet, 22mm. ..   ..   84 *A. calidophila*

75. A. forbesii Balfour *fil.* in H. O. Forbes *Nat. Hist. Sokotra* 511, *t.* XXVIB (1903). – Not included in Berger's Monograph (1908).

Professor Isaac Bayley Balfour's original description was based on a very young plant sent home from Socotra when it flowered for the first time at Edinburgh. His *t.* XXVIB (reproduced herein) is of this plant, grown under unnatural conditions diametrically opposed to those prevailing on sun-drenched Socotra. This figure bears little or no resemblance to normal wild plants, while his description, including characters as "stem sub-sarmentose (= bearing long slender runners), internodes 10—15cm. long" is entirely misleading, so is "leaves often spineless like some of the mesembrianthemums".

Mr. George Popov visited Socotra with the Desert Locust Control in 1953. He collected several plants, some of which were sent to the present author, and one subsequently flowered in his gardens. Mr. Popov also sent material to BM and EA.

DESCRIPTION is based on th BM specimen, and on the plant that flowered in Johannesburg.

Plants solitary or in small groups. *Stem* none or short.

Leaves 16—20, densely rosulate, lanceolate-attenuate, spreading, slightly recurved, 25cm. or more long, 6—7cm. broad, gradually narrowing to an acute apex; *upper surface* dull green, without spots or markings, slightly canaliculate; *lower surface* convex, dull green without spots or markings, *margins* with slight cartilaginous edge armed with very small, pale, deltoid teeth that are only · 5—1mm. long, 4—8mm. apart, smaller and closer low down, longer and more spaced upwards.

Inflorescence a branched panicle, 60—80cm. high, sometimes 2 simultaneously.

Peduncle plano-convex and 12mm. broad at base, terete upwards, branched below the middle with 5 or more branches, the axis of racemes very slender and narrowing to 1mm. thick at apex.

Racemes cylindric, laxly or sublaxly flowered, the terminal about 25cm. long, 5cm. diam., the laterals shorter, 10—15cm. long, the apical buds pale scarlet, grey-green tipped, suberectly spreading, open flowers nutant.

Bracts 3—4mm. long, 1·5mm. broad, thin, scarious 3-nerved.

Pedicels obliquely spreading, the lowest 10—12mm. long, shorter upwards.

Perianth cylindric-clavate, 22—24mm. long, pale scarlet in lower third turning yellowish upwards, broadly obconic at base and shortly stipitate, cylindric across the ovary, thence enlarging upwards and clavate; *outer segments* free for 6—7mm., thinner and paler at the edges, obscurely 3-nerved, the apices subacute, rather straight; *inner segments* themselves free but dorsally adnate to the outer to beyond the middle, broader than the outer, with 3 crowded nerves forming a slight pale scarlet keel, the apices more obtuse and more spreading.

Filaments lemon, the 3 inner narrower and lengthening before the 3 outer, with their *anthers* in turn exserted 1—2mm.; *stigma* at length exserted 4mm.; *ovary* pale olive-brown, 5mm. long, 2mm. diam. (Plate 39, Figs. 196–198).

SOCOTRA. Sagal, 20 March 1953, G. Popov SO279! (BM, EA)—is this *A. forbesii* or a form of *A. perryi?*; Bojhin, coll. Popov 1953, cult. Bryanston, Johannesburg, fl. 23 Nov. 1958, Popov in Reynolds 6922 (PRE).

FIG. 197.

A. forbesii Balf. *f.*

FIG. 196. From H. O. Forbes *Nat. Hist.*, Sokotra 511, *t.* XXVI B (1903) – much reduced.

FIG. 197. Flowers 1/1 from a plant collected at Bojhin, Socotra, by Mr. George Popov, flowering at Johannesburg.

FIG. 196.

PLATE 39

ALOE FORBESII   Balf. *f.*

Young plant from Bojhin, Socotra, flowering in the author's gardens,
Johannesburg. Height 60cm.

Fig. 198.

A. forbesii Balf. *f.* Portion of raceme 1/1 from a plant flowering in Mr. D. H. Hardy's garden, Pretoria. *Photo: by courtesy, The Chief, Botanical Research Institute, Pretoria.*

It appears that Balfour preserved no herbarium specimens, hence there is no holotype at Edinburgh, or any known elsewhere. Popov 279 has axis of racemes purplish tinted, which is a character of *A. perryi* Bak. Is this character common to both *A. forbesii* and *A. perryi*?

When sending plants to the present author in 1953, Mr. Popov wrote "Small plants of *A. forbesii* and *A. perryi* are very similar. There is much variation in both species, but generally speaking, *A. forbesii* is of more slender growth".

It seems that the chief difference between *A. forbesii* and *A. perryi* is that the former has a more-branched, slenderer inflorescence, longer, much more laxly flowered racemes, and longer pedicels (12mm. against 8mm.).

76. **A. perryi** Baker in *Journ. Linn. Soc.* 18: 161 (1880), in *Bot. Mag. t.* 6596 (1881); Balfour *fil. Bot. Socotra, Trans. Roy. Soc. Edinb.* 31: 291 (1888); Durand et Schinz *Consp. Fl. Afr.* 5: 310 (1893); Berger in Engler's *Pflanzenr.* Liliac.–Aloin., 246 (1908).

DESCRIPTION: Since there do not appear to be any later fuller descriptions, or any natural habitat photographs available, Baker's description in *Bot. Mag. t.* 6596 (1881) has been taken over.

Stem simple (in the cultivated Kew specimen), about 30cm. long, 5cm. thick (erect or decumbent).

Leaves 12—20, densely rosulate, lanceolate, 35cm. long, 7·5cm. broad at base, gradually narrowing to an acute apex; *upper surface* glaucous-green with reddish tinge, canaliculate; *marginal teeth* small, deltoid-cuspidate, pale-brown, about 4mm. long, 6mm. distant.

Inflorescence 50—60cm. tall, usually 2—3-branched.

Peduncle purple-tinted, flattened at base.

Racemes oblong-cylindrical, 15—25cm. long, 5—6cm. diam. (rather densely flowered in the *Bot. Mag.* figure).

Pedicels reddish, 8mm. long, the lowest erectly spreading, cernuous.

Bracts lanceolate-deltoid, shorter than the pedicels, scarious, 4—6mm. long, 3-nerved.

Perianth cylindric-clavate (20–) 25mm. long, bright red with greenish tip, turning yellowish at anthesis; *outer segments* free for 8mm.; *anthers* and *style* finally shortly exserted. (Fig. 199).

FIG. 199.

A. perryi Bak. Reproduction – much reduced – *From. Bot. Mag. t.* 6596 (1881). *Photo by courtesy, The Chief, Botanical Research Institute, Pretoria.*

SOCOTRA. Fl. Feb.–March 1880, Prof. Bayley Balfour 473! (K, BM)—(the BM specimen appears to be a mixture of species); received June 17 1881 from Socotra, Dr. I. B. Balfour, the type of *Bot. Mag. t.* 6596! (K); Kischen, 650m., 4 May 1881, Schweinfurth 744! (K)—raceme rather densely flowered. Adho Demalu, 3,000 ft., 16 March 1953, G. Popov SO/224 (BM)—decumbent rooting stem.

Note: In Schweinfurth 744 (K) the inflorescence is 3-branched, 60cm. high, raceme densely flowered, 15cm. long, 5cm. diam., and leaf 30cm. long, 6cm. broad low down.

The description is lacking in several characters. Are stems ascending or decumbent? Are plants solitary, or do they form groups? Are the racemes always as densely flowered as depicted in the *Bot. Mag.* plate? Bayley Balfour states that the racemes are densely flowered. It is probable that plants growing wild on Socotra will be very different in general habit of growth from the Kew-cultivated plant as figured, and described above.

A. perryi was first introduced to Kew in 1878 by Wykeham Perry, and later by Jas. Collins. In 1880 Professor Isaac Bayley Balfour made a thorough exploration of the Island of Socotra and brought home a large collection of plants including Aloes. When two of those Aloe plants flowered at Kew in 1881, the drawing for the *Bot. Mag.* Plate 6596 was prepared.

Balfour found plants of *A. perryi* widely spread through the island especially on limestone tracts, ranging from sea-level to an altitude of 3,000 ft.

AFFINITY: *A. perryi* is nearest allied to *A. forbesii*, from which it chiefly differs in having much more densely flowered racemes, and shorter (8mm. against 12—15mm.) pedicels. *A. perryi* was described as having purple-tinted peduncles. Whether this is a fixed character of one or both species needs further investigation on Socotra.

THE SOCOTRINE ALOES OF COMMERCE

In his Introductory Chapter XXXVIII, Balfour (*l.c.*) gives the following account:

"The most important plant of the island, so far as products are concerned, is the *Aloe perryi*, which yields the 'Socotrine aloes' of commerce. The gum is known as *tâyef* by the natives; the Arabs call it *sobr*. Although this kind of aloe has been so long known, and has the reputation of being finer than either Barbados or Cape aloes, it is only within the past few years that the character of the plant has been made known. It grows abundantly on the island, especially on the limestone plateaux. The collection of the gum is a very simple process, and can be accomplished at any season. The collector scrapes a slight hollow on the surface of the ground in the vicinity of an aloe-plant, into which he depresses the centre of a small portion of goat-skin spread over the ground.

The leaves of the aloe are then cut and laid in a circle on the skin, with the cut ends projecting over the central hollow. Two or three layers are arranged. The juice which is of a pale amber colour, with a slightly mawkish odour and taste, trickles from the leaves upon the goat-skin. After about three hours the leaves are exhausted; the skin containing the juice is then removed from beneath them, and the juice is transferred to a mussock. Only the older leaves are used. The juice thus collected is of a thin, watery character, and is known as *tâyef rhiho*, or watery aloes. In this condition it is exported to Muscat and Arabia, and sells for three dollars the skin of 30 lbs. By keeping, however, the aloes changes in character. After a month the juice, by loss of water, becomes denser and more viscid; it is then known as *tâyef gesheeshah*, and is more valuable – skin of 30 lb. fetches five dollars; whilst in about 15 days more – that is, about six weeks after collection – it gets into a tolerably hard solid mass, and is then *tâyef kasahul*, and is worth seven dollars a skin of 30 lb. In this last condition it is commonly exported."

77. A. scobinifolia Reynolds et Bally in *Journ. S.A. Bot.* 24: 174 (1958).

DESCRIPTION: *Plant* sometimes solitary, usually forming small groups. *Stem* none or short.

Leaves 16—20, densely rosulate, arcuate-ascending, narrowly lanceolate-attenuate, averaging 30cm. long, 7cm. broad at base, 12—15mm. thick, narrowing to an acute spiny point; *upper surface* flat to slightly canaliculate; *lower surface* convex; *both surfaces* unicoloured dull green, rough to the touch; *margins* with very narrow pale pink cartilaginous edge, without teeth; *sap* dries deep brown.

Inflorescence a branched panicle averaging 60—70cm. high, 2—4 simultaneously.

Peduncle basally plano-convex and 15—20mm. broad, terete upwards, brown with a bloom, minutely white-speckled, averaging 5—8-branched, the lowest branch sometimes with a short branch high up.

Racemes corymbose-capitate, densely flowered, 3—4cm. long, 6cm. diam., youngest buds obliquely to horizontally spreading, open flowers nutant to pendulous.

Bracts narrowly deltoid, deflexed, 8mm. long, 2mm. broad, thin, scarious, white, 3—5-nerved.

Pedicels suberectly spreading, 15—18mm. long, the bud pedicels almost as long as those of open flowers.

Perianth yellow, orange or scarlet, cylindric-clavate, trigonous, averaging 22mm. long, basally obtuse and shortly stipitate, 4—5mm. diam. across the ovary, thence trigonous-clavate, the mouth wide open; *outer segments* free for 9—10mm., obscurely 3-nerved, the apices subacute, slightly spreading; *inner segments* broader than the outer and with more obtuse, more spreading apices.

Filaments lemon, filiform-flattened, the 3 inner narrower and lengthening before the 3 outer with their *anthers* in turn exserted 3—4mm.; *stigma* at length exserted 5mm.; *ovary* pale green, 6mm. long, 2·5mm. diam. (Plates 40, 41, Fig. 200).

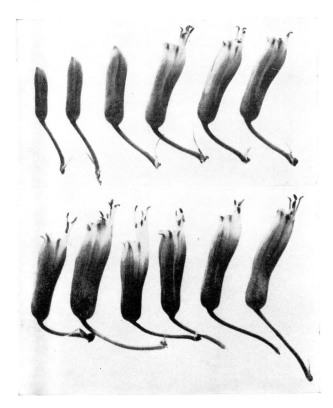

FIG. 200.

Aloe scobinifolia Reynolds et Bally. *Upper-row:* Flowers 1/1 from bud to post-pollination stage. *Lower row:* Flowers 1/1, gathered at random, showing variation.

PLATE 40

ALOE SCOBINIFOLIA   Reynolds et Bally.

Flowering in September, 2 miles W of Erigavo, Somalia North.
Height 60—70cm.

PLATE 41

ALOE SCOBINIFOLIA   Reynolds et Bally.
Colour forms four miles S of Erigavo, Somalia North. Height 65cm.

SOMALIA NORTH (formerly Somaliland Prot.). In considerable numbers near Erigavo, c. 10° 37′ N, 47° 22′ E, alt. 5,500 ft., fl. 8 Sept. 1957, Reynolds 8403 (red flowers) holotype (PRE), isotype (K, EA); same locality, yellow flowers, Reynolds 8402 (PRE, K, EA); Erigavo, coll. P. E. Glover, cult. Nairobi, fl. 9 Aug. 1945, Glover in Bally 6319 (K, EA); between Al Madu Range and Shemis Plains, 4,450 ft., 18 Oct. 1956, Bally 11179 (K, EA); Agasur, eastern Al Madu, 10 Oct. 1956, Bally 11019 (K, EA)—an atypical smooth-leafed form with horny margin; Erigavo, 4,700 ft., 7 Nov. 1954, Bally 10357 (K, EA); ex Al Madu Range, cult. Johannesburg, fl. 14 Sept. 1958, Reynolds 8273 (K).

A. scobinifolia is a smaller plant than photographs suggest; it occurs in vast numbers near Erigavo, for 30 miles along the road southwards towards El Afwein, and along the road north-eastwards towards Medishe.

Flower colours vary from yellow to orange and scarlet, and provide a magnificent blaze of colour when flowering in their hundreds of thousands all around Erigavo.

The typical form is characterized by having leaves that are somewhat rasp-like and rough to the touch, the margins having a very narrow pinkish smooth edge without teeth. Mr. Bally has found considerable quantities much further east on the Al Madu, and at Agasur, where he found a form with much smoother leaves with horny margins with minute widely-spaced teeth.

This charming species prefers exposed stony gypsum soils, and is found mostly between 5,000 ft. and 5,500 ft. Flowering period is from September to November.

The Somalis refer to it only as *Daar*.

A. scobinifolia is nearest allied to *A. elegans* Tod. which grows in Tigre, Northern Ethiopia, and is especially abundant in many parts of Eritrea. *A. elegans* differs in being a much larger plant, with larger, smooth leaves, prominent marginal teeth, and longer, less clavate, flowers.

A. sinkatana Reynolds in *Journ. S.A. Bot.* 23: 39 (1957).

DESCRIPTION: *Plant* succulent, acaulous, growing singly or in groups.
Leaves 16—20, somewhat leathery, densely rosulate, erectly spreading, 50—60cm. long, 6—8cm. broad at base, gradually tapering to a narrowly rounded apex which bears 3—5 very small reddish teeth; *upper surface* canaliculate, dull grey-green, mostly without spots but sometimes spotted throughout; *lower surface* rounded, dull-grey-green, without spots or sometimes copiously spotted in lower half, the spots dull white, lenticular, 5—10mm. long, 1—2mm. broad; *margins* sometimes involute, usually with reddish edge armed with pale-red teeth 2—3mm. long, 15—20—25mm. apart, the teeth firm to subpungent.
Inflorescence a branched panicle 75—90cm. tall.
Peduncle brown with a bloom, plano-convex and 15—20mm. broad at base, somewhat laterally compressed to the first branch, 5—6-branched from about the middle, the branches arcuate-ascending.
Racemes capitate or subcapitate, densely flowered, the terminal averaging 4—6cm. long, 7cm. diam., somewhat corymbose, the youngest buds horizontally disposed, open flowers nutant to subpendulous.
Bracts small, about 3—4mm. long, 2mm. broad, thin, scarious, white, 1-nerved, or with 3 crowded nerves appearing as 1-nerved.
Pedicels 16—20mm. long (18mm. the average), arcuate-spreading with apex nutant, the colour of the base of the perianth.
Perianth scarlet, orange or yellow, clavate, averaging 22mm. long, basally obconic and shortly stipitate, 5mm. diam. across the ovary, thence enlarging to an open mouth; *outer segments* free for 9—10mm. (tube 12mm.) 3-nerved almost to base, thinner at the edges, the apices subacute; *inner segments* themselves free but dorsally adnate to the outer for half their length, broader than the outer, with 3 crowded nerves forming a slight keel, the apices more obtuse and more spreading than the outer.
Filaments filiform-flattened, pale lemon, the 3 inner narrower and lengthening before the 3 outer with their *anthers* in turn exserted 3—4mm.; *style* pale yellow, with *stigma* at length exserted 5mm.; *ovary* pale olive, 6mm. long, 3mm. diam. (Plate 42, Figs. 201–203).

SUDAN. Sinkat, fl. luteo et croceorubro, 11 Sept. 1868, Schweinfurth 206! (K). *Kassala Prov.*, Beja Dist., Red Sea Hills, between Sinkat and Summit, c. 18° 47′ N, 36° 49′ E, 2,890 ft., 4 April 1956, Reynolds 8020 holotype (PRE), isotype (K, Khartoum); between Carthago and Khor Amat, 7 miles WSW of Erkowit, c. 18° 45′ N, 37° 03′ E, 3,200 ft., scarlet flowers, 5 April 1956, Reynolds 8029 (PRE, K), yellow flowers, Reynolds 8030 (PRE, K, G). *Note:* Schweinfurth 274! 275! Wady Sarranib (Sarroweet?), between Sinkat and Erkowit, fl. 17 Sept. 1868 (K), might be an outlying form with racemes much longer than usual.

A. sinkatana was named after the locality which appears to be its specific centre. It occurs abundantly near Sinkat at 2,800 ft., northwards for 8 miles to Gebiet, southwards to Summit, and eastwards across the flats – especially between Carthago and Khor Amat – to hills near Erkowit. A few plants (not flowering) collected near a khor leading up to Jebel De-eb, 2 miles SE of Erkowit at 3,600 ft., appear to belong here.

These localities are in the Beja District, Red Sea Hills, Kassala Province, Sudan, in an area of erratic rainfall averaging only 5 inches per annum. *A. sinkatana* is rare in the higher hills near Erkowit and was not seen in the bleak hills east of Gebiet, or down to Suakin.

PLATE 42

ALOE SINKATANA Reynolds.

Near Sinkat, Red Sea Hills, Kassala Prov., Sudan. Height 85cm.

Fig. 201.   Fig. 202.

A. sinkatana Reynolds.

Fig. 201. Plant near Sinkat.

Fig. 202. Plant between Carthago and Khor Amat, 7 miles WSW of Erkowit, Red Sea
Hills, Kassala Prov., Sudan. 18° 45′ N., 37° 03′ E., alt. 3,200 ft. Height 75cm.

Fig. 203.

A. sinkatana Reynolds. Flowers natural size.

Plants were found in the largest numbers in flat, sandy, stony khors and wadis (small to larger ephemeral water-courses) and sometimes with *Euphorbia abyssinica* and *Dracaena ombet* nearby; not seen on rocky slopes.

Schweinfurth discovered this species in 1868. In *The Heart of Africa*, vol. 1, p. 27, London 1873, he records: "Halfway between Singat and Erkoweet we halted in a wady which bore the name of Sarroweet. Nothing could be more pleasant than the shade of the acacia, nothing more striking than the abundance of bloom of the Abyssinian Aloe transforming the dreary sand-beds into smiling gardens . . . yellow and red were the Aloes, and in such crowded masses that I was involuntarily reminded of the splendour of the tulip beds of the Netherlands."

Schweinfurth's n. 206! (at Kew) was gathered at Sinkat on 11 September 1868. He regarded it as being *A. abyssinica* Lam., but it is not that species.

The identity of *A. abyssinica* Lam. is discussed under *Species non satis cognitae*. The Sinkat Aloe bears no resemblance whatever to the material of *A. abyssinica* so named by Lamarck himself in the Lamarck Herbarium in Paris.

In bracts, pedicels and clavate flowers *A. sinkatana* is perhaps nearest allied to *A. camperi* Schweinf. (found in Eritrea and Northern Ethiopia) but the latter is of shrubby growth with stems up to 1m. long, and with racemes twice as long as broad.

A. sinkatana is acaulous and not a shrub. It sometimes occurs singly, but usually forms groups and bears capitate, somewhat corymbose, racemes with the youngest buds spreading horizontally.

Native name: The Hadendowa name for *A. sinkatana* is *Kalandoy*; they plant it on their graves near Erkowit. The sap is used for stomach troubles.

79. **A. elegans** Todaro in *Hort. Bot. Panorm.* 2: 25, *t.* 29 (1882); Reynolds in *Journ. S.A. Bot.* 22: 153 (1956).

—— *A. Schweinfurthii* Hook. *f.* in *Bot. Mag. t.* 7667 (1899) *non* Baker; Bak. ex Berger in *Gard. Chron.* 23: ser. 3, 197, Fig. 76 (1898), *non* Baker in *Journ. Linn. Soc.* 18: 175 (1880).

—— *A. aethiopica* (Schweinf.) Berger in Engler's *Bot. Jahrb.* 36: 60 (1905), in *Pflanzenr.* Liliac.–Aloin. 243 (1908).

—— *A. vera* var. *aethiopica* Schweinf. in *Bull. Herb. Boiss.* 2: app. 2, 61 (1894); Baker in Th. Dyer *Fl. Trop. Afr.* 7: 465 (1898).

—— *A. abyssinica* var. *peacockii* Baker in *Journ. Linn. Soc.* 18: 175 (1880), in *Bot. Mag. t.* 6620 (1882) – *fide* Todaro; Baker in Th. Dyer *Fl. Trop. Afr.* 7: 468 (1898).

—— *A. abyssinica* Berger (*non* Lam.) in *Pflanzenr. l.c.* 237 (1908).

—— *A. percrassa* Berger (*non* Tod) var. *saganeitiana* Berger *l.c.* 220 (1909).

DESCRIPTION based on personal observations over a wide area in Eritrea and Northern Ethiopia.

Plants usually solitary, rarely dividing into 2—3 rosettes. *Stem none,* or sometimes up to 20—30cm. long in old specimens, decumbent.

Leaves 16—20, densely rosulate (rosettes compact, averaging 60cm. diam.), lanceolate-attenuate, 15—18cm. broad at base, about 60cm. long, 25mm. thick, gradually narrowing to an obtuse shortly-dentate apex; *upper surface* grey-green, flat low down, slightly caniculate upwards, without spots or markings; *lower surface* convex, similar in colour to upper surface; *margins* with reddish edge, armed with brownish-red teeth that are pungent, deltoid, 3—4mm. long, 15—25mm. distant, larger low down, smaller upwards. *Sap* dries reddish-brown.

Inflorescence a many-branched panicle 1m. high, 2—4 simultaneously.

Peduncle basally plano-convex and 25mm. broad, branched from about the middle with about 8 arcuate-ascending branches, the lowest sometimes with 1—2 branchlets.

Racemes conical when young becoming corymbose when flowers open, broadly cylindric, subcapitate, the terminal 8cm. long, 7cm. diam., lateral a little shorter, densely flowered, the youngest buds spreading horizontally to slightly downwards, open flowers nutant to subpendulous.

Bracts narrowly ovate-acuminate, about 8mm. long, 2—3mm. broad, thin, subscarious, 3—5-nerved.

Pedicels averaging 15mm. long, compactly arcuate-ascending, nutant at apex.

Perianth yellow, orange or scarlet, slightly clavate, 25—30mm. long, basally flat to very slightly rounded and shortly stipitate, 6mm. diam. across the ovary, thence very slightly narrowed and trigonously indented, enlarging slightly from the middle to a wide open trigonous mouth; *outer segments* free for half their length, thinner at the margins, obscurely 3-nerved, the apices subacute, slightly spreading; *inner segments* free but dorsally adnate to the outer to the middle, broader than the outer, with 3 crowded nerves forming a keel the colour of the perianth, and with their apices more obtuse and more spreading than the outer.

Filaments pale lemon, the 3 inner narrower and lengthening before the 3 outer with their *anthers* in turn exserted 3mm.; *stigma* at length exserted 4mm.; *ovary* light green, 5mm. long, 3mm. diam. (Plates 43, 44, Figs. 204–206).

N. ETHIOPIA. *Tigre,* near Abba Gerima, 6,000 ft., 7 Nov. 1862, Schimper 927! (K, BM)—this locality is in the Axum District. *Tigre Prov.,* 55km. S of Mekele, at northern foot of Amba Alaji, c. 13° 08′ N, 39° 29′ E, alt. 6,600 ft., 26 April 1956, yellow flowers, Reynolds 8110 (K, PRE), same loc., red flowers, Reynolds 8111 (PRE).

ERITREA. Gorge Goua, near Addingofom, 29 March 1892, Schweinfurth et Riva 1330! (K)—as *A. schimperi* Tod.; Coll. Addingofom hill, at entrance to Gorge of Gua, 2km. S of Saganeiti, cult. Johannesburg, fl. 11 May 1958, Reynolds 8061! (K, PRE); Coll. 11km. S of Nefasit (between Asmara and Ghinda), cult. Johannesburg, fl. 30 March 1959, Reynolds 8058 (K, PRE); 28km. S of Adi Ugri (10km. N of Adi Kwali), 6,000 ft., c. 15° 22′ N, 38° 50′ E, fl. 18 April 1956, Reynolds 8092 (K, PRE, EA).

Plant cult. La Mortola, fl. 20 Feb. 1899, type of *Bot. Mag. t.* 7667 (1899)—wrongly named *A. schweinfurthii* by J. D. Hooker, belongs here.

A. elegans was described and beautifully figured by Todaro in *Hort. Bot. Panorm.* 2: 25, *t.* 29 (1882) and it has not been recognised in the wild state again until very recently. So much confusion was caused by all workers after Lamarck not knowing what *A. abyssinica* Lam. really looked like. For photo of the type specimen in Paris, and discussion on the identity of *A. abyssinica* Lam. – see *Species imperfectly known.* Berger *l.c.* 237 not only wrongly identified *A. abyssinica* Lam., but he wrongly placed *A. elegans* Tod. in synonymy under *A. abyssinica* Lam.

PLATE 43

ALOE ELEGANS　Todaro.

Orange form, at Northern foot of Amba Alaji, 55km. S of Mekele,
Tigre, N. Ethiopia. Height 90cm.

PLATE 44

ALOE ELEGANS   Todaro.

Scarlet form collected 11km. S of Nefasit, Eritrea, flowering in the
author's gardens. Height 1m.

FIG. 204.

A. elegans Tod. Todaro's *t.* 29 in *Hort. Bot. Panorm.* 2: 25 (1882) – much reduced. *Photo by courtesy, The Director, Royal Botanic Gardens, Kew.*

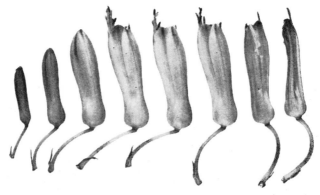

FIG. 205.

A. elegans Tod. Flowers 1/1 from a plant between Adi Kwali and Adi Ugri, Eritrea.

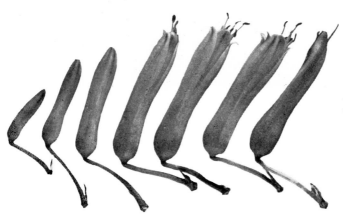

FIG. 206.

A. elegans Tod. Flowers 1/1 from a plant at northern foot of Amba Alaji, 55km. S of Mekele, N. Ethiopia.

Todaro's *t.* 29 is reproduced herein and from this figure it will be seen that one of the most striking characters of *A. elegans* is the racemes with the young buds spreading horizontally to slightly downwards – so different from *A. camperi* in which the buds are suberect.

Schweinfurth also did not recognise *A. elegans*, and he described this species as *A. vera* var. *aethiopica* in *Bull. Herb. Boiss.* 2: app. 2, 61 (1894).

Berger in Engler's *Bot. Jahrb.* 36: 60 (1905), and in *Pflanzenr.* 243, Fig. 94 (1908) described *A. aethiopica* (Schweinf.) Berger from a plant that flowered at La Mortola in February 1899. Material from Berger's type plant is at Kew, together with a photograph of the flowering plant, and it is clearly conspecific with *A. elegans* Tod.

This material is the type of *Bot. Mag. t.* 7667 (1899) and that plate was prepared from Berger's photograph – but the species was wrongly named *A. schweinfurthii* Bak. by Hooker.

This photograph was also used for the figure accompanying the text in *Gard. Chron.* 23: ser. 3, 197, Fig. 76 (1898) but the species was again wrongly named *A. schweinfurthii* Bak.

The author's special visit to Mr. Bangenze, in the SW corner of the Sudan, type locality of *A. schweinfurthii* Bak., settled the identity of that species. As the result of careful investigations in Eritrea and N. Ethiopia the identities of *A. camperi* Schweinf. (= *A. eru* Berger), and *A. elegans* Tod. (= *A. aethiopica* (Schw.) Berger), have at long last been established.

TYPE LOCALITY

Todaro stated that his plants were raised from seeds collected by Schimper in Abyssinia which then included Eritrea and Ethiopia. Material gathered by Schimper on 7 Nov. 1862 near Abba Gerima in the Axum Dist. of Northern Ethiopia (K, BM) suggests that Schimper might have gathered the seeds also at that locality.

DISTRIBUTION

A. elegans Tod. occurs in considerable numbers over a wide area in Eritrea, and Tigre Prov. of Northern Ethiopia. It is abundant near Asmara (7,500 ft.); for 80km. along the road northwards towards Keren; southwards to Adi Ugri (6,200 ft.), Adi Kwale (6,500 ft.); not seen in the Mareb Valley – which is the Eritrea-Tigre border; southwards to Adowa (6,100 ft.), Axum (6,300 ft.) and E of Adowa. East of Asmara the species abounds S of Nefasit in the broad Piana Dalla Valley (5,300 ft.), thence southwards to Decamere (6,400 ft.), Saganeiti (6,900 ft.), Addingfom Hill near the Gorge of Gua (6,700 ft.), Adi Caieh (7,700ft.), on the Kohaito Plateau with *A. camperi* Schweinf. and *A. percrassa* Tod. (8,200 ft.), and near Senafe (7,700 ft.). In Tigre, *A. elegans* occurs abundantly to Adigrat (7,700 ft.), southwards to Mekele (6,700 ft.) and to the foot of Amba Alaji (6,600 ft.), 55km. S of Mekele and 355km. S of Asmara, which was the furthest south seen.

80. **A. wrefordii** Reynolds in *Journ. S.A. Bot.* 22: 141 (1956).

DESCRIPTION: *Plants* solitary, not forming groups, acaulescent or with very short *stem.*

Leaves about 24, densely rosulate, lanceolate-attenuate, suberectly spreading and recurved in upper quarter, about 60cm. long, 15cm. broad at base, 15mm. thick, the acute apex a reddish-brown spine; *upper surface* dull grey-green, sometimes with reddish-brown tinge, mostly without spots or markings, very obscurely lineate, flat low down, slightly canaliculate upwards; *lower surface* convex, pale grey-green, without markings; *margins* sinuate-dentate, armed with reddish-brown deltoid pungent teeth 4mm. long, 10—15mm. distant, forward-uncinate, the interspaces the colour of the leaf. *Sap* dries yellow.

Inflorescence a compactly branched panicle about 120cm. high, sometimes 2—3 consecutively.

Peduncle basally plano-convex and 20—25mm. broad, branched well below the middle, with up to 16 ascending branches, the lowest 1—2 branches with 2—5 branchlets producing a total of up to 25 racemes.

Racemes sub-capitate, the pedicellate portion of terminal racemes 5—8cm. long, 6cm. diam., laterals slightly shorter, densely flowered, the apex a small tuft of dried bracts, the youngest buds green-tipped, suberect, older buds spreading, open flowers nutant to subpendulous.

Bracts ovate-acute, 9mm. long, 4mm. broad, very thin, white, scarious, about 5-nerved.

Pedicels lowest 16mm. long, slightly shorter upwards, 20mm. in the fruit.

Perianth scarlet or orange, cylindric-clavate, 22mm. long, obtusely tapering at base to the pedicel articulation, shortly stipitate, cylindric and 5—6mm. diam. across the ovary, thence narrowly clavate, the mouth slightly up-turned; *outer segments* free for 13mm. (tube about 8mm.), 3-nerved, apices subacute; *inner segments* broader than the outer, with broad white border and 3 crowded nerves forming a keel, the apices more obtuse and more spreading than the outer.

Filaments pale lemon, the 3 inner narrower and lengthening before the 3 outer with their *anthers* in turn exserted 3—4mm.; *stigma* at length exserted 5mm.; *ovary* olive, 6mm. long, 3mm. diam., obtuse at apex. (Figs. 207–211).

UGANDA. *Northern Prov.:* Karamoja, Matheniko County, Katumet, 12 miles SE of Moroto, c. 2° 24′ N, 34° 45′ E, 4,900 ft., cult. hort. Tweedie, Mutamayo, fl. 21 Jan. 1956, Tweedie 659, holotype (PRE), isotype (EA, K); Stony foothills, Mt. Moroto, Nov. 1945, Tweedie 659 (K).

S. ETHIOPIA. *Sidamo,* Borana, coll. 6 miles S of Yavello, cult. Mbabane, Swaziland, fl. 31 May 1964, Reynolds 7072A (K, PRE).

A. wrefordii was named after the late Mr. H. Wreford Smith who has travelled extensively throughout Karamoja, and who first discovered plants at Katumet, 12 miles SE of Moroto, in 1940. Subsequently Mrs. E. M. Tweedie found plants at another locality nearby, and sent material to Kew under her number 659. Plants were later found by Mr. John T. Wilson in numbers at Rupa, 9 miles NE of Moroto, in stony thorn and bush country.

FIG. 207.   FIG. 208.

A. wrefordii Reynolds.

FIG. 207. Plant at Rupa, 9 miles NE of Moroto, Karamoja, Uganda; with dehisced capsules. Height 5 feet.

FIG. 208. Plant from Rupa flowering in Johannesburg.

FIG. 209.

A. wrefordii Reynolds. Flowers 1/1 from a plant near Rupa, Moroto Dist. Karamoja.

A plant collected by the author in 1953, 6 miles S of Yavello in Borana Dist., Sidamo Prov., S. Ethiopia, flowered at Mbabane, Swaziland, in May 1964 and proved to be *A. wrefordii*, with slightly longer racemes.

A. wrefordii occurs mostly as solitary plants, sometimes in very small groups, with little or no stem; it has a tall much-branched paniculate inflorescence with subcapitate racemes of clavate flowers.

A. calidophila Reynolds which also occurs further south in the Borana Dist. between Mega and Moyale is a near ally in shape and size of flowers but that species has much longer racemes, and longer, deeply-channeled, recurved leaves.

A. camperi Schweinf. from Eritrea is another near ally in pedicels, bracts and short clavate flowers, but differs in being of shrubby growth, and in having longer, narrower, spotted leaves and longer racemes.

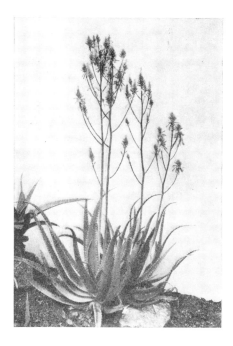

Fig. 210.

A. wrefordii Reynolds. Plant collected 6 miles S of Yavello, Borana, Sidamo, S. Ethiopia, flowering at Mbabane, Swaziland. Height 5 ft.

Fig. 211.

A. wrefordii Reynolds. Flowers 1/1 from the Fig. 210 plant.

FIG. 212.   FIG. 213.

A. sinana Reynolds.

FIG. 212. Plant 17 km. S of Karakore, 121km. S of Dessie, Shoa Prov., Ethiopia. Alt. 4,800 ft. Height 5 feet.

FIG. 213. Plant 17km. NE of Debre Sina, Shoa Prov., Ethiopia. Alt. 4,800 ft. Height 5 feet.

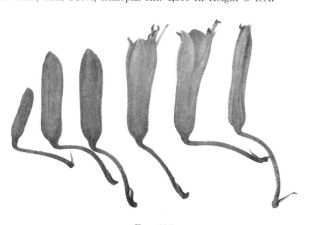

FIG. 215.

A. sinana Reynolds.

FIG. 214. Raceme × 1/5 approx.

FIG. 215. Flowers natural size.

FIG. 214.

81. **A. sinana** Reynolds in *Journ. S.A. Bot.* 23: 3 (1957).

DESCRIPTION: *Plants* of shrubby growth; *stems* up to 1m. long, 8—10cm. diam., erect or divergent, the apical 20cm. foliate.

Leaves 12—16, rosulate, basally sheathing, 10—13cm., broad at base, gradually narrowing to the apex and 60—70cm. long, spreading to recurved; *upper surface* concave low down, canaliculate upwards, dull grey-green, usually with a few scattered pale green elongated lenticular blotches in lower half; *lower surface* convex, grey-green, with numerous more crowded pale-green blotches in lower half; *margins* usually with horny reddish edge armed with pungent deltoid reddish-brown teeth 3—4mm. long, 10—15—20mm. distant; *sap* dries deep brown.

Inflorescence a branched panicle about 1m. high.

Peduncle flattened and 25mm. broad at base, terete upwards, 4—7-branched from about the middle.

Racemes sublaxly flowered, varying from somewhat broadly conical, 6—10cm. long, 8cm. diam., to sub-capitate, the youngest buds spreading horizontally to slightly downwards, open flowers nutant, young racemes at first conical, with development becoming slightly corymbose.

Bracts ovate-attenuate, 5mm. long, 3mm. broad, thin, brown, scarious, 5-nerved.

Pedicels 18—20mm. long, mostly spreading with apices nutant.

Perianth orange-scarlet near base, paler at mouth, slightly clavate, averaging 28mm. long, basally obconic and shortly stipitate, 6mm. diam. across the ovary, thence trigonous-clavate, the mouth wide open; *outer segments* free to the middle, obscurely 3-nerved, apices subacute, slightly spreading; *inner segments* pale orange, broader than the outer, with 3 crowded nerves forming a pale orange keel, the apices more obtuse and more spreading than the outer.

Filaments pale lemon, the 3 inner narrower and lengthening before the 3 outer with their *anthers* in turn exserted 2—3mm.; *style* pale lemon, with *stigma* at length exserted 3—4mm.; *ovary* yellowish-green, 7mm. long, 3mm. diam. (Figs. 212–215).

ETHIOPIA. *Shoa Prov.*: 18km. NE of Debre Sina, c. 9° 54′ N, 39° 50′ E, c. 1410m., 29 April 1956, Reynolds 8126 holotype (PRE), isotype (K, EA); 19km. NE of Debre Sina, 4,700 ft., 29 April 1956, Reynolds 8127 (K. PRE)—racemes more capitate than usual.

This species was named after the locality where it was found in the largest numbers, namely, on mountain slopes from about 8km. (5 miles) to 20km. (12 miles) NE of Debre Sina, from 1,950m. (6,500 ft.) down to about 1,410m. (4,700 ft.). Debre Sina is an Ethiopian village 130km. (81 miles) NE of Addis Ababa, situated below the three tunnels of the Pass previously known as Mussolini Pass, on the road to Dessie, at an elevation of 8,500 ft. *A. sinana* was also seen further north at a point 76km. (47 miles) NE of Debre Sina which is 17km. S of Karakora. Certain plants on mountain slopes east of Dessie, on the road down to Kombolchia, growing among *A. camperi* Schweinf., but not flowering when seen, may belong here.

A. sinana seems to be nearest allied to *A. camperi* Schweinf. in general habit of growth, leaves, and clavate flowers, but differs in having a less-branched inflorescence and longer (28mm.) flowers. It is also characterized by having sublaxly flowered cylindric, slightly conical, racemes with the buds spreading horizontally to slightly downwards. This is also a character of *A. elegans* Tod. which occurs north of Amba Alaji and up into Eritrea, but the latter is a large acaulescent plant with grey-green unspotted leaves forming rather compact rosettes, and with a considerably more branched inflorescence.

Some plants of *A. sinana* were observed with shorter, denser, subcapitate racemes, but in all forms the buds were spreading horizontally to slightly downwards. The only other Aloe species seen between Kombolchia and Debre Sina, mostly in the Rift Valley at about 4,700 ft., were *A. macrocarpa* Tod. and *A. trichosantha* Berger.

82. **A. camperi** Schweinfurth in *Bull. Herb. Boiss.* 2: app. 2, 67 (1894); Reynolds in *Journ. S.A. Bot.* 22: 156 (1957).

—— *A. abyssinica* (*non* Lamarck) Salm Dyck *Cat. rais.* 25 (1817), *Monogr. gen. Al.* ser. 18, fig. 1 (1842); Roem. et Schult. *Syst. veg.* 7: 695 (1829); Kunth *Enum. pl.* 521 (1843); Baker in *Journ. Linn. Soc.* 18: 174 (1880), in Th. Dyer *Fl. Trop. Afr.* 7: 467 (1898); Schweinfurth in *Bull. Herb. Boiss.* 2: app. 2, 66 et 110 (1894).

(*Note: A. abyssinica* Berger (*non* Lam.) in Engler *Pflanzenr.* Liliac.–Aloin. 237 (1908) excl. part syn., is a form of *A. elegans* Tod.).

—— *A. eru* Berger *l.c.* 249 (1908).

—— *A. spicata* Baker (*non* L.f.) in *Fl. capens* 6: 316 (1896), et Bentley et Trimen (*non* L.f.) in *Medic. plants* 4: 284 (1880) appear to be forms of *A. camperi* Schw. – from a plant of unknown origin, hence taxonomically useless.

DESCRIPTION: *Plant* shrubby, branching from base and sometimes forming groups 1—2m. across. *Stem* usually 50cm. long, 6cm. diam., sometimes up to 1m. long, 9—10cm. diam., erect, divergent or decumbent, the apical 10—20cm. densely foliate.

Leaves 12—16, rosulate, averaging 50—60cm. long, 8—12cm. broad at base, tapering to the apex, basally sheathing, recurved and forming open rosettes; *upper surface* dark green, canaliculate, unspotted, or sometimes with a few dull white lenticular spots; *lower surface* convex, deep green, with or without numerous elongated lenticular white spots; *margins* with reddish edge, armed with deltoid, pungent, brownish-red teeth averaging 3—5mm. long, 10—20mm. distant, more crowded near base, more distant upwards.

Inflorescence a branched panicle 70—100cm. high, usually 2—3 simultaneously.

Peduncle basally plano-convex and 15—20mm. broad, brown with a bloom, 6—8-branched from about the middle, the lowest branches sometimes with 1—2 branchlets.

Racemes densely flowered, the pedicellate portion 6—9cm. long, 6—7cm. diam., youngest buds suberect, scarlet, sometimes greyish-green tipped, older buds spreading, open flowers turning orange to yellow, subpendulous.

Bracts very small, deltoid, 2mm. long, 2mm. broad at base, dirty white, 5-nerved.

Pedicels 12—18mm. long, 14mm. the average.

Perianth orange to yellow, cylindric-clavate, averaging 20—22mm. long, basally obconic and shortly stipitate, 5mm. diam. across the ovary, clavate upwards, the mouth wide open, trigonal; *outer segments* free for one-third their length (about 7mm.), obscurely 3-nerved, the apices subacute, slightly spreading; *inner segments* free but dorsally adnate to the outer for two-thirds their length, thinner at the margins, the apices more obtuse and more spreading than the outer.

Filaments lemon, the 3 inner narrower and lengthening before the 3 outer with their *anthers* in turn exserted 2—3mm.; *Stigma* at length exserted 3—4mm.; *ovary* light green, averaging 5mm. long, 2mm. diam. (Plate 45, Figs. 216, 217).

FIG. 216.

A. camperi Schweinfurth. Plant 8km. S of Nefasit, Eritrea, 15° 21′ N., 39° 04′ E. Alt. 5,000 ft. Flowering in April. Height 5 ft.

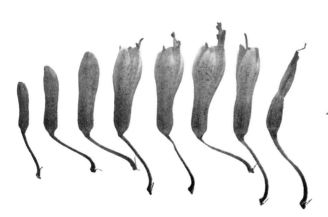

FIG. 217.

A. camperi Schweinfurth. Flowers 1/1 from a plant 8km. S of Nefasit, Eritrea.

PLATE 45

ALOE CAMPERI   Schweinfurth.

20km. S of Waldia (100km. N of Dessie), Wollo Province, N. Ethiopia,
alt. 5,700 ft., Height 1m.

ERITREA. Jebel Schaba, in Wadi Osfir, 10 April 1865, Schweinfurth 19! (K); Gheleb, 1900m., 3 April 1891, Schweinfurth 1234!, 1430! 1796! (K); near Acrur, 1900m., 1–6 April 1892, Schweinfurth 1350! (K)—this would make an excellent lectotype if Schweinfurth's no. 514A cannot be found; 7–25 April 1892, Schweinfurth 1696! (K), 25–30 April 1892, Schweinfurth 1797! (K).—*Note:* Acrur is NE of Saganeiti in Barasio Valley. Near Mahio in the Haddas Valley, 1000–1075m., 16–18 May 1894! Schweinfurth 155! (K); Kohaito Plateau 2600m., 1–10 May 1894, Schweinfurth 154!, 156! (K), Mesillit Pass (N. Eritrea), 4,500 ft. down to 1,800 ft., 24 March 1949, Bally 6686! (K); 6km. E of Asmara, 2250m.; 12 Apri 1956, Reynolds 8036 (PRE, K); in the valley above Ghinda, near Nefasit, 1700m., c. 15° 23' N, 39° 04' E, 13 April 1956, Reynolds 8051! (K, PRE, EA); on the Kohaito Plateau 13km. S of Adi Caieh, 2700m., 15 April 1956, Reynolds 8071! (K, PRE).

ETHIOPIA. *Wollo Prov.,* 20km. south of Waldia (100km. N of Dessie), 1700m., 25 April 1956, Reynolds 8105! (K, PRE, EA).

TYPE LOCALITY

A. camperi Schweinfurth was described in *Bull. Herb. Boiss.* 2: app. 2, 67 (1894) from the Great Valley above Ghinda, Eritrea, 1,400m., Schweinfurth 514a, coll. 1891. Schweinfurth stated that he named the species after his "esteemed friend Manfredo Camperio, who did so much for the Italian Colony of Eritrea", and he also included: Asmara, 2,400m., n. 605, coll. 1891; Arbaschiko, 1,600m., n. 668, coll. 1891; Gheleb, 1,700m., n. 1074, coll. 1891; Acrur, 1,900m., 1342, 1306, coll. 1892, all in Eritrea.

Schweinfurth stated: "Grows at all (above) mentioned places in association with *A. abyssinica* Lam., but more singly and not in communities. It cannot be distinguished by its flowers from *A. abyssinica* Lam., but differs in its broader, shorter leaves not so recurved at the apex . . ."

Salm Dyck's figure in 1842, was the first published of "*A. abyssinica* Lam." and it has misled *all* subsequent workers including Schweinfurth and Berger – see account under *Species imperfectly known* and specially the photograph of the type specimen of *A. abyssinica* Lam. in Paris.

Schweinfurth had obviously followed Salm Dyck's description and figure of "*A. abyssinica* Lam.", which was entirely incorrect. He and others have endeavoured to make two species from forms of one shrubby species of Aloe found in considerable numbers from the valley above Ghinda to Nefasit, up the mountains to Asmara, and elsewhere in Eritrea.

NOTE ON SOME SYNONYMS

Another species is also involved, namely *A. eru* Berger. Berger had wrongly identified *A. abyssinica* Lam. – his concept being a form of *A. elegans* Tod. He also wrongly placed *A. camperi* Schweinf. in synonymy under his concept of *A. abyssinica* Lam. (i.e. *A. elegans* Tod.) which added still more to the confusion.

Berger founded his *A. eru* on Schweinfurth's n. 514 from the Great Valley above Ghinda, but he cited the identical material from Asmara, Gheleb and Acrur that Schweinfurth had cited for his *A. camperi*, notwithstanding that he (Berger) had previously sunk *A. camperi* under "*A. abyssinica* Lam.".

In April 1956, when travelling in Eritrea, the present author specially visited as many of Schweinfurth's localities as he could reach. He found the shrubby species hitherto so well known as *A. eru* Berger, in considerable numbers in the valley between Ghinda and Nefasit (the first place where travellers coming up from the coast would see it) and especially on the mountains up to Asmara at 7,600 ft.

It is now clear that *A. abbysinica* Schweinf. *non* Lam., *A. camperi* Schweinf. and *A. eru* Berger are merely forms of one species from the same locality. *A. camperi* being the earlier name, has priority.

DISTRIBUTION

A. camperi occurs in considerable numbers in many parts of Eritrea, from Meschillit Pass, NE of Keren in the north, to the Ethiopian border in the south. The author found it in the broad Piana Dalla Valley south of Nefasit (5,300 ft.), near the Gua Gorge (6,800 ft.), Adi Caieh (7,700 ft.), on the Kohaito Plateau with *A. percrassa* Tod. and *A. elegans* Tod. (8,300 ft.), and near Senafe (7,700 ft.).

In Ethiopia, *A. camperi* was found in numbers at the northern foot of Amba Alaji (6,700 ft.), near Alamata (4,800 ft.) and Cobbo (4,700 ft.), in the Rift Valley, Tigre Province. In Wollo Province, the species occurs abundantly near Waldia (6,000 ft.), and as far south as near Dessie.

A. camperi is a variable species, weaker forms occurring at lower drier altitudes (4,600 ft.), and more robust forms from 6,000—8,300 ft. Stems vary in length. Leaves vary in length and width and occur with or without spots. Racemes also vary from shorter and denser to longer and laxer. Flowers vary in length and shape, but are invariably clavate, and average 20mm. in length. It is a most handsome species when in full flower.

NATIVE NAME: *Erreh* in Eritrea, *Iret* in Ethiopia.

83. **A. adigratana** Reynolds in *Journ. S.A. Bot.* 23: 1 (1957).
    The following almost certainly belong here: *A. abyssinica* Hook *fil.* in *Bot. Mag. t.* 7712 (1900); *A. eru* Berger var. *hookeri* Berger in *Pflanzenr.* Liliac.–Aloin. 251 (1908).

DESCRIPTION: *Plants* of shrubby growth. *Stems* up to 1m. erect, or 1—2m. decumbent, 12cm. thick, sometimes with shoots forming small to large shrubs.

Leaves about 16—20, rosulate, sometimes with the apical 30cm. of stems subdensely foliate, ensiform, spreading and slightly recurved, 60—80cm. long, 15cm. broad at base, 15—20mm. thick at base; *upper surface* concave low down, canaliculate upwards, dull green with numerous pale green lenticular spots in lower third; *lower surface* rounded, dark green with numerous more crowded pale green lenticular spots in basal quarter; *margins* armed with large deltoid, pungent, reddish to reddish-brown teeth up to 10mm. long, 25—35mm. distant; *sap* dries deep brown.

Inflorescence a 3—5-branched panicle about 90cm. tall.

Peduncle basally flattened and 25—30mm. broad, 3—5-branched from the middle, lowest branch subtended at base by a broadly ovate-acute, many-nerved, thin, scarious bract.

Racemes cylindric-conical, densely flowered, 15—20cm. long, 8—9cm. diam., youngest buds suberect, scarlet with grey-green tips, older buds spreading, open flowers orange to yellow, subpendulous.

Bracts deltoid, thin, scarious, 8mm. long, 3mm. broad, 3—5-nerved.

Pedicels averaging 18mm. long.

Perianth orange or yellow, 28—33mm. long, cylindric-clavate, basally tapering into the pedicel, shortly stipitate, 6mm. diam. across the ovary, thence trigonous-clavate, the mouth wide open; *outer segments* free to the middle, obscurely 3-green-nerved, apices subacute, spreading; *inner segments* adnate to the outer to the middle, broader than the outer, orange-keeled, the apices brownish-tipped and more spreading than the outer.

Filaments lemon, the 3 inner narrower and lengthening before the 3 outer with their *anthers* in turn exserted 5mm.; *stigma* at length exserted 6mm.; *ovary* pale green, 8mm. long, 4mm. diam. (Figs. 218–220).

FIG. 218.

A. adigratana Reynolds. Plants 19km. N of Adigrat, Tigre Province, N. Ethiopia, c. 14° 21′ N., 39° 25′ E., alt. 2,370m. (7,800 ft.).

ETHIOPIA. *Tigre Prov.*, 10km. W of Adigrat, c. 14° 21′ N, 39° 23′ E, c. 2,700m., 15 April 1956, Reynolds 8076 holotype (PRE), isotype (K); 19km. north of Adigrat, c. 14° 21′ N, 39° 25′ E, c. 2370m., 16 April 1956, Reynolds 8073 (PRE, K)- Plant of unknown origin, fl. 13 May 1899, type of *Bot. Mag. t.* 7712 (1900) is doubtfully placed here, the tall stem de. picted being the result of unnatural growth conditions under glass.

This species takes its name from the town and district of Adigrat, Tigre Province, Northern Ethiopia, which appears to be its specific centre. *A. adigratana* was found from Adigrat for 20km. northwards to the Eritrean border at elevations of 2100—2600m. Along the main road to the south considerable numbers were seen 13 to 23km. from Adigrat at 2600m., also at 58km. near Agula, S of Wogerra (1800m.), and on rocky hills near Mekele, 124km. S of Adigrat, at 2100m.

On the road westwards over the mountains to Adowa, numbers of plants were observed for the first 10km. from Adigrat up to 2700m. (9,000 ft.), thence at km. 23 (2500m.), km. 46 (2250m.) and near km. 85 (2100m.), which is 20km. W of Adi Aboun near Adowa; not seen again further west, or north of Adowa.

Below 2400m. (8,000 ft.) *A. adigratana* was sometimes found in asociation with *A. elegans* Tod.; above that altitude and up to 2850m. (9,500 ft.) it sometimes occurs with *A. percrassa* Tod.

A. adigratana is nearest allied to *A. camperi* Schweinf. (= *A. eru* Berger) but differs in having longer, thicker stems, longer leaves, longer, denser, more conical racemes, and much larger but less clavate flowers. Near Adigrat the maximum flowering period is March – a month earlier than *A. camperi*.

NATIVE NAME: *Iret* (Tigrinya).

FIG. 219.

A. adigratana Reynolds. Flowers 1/1 from a plant 10km. W of Adigrat, Tigre Province, N. Ethiopia.

FIG. 220.

A. adigratana Reynolds. Flowers 1/1 gathered at random showing variation; 19km. N of Adigrat.

84. **A. calidophila** Reynolds in *Journ. S.A. Bot.* 20: 26 (1954).

DESCRIPTION: A succulent low shrub, forming small to large dense groups. *Stem* short, or, in very old specimens procumbent for 1m., thence ascending for 1m., with old dried leaf remains persistent, sometimes with shoots from base forming dense groups.

Leaves about 20, rather leathery, densely aggregated at apex of stems, basally sheathing and about 16cm. broad when pressed flat, gradually tapering to the apex, about 80cm. long, spreading and much recurved with the apices usually pointing downwards; *upper surface* dull olive-green, without spots or lineation, deeply canaliculate; *lower surface* rounded, of similar colour to the upper surface; *margins* armed with firm, cartilaginous, dull white teeth which are pale reddish-brown tipped, 4—5mm. long, 20—25mm. distant, the interspaces straight and the colour of the leaf. *Sap* dries deep brown.

Inflorescence a branched panicle, 1—1·3m. high.

Peduncle plano-convex and 23mm. broad at base, terete upwards, brown, with a grey powdery bloom, branched about the middle, with about 12 arcuate-ascending branches, the lowest of which with 1—2 branchlets.

Racemes erect, slightly conico-cylindric, 10—13cm. long, 5cm. diam., rather densely flowered, the buds suberect, dull scarlet at base turning orange upwards.

Bracts ovate-acuminate, 3—4mm. long, 2mm. broad at base, thin, scarious, with 3 congested nerves down the middle.

Pedicels averaging 10mm. long, curved, with apex nutant.

Perianth scarlet at base, turning orange towards the throat, 22mm. long, cylindric-trigonous-clavate, obtusely tapering at base, cylindric and 6mm. diam. across the ovary, thence laterally compressed-trigonous and enlarging to the throat; *outer segments* free for 11mm., with broad pale-lemon borders in upper half, 3-nerved throughout, the apices subacute, slightly spreading; *inner segments* themselves free but dorsally adnate to the outer to the middle, much broader than the outer and with an orange keel throughout, the apices brown-edged, more obtuse and more spreading than the outer.

Filaments filiform-flattened, the 3 inner narrower and lengthening before the 3 outer; *anthers* scarcely exserted; *style* filiform, yellow, with the *stigma* at length exserted 1—2mm.; *ovary* pale olive-green, 5mm. long, 2mm. diam. (Plate 46, Fig. 221).

ETHIOPIA. *Sidamo Prov.:* Borana Dist., on the arid Dida Cheena Plains, 49 miles WNW of Moyale on the road to Mega, 4,400 ft., c. 3° 53′ N, 38° 35′ E, 6 Sept. 1953, Reynolds 7029 holotype (PRE), isotype (K).
KENYA. *Northern Prov.,* near Moyale, 1080m., Oct. 1952, J. B. Gillett 12944! (EA); El Wak, 29 May 1952, Gillett 13393! (EA).

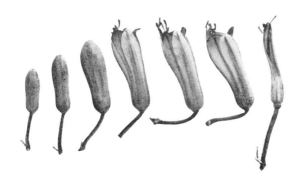

FIG. 221.

A. calidophila Reynolds. Flowers natural size.

NATIVE NAME: Called *Hargeisa Sodu* by the Boran – J. B. Gillett.

DISTRIBUTION: Kenya, abundant in the area 64 miles N of Wajir (14 miles S of Buna), to Korondil and near Moyale; along the Wajir–El Wak road.

S. Ethiopia, Borana: Occurs in numbers for 60 miles along the Moyale–Mega road, especially on the Dida Cheena plains; 3—5 miles N of Mega; near Dubuluch and for 25 miles northwards to near Yavello; repeatedly for 66 miles along the Daua Parma road at 4,200—4,800 ft.; not seen east of the Daua Parma River.

This species is characterised by having large, deeply channelled, very recurved leaves, a much-branched inflorescence with erect subdense racemes and clavate flowers, which are dull scarlet near base, turning orange towards the mouth.

In leaf characters, *A. calidophila* approaches *A. microdonta* Chiov. in Southern Somalia, but the latter is immediately separated by its oblique lax racemes with secund red flowers, and minute marginal teeth.

The clavate flowers of *A. calidophila* resemble those of *A. camperi* but the latter has entirely different leaves, and a lower inflorescence with slightly shorter flowers. The largest numbers of plants were found on arid plains, in intensely hot places, which suggested the specific epithet.

PLATE 46

ALOE CALIDOPHILA Reynolds.

On the Dida Cheena Plains, 49 miles WNW of Moyale on Mega road,
Borana Dist., Sidamo Prov., S. Ethiopia. Height 1·30m.

GROUP 14

(Sub-Sect. *Ortholophae* Christian, amended)

RACEMES OBLIQUE, FLOWERS ± SECUND

Plants mostly acaulescent, sometimes caulescent. *Leaves* laxly to densely rosulate, spreading or incurved, green or glaucous. *Inflorescence* erect or suboblique, simple or divaricately many-branched. *Racemes* oblique to almost horizontally disposed, sublax to densely flowered; flowers secund or subsecund. *Bracts* small. *Pedicels* short. *Perianth* cylindric-trigonous, ventricose or clavate; *outer segments* connate for one-quarter to two-thirds their length; *anthers* shortly to long exserted.

Type Species: *A. secundiflora* Engler.

The species comprising this group are characterised by having inflorescences that are erect or slightly oblique, with racemes that are suberectly to obliquely or horizontally disposed with their flowers slightly to prominently secund.

The well-known Transvaal, Zululand and Swaziland species *A. marlothii* Berger has oblique racemes and secund flowers, but is not included in this work because exceedingly few plants occur in Moçambique north of lat. 22° S – see *Aloes of S. Africa* (1950) for full treatment with colour plate and several figures.

Another species, *A. gossweileri* Reynolds, in Angola, has a paniculate inflorescence with oblique racemes and subsecund flowers, but being a shrub it is included under Group 19 – Shrubs.

A. globuligemma has clavate flowers, but is included here because its oblique racemes with secund flowers are more prominent characters.

KEY TO THE SPECIES

A. PERIANTH CYLINDRIC-TRIGONOUS

Inflorescence many-branched, 1—1·5m. high, *anthers* and *stigma* shortly (2—4mm.) exserted:
  (a) *Leaves entire*, 25—30cm. long, 6cm. broad:
    1. *Racemes* 10—15cm. long; *pedicels* 5mm., *perianth* scarlet or yellow, 22—24mm. .. .. 85 *A. inermis*
  (b) *Leaves with dentate margins:*
    1. *Leaves* 55cm. × 10cm., marginal teeth 2mm. long. *Racemes* lax, 25—30cm. long, *pedicels* 5mm. *Perianth* 25mm. long.. .. 87 *A. turkanensis*
    2. *Leaves* 35 × 6cm. *Inflorescence* divaricately 7—10-branched, 1m. high. *Racemes* very lax, 15—20cm. *Pedicels* 6—8mm. *Perianth* 30mm., *outer segments* free for 15mm. .. .. .. 88 *A. leachii*
    3. *Leaves* 40cm. × 6—7cm. broad, marginal teeth 4—5mm. long. *Racemes* sublax, 20cm. long. *Pedicels* 5mm. *Perianth* scarlet, 40mm. long .. .. 89 *A. guerrai*
    4. *Leaves* 45cm. × 12—14cm. *Pedicels* 8—10mm. *Perianth* 35mm. long, scarlet, minutely white-speckled .. .. 90 *A. secundiflora*

B. PERIANTH CLAVATE

Anthers and *stigma* exserted 10—14mm.:
    1. *Leaves* 45—50cm. × 8—9cm. *Inflorescence* many-branched, up to 1m. tall. *Racemes* subdense, 30—40cm. long. *Pedicels* 3—4mm. *Perianth* 26mm. long, sulphur-yellow to ivory .. .. 86 *A. globuligemma*

C. PERIANTH VENTRICOSE

Racemes densely-flowered, 30cm. long. *Anthers* and *stigma* much (10—15mm.) exserted:
    1. Acaulescent, *leaves* 50cm. × 12—14cm., compactly incurved. *Inflorescence* 90cm. high, 2—4-branched. *Pedicels* 8mm. long. *Perianth* orange-scarlet, 40mm. long.. .. .. 91 *A. ortholopha*

2. *Stem* 1—2m. high, simple or branched, *leaves* 50cm. × 10cm.
Inflorescence stout, to 1m. long, spreading arcuate-horizontal.
Pedicels 1—2mm. long. *Perianth* 35—40mm., red or orange.. ..   92 *A. mawii*

A. marsabitensis Verdoorn et Christian, and *A. microdonta* Chiov. have oblique racemes and subsecund flowers, but are included under Group 17 – plants with large, deeply canaliculate, recurved leaves.

85. **A. inermis** Forskal in *Fl. Aeg. Arab.* 74 (1775); Baker in *Journ. Linn. Soc.* 18: 181 (1880); Berger in Engler's *Pflanzenr.* Liliac.–Aloin. 268 (1908); Blatter in *Fl. Arab. Rec. Bot. Surv. India* 8: 6, 463 (1936); O. Schwartz in *Fl. Trop. Arab.* 351 (1939); Christensen in *Dansk. Bot. Ark.* 4: No. 3, 18 (1922); Reynolds in *Journ. S.A. Bot.* 24: 173 (1958); Lavranos in *Journ. S.A. Bot.* 31: (1965).
—— *A. luntii* Bak. in *Kew Bull.* 342 (1894), in *Bot. Mag. t.* 7448 (1895).

DESCRIPTION: *Plants* suckering and forming small to large groups. *Stems* slender, up to 50cm. long, decumbent or ascending to erect, the apical 20cm. sub-densely foliate.
Leaves about 12—16, densely or subdensely rosulate, narrowly lanceolate- or ensiform-attenuate, 25—30cm. long (sometimes up to 45cm. long), 5—7cm. broad at base, more or less horizontally spreading and slightly- to much-recurved, sometimes with the apices of oldest leaves curved downwards; *upper surface* grey-green or dull pale-olive green, uni-coloured or sometimes with few to many scattered small dull-white lenticular spots low down; basally flat, slightly canalic-ulate upwards; *lower surface* convex, the colour of the upper surface, sometimes with numerous dull-white elongated spots in lowest quarter; *margins* entire, slightly rounded, smooth, with whitish cartilaginous edge.
Inflorescence a many-branched panicle about 70cm. high, produced sub-erectly or obliquely, rarely erect, about 6—9-branched, the lowest 2—3 branches sometimes with 2—3 or more branchlets, making a total of up to 25—30 racemes per inflorescence.
Peduncle basally plano-convex and 12—15mm. broad, divaricately branched from the middle or lower, the branches slender, about 4mm. thick, brown with a bloom.
Racemes suberect to oblique, sublaxly-flowered, the terminal about 15cm. long, the others a little shorter, the more oblique the racemes the more secund the flowers, the youngest buds grey-green tipped.
Bracts very small, ovate-acute, thin, scarious, white, 4mm. long, 2—3mm. broad at base, 3-nerved with 1 prominent nerve flanked by one paler nerve on each side.
Pedicels 5mm. long.
Perianth dull scarlet with a bloom, or yellow, cylindric-trigonous, up to 28mm. long, 7—8mm. diam. across the ovary, thence very slightly narrowed above the ovary and trigonously very slightly enlarging to the throat; *outer segments* free for 7mm., paler at the margins, obscurely 3-nerved; *inner segments* free but dorsally adnate to the outer to beyond the middle, broader than the outer and with more obtuse more spreading apices.
Filaments pale lemon, filiform-flattened, the 3 inner narrower and lengthening before the 3 outer with their *anthers* exserted 2—3mm.; *stigma* at length exserted 3—4mm.; *ovary* brownish, 5mm. long, 2mm. diam. (Plate 47, Figs. 222, 223).

YEMEN. Near the town Taaes—Forskal. (Ta'izz of Hugh Scott). Between Heis and Taizz—Deflers, and others.
S.-W. ARABIA. In large numbers in the Wadi Hardaba, 2,500 ft., flowers yellow, Jan. 1962, J. Lavranos 1891! (PRE).— This locality is in the Haushabi and Amiri country, below the Pass leading up to the Dhala Plateau, about 10 miles SE of Dhala, about 80 miles N of Aden.
S. ARABIA. Hadhramaut, Jol. On hills near Dobaibah (near Gambla), 3,000 ft., fl. 28 Feb. 1894, W. Lunt 225! (K)—the type of *A. luntii* Bak; Jol, Moola Mutan, 5,500 ft., cult. Nairobi, fl. 16 Aug. 1949, Ken Guichard HAD 210! (K, EA); Coll. Ken Guichard, cult. Johannesburg, fl. 27 March 1954, Reynolds 6225! (PRE).
SOMALIA NORTH (formerly Somaliland Prot.). Las Anod, 23 Oct. 1954, Bally B10177! (K, EA); Las Anod, 12 June 1958, C. F. Hemming 1346! (K, EA); between Halin and Helidera Tug, 2,300 ft., 29 Aug. 1956, Bally B10879! (K, EA); 3 miles N of Helidera Tug (84 miles S of Buran), fl. 15 Sept. 1957, Reynolds 8453 (PRE).

A. inermis was discovered by Forskal in 1774, near Taizz, in the Yemen, and was described by him a year later. No holotype was preserved, while Christensen in his revision of the Forskal Herbarium lists *A. inermis*, but classes it as *ignota*.

Deflers also collected *A. inermis* near Taizz, over 100 years later.

The typical (western) form with red flowers is reported by Mr. J. Lavranos to occur rather frequently throughout the upper Wadi Hardaba from Thumair in Kutaibi country, at 2,000 ft., to the head of Wadi Hardaba in the Haushabi and Amiri country below the Khureba Pass (which is about 10 miles SE of Dhala, and 80 miles N of Aden) and which leads up to the Dhala Plateau; also observed in Wadi Dareija, near Dhala. These localities are in the western sector of the South Arabian Federation – formerly Western Aden Protectorate. The western limit of the typical form appears to lie some 25 miles SE of Dhala on the road to Aden.

Mr. Lavranos saw no trace of *A. inermis* between that point and the limestone hills of Hadhra-maut in the east. This eastern form (named *A. luntii* Bak. in 1894, and now in synonymy), was collected by W. Lunt who was attached as botanical collector from Kew to the expedition organised by J. Theodore Bent in the winter of 1893–94 to explore the ruined cities of the Hadhramaut of Southern Arabia. Ken Guichard and others have collected it in the Hadhramaut.

PLATE 47

ALOE INERMIS   Forskal.

At the head of Wadi Hardaba, below the Khureba Pass leading up to
the Dhala Plateau, SW. Arabia. Height 70cm.
From a Kodachrome by Mr. J. Lavranos.

FIG. 222.

A. inermis Forskal. Starved plants 21 miles NE of Halin (3 miles N of Helidera Tug), Somalia North. Alt. 2,600 ft.

Mr. Lavranos records this eastern form on the seaward slopes of the escarpment, above 4,000 ft. The last plants seen on the road inland grew at Bain al Jibal at 6,500 ft., near the watershed separating the Wadi flowing south to the coast from those flowing north to the Wadi Hadhramaut. The eastern form differs from the western typical form in growing mostly as single plants, with a procumbent or ascending stem rarely 25cm. long. Leaves are fewer, about 8—10, perianth is red, and 25mm. long.

This form occurs in large numbers all round Mola Mata which is 54 miles N of Mukalla on the road inland to Wadi Doan at 6,000 ft., and at Bain al Jibal, 8 miles NW of Mola Matr. at 6,500 ft. Also occurs on the Qara Mountains, in Dhufar, S. Arabia.

In Somalia North (formerly Somaliland Prot.), *A. inermis* occurs in large numbers all round Las Anod in the far eastern parts of the country. The present author did not see *A. inermis* for a hundred miles across the Nogal Plain, but found it near Taleh, Halin and beyond, near Buran.

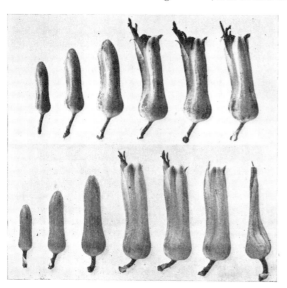

FIG. 223.

A. inermis Forsk. Flowers natural size. *Upper:* from a plant 21 miles NE of Halin, Somalia North. *Lower:* from a plant from the Jol of the Hadhramaut Arabia, flowering in Johannesburg.

The Somalia North plants appear to be a weaker form than those in Arabia.

A. inermis is characterized (as the name implies) by having leaves without marginal teeth. The inflorescence is produced suberectly to obliquely. The more oblique the raceme, the more noticeably secund the flowers are, while in suberect racemes the flowers are more evenly distributed around the axis.

Young plants remain in the distichous stage for some time and develop slowly.

86. **A. globuligemma** Pole Evans in *Trans. Roy. Soc. S. Afr.* 5: Part 1, 30, Plates 10, 11 (1915), in *Fl. Pl. S. Afr.* 1: Plate 2 (1921); Christian in *Rhod. Agric. Journ. Bull.* 905 (1933), et in *Journ. S.A. Bot.* 6: 188 (1940); Reynolds in *Aloes of S. Afr.* 443–46 (1950).

Plants with creeping rooting stems up to 50cm. long with suckers and offshoots forming dense groups.

Leaves about 20, densely rosulate, lanceolate-attenuate, erectly spreading with the apical portion slightly recurved, 45—50cm. long, 8—9cm. broad at base; *upper surface* somewhat glaucous, flat low down, subcanaliculate upwards, glabrous, without spots or lines; *lower surface* convex; *margins* with dull white to very pale pink narrow cartilaginous edge, armed with firm deltoid teeth about 2mm. long, up to 10mm. apart, the teeth dull white, pale-brown tipped, mostly curved towards apex of leaf, smaller more crowded low down, larger and more distant upwards.

Inflorescence a branched panicle up to 1m. high, sometimes 2 simultaneously, branched about the middle with 8—12 branches, the lowest sometimes 1—2-rebranched, all branches and racemes oblique to almost horizontally disposed.

Racemes subdensely flowered, 30—40cm. long, oblique to nearly horizontal, the flowers secund and all pointing towards base of branch; the youngest buds rather globular, dull-reddish with a bloom, open flowers sulphur-yellow to ivory, reddish-tinged near base, with a bloom.

Bracts ovate-acute, thin, scarious, 6mm. long, 3—5-nerved.

Pedicels 3—4mm. long.

Perianth cylindric-clavate, averaging 26mm. long, 5mm. diam. across the ovary, 10mm. diam. at the throat, narrowing slightly to the mouth; *outer segments* free for two-thirds their length (tube about 8mm.), 3—5-nerved, the nerves rose-coloured; *inner segments* free, broader than the outer, with 3 crowded nerves forming a keel, the apices more obtuse and more spreading than the outer.

Filaments filiform-flattened, the exserted portion deep brown to purplish almost black, the 3 inner narrower and lengthening before the 3 outer with their *anthers* in turn exserted 10—12mm.; *stigma* at length exserted 12—14mm. (Figs. 224, 225).

TRANSVAAL. Plants ex M'Phathlele's Location, fl. in Pretoria 21 Aug. 1914, I. B. Pole Evans in *Govt. Herb.* No. 20! (?) type (PRE). *Note:* M'Phathlele's Location lies between Chunies Poort and the Olifants River, in the Pietersburg Dist. of the N. Transvaal.

FIG. 224.

A. globuligemma Pole Evans. Plants on north side of the Nyanyadzi River, 61 miles S of Umtali, 20 miles S of Junction, Rhodesia, alt. 2,000 ft. Height 5 feet.

RHODESIA. Sabi Valley near Nyanyadze, 3 July 1952, H. Wild 3841! (K, PRE, SRGH); north side of Nyanyadzi River, 61 miles S of Umtali (20 miles S of Hotsprings), 2,000 ft., 24 July 1956, Reynolds 8240 (SRGH, K, PRE); near Birchenough Bridge, W bank of Sabi River, cult. Greendale, 21 July 1958, L. C. Leach 381 (PRE, SRGH); near Plumtree, 13 Aug. 1930, G. van Son (PRE).

BECHUANALAND PROT. 12 miles S of Bechuanaland border on Plumtree–Francistown Road, 4,300 ft., cult. Greendale, 16 Aug. 1961, L. C. Leach 11227 (SRGH, PRE).

This most attractive species of Aloe was first collected by Messrs. Wickens and Pienaar in M'Phathlele's Location in the Pietersburg District of the Transvaal in January 1914. Specimens brought to the then Botanical Laboratories in Pretoria (later the Division of Botany, and now the Botanical Research Institute) flowered during July and August 1941.

Although it spills over into the southern parts of Rhodesia, *A. globuligemma* is essentially a species of the Northern and North-eastern Transvaal. It occurs in vast numbers in Sekukuniland, and is especially abundant around Steelpoort in the Eastern Transvaal – see Colour Plate etc., in *Aloes of South Africa* 443 (1950).

In Rhodesia, *A. globuligemma* is found in large colonies among trees with *A. cryptopoda* NW of Plumtree, and W and S of that town on the Bechuanaland border.

It grows plentifully near Birchenough Bridge, and in the Sabi Valley, especially near Nyanyadzi in the eastern parts of Rhodesia.

FIG. 225.

A. globuligemma Pole Evans. Flowers natural size.

87. A. turkanensis Christian in *Journ. S.A. Bot.* 8: 173, pl. 6 (1942).

DESCRIPTION based on many plants 12 miles N of Isiolo (188 miles N of Nairobi), Northern Prov., Kenya.

Plants in small to large dense groups sometimes 2—3m. across. *Stems* procumbent, creeping and rooting, up to 4cm. thick, with shoots from base or at random, the terminal 20—30cm. subdensely foliate, the stems bare along the ground.

Leaves about 25, rosulate, basally sheathing, thence lanceolate long-attenuate, up to 55cm. long, 10cm. broad at base; *upper surface* dull bluish grey-green, rather rough to the touch, with few to many long-oblong or lenticular dull-white spots about 10mm. and more long, up to 5mm. broad at middle, irregularly scattered; *lower surface* convex, and resembling the upper surface. *Note:* The spotting is irregular and varies from few to many on both surfaces. *Margins* usually with a thin, dull-white, cartilaginous edge armed with laterally compressed deltoid teeth which are dull-whitish at base, reddish-brown-tipped, 2mm. long, 10—15mm. distant, more crowded low down, obsolescent towards apex. *Sap* dries glossy brown.

Inflorescence a branched panicle, 1·40m. high, about 12-branched from below the middle, the lowest branches with 2—5 branchlets, producing a total of about 26 racemes, the branches divaricately spreading, the terminal rhachis also turned obliquely, with all flowers more or less secund.

Peduncle flattened at base and 2cm. diam., heavily covered with a grey powdery bloom, lowest branch subtended at base by a thin, dry, ovate-acuminate 5—7-nerved bract.

Racemes the terminal sub-erect, up to 30cm. long, laxly flowered, the pedicels about 5—10mm. apart, flowers subsecund; in the more widely spreading branches the flowers are mostly secund and directed backwards.

Bracts very small, ovate-acute, about 3mm. long, and broad, thin, scarious, about 3-nerved.

Pedicels 5mm. long, deep brownish.

PLATE 48

ALOE TURKANENSIS   Christian.

12 miles N of Isiolo (189 miles N of Nairobi), Kenya. Alt. 4,000 ft. Height 5 ft.

Perianth dull pinkish-scarlet, 25mm. long, cylindric-trigonous, cylindric around the ovary and 7mm. diam., exceedingly slightly constricted above the ovary (mostly on the underside) thence trigonous and enlarging towards the throat, with the mouth wide open; *outer segments* free to the middle (tube 13mm.), with thinner paler margins and subacute spreading apices, 3-nerved; *inner segments* themselves free, but dorsally adnate to the outer for half their length, broader than the outer and with broader thin border and more obtuse, more spreading, brown-tipped apices.

Filaments pale lemon, filiform-flattened, the 3 inner narrower and lengthening before the 3 outer with their *anthers* in turn exserted 2mm.; *style* pale yellow, filiform, with the *stigma* at length exserted 4mm.; *ovary* pale brownish-green, 3-angled (not cylindric). (Plate 48, Fig. 226).

KENYA. *Turkana Desert*, below the second escarpment, c. 180 miles N of Kapenguria, coll. J. Erens 1610, 2 August 1938, cult. Ewanrigg, fl. 7 May 1941, Christian 987 holotype (SRGH), isotype (PRE). *Note:* This locality is in N.-W. Kenya, W of Lake Rudolph, beyond the foot of Napau Pass, about 150 miles N of Kitale). Plant coll. J. Erens, fl. D.O.B. Pretoria, 13 May 1940, J. Erens 1610! (SRGH). *Northern Prov.*, 12 miles N of Isiolo, 4,000 ft., 21 April 1952, Reynolds 6571 (K, PRE), Bally 8188 (EA). *Turkana*, foot of Napau Pass, 3,000 ft., Nov. 1958, Mrs. E. M. Tweedie 1753! (K); Loya River, Nov. 1962, Mrs. E. M. Tweedie 2506! (EA); 15 miles N of Kangetet, 14 July 1954, Hemming 321! (EA); 10 miles N of Lokichar, 2 April 1954, Hemming 274! (EA).

A. turkanensis is found in intensely hot arid places to the west, south and east of Lake Rudolph, in Kenya, at altitudes of 3,000 ft. to 4,000 ft., also in the eastern parts of Karamoja, Uganda, near Amudat and south of Toror Mountain, near the Kenya border.

Stems are decumbent, creeping and rooting, with the ascending apical portion subdensely foliate.

Plants sometimes form groups up to 1—3m. across.

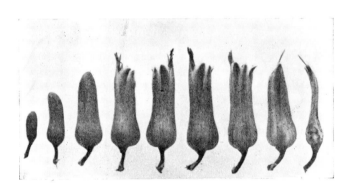

FIG. 226.

A. turkanensis Christian. Flowers 1/1 from a plant from the type locality.

88. **A. leachii** Reynolds in *Journ. S.A. Bot.* 31: 275 (1965).

DESCRIPTION: *Plant* succulent, acaulous or shortly caulescent, growing singly or with a few offshoots from base forming small groups.

Leaves about 20, rosulate, suberectly spreading up to 35cm. long, 6cm. broad at base, gradually narrowing to an acute apex; *upper surface* flat low down, slightly canaliculate upwards, uniformly dark green with reddish tinge, without spots or markings; *lower surface* convex, otherwise as the upper; *marginal teeth* reddish-brown, pungent, deltoid, about 5mm. long and 10—20mm. distant.

Inflorescence 2 simultaneously, up to 1m. high, divaricately 7—10-branched from below the middle, the lowest branches sometimes with 1—2 branchlets, the *peduncle* plano-convex and 15—20mm. broad at base.

Racemes cylindric, 15—20cm. long, 7cm. diam., very laxly flowered, the terminal ascending with the flowers more or less evenly distributed around the axis, the others sometimes almost horizontal and with their flowers more or less secund.

Pedicels 6—8mm. long.

Bracts small, ovate-acute, dirty-white, 5mm. long, 4mm. broad, 3—5-nerved.

Perianth scarlet, paler at mouth, slightly striped, cylindric-trigonous, 30mm. long, basally rounded, cylindric and 7mm. diam. across the ovary, trigonous upwards; *outer segments* free to the middle (15mm.), paler at the margins, the pale colour continuing to base and giving the flower a somewhat striped effect; *inner segments* broader than the outer, with broad pale-orange border and with 3 crowded nerves forming a scarlet keel, the apices more obtuse, more spreading than the outer.

Anthers exserted 1—2mm.; *stigma* at length exserted 2—3mm.; *ovary* olive-green, 6mm. long, 3mm. diam. (Figs. 227—229).

TANZANIA (TANGANYIKA). *Eastern Prov.*, 18 miles W of Bagamoyo Ferry on road westwards to Msata, cult. "Farview", Greendale (Rhodesia), fl. 26 May 1963, Leach et Brunton 10178 holotype (PRE); cult. Mbabane, Swaziland, fl. 15 Aug. 1964, Leach 10178 in Reynolds 10125 (K).

A. leachii was named after Mr. L. C. Leach of Greendale, Salisbury, who discovered plants about 18 miles inland (westwards) from Bagamoyo Ferry, Tanzania, on the road to Msata, more or less in open woodland, at an altitude of about 900 ft.

A. leachii is allied to *A. secundiflora* Engler in having widely spreading inflorescence branches and more or less subsecund flowers but differs in being a smaller plant, with much laxer racemes that are not so markedly secund, and in having smaller flowers that are not, or only very slightly, minutely white-flecked. In *A. leachii* the terminal raceme is ascending with the flowers more evenly distributed around the axis; the flowers also have a slightly striped effect compared with those of *A. secundiflora*.

FIG. 227.   FIG. 228.

A. leachii Reynolds.

FIG. 227. Plant from 18 miles W of Bagamoyo Ferry, on road to Msata, Tanzania (Tanganyika) flowering in Mr. Leach's gardens at Greendale, Salisbury, Rhodesia. Height 1m.

FIG. 228. Plant from type locaiity, flowering at Mbabane, Swaziland, Height 1m.

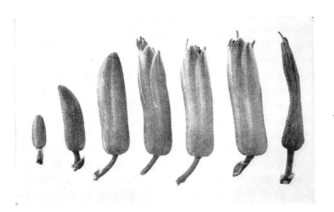

FIG. 229.

A. leachii Reynolds. Buds and flowers 1/1.

89. **A. guerrai** Reynolds in *Journ. S.A. Bot.* 26: 85, pl. 6, 7 (1960).

DESCRIPTION: *Plant* solitary, acaulous or with very short stem, the rosette of leaves usually with a slight tilt.

Leaves about 24, densely rosulate, narrowly lanceolate, long-pointed, the youngest suberectly spreading, the oldest spreading with apical portion slightly recurved, averaging 40cm. long, 6—7cm. broad at base; *upper surface* flat low down, slightly canaliculate upwards, dull green, obscurely lineate, without spots or markings; *lower surface* convex, grey-green, without markings; *margins* sinuate-dentate, armed with pungent pale-brown or reddish-brown teeth that are 4—5mm. long, 10—15mm. apart, more crowded lower down, more distant upwards; *sap* dries yellow.

Inflorescence a branched panicle 90—100cm. high.

Peduncle brown with a bloom, basally plano-convex and 25—30mm. broad, divaricately about 8—10-branched from about the middle, the lowest 1—2 branches sometimes with 1—2 branchlets, and with a few sterile bracts below the racemes.

Racemes all (including the terminal) produced obliquely to almost horizontally, averaging 20cm. long, sublaxly flowered, the buds and open flowers secund.

Bracts ovate-acute, 6—8mm. long, 4mm. broad, thin, dirty-white, about 7-nerved, reflexed at the middle.

Pedicels averaging 5mm. long.

Perianth scarlet with a bloom, averaging 40mm. long, cylindric-trigonous, straight or sometimes very slightly curved, flat at base, cylindric and 8mm. diam. across the ovary, thence trigonous upwards with the mouth slightly upturned; *outer segments* free for 10—12mm., paler at the margins, very obscurely nerved, the apices subacute, slightly spreading; *inner segments* themselves free but dorsally adnate to the outer to beyond the middle, with broad white border and a scarlet keel, the apices more obtuse and more spreading than the outer.

Filaments lemon, the 3 inner narrower and lengthening before the 3 outer, with their *anthers* in turn exserted 2mm.; *stigma* at length exserted 3mm.; *ovary* green, 6—7mm. long, 3—4mm. diam. (Plate 49, Figs. 230, 231).

FIG. 230.

A. guerrai Reynolds. Plant 23 miles E of Monte Belo 104 miles E of Lobito, Benguela Dist., Angola. Alt. 4,000 ft. Height 6 ft.

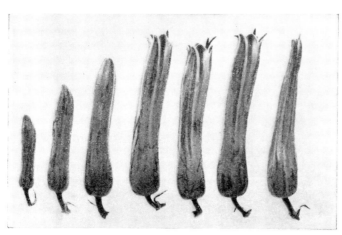

FIG. 231.

A. guerrai Reynolds. Flowers 1/1 from a plant near General Machado, Angola.

ALOE GUERRAI   Reynolds.

Plant 3 miles E of General Machado, Bié Dist., Angola. Flowering in
June. Height 1m.

ANGOLA. *Bié Dist.*, 3 miles E of General Machado, c. 12° 02′ S, 17° 30′ E, alt. 4,500 ft., fl. 18 June 1959, Reynolds 9218 holotype (PRE), isotype (K, LUA). *Benguela:* 6 miles W of Balombo, c. 12° 21′ S, 14° 42′ E, alt. 4,000 ft., fl. 3 July 1959, Reynolds 9325 (PRE, LUA, K).

This fascinating species was named after Senhor Guilherme Guerra, Engenheiro Agronomo (Director of Agriculture and Forests, Luanda, Angola) who first collected and sent plants to the author in 1952 from Posto do Cunje, 5 miles N of Silva Porto, the capital of the District of Bié. A plant collected by Dr. Guerra flowered in Johannesburg in August 1956, when it was recognised as a distinct new species.

In June and July 1959, during the author's travels in Angola investigating the Aloes, he found a large number of flowering plants near General Machado (about 50 miles E of Dr. Guerra's locality, Posto do Cunje) in grasslands with bush, at 4,500 ft., c. 12° 02′ S., 17° 30′ E.

Subsequently, it was found that *A. guerrai* occurred from about 20 miles E of General Machado westwards to Posto do Cunje and Silva Porto, Chinguar (5,500 ft.), near Nova Lisboa; and abundant near Moma, 38 miles S of Bela Vista.

On the main road inland from Lobito, *A. guerrai* was observed repeatedly from Monte Belo, 30 miles W of Balombo, to Balombo (4,000 ft., c. 12° 21′ S, 14° 42′ E), and for 12 miles eastwards. Northwest of Luimbale and 15—20 miles NW of Cassongue (5,000 ft., c. 11° 51′ S, 14° 55′ E), more plants were found.

A very robust form was observed in seed on 10 July, 8 miles E of Salazar in Luanda Province, on the road to Malange, c. 9° 42′ S, 15° 34′ E.

A. guerrai is characterized by having a divaricately-branched inflorescence with oblique to sub-horizontal racemes of secund flowers. In this respect it is nearest allied to the East African species *A. secundiflora* Engler, but the latter has longer, broader, thicker leaves, and perianths with outer segments free for half their length.

With slightly tilted rosettes, in kind and size of leaves, and with perianth outer segments free for 10—12mm., *A. guerrai* is nearer *A. christianii* Reynolds. The latter, however, produces a compactly-branched inflorescence 6 ft. and more high, with erect racemes.

NATIVE NAME: *Chaudala* (Silva Porto).

FLOWERING PERIOD: May, June.

90. **A. secundiflora** Engler in *Pflanzenwelt Ostafrikas* 140 (1895); Baker in *Fl. Trop. Afr.* 7: 457 (1898); Berger in Engler's *Pflanzenr.* Liliac.-Aloin. 267 (1908); Reynolds in *Journ. S.A. Bot.* 19: 13 (1953); Verdoorn in *Fl. Pl. Afr.* 34: Pl. 1341 (1961).
—— *A. engleri* Berger in Engler's *Bot. Jahrb.* 36: 60 (1905), in Engler's *Pflanzenr. l.c.* 252 (1908).

DESCRIPTION: *Plants* acaulescent or very shortly caulescent; mostly solitary, or in small groups, rarely soboliferous.

Leaves about 20, densely rosulate, erectly spreading, slightly recurved near apex, ovate-lanceolate-attenuate, averaging 45cm. long, 12—14cm. broad at base, dull-green, rather glossy, without spots; *upper surface* flat low down, slightly canaliculate towards apex; *lower surface* rather flat low down, more rounded upwards; *margins* obtuse, sinuate-dentate, armed with laterally compressed deltoid teeth which are pungent, brown with paler tips, straight or hooked forward, averaging 4mm. long, 15mm. distant, the teeth isolated in younger leaves, sometimes joined by a horny brown marginal edge in older leaves. Sap dries yellow.

Inflorescence a divaricately branched panicle 1—1·5m. high, sometimes 2 simultaneously, branched from below the middle with about 10—12 slender oblique branches, sometimes producing 50 and more racemes per inflorescence, the lowest branch subtended at base by a broadly ovate, thin, scarious, pale-brown, 7-nerved bract about 12mm. long, 20mm. broad at base.

Peduncle brown with a grey powdery-bloom, plano-convex and 35mm. diam. at base, terete upwards, the branches slender, oblique.

Racemes more or less oblique, 15—20cm. long, rather laxly about 18-flowered, the flowers more or less secund, the buds rose-pink and greyish tipped, clearly spotted, the open flowers clearly spotted; the buds suberect and grouped along the top of the branch, open flowers cernuous to pendulous, after pollination the drying perianth and fruit becoming erect.

Bracts ovate-acute or deltoid, thin, scarious, about 4—5mm. long, 4—5mm. broad at base, 3—5-nerved.

Pedicels 8—10 mm. long.

Perianth rose-pink to dull scarlet-red, paler at mouth, obscurely to clearly minutely white-spotted, averaging 35mm. long, cylindric, basally flat and not at all stipitate, 9mm. diam. over the ovary, slightly constricted above the ovary, thence slightly trigonous and slightly enlarging to the open mouth; *outer segments* free for half their length, with paler margins and subacute spreading apices, obscurely 3-nerved, the nerves turning brownish at apex; *inner segments* themselves free but dorsally adnate to the outer and with broad pale border, with 3 congested nerves forming a keel throughout, the apices more obtuse and more spreading than the outer.

Filaments very pale lemon, filiform-flattened, the 3 inner narrower and lengthening before the 3 outer, with their *anthers* in turn exserted 5mm.; *style* lemon, filiform, with *stigma* at length exserted 6mm.; *ovary* pale green, 6mm. long, 3mm. diam., finely 6-grooved. (Plate 50, Figs. 232–236).

PLATE 50

ALOE SECUNDIFLORA   Engler.

At Kifaru (type locality), 10 miles S of Himo, Tanga Prov., Tanzania
(Tanganyika). Height 5 ft.

Fig. 232.   Fig. 233.

A. secundiflora Engler.

Fig. 232. Lower foothills of Mt. Meru 22 miles W of Arusha, Tanzania (Tanganyika) – with Botanical Assistant Kirrika.

Fig. 233. At south end of L. Naivasha, Kenya. Height 4 ft. 6 ins.

Fig. 234.

A. secundiflora Engler. 10 miles NW of Moyale on road to Mega, Borana, Sidamo, S. Ethiopia, 3° 40′ N., 38° 38′ E., Height 4 feet.

FIG. 235.

A. secundiflora Engler. Raceme × 1/3, at the angle produced.

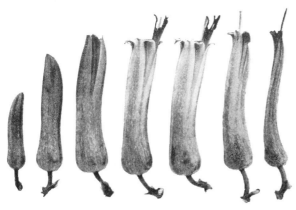

FIG. 236.

A. secundiflora Engler. Flowers natural size from a plant at the type locality.

TANZANIA. *Kilimanjaro Dist.*, at the foot of the Rhino Hills at 700—800m., fl. 4 July 1893, G. Volkens 530, holotype (B). *Tanga Prov.*, Mwembe and Vudea Valleys, W side of S. Pares, 3,000 ft., 30 June 1942, P. J. Greenway 6506! (EA, PRE); 10 miles S of Himo, 2,200 ft., 30 July 1957, Bally 11621! (K, EA); at Kifaru, 10 miles S of Himo (type loc.), 2,500 ft., 5 July 1958, Reynolds 8782 (K, PRE, EA). *Lake Prov.*, Shinyanga, Mahumbu River Flats, 3,900 ft., June–July 1935, B. D. Burtt 5138 (K, PRE, SRGH), 5139! (K), 5159! (K, PRE, EA, SRGH); 68 miles SE of Biharamulu, 3900!, 15 July 1958, Reynolds 8872 (K, PRE, EA). *Musoma Dist.*, between Junction of the Seronera and Oranji Rivers, 28 May 1961, Greenway 10335 (EA). *Northern Prov.*, Masai Dist., 49 miles W of Endulen (W of Ngorongoro Crater), 5,500 ft., 27 July 1957, Bally 11608 (K); lower western foothills of Mt. Meru, 22 miles W of Arusha, 4,600 ft., 28 March 1952, Reynolds 6367 (K, PRE, EA). *Central Prov.*, between Iringa and Dodoma, in dry, thorny country, coll. 18 June 1938, cult. DOB, fl. 25 April 1940, Pole Evans et Erens 807 (PRE, SRGH, EA); 7 miles S of Bubu River, S of Kondoa, 19 June 1938, Pole Evans et Erens 828! (PRE, K). On the hills at Oldango, fl. 28 March 1940 at Pretoria, Pole Evans et Erens 1019 (PRE, SRGH)ex seeds from Mpwapwa, 6,000 ft., cult. Amani, 16 May 1942, Greenway 6459 (EA, PRE); Coll. Major A. C. McLoughlin 694! near Nanyuki, Kenya, fl. DOB, Pretoria, April 1948, no. 28669 (PRE), figured for FPA, May 1948.

KENYA. Baringo, 3,400 ft., March 1901, Sir H. H. Johnston (K). *Teita Dist.*, near Maktau, between Taveta and the Bura Hills, 30 March 1952, Reynolds 6374 (PRE, K, EA). *Northern Prov.*, near Moyale, 3,800 ft., 25 April 1952, J. B. Gillett 12943 (K, EA, PRE); abundant 8 miles E of Thomson's Falls on road to Nanyuki, 6,000 ft., 20 April 1952, Reynolds 6560 (K, PRE); Olorgesailie, 42 miles SW of Nairobi, 2,500 ft., 23 May 1952, Reynolds 6360 (PRE, K, EA); Chyulu North, 5,200 ft., rocky ledge of small crater, 21 May 1938, Bally 823! (K, EA).

SUDAN. *Equatoria Prov.*, 26 miles SW of Juba, 2,400 ft., 13 July 1954, Reynolds 7490 (K, PRE, B).

S. ETHIOPIA. Borana, 22 miles W of Yavello, 4° 58′ N, 37° 53′ E, 4,000 ft., 18 Aug. 1953, Reynolds 7065! (K, PRE).

DISTRIBUTION

A. secundiflora is widely distributed in parts of Tanzania and Kenya, and extends northwards into Southern Ethiopia and the Southern Sudan. The material cited above gives an idea as to its range.

The southern limit appears to be near Iringa in Central Tanzania, with Igalula–Tabora–Kahama–Biharamulu in the west, and eastwards through Lake Prov., Northern Prov. and Central Prov. to Tanga Prov.; all round the base of Kilimanjaro; also occurs along the Tanga–Mombasa road.

In Kenya *A. secundiflora* is abundant along the Tanga–Mombasa road from 64 miles to near Kinango, 30 miles from Mombasa; not seen N of Mombasa on the Malidni–Lamu road. From Mombasa, westwards near Mariakani (20 miles NW of Mombasa), along the road to Voi, thence westwards to Maktau and Taveta; Sultan Hamud, occasional on the Kapiti Plains; Machakos; at the foot of Lukenya Hill; abundant at the Athi River road bridge, Stony Athi (20 miles SE of Nairobi); E of Thika, near Donyo Sabuk; in the Kedong Valley (NW of Nairobi); Mt. Margaret; near Mt. Longonot and at the southern end of Lake Naivasha; near Elmenteita; southwards along the Rift Valley to Olorgesailie Prehistoric Site; Kajiado; near Nanyuki (122 miles N of Nairobi); tremendous quantities 34 miles W of Nanyuki near the Mutara Police Post where, in April, the countryside is pink with flowers for a few miles; in the Ngobit Valley, 16 miles SE of Mutara; near Moyale, and across the border in Ethiopia for 30 miles along the road to Mega, to 15 miles N of Yavello and 25 miles W of Yavello towards the Sagan River, in Borana Dist., Sidamo Prov. SUDAN: A form with racemes less oblique than usual was seen 26 miles SW of Juba, on road to Yei, in Equatoria Prov.

VARIATION

At Kifaru, at the northern tip of Tanga Province in Tanzania (type locality), also near Lake Chala and Maktau, Mariakani, that is the localities furthest east, *A. secundiflora* occurs as large solitary plants and not in groups. In the Rift Valley of Kenya, small groups are found increasing by division and not from suckers, while in the furthest west localities, i.e. in the Biharamulu district, dense groups from suckers occur, leaves being darker green, narrower and more long-pointed than elsewhere. This form was also noticed plentifully around the base of large termite mounds in partial shade in *Brachystegia-Pseudoberlinia* woodland 38—46 miles SSW of Tabora on road to Igalula and Mpanda.

SPOTTED PERIANTH

A character not mentioned in Volken's original description (or by Berger subsequently) is the perianth which has numerous small white specks or spots throughout. No sooner are racemes scalded, pressed and dried in the field, when this distinguishing character is irretrievably lost, and when dried flowers are later soaked, the spotting is absent.

The late Mr. H. Basil Christian once submitted racemes of these "spotted" flowers to Dr. J. C. Hopkins, then Chief Botanist and Plant Pathologist, Salisbury, Rhodesia, who reported : "The pale specks on flowers are not due to a pigment, but are pale translucent spots or stripes caused by the presence of bubbles of gas in the sub-epidermal tissue. The gas does not appear to be enclosed in any special structure".

NATURAL HYBRID

Crosses of *A. secundiflora* with *A. otallensis* var. *elongata* (with both parents nearby), were noticed 6 and 8 miles N of Dubuluch, which is 27 and 29 miles N of Mega on the road to Yavello in Boran, Sidamo, S. Ethiopia. In this cross, rosettes and leaves were nearer *A. secundiflora* but large white bracts, pedicels, and shorter perianths narrowing at base were nearer *A. otallensis* var. *elongata*. This is the cited locality for *A. boranensis* Cufod., and plants of this cross fit the description of that species, hence the name should be dropped.
MATERIAL: *S. Ethiopia*, Borana, 8 miles N of Dubuluch (29 miles N of Mega), 4° 27' N, 38° 17' E, 16 Sept. 1953 Reynolds 7047 (PRE).

91. **A. ortholopha** Christian et Milne-Redhead in *Kew Bull.* No. 10, 478 (1933); Verdoorn in *Fl. Pl. S. Afr.* 23: Plate 882 (1943).

DESCRIPTION based on plants at type locality.
  Plant succulent, stemless, solitary.
  Leaves 30 or more, densely rosulate, spreading-erect, slightly in-curved, broadly lanceolate, up to 50cm. long, 12—14 cm. broad near base, about 14mm. thick; *upper surface* flat low down, slightly canaliculate upwards, dull grey-green, with pinkish tinge, without spots or markings; *lower surface* convex, otherwise as upper surface; *margins* with pinkish to reddish-brown edge armed with pungent, deltoid teeth, smaller and crowded low down and 4mm. apart, larger and 10mm. apart at the middle, more distant and 20mm. apart, 4mm. long, upwards.

PLATE 51

ALOE ORTHOLOPHA   Christian et Milne-Redhead.

Mtoroshanga Pass, Umvukwes, 61 miles NNW of Salisbury, Rhodesia.
Alt. 4,000 ft. Height 3 feet.

11

Inflorescence usually one, rarely 2, averaging 80—90cm. high, 2—3-branched high up (rarely 5-branched); peduncle basally plano-convex and 4cm. broad, 2·5cm. thick.

Racemes almost horizontal, very densely-flowered, averaging 30cm. long, the flowers markedly secund and pointing slightly backwards.

Bracts narrowly lanceolate-attenuate, 10—15mm. long, 5mm. broad, thin, subscarious, 5—7-nerved.

Pedicels thick, about 8mm. long, laterally compressed, 5mm. broad.

Perianth orange-scarlet to blood-red, averaging 40mm. long, cylindric-ventricose, roundly trigonal, 6—7mm. diam. at base, 10—11mm. diam. at the middle, then narrowing to 6—7mm. at the rather closed mouth; *outer segments* free for 30mm. (tube 10mm.), rather thick and fleshy, obscurely 3—5-nerved, the apices subacute; *inner segments* free, but dorsally adnate to the outer for 10mm., broader than the outer, thin at the edges, with a prominent scarlet keel, the apices dark-brown tipped, and more obtuse and more spreading than the outer.

Filaments almost white within, the exserted portion purple-black, the 3 inner narrower and lengthening before the 3 outer with their *anthers* in turn exserted 10—15mm.; *stigma* at length exserted 15—18mm.; *ovary* green, 9mm. long. (Plate 51, Fig. 237).

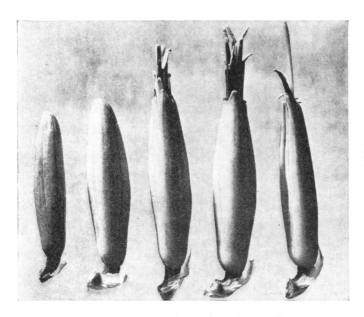

Fig. 237.

A. ortholopha Christian et Milne-Redhead. Flowers 1/1 from bud to post-pollination stages.

RHODESIA (formerly Southern Rhodesia). Mtoroshanga Pass in the Umvukwe Hills on the Great Dyck, 5,000 ft., cult. at Salisbury, 19 Aug. 1926, Herb. Dept. Agric. S. Rhod. 1201 (Eyles 5448 in Herb. Eyles; type). *Mazoe Dist.*, Umvukwe, cult. Div. of Bot, Pretoria, fl. Aug. 1942, Christian 289! (PRE, K) the type of *Fl. Pl. S. Afr.* 23: Plate 478 (1933): Umvukwe, Ntoroshanga Pass, 61 miles NNW of Salisbury, 5,000 ft., fl. 12 July 1957, Reynolds 8194 (PRE, SRGH, K). *Darwin Dist.*, Mt. Bandilombidzi, 17 May 1955, R. Watmough 137! (SRGH, PRE)—this is at the extreme western end of the Mvuradona Range, at 5,000 ft., almost overlooking the Umsengedzi Valley.

Mr. J. A. Whellan has also found *A. ortholopha* on the Zambezi Escarpment, Mvuradona Range.

The specific epithet refers to the crest-like appearance of the horizontal racemes of upright flowers. – Mr. E. Milne-Redhead.

The late Mr. H. B. Christian stated that plants of *A. ortholopha* were first brought into Salisbury by Mr. G. Mainwaring, Dept. of Agriculture, Salisbury, about 1926.

The Mtoroshanga Pass is 61 miles NNW from Salisbury, and consists mostly of rocky, treeless hills, the formation being serpentine rock. More plants are found along the south side of the Pass for a distance of 3—4 miles from the eastern entrance, and no other species of Aloe has been found nearby. The flower colour varies in different plants from light orange-red, to deep blood-crimson.

FLOWERING PERIOD: Late July, August.

PLATE 52

ALOE MAWII   Christian.

On Zomba Plateau, Southern Prov., Malawi. Alt. 4,000 ft. Height 6 ft.

92. **A mawii** Christian in *Journ. S.A. Bot.* 6: 186, pl. 23 (1940); Reynolds in *Aloes of Nyasaland* 40 (1954).

DESCRIPTION: *Plant* arborescent, 1—2m. high, the heads sometimes dividing and becoming branched. *Stems* stout, 10—12cm. thick.

Leaves 20 and more, densely rosulate, spreading or erectly spreading, more or less recurved, ensiform, 50cm. long, up to 10cm. broad at base; *upper surface* green with a bluish tinge, unspotted, somewhat striate, broadly concave or canaliculate; *lower surface* convex or rounded, striate; *margins* acute, with narrow reddish border armed with pinkish-tipped uncinate deltoid teeth 3mm. long, 15mm. apart at middle of leaf, closer towards base and apex; the interspaces usually straight.

Inflorescence simple or with one lateral branch, arising obliquely, up to 1m. long.

Peduncle green low down, brown upwards, laterally compressed low down and 25mm. broad, slightly furrowed, sparsely sterile-bracteate below the raceme; *sterile bracts* broadly triangular-acute, shortly cuspidate, 4mm. long, 10mm. broad, smaller upwards.

Racemes densely secund-flowered, averaging 30cm. long, the flowers slightly retrorse.

Bracts small, 1mm. long, 3mm. broad, triangular-acute, shortly cuspidate.

Pedicels stout, green with a pinkish globose swelling above, sharply constricted at junction with perianth, 1—2mm. long, 3—4mm. thick.

Perianth red (or orange), 35—40mm. long, sometimes longer (45—48mm.), 7mm. diam. across the ovary, gradually widening to 10mm. at the middle, thence gradually constricted towards the mouth (ventricose), broadly trigonous; *outer segments* free for 22mm., obscurely 8-nerved, the apices straight, subacute; *inner segments* free, yellowish-white with a 3-nerved red keel, 11mm. broad, apices subobtuse, straight, tightly clasping the filaments.

Filaments exserted for about 12mm., the included portion yellow, exserted portion blackish-purple, widened and flattened, tightly pressed together; *anthers* terra-cotta, 9mm. long, 2mm. broad, at length withdrawn into the perianth; *style* yellow, exserted; *ovary* pale-green, cylindric-acuminate, 9mm. long, 4mm. diam.—H. B. Christian. (Plate 52, Figs. 238–242).

MALAWI (formerly Nyasaland): Zomba Plateau, 4,000 ft., col. June 1938, cult. Ewanrigg, 5 June 1939, Christian 942! holotype (SRGH); Zomba Mtn., June 5, 1946, L. J. Brass 16273! (K, SRGH); Mt. Mlanje, Tuchilla Plateau, 5,700 ft., 26 July 1956, Newman et Whitmore 240! (BM, SRGH).

MOÇAMBIQUE. Tumbini Mountains (near Nyasaland border and Mt. Mlanje), Aug. 1942, A. J. W. Hornby 2754! (PRE). *Zambesia Dist.*, granite slopes on west face of Namuli Peaks near Vila Junqueiro (Gurue), c. 4,000 ft., 26 July 1962, Leach et Schelpe 11481! (SRGH).—Plants arborescent to 12 ft. high, branched near base or higher.

The following material is from plants that are acaulescent or almost so, and growing singly or in very small groups from division. Flowers are mostly smaller than in the typical form.

Moçambique Dist.: Bare granite hill, 9 miles E of Camuana (34 miles E of Nampula), 1,000 ft., 15° S, 39° 40′ E, cult.

FIG. 238.

A. mawii Christian. On Zomba Plateau, Malawi.
Photo: By courtesy, Dr. Harold E. Antony.

FIG. 239.

A. mawii Christian. Raceme × 1/4 from a plant ex Mlanje Mountain, Malawi – at the angle produced.

FIG. 240.

A. mawii Christian. Flowers 1/1 from a plant on Zomba Mountain, Malawi.

FIG. 241.

A. mawii Christian. An acaulescent form 32 miles E of Malema, 30 miles W of Ribaue, Moçambique Dist., Moçambique.
Photo: Mr. L. C. Leach.

FIG. 242.

A. mawii Christian. Flowers 1/1 from a small form on the Matagoro Hills, 4 miles SE of Songea, Southern Province, Tanzania (Tanganyika).

Farview, Salisbury, flowers in summer, Leach et Schelpe 11439! (SRGH, PRE); 37 miles W of Nampula, 15° 01′ S, 38° 50′ E, 2,000 ft., 23 May 1961, Leach et Rutherford Smith 10973 (SRGH, PRE)—raceme in bud, W slopes of granite hill, 32 miles E of Malema (Entre Rios), 2,000 ft., c. 14° 55′ S, 37° 51′ E, 18 July 1962, Leach et Schelpe 11397 (SRGH, PRE)—plants acaulescent, solitary, leaves red-brown, spreading-recurved to suberect, inflorescence frequently 2-branched, flowers red, orange. *Zambesia Dist.*,10 miles S of Lioma, 15° 19′ S., 36° 47′ E, 2,400 ft., 25 July 1962, Leach et Schelpe 11447! (SRGH, PRE)—acaulescent, racemes red, marginal teeth sometimes closely set.

TANZANIA. *Southern Prov.:* Songea Dist., Matogoro Hills, 1320–1440m., 14 July 1956, Milne-Redhead et Taylor 10827! (K); Matengo Hills, Kihuru Hill, Ngwambo, 1770m., 22 May 1956, Milne-Redhead et Taylor 10413 (K); Matogoro hills, 4 miles SE of Songea, abundant along the top at 4,800 ft., 25 June 1958, Reynolds 8696! (K, PRE, EA).

TYPE LOCALITY: Zomba Plateau, 4,000 ft., Malawi.

DISTRIBUTION

MALAWI. At south end of the Kirk Range, east of Zobue (Moçambique) Customs, and south of Mwanza (Malawi) Customs – found there by Mr. L. C. Leach. Abundant on Mlanje Mountain, up the Likabula trail to Luchenya before reaching the cedar line, also on Simpson's Peak on Luchenya Plateau; also on the Tuchila Plains SW of Mlanje – also across the Moçambique border on Tumbini Hill.

The late Mr. W. H. J. Rangeley reported the species on top of Ndirandi Hill, Blantyre, also between Blantyre and Zomba on Chiradzulu Mountain. Abundant on the plateau edge and slopes of Zomba Mountain. Top ridge of plateau of Chingoni Mountain, 20 miles N of Dedza. Also observed by the present author on rocks at Manchewe Falls, 4 miles N of Livingstonia, Northern Province.

TANZANIA, Southern Province: Abundant in the Songea Dist. on granite from 4,400 ft. to 6,000 ft. Mr. E. Milne-Redhead of Kew found forms of *A. mawii* along the top of the Matogoros, 4 miles SE of Songea, and generally in the Matengo Highlands, 3 miles SE of Litembo Mission (5,900 ft.); Kihuru Hill, Luiri Kitesi Hill, near Mpapa on the Mbamba Bay road SW of Songea. Also found near Masasi – about 285 miles E of Songea.

MOÇAMBIQUE. Thanks to the investigations of Mr. L. C. Leach, *A. mawii* in various forms has now been found to occur abundantly in parts of the Moçambique and Niassa Districts, along the main road westwards from Lumbo (on the coast opposite Moçambique town and Island) to Nampula and beyond.

An acaulescent form, 80 miles W of Lumbo and 34 miles E of Nampula, growing singly, with red leaves and flowering in October needs further investigation; it might merit varietal rank.

Further inland from just E of Nampula, repeatedly westwards to Ribane, all plants seen had little or no stems, while in Niassa Dist. on W face of Namuli Peaks near Vila Junqueiro (Gurue), typical

A. mawii with stems to 10 ft. was seen.

Mr. Leach observed that the acaulescent form occurs in several localities and in large numbers, but always between 1,800 ft. and 2,400 ft., with typical caulescent *A. mawii* occurred (in large numbers) between 4,000 ft. to 4,500 ft. It is noteworthy that in the Moçambique and Tanzania forms some plants are found with shorter flowers than in Malawi. This was particularly noticed on the Matogoras, near Songea, in Tanzania.

A. mawii was named after Capt. A. H. Maw of "Namadidi", Zomba, on whose property on Zomba Plateau numbers of plants occur on the edge of a precipice, and on steep mountain slopes nearby, mostly facing east.

A. mawii is a striking species with its horizontally disposed racemes of flowers that are secund, i.e., grouped along the top of the axis and pointing slightly backwards.

In this respect it is allied to *A. ortholopha* Christian et Milne-Redhead, on the Umvukwes, NW of Salisbury, but the latter is always acaulescent, and has shorter, broader, thicker, grey leaves in a compact rosette.

In its widely distributed localities *A. mawii* varies considerably. It occurs as single plants with no stem, to shrubby with branched stems up to 10 ft. high. Leaves vary in shape and colour, and marginal teeth from crowded and smaller to larger and more spaced. Racemes vary in length, and flowers vary from orange to red, and from 30mm. to 50mm. long, the average being 35—40mm.

GROUP 15

Flowers Sessile Or Very Shortly Pedicellate
Racemes Very Densely Flowered, Bottlebrush-Like

Plants with little or no stem. *Leaves* large, compactly rosulate, or spreading-recurved. *Inflorescence* simple or few-branched. *Bracts* small to large. *Pedicels* 1—4mm. long. *Perianth* mostly cylindric-ventricose, up to 40mm. long; *outer segments* free to the middle, or to near base; *filaments* long-exserted.

Type species: *A. aculeata* Pole Evans, Rhodesia.

A species with 1mm. pedicels and dense racemes, *A. exselsa* Berger, fits better into Group 18, and is included there.

A. *Racemes 30—50cm. long, erect:*

1. *Leaves* arcuate-incurved. *Inflorescence* 2—4-branched. *Perianths* cylindric-ventricose, orange, 36mm. long .. ..   93 *A. aculeata*
2. *Leaves* spreading. *Inflorescence* simple or forked. *Bracts* 20—25mm. long. *Perianth* bright-red, up to 40mm. .. ..   94 *A. rubroviolacea*

B. *Racemes 15—20cm. long, decurved:*

Leaves spreading-recurved. *Inflorescence* simple or forked. *Perianth* bright-red, 38mm. .. ..   95 *A. decurva*

93. **A. aculeata** Pole Evans in *Trans. Roy. Soc. S. Afr.* 5: Part 1, 34, Plates 14—15 (1915), in *Fl. Pl. S. Afr.* 10: Plate 371 (1930); Christian in *Rhod. Agric. Jnl.* Bull. 876 (1933); Reynolds in *Aloes S. Afr.* 447 (1950).

Description based on plants 5—8 miles N of Fort Victoria, Rhodesia.

Plants solitary, never in groups. *Stem* none or short.
Leaves densely rosulate, about 30, up to 50—60cm. long, 10cm. broad, arcuate-erectly-incurved and forming a compact rosette, 40—50cm. diam.; *upper surface* greyish-green, flat low down, slightly caniculate upwards, with a few scattered prickles in upper half; *lower surface* convex, with numerous reddish-brown prickles irregularly scattered throughout; *margins* armed with pungent, deltoid, reddish-brown teeth about 4mm. long, 10mm. apart, smaller and more crowded low down, larger and more distant upwards, all springing from a white tubercle-like raised base.
Inflorescence usually compactly 2—4-branched, 1—1·3m. high.
Racemes very densely flowered, cylindric-acuminate, up to 50cm. long, 7cm. diam. low down, the buds reddish, open flowers orange.
Pedicels 1—2mm. long.

Left: ALOE ACULEATA   Pole Evans.

Centre: *A. chabaudii* Schonl. Right: Natural hybrid of these two species.
3 miles S of Lundi River, between Beit Bridge and Fort Victoria,
Rhodesia.

Bracts lanceolate-acute, thin, dry, brownish, 9mm. long, 5mm. broad at base, very deflexed.

Perianth orange, cylindric, slightly ventricose, 36mm. long, 10mm. diam. at the middle; *outer segments* free for 24mm. (tube 12mm.) with 3 greenish-nerves, the apices brownish-tipped, slightly spreading; *inner segments* free but dorsally adnate to the outer for 10mm., broader than the outer, with more obtuse more spreading apices.

Filaments filiform-flattened, the 3 inner and 3 outer lengthening in turn with their *anthers* exserted 15mm.; *stigma* at length exserted 17mm.; *ovary* green, 7mm. long, 4mm. diam. (Plate 53. Figs. 243–245).

RHODESIA. Coll. 5 miles N of Fort Victoria, fl. 25 July 1942, in Johannesburg, Reynolds 3299 (PRE); 8 miles N of Fort Victoria, 3,500 ft., 31 July 1952, Reynolds 6727 (PRE, SRGH, K, EA); 4 miles NW of Birchenough Bridge, cult. Greendale, fl. 21 July 1958, L. C. Leach 333 (SRGH); N of Fort Victoria, 13 July 1959, L. C. Leach 9219 (SRGH); between Tokwe Bridge and Chibi, 10 July 1959, L. C. Leach 9218 (SRGH); 5 miles N of Shabani, 6 Aug. 1962, L. C. Leach 11512 (SRGH).

DISTRIBUTION: Rhodesia, from south of West Nicholson to near Gwanda, near Bulawayo; 4 miles S of Lundi River, 5—9 miles S of Tokwe River, 5—8—24 miles N of Fort Victoria, near Enkeldoorn; 6 miles W, 6 and 28 miles S of Umtali, near Birchenough Bridge; abundant at mouth of Sabi River Gorge. It appears that the largest numbers are to be found in the Pietersburg and Lydenburg Districts of the Transvaal.

TYPE LOCALITY: Northern Transvaal, Pietersburg Dist., E of Smit's Drift, about 26 miles E of Pietersburg, first collected by Messrs. Pienaar and Wickens in January 1914.

TYPE MATERIAL: From Smits Drift, fl. in Pretoria, 14 June 1914, I. B. Pole Evans, in Govt. Herb. No. 55! (PRE).

One can almost always recognise the Rhodesian form of *A. aculeata* because it differs from the Transvaal form in having its marginal teeth and leaf surface prickles spring from a raised whitish tubercule-like base. The racemes are also usually more acuminate, pointed.

FIG. 243.   FIG. 244.

A. aculeata Pole Evans.

FIG. 243. Plant 8 miles N of Fort Victoria, Rhodesia. Height 4 ft.

FIG. 244. A form, 5 miles N of Fort Victoria, Rhodesia.

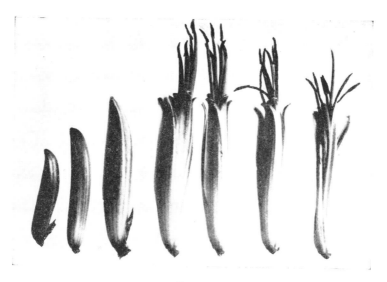

Fɪɢ. 245.

A. *aculeata* Pole Evans. Flowers 1/1 from bud to post-anthesis stages from
the Fig. 243 plant.

NATURAL HYBRIDS

The accompanying colour plate illustrates a natural cross between *A. aculeata* and *A. chabaudii*
Schonl.

A. aculeata × *A. excelsa* is reported to have been collected on the farm "Spes Bona" in the
Fort Victoria District.

A. aculeata × *A. globuligemma* has been collected by Mr. L. C. Leach near Birchenough
Bridge.

94. **A. rubroviolacea** Schweinfurth in *Bull. Herb. Boiss.* 2: App. 2, 71 (1895); Engler in *Notizblatt.
Berl. Bot. Gart.* 1: 5 (1897); Hook. *f.* in *Bot. Mag. t.* 7882 (1903); Berger in Engler's *Pflanzenr.*
Liliac.–Aloin. 296 (1908); Blatter in *Fl. Arab. Rec. Bot. Surv. India* 8: 6, 464 (1936); O. Schwartz
in *Fl. Trop. Arab.* 351 (1939).

Dᴇsᴄʀɪᴘᴛɪᴏɴ based on Schweinfurth's and Berger's accounts.
    Stem thick, curved, simple, scarcely 1m. high.
    Leaves densely rosulate, spreading-recurved, somewhat falcate, 60cm. long, 10—11cm. broad, broadly lanceolate-
ensiform, somewhat glaucous; *upper surface* flat low down, a little canaliculate upwards, reddish or purplish-violet
near base, rose-flesh towards apex, covered with a violaceous bloom; *lower surface* convex; *margins* with a reddish
cartilaginous edge armed with small hooked teeth about 2—3mm. long, 20—25mm. distant.
    Inflorescence arcuate-ascending, 1m. high.
    Peduncle stout, simple or forked, laterally compressed.
    Racemes very densely many-flowered, 30—40cm. long, 8—10cm. broad, the flowers pendulous, densely imbricate,
bright red, very shortly pedicellate.
    Bracts large, lanceolate-acute, 20—25mm. long, scarious, white, many-nerved.
    Pedicels 3—4mm. long.
    Perianth bright red, almost 40mm. long (Berger), orange, 23—30cm. long (Schweinfurth), ventricose-cylindric,
slightly compressed laterally; *outer segments* free to the middle, linear-lanceolate, acute, 3-nerved, the apices slightly
spreading; *inner segments* broader, with 3 crowded nerves forming a keel.
    Filaments reddish, exserted 10—15mm. (Figs. 246–248).

Yᴇᴍᴇɴ. On peaks of Mt. Schibam, above Menhaka, near the Old Castle, at about 2900m. (9,500 ft.), above sea level,
fl. 2 March 1889, Schweinfurth 1658! (K)—presumably the holotype.

The type locality is in the high altitudes of the Haraz mountains, on the western escarpment of
the Yemen, Southern Arabia.

It seems that Schweinfurth 1658 at Kew is the only gathering of this species since Berger (1908)
mentions no other, while Blatter (1936) and O. Schwartz (1939) also cite no other material. Berger
states that the plant that flowered at La Mortola in the spring of 1900, had been received from the
Berlin Botanical Gardens – where it had previously been introduced by Schweinfurth himself.

Fig. 246.

A. rubroviolacea Schweinfurth. An uncoloured plate of
Bot. Mag. t. 7882 (1903) – much reduced.
By courtesy The Director, Royal Botanic Gardens, Kew.

Fig. 247.

A. rubroviolacea Schweinf. Berger's Fig. 123
in Engler's *Pflanzenreich Liliac-Aloin*. p. 297.
(1908).

Fig. 123. *Aloe rubroviolacea* Schweinfurth. Habitus. (Icon. orig.)

246 *Aloe decurva*

Fig. 122. *Aloe rubroviolacea* Schweinfurth. *A* Bractea. *B* Alabastrum cum bractea. *C* Perigonium. *D* Folii margo. (Icon. orig.)

FIG. 248.

A. rubroviolacea Schweinf. Berger's Fig. 122 from Engler's *Pflanzenreich* (*lc.*) p. 297.
Photostats by courtesy, The Chief, Botanic Research Institute, Pretoria.

A photograph, together with a flowering raceme and a leaf were sent to Kew in March 1902, and those formed the type of *Bot. Mag. t.* 7882.

AFFINITIES: Berger gives *A. salm-dyckiana* Schult. f. as its closest ally – but this is a natural hybrid of *A. arborescens* Mill. and *A. ferox* Mill.

The Cape species *A. speciosa* Bak. appears to be a near ally, while the Madagascar species *A. macroclada* Bak. also appears to be a close affinity.

From all of these, however, *A. rubroviolacea* differs in having considerably larger bracts, 25mm. long.

Schweinfurth describes his *A. rubroviolacea* as being "*Caulescens dependens glaberrima*", while Berger described his plant as having a thick, curved, simple stem scarcely 1m. long.

This suggests that in the wild state plants on very steep slopes might have somewhat hanging stems; otherwise stems might be "curved" as the result of lying along the ground with the rosulate apex ascending.

95. **A. decurva** Reynolds in *Journ. S.A. Bot.* 23: 15 (1957).

DESCRIPTION: *Plants* acaulescent or with very short stem, solitary, sometimes dividing into 2 rosettes.

Leaves 20—24, densely rosulate, ensiform, spreading and recurved near apex, up to 9cm. broad at base, 15—20mm. thick, gradually attenuate and up to 55cm. long; *upper surface* dull green with reddish tinge, without spots or markings, concave at base, canaliculate upwards; *lower surface* rounded, dull-green, without spots or markings; *margins* sinuate-dentate, armed with pungent, deltoid teeth, averaging 3mm. long, irregularly 8—15mm. distant; *sap* dries yellow.

Inflorescence simple, very rarely furcate, up to 90cm. long, sometimes 2—3 from a rosette.

Peduncle curved obliquely, with the raceme decurved, basally plano-convex and 20mm. broad, brown and somewhat sulcate, with several sterile-bracts, the lowest broadly ovate-acute, 20mm. long, 15mm. broad at base, thin, scarious, many-nerved, smaller upwards.

Racemes very densely flowered, broadly cylindric, very slightly acuminate, 15—20cm. long, 10—12cm. diam., youngest buds minutely spotted and spreading slightly downwards, the whole raceme curved downwards, the flowers deflexed and opening first on the sunny side.

Bracts very small, broadly ovate-obtuse, 2mm. long, 3mm. broad at base, thin, subscarious, 3-nerved.

Pedicels negligible, at most 1mm. long.

Perianth bright red, sometimes orange, cylindric-ventricose, trigonal, averaging 38mm. long, 5mm. diam. across the ovary, 11mm. at the middle, thence narrowing to a constricted mouth with the segment apices pressing on the exserted filaments; *outer segments* free almost to base (tube 5mm. at most), 5-nerved, the apices subacute, straight; *inner segments* broader than the outer, thinner at the edges, the apices more obtuse.

Filaments filiform-flattened, rather thick, pink within, the exserted portion orange, the 3 inner narrower and lengthening before the 3 outer with their *anthers* in turn exserted 10—12mm.; *stigma* at length exserted 15—20mm.; *ovary* pale green, 6mm. long, 3·5mm. diam. (Plate 54, Figs. 249–251).

MOÇAMBIQUE. *Manica Sofala:* Along the top of Zembe Mountain, 18 miles S of Vila Pery, 3,500 ft., cult. hort. Munch, Rusape, fl. 15 July 1956, Reynolds 8200 holotype (PRE), isotype (SRGH, K); same locality, fl. 16 June 1959, L. C. Leach 9134! (K, SRGH); same locality, cult. Greendale, fl. 10 June 1960, L. C. Leach 9987! (SRGH).

PLATE 54

ALOE DECURVA Reynolds.

Plant from Zembe Mtn., 18 miles S of Vila Pery, Moçambique, flowering
in Mr. R. C. Munch's gardens near Rusape, Rhodesia. Height 3 ft.

FIG. 249.   FIG. 250.

A. decurva Reynolds. Plants along the top of Zembe Mtn., 18 miles S of Vila Pery, Moçambique.
Alt. 3,500 ft. Height 3 feet.

FIG. 251.

A. decurva Reynolds. Flowers 1/1 from
bud to post-anthesis stages.

Mr. Leach noted that the inflorescences were not so markedly bent downwards as on Mt. Zembe, and that flowers varied from orange to deep red.

This very distinctive, unique species was discovered in 1949 by Mr. R. C. Munch of "Mona", Rusape, Rhodesia, on Zembe Mountain, 18 miles S of Vila Pery (on the Umtali–Beira road) and about 93 miles by road E of Umtali.

In July 1956, Mr. and Mrs. Munch conducted the author to Zembe Mountain, and after a steep climb of a thousand feet, large numbers of plants were found growing in shallow pockets of soil on semi-denuded granite slopes along the top of Zembe Mountain (with *A. excelsa* Berger, *A. chabaudii* Schonl. and *A. cameronii* Hemsl. nearby), but only two plants were found with a few flowers left.

A. decurva is distinguished from all other known species by having a somewhat sulcate, curved peduncle bearing a short, densely-flowered "bottle-brush"-like raceme that is always deflexed or decurved. The bracts and the almost sessile flowers are also deflexed.

The 38mm. cylindric-ventricose flowers of *A. decurva* appear to be nearest allied to those of *A. ortholopha* Christian et Milne-Redhead from Mtoroshanga Pass in the Umvukwes, 61 miles NNW of Salisbury, but the latter has a 2—4-branched inflorescence, much longer horizontal racemes, 8mm. pedicels, secund flowers, and very different leaves.

In leaf characters only, *A. decurva* is near *A. sessiliflora* Pole Evans, which differs in having much longer, narrower "bottle-brush"-like racemes of sessile considerably shorter campanulate flowers.

Only two plants were found on Zembe Mountain with forked peduncles, all the others being simple. Two and three inflorescences are produced from a rosette, and flowers open first along the sunny side of racemes.

GROUP 16

MEDIUM TO LARGE PLANTS WITH DENSELY ROSULATE

LEAVES FORMING RATHER COMPACT ROSETTES

Stems none or short, decumbent or erect. *Bracts* minute to large. *Pedicels* up to 20mm. long. *Perianth* cylindric-trigonous, yellow or red (vinaceous in one species); *outer segments* free for one-quarter to one-half their length.

Type species: *A. percrassa* Tod.

Species comprising this group have rather compact rosettes of leaves as in *A. percrassa*, as distinguished from species in Group 17 which have large, open rosettes with spreading to recurved, slightly to deeply-channelled leaves as in *A. megalacantha* Bak.

KEY TO THE SPECIES

1—MEDIUM-SIZED PLANTS

A. PEDICELS LESS THAN 10MM. LONG, FLOWERS YELLOW:

1. *Leaves* 28cm. long, 7·5cm. broad, somewhat falcate. *Inflorescence* 4—9-branched, 60cm. high. *Racemes* 16—20cm. long, sublax. *Perianth* 30mm., yellow .. ..   96 *A. lavranosii*
2. *Leaves* 50—60cm. long, 12cm. broad; *marginal teeth* only ·5mm. long. *Inflorescence* many-branched, 1·5m. high. *Racemes* densely capitate, flowers yellow, 16—20mm. long .. ..   97 *A. ruspoliana*

B. PEDICELS 8—10MM. LONG, FLOWERS VINACEOUS:

1. *Leaves* 35—40cm. × 7—8cm. *Inflorescence* a branched panicle 60cm. high. *Racemes* lax, 7 cm. long. *Perianth* 20mm. long, dark brownish-vinaceous .. ..   98 *A. classenii*

C. PEDICELS 10—18MM. LONG, FLOWERS RED:

(*a*) Buds covered by imbricate bracts:
1. *Leaves* 40cm. long, 6cm. broad. *Inflorescence* 2—4-branched, 60—70cm. high. *Pedicels* 14—18mm. long. *Racemes* cylindric-conic, 15—20cm. long. *Perianth* dull scarlet, 30mm. long .. ..   99 *A. sereti*
(*b*) Buds visible:
Leaves 25cm. long, 9cm. broad. *Inflorescence* 8-branched, 50—60cm. high. *Racemes* 15—18cm. long, subdense to sublax. *Perianth* slender, scarlet, 28mm. .. ..   101 *A. wilsonii*
2. Forms dense groups. *Leaves* 30cm. long, 6·5cm. broad. *Inflorescence* 8-branched, 70—90cm. high. *Racemes* sublax, 10cm. long, the lowest sometimes sub-secund. *Perianth* brick-red, 30mm.   100 *A. mubendiensis*

D. Terminal Racemes Only Slightly Higher Than Apices of
Leaves, Inflorescence 50cm. High:

(a) *Inflorescence 2—3-branched:*
  1. *Leaves* dentate, up to 50cm. long, 10—12cm. broad. *Racemes* densely capitate. *Pedicels* 18—20mm. long. *Perianth* bright red, 40mm.   .. ..   102 *A. ukambensis*

(b) *Inflorescence 4—8-branched:*
  1. *Leaves* entire, 30cm. long, 8cm. broad. *Racemes* lax, 20—25cm. long. *Pedicels* 10—14mm. long. *Perianth* scarlet, 26—30mm.   .. ..   103 *A. breviscapa*

2—LARGE PLANTS

Mostly solitary or in small groups.

A. Pedicels Less Than 10mm. Long, Bracts Minute:

  1. *Leaves* 50cm. long, 13cm. broad. *Inflorescence* many-branched, 1·20—1·50m. high. *Racemes* sub-lax, 15cm. long. *Perianth* 24mm., rose-pink   .. ..   104 *A. tweediae*

B. Pedicels 12—15—20mm. Long, Bracts Larger

(a) *Perianth averaging 20mm. long:*
  1. *Leaves* 40—50cm. long, 10—15cm. broad. *Inflorescence* 5—6-branched, 60—80cm. high. *Raceme* sub-dense, 10—15cm. long. *Perianth* scarlet, 20mm.   .. ..   105 *A. percrassa*

(b) *Perianth 30—40mm. long:*
  1. *Leaves* 50cm. long, 12cm. broad. *Inflorescence* 70—90cm. high, 6—8-branched. *Racemes* conic-capitate 10cm., to cylindric-acuminate 15—20cm. long. *Perianth* 33mm., deep red   ..   106 *A. harlana*
  2. *Leaves* 60cm. long, 12cm. broad. *Inflorescence* 70—90cm. high, 3—5-branched. *Racemes* elongate, 15—18cm. long, sublax. *Bracts* 15—20mm. *Perianth* thick and fleshy, 40—45mm. long, *outer segments* free almost to base   .. ..   107 *A. steudneri*
  3. *Leaves* 50—60cm. long, 15cm. broad. *Inflorescence* many-branched, 1m. high. *Racemes* subcapitate 6—8cm. long. *Perianth* curved, scarlet, 30—35mm. long   .. ..   108 *A. berhana*
  4. *Leaves* 60—70cm. long, 14—16cm. broad, glossy, olive-green. *Inflorescence* 8-branched, 1m. high. *Racemes* slightly conic to capitate-corymbose. *Perianth* mostly yellow, 38mm. long .. ..   109 *A. monticola*

96. **A. lavranosii** Reynolds in *Journ. S.A. Bot.* 30: 225 (1964).

DESCRIPTION: *Plant* succulent, acaulescent or with short decumbent stems up to 15cm. long, rarely solitary, usually in groups of 5—8 rosettes.

Leaves 10—14, densely rosulate, obliquely ascending-spreading, deltoid-acute, somewhat falcate, with apices slightly recurved, 28cm. long, 7·5cm. broad at base, 15mm. thick, very stiff and rigid; *upper surface* uniformly olive-green with brownish tinge, flat near base, broadly canaliculate upwards; *lower surface* convex, otherwise as in the upper surface; *margins* horny, continuous pinkish-brown, armed with pungent, deltoid, brownish teeth 3mm. long, 6—12mm. apart, more crowded low down, the apex acute and armed with 2—4 small sharp teeth.

Inflorescence usually 2 successively from a rosette, ascending to suberect, 60cm. high, 4—9-branched.

Peduncle basally plano-convex and 12mm. broad, biconvex upwards, brown, the base of lateral branches enveloped by 2 sterile-bracts, one above and one below; *sterile bracts* broadly deltoid, acute, papery, whitish, many-nerved.

Racemes cylindric-acuminate, sublaxly flowered, the terminal 16—20cm. long, the lateral a little shorter, about 5cm. diam., youngest buds sub-erect, older buds spreading, open flowers pendulous.

Bracts ovate-lanceolate, acute, 8mm. long, 3mm. broad at base, thin, scarious, whitish, 7-nerved.

Pedicels yellowish-green, 8mm. long.

Perianth bright yellow, smooth (without indumentum), cylindric-trigonous, 30mm. long, basally obtuse, 7mm. diam. across the ovary, very slightly constricted above the ovary, thence trigonous and slightly compressed laterally, the mouth open; *outer segments* free for 10mm., 3-nerved, the nerves brownish becoming greenish and confluent at apex, the apices subacute, slightly spreading; *inner segments* free but dorsally adnate to the outer for 20mm., broader than the outer, with 3 crowded bright yellow nerves forming a keel becoming greenish near apex, the broad margins white, the apices more obtuse than the outer.

Filaments pale yellow, filiform-flattened, the 3 inner narrower and lengthening before the 3 outer with their *anthers* in turn exserted 1—2mm.; *stigma* at length exserted 2mm.; *ovary* bright green, 7mm. long, 2·5mm. diam. (Plate 55, Figs. 252, 253).

South Arabian Federation. Amiri Highlands, 2 miles N of Dhala, c. 13° 43′ N, 44° 45′ E, 25 Aug. 1962, Lavranos 1890 holotype (PRE), isotype (K).

Fig. 252.

A. lavranosii Reynolds. From Amiri Highlands 2 miles N of Dhala, about 86 miles N of Aden, SW Arabia, flowering in Mr. Lavranos's garden in Johannesburg. Height 70cm.

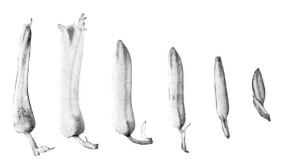

Fig. 253.

A. lavranosii Reynolds. Yellow flowers. 1/1.

PLATE 55

ALOE LAVRANOSII Reynolds.

Two miles N of Dhala, Amiri Highlands, SW. Arabia. Height 70cm.
From a Kodachrome by Mr. J. Lavranos.

Numbers of plants were found on a low rocky basalt hill on the Amiri Highlands about 2 miles N of Dhala, which is about 87 miles N of Aden, at an altitude of approximately 4,500 ft., and in an area receiving about 15 in. of rainfall annually.

A. lavranosii with its bright yellow flowers is a strikingly attractive species, and belongs to a group of Aloes characterized by having racemes about 15—20cm. long, short pedicels 5—10mm. long, and perianths averaging 30mm. long with outer segments connate to beyond the middle. It is not closely allied to any species hitherto described, but shows some affinities with *A.massawana* Reynolds and *A. breviscapa* Reynolds, both from the African mainland.

A. massawana differs in having longer, broader, less rigid leaves, and an inflorescence that is only 3—4-branched and twice as high, with perianths that are pale scarlet and somewhat white-striped. *A. breviscapa* is separated from *A. lavranosii* by having larger leaves, an inflorescence that is only slightly higher than the apices of the leaves, longer laxer racemes, and longer pedicels.

97. **A. ruspoliana** Baker in *Fl. Trop. Afr.* 7: 460 (1898); Berger in Engler's *Pflanzenr.* Liliac.–Aloin. 266 (1908); Reynolds in *Journ. S.A. Bot.* 20: 34 (1954).
—— *A. stephaninii* Chiov. in *Result. Sci. Miss. Stefani.* 1: 171 (1916).
—— *A. jex-blakeae* Christian in *Journ. S.A. Bot.* 8: 176 (1942).

Plants acaulescent, or with stems up to 50cm. long, decumbent or ascending, forming small to large dense groups sometimes a few metres across.
Leaves about 16, densely rosulate, lanceolate-attenuate, 50—60cm. long, 12cm. broad, the youngest suberect, the older erectly spreading and forming compact rosettes; *upper surface* yellowish-green, usually without spots or markings, but sometimes with a few narrow lenticular white spots low down, flat low down, slightly canaliculate upwards; *lower surface* convex, otherwise as in the upper surface; *margins* with exceedingly narrow cartilaginous edge armed with very small white teeth that are only ·5mm. or less long, close low down, 5—8mm. apart at the middle, becoming obsolescent upwards.
Inflorescence a many-branched panicle averaging 1·5m. or more high.
Peduncle basally plano-convex and 20mm. broad, 12-branched or more from above the middle, the 2—4 lowest branches sometimes with 4—5 branchlets.
Racemes densely flatly capitate, 2—4cm. long, about 5cm. diam., the buds and flowers more or less horizontally disposed.
Bracts narrowly deltoid-acute, 3mm. long, 1·5mm. broad, thin, scarious, 3-nerved.
Pedicels 5mm. long.
Perianth yellow, 16—20mm. long, cylindric-trigonous, 5mm. diam. across the ovary, enlarging a little to 6—7mm. across the mouth; *outer segments* free for 6—8mm., 3-nerved; *inner segments* broader, with 3 crowded nerves forming a keel, the apices broader and more obtuse.
Anthers in turn exserted 2—3mm.; *stigma* at length exserted 3—4mm.; *ovary* 4mm. long, 2mm. diam. (Figs. 254–256).

ETHIOPIA. *Harar Prov.*, Ogaden: At Milmil and Imi, dry rocky places in shade, 9 Jan. 1893, Riva 918 (FI, holotype). *Note:* Milmil is about 100 miles S of Hargeisa (Capital of Somalia North), between Auareh (Awareh) and Dagabur (Daggah Bur), c. 8° 15′ N, 43° 55′ E, in the Ogaden, Ethiopia. Imi is about 180 miles SW of Milmil, about halfway to Dolo.

SOMALIA SOUTH. Habr Anal, July-Aug. 1891, Robecchi Brichetti, n. 18 (FI). *Note:* Habr Anal lies somewhere to the W of Obbia which is on the coast NE of Mogadiscio.

Near Hemin-Gurei (Heima Guieri) 22 July 1913, Paoli n. 687 (FI) – the type of *A. stefaninii* Chiov. *Note:* Heima and Gurei are wells SE of Bardera to the E of Anole Hill (which hill is about 25 miles S of Bardera on the east side of the Juba River) on the bush-clad Agiuran plains at approx. 1,000 ft. When the present author investigated the Aloes at and near Anole Hill in 1953 he found large numbers of *A. ruspoliana* in places, and it became obvious that *A. stefaninii* was merely a form of *A. ruspoliana* with flowers a little shorter than usual.

Arid desert flats, 1 mile W of Dolo, leaf only, 25 Sept. 1953, Reynolds 7083 (PRE); 1 mile NW of Lugh Ferrandi, leaf only, 27 Sept. 1953, Reynolds 7085 (PRE).

KENYA, Northern Prov., Horr Valley, E of Lake Rudolph, cult. Nairobi, fl. May 1940, Jex Blake in Cor. Mus. 7398, as *A. jexblakeae* Christian, Christian 1109 (SRGH, EA); Mazinga Hill near Voi, 8 Feb. 1953, Bally 8791! (EA).

DISTRIBUTION

Type locality is Milmil, 100 miles S of Hargeisa in the Ogaden, Ethiopia. The author did not see this species in Borana; occurs from Moyale to Mega, Yavello, Neghelli and Dolo. Abundant in most parts of Somalia North, Lugh Ferrandi and Iscia Baidoa, to Bardera, from Bulo Burti (130 miles N of Mogadishu) at 550 ft. to Mogadishu and along the coastal road SW to Kismayo

FIG. 254.   FIG. 255.

A. ruspoliana Baker.

FIG. 254. Plant 120 miles S of Bardera, 36 miles N of Gelib, on east side of Juba River, Somalia. – Stems 50cm. Dried inflorescence remains 6 feet.

FIG. 255. Inflorescence and leaf × 1/12 approx. from a plant from the Horr Valley, Northern Prov., Kenya. Photographed by Mr. P. R. O. Bally when flowering in Lady Jex–Blake's garden in Nairobi.

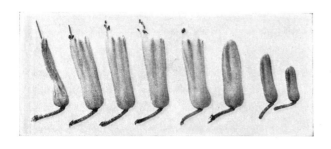

FIG. 256.

A. ruspoliana Bak. Flowers natural size from bud to post-pollination stages.

near Afgoi and the turn-off for Merca, and at Modun. NE and S of Bardera, especially 120—130 miles S of Bardera, not seen anywhere between Kismayo (Somalia) and Beles Cogani, to Garissa in Kenya.

In Kenya, abundant 57 miles W of Garissa (178 miles E of Nairobi), in Tsavo National Park, above Lugards Falls, Mzinga Hill near Voi, Horr Valley, E of Lake Rudolph, and elsewhere.

AFFINITY

A. ruspoliana is a very distinctive species, chiefly distinguished by its leaves having minute marginal teeth that are only ·5mm. long low down, and becoming obsolescent towards apex of leaf; the yellow flowers are only 16—20mm. long, and are slightly wider across the mouth than at base. The pedicels are 5—7mm. long.

Rosettes of leaves are rather compact, and plants form dense groups sometimes some yards across.

A. ruspoliana does not fit well into any existing section of Berger's Key. It is nearest to *A. gracilicaulis* Reynolds et Bally (from the Erigavo Dist. of Somalia North) which also has large leaves with 1mm.-long marginal teeth and yellow flowers 18mm. long on 5—6mm. pedicels, but *A. gracilicaulis* develops stems 2—4m. tall, with the leaves curved downwards, and has a very much lower inflorescence with much longer racemes.

Var. 1. **A. ruspoliana** Bak. var. **dracaeniformis** Berger. Berger states this var. is arborescent, whole plant woody, Dracena-like, differing from the typical form in having narrower leaves 5·5cm. broad, capsule globose-oblong, subtrigonous, woody, greyish, transversely rugose, 10—14mm. long.

ETHIOPIA. Ogaden, Aradeis (Araday), 13 Dec. 1892, Riva no. 227 (FI).

98. **A. classenii** Reynolds in *Journ. S.A. Bot.* 31: 271 (1965).

DESCRIPTION: *Plants* acaulescent or with stems 50cm. long, increasing freely from shoots and forming dense groups sometimes a few metres across.

Leaves about 24, densely rosulate, lanceolate, 35—40cm. long, 7—8cm. broad at base, suberectly spreading and forming rather compact rosettes about 40cm. across; *upper surface* deep olive-green to reddish-bronze without spots or markings, flat low down, slightly concave upwards; *lower surface* convex, more or less as the upper surface except sometimes with a few small elongated pale spots near base; *margins* sinuate-dentate, armed with pale-brownish, pungent, deltoid teeth up to 5mm. long, 10—15mm. apart, the leaf apex a spine.

Inflorescence a many-branched panicle about 60cm. high, about 10-branched from below the middle, the branches slender, the lowest with 2—3 branchlets, producing a total of about 25 racemes.

Peduncle minutely white-flecked, with a powdery bloom, basally plano-convex and 14mm. broad.

Racemes laxly flowered, cylindric-acuminate, about 7cm. long, 4cm. diam., the buds rather globular.

Pedicels 8—10mm. long, nutant at apex.

Bracts very small, ovate-acute, 3mm. long and broad, 3-nerved.

Perianth deep brownish-vinaceous (R.C.S. XXXIX) with a powdery bloom, cylindric-trigonous, straight, 20—25mm. long, 7mm. diam. across the ovary, trigonous upwards, the mouth open; *outer segments* free for 10mm., obscurely 3-nerved; *inner segments* free but dorsally adnate to the outer to the middle, with a broad, large, vinaceous keel which is raised and separates the margins of the outer segments by 1mm. or more.

Filaments very pale lemon, with their *anthers* in turn exserted 3—4mm.; *stigma* at length exserted 4mm.; *ovary* pale-green, 4mm. long, 2mm. diam. (Figs. 257, 258).

KENYA. On Kirima Rocks, about 15 miles SSW of Mackinnon Road Railway Station, cult. Mbabane, Swaziland, fl. 20 June 1965, Reynolds 10117 (Classen C.128), holotype (PRE), isotype (K, EA).

FIG. 257.

A. classenii Reynolds. Plant collected by Mr. George Classen of Nairobi on Kirima Rocks, 15 miles SSW of Mackinnon Road (between Mombasa and Voi), Kenya, flowering at Mbabane, Swaziland. Height 60cm.

Fig. 258.

A. classenii Reynolds. Buds and flowers 1/1 – Note the broad raised keel of upper half of inner segments separating the margins of the outer segments.

This most interesting Aloe was collected by Mr. George Classen of Nairobi, Kenya, on prominent gneissic outcrops called Kirima, 2 miles S of a small rock Pika Pika, about 15 miles SSW of the Mackinnon Road railway station on a track leading to Kilibasi, at approx. 3° 53′ S, 38° 53′ E. Plants form dense groups sometimes a few yards across. When in full sun on rocks, leaves turn a bronze-red colour, but are a dark green with reddish tinge in partial shade. The leaf apex is a spine.

The perianth is unique in having a broad raised median keel in the upper half of the inner segments, which keel actually separates the outer segment margins by 1mm. and more. In the bud stage the double indentation can be clearly seen.

A. classenii appears to be nearest allied to *A. percrassa* Tod. in floral characters, but differs in being a much smaller plant with an inflorescence only 60cm. high, and in having rosy-vinaceous flowers much resembling those of *A. myriacantha* (Haw.) R. & S. in colour. In cultivation *A. classenii* does not flower freely; in each raceme only a few flowers open at a time. If not watered freely, buds and flowers tend to dry out and fall.

99. **A. sereti** De Wild in *Plantae Bequaertianae* 1: 28 (1921); Reynolds in *Journ. S.A. Bot.* 20: 185 (1954).

DESCRIPTION based on plants observed near Bunia, and near Fataki, in the Kibali–Ituri Dist., Oriental Prov., Congo (Leo).

Stem none or short, suckering from base and forming small to large dense groups on rocks.

Leaves about 16, densely rosulate, erectly spreading, with upper quarter recurved and with a twist, lanceolate-attenuate, averaging 40cm. long, 6—7cm. broad at base; *upper surface* flat low down, canaliculate upwards, grey bluish-green with a reddish tinge, mostly without spots, sometimes obscurely dull white-spotted; *lower surface* convex, similar in colour to upper surface, mostly without spots; *margins* sinuate-dentate with pinkish edge, armed with pungent deltoid teeth which are white at base and reddish-brown-tipped, averaging 3—4mm. long, 8—10mm. distant, more crowded near base of leaf, more distant upwards, the interspaces rounded.

Inflorescence a sparsely-branched panicle 60—70cm. high.

Peduncle brown, minutely speckled, flattened and 15mm. diam. at base, mostly compactly 3-branched from the middle or lower (sometimes 4-branched), the lowest branch subtended at base by a broadly ovate-acute subscarious, many-nerved bract, 25mm. broad, 12mm. long.

Raceme cylindric-conical, 15—20cm. long, 5—6cm. diam., subdensely flowered, the apical buds covered by densely imbricate bracts, older buds grey-green tipped and horizontally disposed, the open flowers subpendulous.

Bracts ovate-acute, pink, rather fleshy, varying from 9—15mm. long, and from 5—10mm. broad, with 3—5 pinkish nerves.

Pedicels nutant at apex, 14—18mm. long, the colour of the perianth.

Perianth dull to bright scarlet, cylindric-trigonous, 28—33mm. long, obtusely tapering at base and shortly stipitate, 7mm. diam. across the ovary, thence very slightly narrowed on underside only, the mouth wide open; *outer segments* free for 9—10mm., obscurely nerved, the apices subacute; *inner segments* themselves free but dorsally adnate to the outer for two-thirds their length, broader than the outer, scarlet-keeled, and with more obtuse, more spreading apices.

Filaments pale rose turning lemon near the mouth, the 3 inner narrower and lengthening before the 3 outer, with their *anthers* in turn exserted 1—3mm.; *style* pale yellow, with *stigma* at length exserted 3—4mm.; *ovary* green, 5mm. long, 2·5mm. diam. (Plate 56, Figs. 259, 260).

CONGO (LEO). *Oriental Prov., Uele Dist.*, between the villages Bo and Gongo, 28 Oct. 1903, F. Seret 299 (BR, holotype)—flowers salmon, rocky ground on arid plateau; native name *Abungubete* (Amadi)—F. Seret. *Oriental Prov., Kibali–Ituri Dist.*: Irumu, grassy savannah on rocks, flowers carmine-red, 2 July 1914, J. Bequaert 4893 (BR); 6 miles N of Bunia, across the Shari River, on granite hill "Mbeye", fl. 2 July 1954, Reynolds 7280! (BR, K, PRE, EA); 8 miles NE of Fakati Hotel, = half-mile SW of Chief Libi's village, 14 miles SW of Nioka P.O., 5,800 ft., 4 July 1954, Reynolds 7281! (BR, K, PRE).

A. sereti was one of the five species of Aloe collected by Dr. J. Bequaert in 1914 in the (then Belgian) Congo, and it was described by De Wildeman in his *Plantae Bequaertianae* 1: 28 (1921).

PLATE 56

ALOE SERETI   De Wild.

On granite hill "Mbeye", 6—7 miles north of Irumu, Kibali-Ituri Dist.,
Oriental Prov., Congo (Leo.). Height 70cm. Approx. × 1/10.

FIG. 259.

A. sereti De Wild. Plants 8 miles NE of Fataki, 14 miles SW of Nioka, Kibali Dist., Oriental Prov., Congo (Leo); Alt. 5,000 ft. Height 80cm.

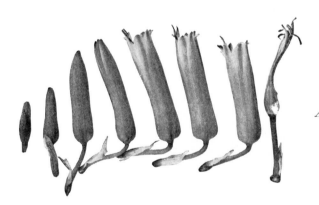

FIG. 260.

A. sereti De Wild. Flowers natural size.

No holotype was cited, but Professor W. Robyns, Director of the Jardin Botanique de l'Etat, Brussels, informed the author that Seret 299 is the type, and that the type locality is near Amadi, W of Niangara, in the Uele District, Oriental Province.

There were no figures, and the description did not give the size of the plant, the number of leaves, or their markings if any, and lacked other details.

Dr. Bequaert very kindly informed the present author (in 1953) that "*A. sereti* grew on rocks in a grass-savanna (mostly *Andropogon*), 2 hours walk N of Irumu. This was an acaulescent species, with leaves in a rosette, leaves green without blotches. The locality, 2 hours walk N of Irumu, was on a pathway serving as a road in 1914 between Irumu and Kilo, and about halfway between Irumu and a village called Pania." Dr. Bequaert also kindly sent a sketch he had made in 1914, of a flower with pedicel and bract, natural size.

Irumu is in the Oriental Province, Kibali–Ituri District, of the (then Belgian) Congo, about 60 miles W of Lake Albert (Kasenyi), on the south bank of the Shari River, at about 1° 20′ N, 29° 50′ E, alt. 3,100 ft.

In July 1954, the author visited Irumu and succeeded in tracing the old track to Pania village. Crossing the Shari River, and walking northwards up hill and down dale for two hours along the old Pania footpath, he eventually reached a granite hill known to local natives as "Mbeye", where numbers of Aloes were found, many being in flower. The distance north of Irumu would be 6—7 miles. This was clearly Dr. Bequaert's locality, and flowers matched his sketch.

Photographs were secured, herbarium material gathered, and a full description drawn up on the spot. (On a nearby hilltop, *A. dawei* Berger = *A. beniensis* De Wild. was also found.)

Continuing the journey eastwards to Bunia, thence north-eastwards along the road to Nioka, *A. sereti* was found close to Chief Libi's Village, 8 miles NE of Fataki and 14 miles SW of Nioka Post Office, at 5,800 ft., on granite.

Bracts were a little larger and more fleshy, and young buds were entirely hidden by densely imbricate bracts. Herbarium material was gathered at this locality also.

Four miles NE of Libi's Village (10 miles SW of Nioka) large numbers were again seen on granite.

Near Adranga, and along the Congo–Sudan border, a closely allied but distinct species, *A. schweinfurthii* Bak., takes over.

In all herbarium specimens cited above the bracts are more or less densely imbricate at apex of racemes, and are larger than in *A. schweinfurthii*. *A. sereti* also produces a much less-branched and lower inflorescence than *A. schweinfurthii*, and the leaves are smaller.

100. A. mubendiensis Christian in *Journ. S.A. Bot.* 8: 172 (1942).

DESCRIPTION based on observations at the type locality, 33 miles W of Mubende, Toro, Uganda.

Plants freely suckering and forming rather large dense groups. *Stem* none or short.

Leaves about 16, densely rosulate, averaging 30—35cm. long, 6·5cm. broad, narrowly lanceolate, erectly spreading, slightly recurved near apex; *upper surface* flat low down, slightly canaliculate towards apex, dull grey-green varying from unspotted to sparingly spotted with elongated-lenticular whitish spots, and obscurely slightly lineate; *lower surface* convex, greyer-green, mostly unspotted; *margins* sinuate-dentate, with slight pinkish cartilaginous edge armed with reddish-brown spreading teeth that are paler tipped, from a whitish base, 3—4mm. long, 10—15mm. apart; *sap* dries yellowish.

Inflorescence a branched panicle 70—90cm. high.

Peduncle basally plano-convex and 18mm. broad, 8-branched from the middle or higher, the lowest branches sometimes with 2—3 branchlets, subobliquely spreading and only slightly arcuate-ascending.

Racemes shortly cylindric, sublaxly flowered, about 10cm. long, 6—7cm. diam., suberect to oblique, some lateral racemes with flowers somewhat subsecund, buds grey-tipped, open flowers spreading to pendulous.

Bracts very small, ovate-acuminate, whitish, thin, subscarious, 3—4mm. long, 2—3mm. broad.

Pedicels averaging 10mm. long, the colour of the perianth.

Perianth cylindric-trigonous, dark brick-red, paler at mouth, averaging 30mm. long, 7mm. diam. across the ovary, thence narrowing very slightly on the underside only and widening slightly at the throat; *outer segments* free for 8—9mm., the margins paler, prominently 3-nerved from base to apex, the apices sub-acute, spreading; *inner segments* free, but dorsally adnate to the outer for two-thirds their length, apices brownish, more obtuse and more spreading than the outer.

Filaments filiform-flattened, with their *anthers* in turn exserted 2—3mm.; *style* yellow, with *stigma* at length exserted 4mm.; *ovary* green, 5mm. long, 2·5mm. diam. (Plate 57, Figs. 261, 262).

UGANDA. Buganda, Toro, 35 miles W of Mubende on Fort Portal road, c. 4,000 ft., cult. Ewanrigg, 6 May 1940, I. B· Pole Evans et J. Erens 1685! holotype (SRGH), isotype (PRE); 35 miles SW of Mubende, coll. J. Erens 1938, cult. Johannesburg, fl. 27 Jan. 1953, Reynolds 5760 (PRE, K), fl. again 17 May 1953 (PRE); 33 miles W of Mubende, 27 July 1954, Reynolds 7495 (PRE, K, EA); Plant received from Ewanrigg, fl. 28 April 1959 at Greendale, L. C. Leach 445! (SRGH).

A. mubendiensis was collected on 12 August 1938 by Mr. J. Erens, on the Pole Evans Central and E. Tropical African Expedition. It was named after the locality where it grows in abundance, namely from 30 to 40 miles westwards from Mubende on the road to Fort Portal in Uganda, growing on granite, and forming large groups.

It appears to be nearest allied to *A. schweinfurthii* Bak. in general habit of growth, leaves, rosettes and flowers, but the latter is readily distinguished by its erect, longer cylindric-acuminate racemes with flowers evenly distributed around the axis.

In *A. mubendiensis* the lowest more obliquely disposed racemes sometimes have slightly subsecund flowers.

ALOE MUBENDIENSIS   Christian.

Young plant from 33 miles W of Mubende, Toro, Uganda; flowering
in Johannesburg. Height 2 ft. 9 ins.

FIG. 261.

A. mubendiensis Christian. Plants on granite 33 miles W of Mubende, Toro, Western Prov., Uganda (Type locality) Height 3′ 6″.

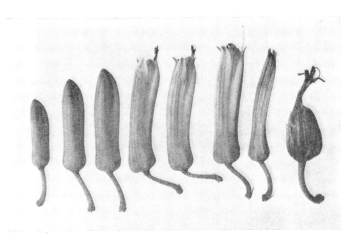

FIG. 262.

A. mubendiensis Christian. Flowers 1/1 from bud to fruit stages.

101. **A. wilsonii** Reynolds in *Journ. S.A. Bot.* 22: 137 (1956).

DESCRIPTION: *Plant* succulent, solitary or sometimes in small groups. *Stem* short, or sometimes 50—80cm. long, 6cm. diam., decumbent, glabrous, old leaves not persistent.

Leaves about 24, densely rosulate, lanceolate-attenuate, erectly spreading to spreading, up to 25cm. long, 9cm. broad at base, 2cm. thick low down; *upper surface* flat to slightly canaliculate, unicoloured deep green with yellowish tinge, slightly glossy, without spots or markings; *lower surface* convex, of similar colour to upper surface, usually without but sometimes with a few crowded white spots in lower quarter; *margins* sinuate-dentate, with pale brown horny edge armed with flat-deltoid, pungent, reddish teeth averaging 3—4mm. long, 10mm. distant.

Inflorescence a branched panicle 50—60cm. high, sometimes 2 consecutively.

Peduncle basally plano-convex and 25mm. broad, brown with a bloom, minutely white-speckled throughout, branched from below the middle with about 8 arcuate-ascending branches, the lowest branch subtended at base by a fleshy 3-nerved, broadly ovate-acute bract 10mm. long, 20mm. broad.

Racemes cylindric-acuminate, erect, 15—18cm. long, 5—6cm. diam., rather laxly flowered, the lowest flowers 10—15 mm. apart, gradually denser upwards, the youngest buds suberect, round-oval and only 1—2mm. long, older buds grey-green tipped, erectly spreading, open flowers cernuous to sub-pendulous.

Bracts ovate-acuminate, the lowest 5mm. long, 3mm. broad, white, thin, scarious, 1-nerved.

Pedicels reddish-brown, suberect, 15mm. long, nutant at apex.

Perianth dull scarlet with a bloom, cylindric, 28mm. long, obtusely obconical at base and shortly stipitate, slender and 7mm. diam. across the ovary, thence slightly trigonous to the mouth; *outer segments* free for half their length (tube 14mm.), pale lemon at the edges, 3-nerved, apices subacute, spreading; *inner segments* free but dorsally adnate to the outer to the middle, broader than the outer, with broad pale borders, scarlet-keeled, the apices brownish-tipped on the inside, more obtuse and more spreading than the outer.

Filaments lemon, filiform-flattened, the 3 inner narrower and lengthening before the 3 outer with their *anthers* in turn exserted 1—2mm.; *style* pale yellow, with *stigma* at length exserted 2—3mm.; *ovary* deep green, 6mm. long, 3mm. diam. (Figs. 263–267).

Fig. 263.

Imagit Peak, Mount Moroto (alt. 8,500 ft.), Matheniko County, Karamoja, Uganda. c. 2° 45′ N., 34° 44′ E. The arrow indicates type locality of *A. wilsonii* Reynolds.

UGANDA. *Northern Prov.*: Karamoja, Matheniko County, Mount Moroto near Imagit Peak, 8,500 ft., c. 2° 45′ N., 34° 44′ E, cult. hort. Tweedie, Mutamayo (near Endebess, Kenya), fl. 30 Oct. 1955, Tweedie 1365 (Reynolds 8804), holotype (PRE), isotype (EA). *Mount Elgon*: Mile 59 from Kitale on the Bugishu Mountain road, north slopes of Mt. Elgon, 7,500 ft., January 1957, Mrs. D. R. Tweedie 1425! (K, PRE); Mile 61 on same road, 1 mile SE of Kaburoni, on N slopes of Mt. Elgon, 7,500 ft., c. 1° 50′ N, 34° 50′ E, Mrs. D. R. Tweedie 1424! (K, PRE); cult. Mbabane, fl. 21 Feb. 1965, Reynolds 9041 (K, PRE).

A. wilsonii was named after Mr. John T. Wilson, then Ecologist, Dept. of Agriculture, at Moroto, in Karamoja, Uganda. He had first discovered the species near Imagit Peak, on Mt. Moroto, at an altitude of nearly 8,500 ft.

On Mt. Moroto, plants are solitary, acaulescent, or sometimes develop a decumbent smooth stem 50—80cm. long. Mr. Wilson has also found this species on north-western slopes of Kadam Mountain (Debasien), about 40 miles S of Moroto, at 5,000—8,000 ft., c. 1° 49′ N, 34° 42′ E. At this locality, Mr. Wilson found some plants solitary, and others forming small groups.

Much further south, Mrs. D. R. Tweedie has found numbers of *A. wilsonii* in Uganda, along the Bugishu Mountain road—leading to Kaburoni and Mbale around the north side of Mt. Elgon—from mile 45 to mile 68 from Kitale (Kenya), at an altitude of about 7,500 ft. Mrs. Tweedie noticed plants all along the upper edges of cliffs, and sometimes hanging down on their thick stems.

A striking character of *A. wilsonii* is the very acuminate racemes that taper to an acute point. The youngest buds, not hidden by bracts, are round–oval, and only 1—2mm. long. The perianth is basally rather obconical and tapers into the pedicel articulation, while outer segments are free to the middle. Although racemes vary from longer and laxer to shorter and denser, the flowers are identical.

NATIVE NAME: *Echuchukua* (Karamojong), used throughout Karamoja for Aloe in general.— J. T. Wilson.

FIG. 264.   FIG. 265.

A. wilsonii Reynolds.

FIG. 264. Plant collected by Mrs. E. M. Tweedie on the Bugishu mountain road, 45 miles from Kitale, on north slopes of Mount Elgon, Uganda, alt. 6,800 ft., flowering at Mbabane, Swaziland.

FIG. 265. Plant from Imagit Peak, Mount Moroto, flowering in the author's gardens.

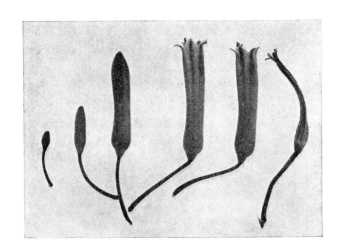

FIG. 266.

A. wilsonii Reynolds. Flowers 1/1 from the Fig. 264 plant.

FIG. 267.

A. wilsonii Reynolds. Flowers 1/1 from bud to post-anthesis stages – from the Fig. 265 plant.

102. **A. ukambensis** Reynolds in *Journ. S.A. Bot.* 22: 33 (1956).

DESCRIPTION: An acaulescent plant forming small to large dense groups on gneiss outcrops. *Stem* none or very short.

Leaves 30—40, densely rosulate, lanceolate-attenuate, up to 50cm. long, 10—12cm. broad at base; *upper surface* flat low down, slightly canaliculate upwards, grey-green with reddish tinge, conspicuously striate longitudinally, with or without a few scattered oval to lenticular white spots low down; *lower surface* convex, similar to upper surface in colour and lineation, varying from unspotted to spotted in lower half, the spots H-shaped, in line with, and interrupting the veins; *margins* sinuate-dentate, armed with compressed-deltoid, reddish-brown teeth which are paler at apex, 3—4mm. long, 8—10mm. distant. *Sap* dries pale-orange.

Inflorescence 2—3-branched, 50 cm. high, the racemes usually only slightly higher than the apices of leaves.

Peduncle plano-convex and 15mm. broad at base, brown with a bloom, with 2—3 branches (sometimes 4) from about the middle, the lowest branch subtended at base by a broadly ovate, thin, scarious, brownish many-nerved bract about 15mm. long and broad.

Racemes densely flowered, capitate or sub-capitate, 6cm. diam., the pedicellate portion 4—6cm. long, youngest buds bright-red with greyish tips, suberect, older buds spreading, open flowers pendulous.

Bracts ovate-deltoid, dull white, scarious, thin, 5mm. long, 2·5mm. broad at base, with 3 crowded nerves in median line.

FIG. 268.

A. ukambensis Reynolds. On Mabolini Hill, 37 miles E of Thika, Kenya, c. 1° 05′ S., 37° 28′ E. Alt. 4,500 ft. Height 75cm.

Pedicels slender, suberect, 18—20mm. long, deflexed at apex, reaching 30mm. in the fruit.

Perianth bright red, averaging 40mm. long, cylindric-trigonous, basally tapering to the pedicel and shortly stipitate, cylindric and 7mm. diam. across the ovary, above the ovary slightly narrowed on underside and slightly decurved, cylindric-trigonous upwards, the mouth wide open; *outer segments* free to the middle (tube 20mm.), obscurely 3-nerved at apex, apices subacute, slightly spreading; *inner segments* free but dorsally adnate to the outer to the middle, broader than the outer, with 3 crowded nerves forming a scarlet keel in upper half, the apices more obtuse and more spreading than the outer.

Filaments pale-pink, filiform-flattened, the 3 inner narrower and lengthening before the 3 outer with their *anthers* in turn exserted 2—3mm.; *stigma* at length exserted 4—5mm.; *ovary* orange-brown, 5mm. long, 2·5mm. diam.; *capsule* 18—20mm. long, 8—9mm. diam. (Figs. 268–271).

KENYA. Maboloni Hill, Yatta, coll. Benton, fl. 7 Dec. 1952, Bally 8382! (EA, K); Maboloni Hill, Ndaleni Ranch, 47 miles E of Thika, 73 miles NE of Nairobi, alt. 4,500 ft., c. 1° 05′ S, 37° 28′ E, fl. 6 June 1955, Reynolds 7651, holotype (EA), isotype (PRE, K). *Kibwezi Dist.*, 5 Jan. 1958, Bayliss in CM22047 (EA); N. Kitui, 5 miles N of Migwani, 5 May 1960, Napper 1619! (EA, PRE).

Also reported to occur on Ngomeni Rock, 10 miles N of Nguni, N of the Nairobi–Garissa Road, Kitui Dist., c. 0° 39′ S, 38° 24′ E—but not seen personally.

A. ukambensis was first discovered by Mr. P. R. O. Bally in January 1952, on Mbwinzao Hill between Makindu and Kibwezi, on the Nairobi–Mombasa main road. (Alt. 4,500 ft., c. 2° 22′ S, 37° 54′ E). In 1943 Mr. Bally found the species on the Yatta Plateau near Kitui.

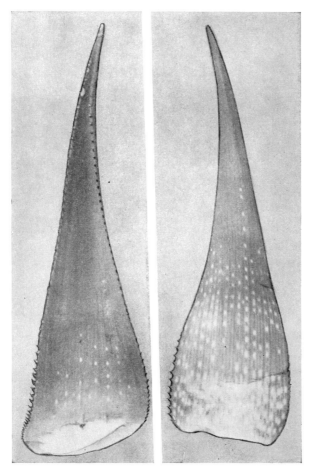

FIG. 269.　　　　　FIG. 270.

A. ukambensis Reynolds.

FIG. 269. Leaf upper surface × 1/4.

FIG. 270. Leaf lower surface × 1/4.

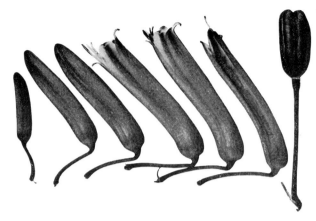

FIG. 271.

A. ukambensis Reynolds. Flowers natural size.

In January 1952, Police Officer Benton found plants on Maboloni Hill, near the Thika River, about 47 miles E of Thika. The species has also been collected by Mr. David Sheldrick, on Yamanyani Hill, about 25 miles N of Voi.

The author found several plants in flower on Mabolini Hill in June 1955, although the maximum flowering period is December—January.

A striking character of *A. ukambensis* is the leaf lineation, and the arrangement of the H-shaped spots. The leaves are conspicuously dark-veined longitudinally, the veins being 1—2mm. wide. The H-spots are almost square and occur only in line with, and interrupting the veins. In some plants the spots disappear with age, while in others the basal half of the lower surface of leaves may be copiously H-spotted.

The capitate racemes are usually only a little higher than the leaves, while in the flowers, the filaments and style lie along the lowest side of the perianth.

A. ukambensis appears to be allied to the Northern Ethiopian species *A. monticola* in rosettes and floral characters but the latter is a larger plant with a much taller, much more branched inflorescence.

A. breviscapa from Somalia North is a near ally with its inflorescence only slightly higher than the leaf apices, but differs in having longer, laxer racemes, with shorter pedicels and flowers.

103. **A. breviscapa** Reynolds et Bally in *Journ. S.A. Bot.* 24: 176 (Plate XIX) (1958).

DESCRIPTION: *Plants* forming small to large dense groups. *Stem* short or to 50cm. long, decumbent, sometimes up to 1m. in very old specimens, with old dried leaf remains persistent, the rosettes usually decumbent.

Leaves about 24, densely rosulate, lanceolate-attenuate, averaging 30—35cm. long, 8—10cm. broad at base, narrowing to an acute apex; *upper surface* unicoloured bluish-grey with reddish tinge, without spots or markings, flat low down, slightly canaliculate upwards; *lower surface* convex; *margins* usually entire, sometimes with a few very short blunt teeth 1—2mm. long, 10mm. apart in basal quarter only, thence entire upwards; *sap* dries yellow.

Inflorescence a branched arcuate-ascending panicle about 50cm. tall, the terminal raceme usually only slightly higher than the tips of the leaves.

Peduncle brown with a bloom, plano-convex and 12mm. broad at base, terete upwards, divaricately 4—8-branched from low down.

Racemes ascending, rather laxly-flowered, cylindric, 20—25cm. long, 6cm. diam., youngest buds obliquely spreading, open flowers nutant.

Bracts ovate-acute, 6mm. long, 3mm. broad, thin, scarious, white, 1—3-nerved.

Pedicels 10—14mm. long, obliquely spreading with apex nutant.

Perianth glabrous, cylindric-trigonous, 26—30mm. long, scarlet with a bloom, greenish at mouth, 8mm. diam. across the ovary, thence slightly narrowed on underside and slightly decurved, the mouth wide open; *outer segments* free for 10mm., thinner at margins, 3-nerved, the nerves turning greenish at apex, the apices subacute slightly spreading; *inner segments* broader than the outer, with broad white marginal border, prominently keeled, the apices more obtuse and more spreading than the outer.

Filaments lemon, the 3 inner narrower and lengthening before the 3 outer with their *anthers* in turn exserted 2—3mm.; *stigma* at length exserted 3—4mm.; *ovary* pale green, 6mm. long, 3mm. diam. (Plate 58, Figs. 272, 273).

SOMALIA NORTH (formerly Somaliland Prot.): 40 miles E of Erigavo, 4,700 ft., 20 Oct. 1956, Bally 11188 (EA); 48 miles E of Erigavo on road to Hadaftino, 4,600 ft., c. 10° 45′ N, 48° 03′ E, 14 Sept. 1957, Reynolds 8542, holotype (PRE), isotype (K, EA); 47 miles E of Erigavo, 30 July 1960, Hemming 1982! (EA).

A. breviscapa occurs in considerable numbers on arid, stony, gypsum plains on the road eastwards from Erigavo to Hadaftino from mile 40 to mile 54, near Hadaftino, at about 4,600 ft. alt., thence eastwards towards Baran for 20 miles, and occasionally on the Shemis Plain to near Huberra.

PLATE 58

ALOE BREVISCAPA   Reynolds et Bally.

Plant on gypsum plains 48 miles E of Erigavo on road to Hadaftino,
Somalia North. Height 50cm.

FIG. 272.

A. breviscapa Reynolds et Bally. On the Shemis Plain, about 50 miles E of Erigavo on road to Hadaftino and Buran, Somalia North.

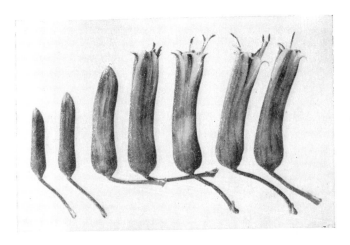

FIG. 273.

A. breviscapa Reynolds et Bally. Flowers natural size.

It occurs occasionally in broken country for about 40 miles south-eastwards from Huberra to near Buran, near the Somalia South border.

Plants near Buran were not flowering when the author was there, but they appear to be weaker forms of the species.

A. breviscapa is characterized by forming small to large dense groups, and by having leaves that vary from entire to partly dentate. When marginal teeth are present they occur only on the lowest third of leaf margins, the teeth being obtuse, 1—2mm. long and 10mm. apart, obsolescent upwards. The rosettes almost lie on their sides, and the terminal raceme of the arcuate-ascending inflorescence is usually only slightly higher than the tips of the uppermost leaves. The perianths are smooth.

In habit of growth, and in leaf characters only, *A. breviscapa* bears a striking resemblance to *A. tomentosa* Deflers which occurs in vast numbers near Moledera, 40 miles S of Erigavo, on the road to El Afwein, but the latter has a much taller, less branched, erect inflorescence, denser racemes, larger bracts and shorter, remarkably shaggy-tomentose perianths.

104. A. tweediae Christian in *Journ. S.A. Bot.* 8: 175 (1942).

DESCRIPTION based on personal observations at the type locality, Amudat, and throughout Karamoja, N. Prov., Uganda.

Plant succulent, usually solitary, sometimes in small groups. *Stem* usually none or very short, rarely up to 50cm. with old dried leaves persistent.

Leaves about 20, densely rosulate, varying from arcuate-ascending to spreading and recurved in upper quarter, broadly lanceolate-attenuate, averaging 50cm. long, 13cm. broad at base, 15mm. thick low down; *upper surface* flat low down, slightly canaliculate upwards, dull to glossy green, with numerous pale green lenticular markings in lower half averaging 10—15mm. long, 3mm. broad at the middle; *lower surface* convex, dull green, with numerous lenticular markings throughout (sometimes entirely without markings); *margins* sinuate-dentate, with reddish-brown horny edge armed with pungent reddish-brown deltoid teeth averaging 4mm. long, 10—15mm. distant, the teeth usually proclivent or forward-uncinate. *Sap* dries deep purple.

Inflorescence a many-branched pyramidal panicle, 120—150cm. high, sometimes 2—3 simultaneously.

Peduncle plano-convex and 3cm. broad at base, brown with a bloom, divaricately branched below the middle with 15—20 arcuate-ascending branches, the 2—3 lowest branches sometimes with 4—5 branchlets sometimes producing a total of about 40 racemes per inflorescence, the terminal raceme the highest.

Racemes ascending, sublaxly flowered, cylindric-acuminate, up to 15cm. long, 5cm. diam., the terminal erect with flowers evenly distributed, the lateral occasionally sub-oblique with their open flowers subpendulous.

Bracts very small, ovate-acute, thin, scarious, 2mm. long, 2mm. broad, 3—5-nerved.

Pedicels slender, averaging 7mm. long.

Perianth deep rose-pink below, paler upwards, slightly yellowish at mouth, averaging 24mm. long, slightly rounded at base, 8mm. diam. across the ovary, thence trigonous upwards, with the mouth upturned; *outer segments* free for two-thirds their length (tube 8mm.), yellowish at the margins, 3-nerved almost to base, the 2 upper with apices subacute, spreading, the lowest up-curved and giving the mouth a slightly upturned effect; *inner segments* free but dorsally adnate to the outer for 8mm., broader than the outer, with lemon borders, keeled, the apices more obtuse than the outer.

Filaments lemon, filiform-flattened, the 3 inner narrower and lengthening before the 3 outer with their *anthers* in turn exserted 3—4mm.; *style* pale yellow, with *stigma* at length exserted 5mm.; *ovary* green, 6mm. long, 3mm. diam. (Plate 59, Fig. 274).

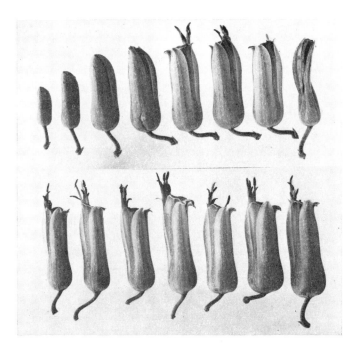

FIG. 274.

A. tweediae Christian'. Flowers natural size. *Upper Row:* From bud to post-anthesis. *Lower Row:* From various plants at random, showing variation.

UGANDA. *Northern Prov.:* Karamoja, at Amudat, coll. Mrs. E. M. Tweedie No. 262, 27 Nov. 1934, cult. Ewanrigg, fl. 6 Sept. 1941, Christian 1080!, holotype (SRGH), isotype (PRE, K); ex Amudat, Mrs. Tweedie 660, cult. Johannesburg, fl. 8 March 1953, Reynolds 6324 (K, SRGH); at Amudat, 91 miles N of Kitale, c. 1° 58′ N, 34° 57′ E, 4,400 ft., 12 Oct. 1955, Reynolds 7943 (K, PRE, EA); Karamoja, S of Mt. Moroto, 4,500 ft., 13 Sept. 1956, Bally B10797 (K, EA); Karamoja, Amudat, Nov. 1962, Mrs. E. M. Tweedie 2494 (EA).

Mrs. E. M. Tweedie has been collecting and painting the flora of the Mt. Elgon District of Kenya and elsewhere for many years. *A. tweediae* was described from plants collected by Mrs. Tweedie at Amudat, Karamoja, about 91 miles N of Kitale on the Uganda side of the border – not in West Suk across the border in Kenya as was at first thought.

ALOE TWEEDIAE   Christian.

At the type locality, Amudat, Karamoja, Uganda; Height 5′ 6″ and 6 ft.
With Mrs. E. M. Tweedie.

DISTRIBUTION

UGANDA: Common almost throughout Karamoja from the Suam River northwards to Amudat, Moroto, Kangole, Kotido, Loyoro; also abundant SW of Kotido to the Labwor Hills; and from the Moroto turn-off to Napau Pass.

KENYA: Considerable numbers occur in West Suk, on the Kapenguria–Ortum road from 5,500 ft. down to 4,800 ft., especially in the Marich Valley and near Moropus Mountain; also in the Ndo Valley, and the upper reaches of the Kerio.

AFFINITY

A. tweediae appears to be nearest allied to *A. secundiflora* in leaves, rosettes, and some inflorescence characters, but the two could hardly be confused. In *A. secundiflora* the racemes are oblique, the flowers are much longer, minutely white-spotted and secund. In *A. tweediae* the racemes are ascending to erect, the flowers much shorter (24mm.) and evenly distributed around the axis.

VARIATION

A. tweediae is very variable in different localities. Near Amudat and in the south of Karamoja, plants are mostly solitary, acaulescent, and produce 1—2 inflorescences, the leaves varying from unspotted to spotted on both surfaces, with or without a horny leaf margin. Robust forms near Moroto northwards to Loyoro sometimes develop a 50cm. stem with old leaves persistent, horny leaf margins, copiously spotted leaves, and 3—4 inflorescences simultaneously. Sometimes, in oblique racemes there is a tendency for flowers to become slightly subsecund.

NATIVE NAMES

Chokokwet in the Sebei tongue of the tribe living on the foothills to the north of Mt. Elgon; *Etchuka* or *Achuka* by the Suk tribe at Amudat; *Echuchukua* by the Karamajong in general throughout Karamoja.

MEDICINAL USES

Mr. John T. Wilson, Ecologist at Moroto, states that the Karamojong cut the leaves into slices and rub a slice across the eyelids as a remedy for conjunctivitis. The juice extracted from pulped leaves is drunk as a remedy for anthrax. The juice is also used for applying to cuts and wounds to prevent infection.

NATURAL HYBRIDS

At the type locality, Amudat, *A. tweediae* crosses with *A. amudatensis*, while in the Labwor Hills, 30 miles SW of Kotido, crosses with the yellow-flowered *A. schweinfurthii* var. *labworana* were seen.

105. **A. percrassa** Todaro in *Hort. Bot. Panorm.* 1: 81, *t.* 21 (1875) *non* Schweinfurth; Berger in Engler's *Pflanzenr.* Liliac.–Aloin. 220 (1908).

—— *A. abyssinica* var. *percrassa* Bak. in *Journ. Linn. Soc.* 18: 175 (1880), *non* in Th. Dyer *Fl. Trop. Afr.* 7: 465 (1898).

—— *A. schimperi* Schweinf. in *Bull. Herb. Boiss.* 2: app. 2, 70 et 110 (1894) *non* Todaro.

—— *A. oligospila* Bak.in *Bot. Mag. t.* 7834 (1902).

—— *A. schimperi* Karsten et Schenck in *Vegetationsbilder* 2: *t.* 59 (1905) *non* Tod. *Note:* With perianth only 20mm. long, this belongs here, but when the present author visited the Gorge of Gua, near Saganeiti, in Eritrea, he found *A. elegans* Tod. growing there.

—— *A. debrana* Christian in *Fl. Pl. Afr.* 26: Plate 1016 (1947).

(*Note: A. percrassa* Schweinf. (*non* Tod.) is *A. trichosantha* Berger from Ghinda, between Massawa and Asmara, Eritrea.)

DESCRIPTION based on many plants on the Kohaito Plateau, E of the Adi Caie–Senafe road, at approximately 8,200 ft., Eritrea.

Plants solitary or in groups, acaulescent or developing decumbent or erect stems up to 50—80cm. long, 10—15cm. thick, in very old specimens, the old dried leaf remains persistent.

Leaves densely rosulate, 24 or more, somewhat deltoid, averaging 40—50cm. long, 10—15cm. broad at base, the rosettes rather compact; *upper surface* flat low down, slightly canaliculate upwards, green with slight bluish to reddish tinge, unspotted except sometimes spotted in young plants the spots disappearing with age; *lower surface* convex, without spots or markings; *margins* with whitish to pinkish cartilaginous edge armed with deltoid teeth 3—4mm. long, 10—15mm. apart; *sap* dries yellow.

Inflorescence a branched panicle 60—80cm. high, sometimes 2—3 simultaneously.

Peduncle basally plano-convex, 20mm. broad, rather compactly 5—7-branched from about the middle, the lowest branch subtended at base by a thin, scarious, many-nerved bract about 20mm. long, 15mm. broad.

Racemes cylindric-conic, densely flowered, 10—15cm. long (20cm. long in fruit), 5—6cm. diam., youngest buds at first partly hidden by densely imbricate bracts, older buds spreading, open flowers a little laxer and subpendulous.

Bracts ovate-acuminate, thin, dry, 10—15mm. long, 4—5mm. broad, 5-nerved.

Pedicels 15—20mm. long, the colour of the perianth.

Perianth scarlet, paler at mouth, averaging 20mm. long, cylindric-trigonous, basally rounded and shortly stipitate, 6mm. diam. across the ovary, the mouth wide open and slightly upturned; *outer segments* free for 6mm., thinner and paler at the edges, 3-nerved, the apices subacute, slightly spreading; *inner segments* broader than the outer with broad pale border and 3 crowded nerves forming a scarlet keel, the apices brown-tipped, more obtuse, more spreading.

Filaments lemon, filiform-flattened, the 3 inner narrower and lengthening before the 3 outer with their *anthers* in turn exserted 1—2mm.; *stigma* at length exserted 3mm.; *ovary* pale green, 6mm. long, 3mm. diam. (Plate 60, Figs. 275–278).

ERITREA. Saganeiti, Gorge of Goua, near Addingofom (Hill), alt. 2100—2200m., 29 March 1892, Schweinfurth et Riva 1330! (K)—as *A. schimperi* Tod. *Note:* In this specimen the racemes are longer and the bracts larger than elsewhere. *Kohaito Plateau*, 2600—2700m., 1—10 May 1894, Schweinfurth 153! (K)—as *A. schimperi* Tod. *Kohaito Plateau*, 4 miles NE of the Adi Caie–Senafe road, 14° 48′ N, 39° 16′ E, 8,300 ft., 15 April 1956, Reynolds 8065 (K, PRE, EA).

ETHIOPIA. *Tigre Prov.:* Seed ex Gondar cult. Johannesburg, fl. August 1958, Reynolds 7623 (K, PRE, SRGH); Mountains 41km. N of Mai Chau (78km. S of Mekele), 8,800 ft., 26 April 1956, Reynolds 8115 (PRE); Mountains 38km. N of Mai Chau (81km. S of Mekele), 9,200 ft., 26 April 1956, Reynolds 8116 (K, PRE); 20km. from Debarek on Gondar–Axum road, 8 Jan. 1963, Tekle Hagos 95! (K, ETH, PRE). *Shoa Prov.,* Mulu, 54km. N of Addis Ababa, 20 Feb. 1944, Bally B11425 (K, G); Debre Berhan, on Addis–Dessie road, coll. M. C. Loughlin 812, cult. Ewanrigg, fl. Sept. 1942, Christian 1165—as *A. debrana* (SRGH); cult. Pretoria, fl. August 1943, McLoughlin 812A, type of *Fl. Pl. Afr.* 26: Plate 1016 (1947), no. 27173 in Nat. Herb. (PRE).

FIG. 275.

A. percrassa Todaro. From Todaro's *Hort. Bot. Panorm.*
1: 81, *Tab.* XXI (1875) – much reduced. *Photo: By courtesy
The Director, Royal Botanic Gardens. Kew.*

PLATE 60

ALOE PERCRASSA   Tod.

Young plant on the Kohaito Plateau, between Adi Caie and Senafe,
Eritrea; alt. 8,200 ft. Height 3 ft.

Fig. 276.   Fig. 277.

A. percrassa Tod.

Fig. 276. On the Kohaito Plateau, Eritrea, alt. 8,300 ft. Height 3 ´6˝.

Fig. 277. In the mountainous country 50 miles S of Mekele, 25 miles N of Mai Chau, Tigre. N. Ethiopia, alt. 8,800 ft. Height 5 feet.

TYPE LOCALITY: "Abyssinia, in elevated places at about 8,000 ft. above sea level, cultivated in the R. Botanic Gardens since 1873, thanks to the seeds obtained from the Imperial Botanic Gardens of Pietersburg, derived from the seeds collected by Schimper in Abyssinia." – Todaro.

Todaro's type plant was, therefore, a garden plant raised from seed, originally gathered by Schimper in N. Ethiopia. His splendid colour-plate illustrates a form with cylindric-acuminate racemes. This form occurs on the Kohaito Plateau, Eritrea – see accompanying colour plate – but usually the racemes are shorter.

Todaro mentions an altitude of 8,000 ft. This is noteworthy because in all the mountainous localities where the author found *A. percrassa* growing wild in Eritrea and in Ethiopia, not once was the altitude below 8,000 ft. Plants were also seen at nearly 10,000 ft.

A. percrassa is a variable species. It grows singly or in groups. Stems may be short or up to 60—80cm. long, 10—15cm. thick, erect or decumbent. Leaves are large and somewhat deltoid. Racemes vary from longer and laxer to shorter and denser, while flowers average 20mm. long. It appears that in the furthest north localities (Kohaito Plateau, Eritrea) flowers are 18—20mm. long, while in the furthest south localities (north of Addis Ababa, Ethiopia) they may be up to 25mm. in length.

A. percrassa seems nearest allied to *A. berhana* Reynolds near Debre Berhan, in Shoa Province, Ethiopia, but the latter differs chiefly in having densely capitate racemes and 30mm. slightly curved flowers.

A. elegans Tod. has clavate flowers and quite different racemes with the buds spreading to pointing slightly downwards.

NATIVE NAME: *Erreh* in Eritrea, *Iret* or *Arret* in Tigre, N. Ethiopia.

NATURAL HYBRID: A cross of *A. percrassa* with *A. camperi* Schw. was noticed among both parents on the Kohaito Plateau.

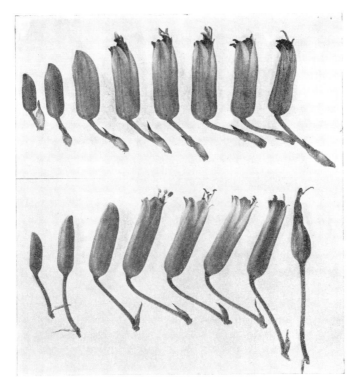

Fig. 278.

A. percrassa Tod. Flowers 1/1 from bud to post-anthesis. *Upper Row:* From a plant on the Kohaito Plateau, Eritrea. *Lower Row:* From a plant in the mountains 25 miles N of Mai Chau, Tigre, N. Ethiopia.

106. **A. harlana** Reynolds in *Journ. S.A. Bot.* 23: 9 (1957).

DESCRIPTION: *Plants* acaulescent or with short stem, growing singly or sometimes dividing into 2—4 rosettes that are up to 60cm. diam.

Leaves about 24, densely rosulate, lanceolate-attenuate, spreading to a little recurved, 50cm. long, 12—15cm. broad at base; *upper surface* pale to dark olive-green, sometimes a little glossy, without spots or markings except when young, flat low down, slightly canaliculate upwards; *lower surface* convex, similar to upper surface but sometimes with a few dull obscure elongated pale-green blotches near base; *margins* sinuate-dentate, mostly with horny reddish-brown edge armed with teeth the same colour, that are deltoid, pungent, 3—4mm. long, 10—15mm. distant; *sap* dries deep brown.

Inflorescence a branched panicle about 70—90cm. high.

Peduncle flattened and 20—25mm. broad at base, 6—8-branched from the middle or lower, marked below the first branch with many elongated very narrow pale-green lines that are broken at intervals.

Racemes conic-capitate or cylindric-acuminate, the terminal 10—20cm. long, laterals a little shorter, the buds sub-erect, crowded and hidden by densely imbricate bracts, older buds spreading, open flowers laxer, subpendulous.

Bracts broadly ovate-acute, 10mm. long, 5—7mm. broad, thin, scarious, brownish, 5-nerved.

Pedicels lowest 15mm.

Perianth deep red, sometimes yellow, 33mm. long, cylindric-trigonous, rather thick and fleshy, basally obconic, shortly stipitate, 11mm. diam. across the ovary, thence trigonous upwards; *outer segments* free for 10mm., obscurely 3-nerved, apices subacute, slightly spreading; *inner segments* broader than the outer and with more obtuse, more spreading apices.

Filaments pale lemon, the 3 inner narrower and lengthening before the 3 outer with their *anthers* in turn exserted 3—4mm.; *stigma* at length exserted 5mm.; *ovary* pale brown, 7mm. long, 3·5mm. diam. (Figs. 279, 280).

ETHIOPIA. *Harar Prov.*, near Harla Village, 9 miles SE of Dire Dawa on the Harar road, c. 9° 30′ N, 41° 52′ E, c. 1650m., 8 May 1956, Reynolds 8158 holotype (PRE), isotype (K); same locality, 3 Sept. 1957, Reynolds 8383 (K, PRE)—a form with more capitate racemes; Reynolds 8384 (K, PRE)—a form with more conical racemenes.

This species was found at the village of Harla, 9 miles SE of Dire Dawa on the road up the mountain to Harar, at 5,500 ft., and for 2 miles further on up to 6,000 ft. At lower altitudes *A.*

harlana was mostly in bud on 8 May 1956, and grew in association with *A. mcloughlinii* Christian (see *Fl. Plants Afr.* 28: Plate 1112 (1951) and *A. megalacantha* Baker (= *A. magnidentata* Verdoorn et Christian).

Larger plants, with rosettes 60—70cm. in diameter, were found at 6,000 ft., but there was no sign of flowers. It seems that at higher altitudes this species flowers in July—August, and in May—June lower down.

A. harlana appears to be nearest allied to *A. monticola* in size of leaves and horny leaf margins, and branching of inflorescence, but differs in having slightly smaller bracts, shorter flowers, and especially in cylindric-acuminate racemes 15—20cm. long.

Fig. 279.

A. harlana Reynolds. Plant × 1/10 approx., near Harla, 9 miles SE of Dire Dawa on road to Harar, Ethiopia.

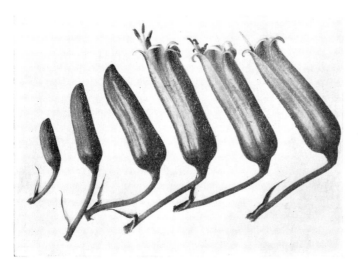

Fig. 280.

A. harlana Reynolds. Flowers natural size.

The peduncle in *A. harlana* is marked below the first branch with many very narrow elongated pale green lines that are broken at invervals. This is a character of *A. mcloughlinii* (abundant in the neighbourhood of Dire Dawa), but the latter could never be confused with its much smaller, glossy spotted leaves and squat flowers only 20mm. long.

Racemes of *A. harlana* vary from conic-subcapitate 10cm. long, 8cm. broad, to cylindric-acuminate 15—20cm. long, while flowers vary from deep red to sometimes yellow.

107. **A. steudneri** Schweinfurth in *Bull. Herb. Boiss.* 2: app. 2, 73 (1894); Baker in Th. Dyer *Fl. Trop. Afr.* 7: 458 (1898); Berger in Engler's *Pflanzenr.* Liliac.–Aloin. 287 (1908); *Bot. Mag. t.* 8448 (1912).

Note: Schweinfurth's original description (1894) gave no details of habit of growth and leaves, while Berger (1908) states "habit of growth and leaves unknown." The first reliable description was given in *Bot. Mag. t.* 8448 (1912). A plant given to Kew in 1896 by Penzig (collected in Eritrea) did not flower. Another plant brought from Eritrea by Penzig, and given to the Cambridge Botanic Gardens, flowered there in 1901. A sheet of material, and a water colour of a leaf and a raceme are at Kew. The type of *Bot. Mag. t.* 8448 (1912) is based on a third plant given by Penzig to Sir Thomas Hanbury in 1901, and which eventually flowered at La Mortola in 1911 when a photograph was taken and sent to Kew, together with a description drawn up by Alwin Berger. These were received at Kew on 28 April 1912.

DESCRIPTION is founded on Berger's description, and *Bot. Mag. t.* 8448.

Plants shortly caulescent, branching at base.

Leaves about 25, densely rosulate, the rosettes 90cm. across, erect and somewhat spreading or incurved towards apex, about 60cm. long, 12—15cm. broad at base, gradually narrowing to an acute apex, with a narrow hyaline somewhat rose-coloured edge armed with small teeth about 2mm. long, from 7—10mm. apart low down to 30—40mm. apart towards apex of leaf; *upper surface* flat low down, slightly canaliculate upwards (colour not stated, but photograph suggests grey-green, without markings); *lower surface* convex, hardly keeled.

FIG. 281.

A. steudneri Schweinf. From *Bot. Mag. t.* 8448 (1912) – much reduced. *Photo: By courtesy The Chief, Botanic Research Institute, Pretoria.*

Inflorescence 2—3 from a rosette simultaneously, the peduncles erect, simple or 3—5-branched, 70—90cm. high, glaucous with a purple tinge upwards, the branches 40—50cm. long, sterile-bracteate the sterile-bracts deltoid-lanceolate, long-acuminate, 25mm. long, many-nerved.

Racemes elongated, sub-laxly flowered, 15—18cm. long, the rhachis sulcate. (Photograph of the La Mortola plant shows deep red buds and pale—perhaps yellow-orange—open flowers).

Bracts enfolding the pedicels, 15—20mm. long, ovate-lanceolate, acuminate, many-nerved.

Pedicels 15—20mm. long, recurved at the tip, the lowest up to 25—30mm. long in the wild state.

Perianth cylindric-trigonous, deep red, thick and fleshy, 40—45mm. long, 12—14mm. diam., *outer segments* free almost to base.

Filaments pale yellow; *anthers* and *style* shortly exserted. (Fig. 281).

ERITREA. On peaks of Mt. Saber (Ssabr, Sabr) near Gheleb (Geleb), 2,600m., 5 April 1891, Penzig 1424 (K)—holotype or isotype?

ETHIOPIA. *Tigre:* Semien Mountains, Ghaba (Ataba?), Hochtal (valley), 3500m., 14 Jan. 1862, Steudner 448 (B, K)—this locality is approximately 13° 22' N, 38° 18' E; a few miles from Debarec on Gondar–Axum road, c. 13° 11' N, 37° 55' E, 8,600 ft., 10 Dec. 1961, flowers bright orange-red, B. T. Thomset 20! (K, PRE); a few miles W of Adigrat, on road to Axum, 6 Jan. 1963, Tekle Hagos 82! (PRE, ETH).

Plant brought from Eritrea by Prof. Penzig, flowered at Cambridge University Garden, 27 March 1901, with water-colour of leaf and flowers (K); Coll. Penzig in Eritrea, cult. La Mortola, fl. 8 April 1912, the type of *Bot. Mag. t.* 8448, with photograph (K).

TYPE LOCALITY

A. steudneri was originally collected by Dr. Steudner in 1862, in the Ghaba (Ataba ?) valley of the Semien Mountains, in N. Ethiopia, but Schweinfurth established his species on inflorescences collected by Prof. Penzig, in April 1891, on peaks of Mt. Saber near Geleb in Northern Eritrea.

Gheleb (or Geleb) is a mission station just NNW of the peak named Saber, 8,515 ft., approximately 15° 48' N, 38° 48' E, which is about 23 miles E of Cheren (Keren).

When the author was at Keren in April 1956, he was informed that Geleb could be reached only by mule trains over bad mountain tracks, the starting point being Elaberet, about 15 miles SE of Keren. The heavy rains had started, and with plants not in flower, any hopes of seeing plants on Mount Saber had to be abandoned.

DISTRIBUTION

Northern Eritrea, and the Tigre Province of Northern Ethiopia, at high altitudes, always over 8,000 ft. it seems.

Ato Tekle Hagos, Curator of the University Herbarium, Addis Ababa, Ethiopia, has found plants in the mountains W of Adigrat, on the road to Axum, at over 8,500 ft., flowering in January.

It seems that *A. steudneri* is characterized by having little or no stem, large leaves up to 60cm. long, 12—15cm. broad with small marginal teeth 2mm. long, 10—40mm. apart, a sparingly-branched inflorescence up to 1m. high, very large bracts, pedicel 20—25mm. long, with large, thick, fleshy flowers 40—45mm. long.

108.   A. berhana Reynolds in *Journ. S.A. Bot.* 23: 5 (1957).

DESCRIPTION: *Plants* mostly solitary, rarely in small groups, acaulescent or with short procumbent stem.

Leaves 24 or more, densely rosulate, spreading, slightly recurved in upper third, 50—60cm. long, 15cm. broad, gradually narrowing to the apex; *upper surface* unicoloured green without spots or markings, flat low down, slightly channelled upwards; *lower surface* convex, similar to upper surface; *margins* with horny reddish-brown edge armed with reddish-brown teeth that are pungent, deltoid, 3—4mm. long, about 15mm. apart.

Inflorescence a many-branched panicle, 1m. or more high.

Peduncle basally plano-convex and 3—4cm. broad, about 15-branched from the middle or lower, the lowest branch with 2—3 branchlets.

Racemes subcapitate, the terminal 6—8cm. long, 6—7cm. diam., rather densely flowered, youngest buds suberectly spreading, older buds horizontal, open flowers nutant to subpendulous.

Bracts narrowly ovate-acuminate, 8mm. long, 3mm. broad, thin, scarious, 1—3-nerved.

Pedicels 12—15mm. long, the colour of the perianth.

Perianth scarlet, paler at mouth, 30—35mm. long, cylindric, slightly curved, basally obtuse and very shortly stipitate, 8mm. diam. across the ovary, thence trigonous and very slightly narrowed on the underside only; *outer segments* free for 9mm., obscurely 3-nerved, apices subacute, slightly spreading; *inner segments* broader than the outer, pale yellow with scarlet keel, the apices more obtuse and more spreading than the outer.

Filaments pale lemon, the 3 inner narrower and lengthening before the 3 outer with their *anthers* in turn exserted 2—3mm.; *stigma* at length exserted 3mm.; *ovary* pale green, 7mm. long, 3mm. diam. (Plate 61, Fig. 282).

ETHIOPIA. *Shoa Prov.,* 9km. SW of Debre Berhan (121km. NE of Addis Ababa), c. 9° 40' N., 39° 40' E, c. 2,670m., 30 April 1956, Reynolds 8135 holotype (PRE), isotype (K).

PLATE 61

ALOE BERHANA   Reynolds.

Near Debre Berhan, 80 miles NE of Addis Ababa, Shoa Prov., Ethiopia.
Alt. 8,900 ft. Height 3′ 6″.

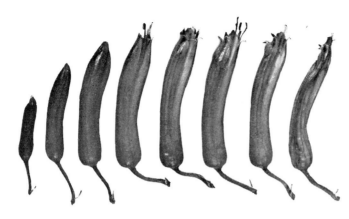

Fig. 282.

Aloe berhana Reynolds. Flowers 1/1 from a plant 9km. SW of Debre Berhan (121km. NE of Addis Ababa), Shoa Prov., Ethiopia, approx. 9° 40′ N., 39° 40′ E.

A. berhana was named after the locality where the author found it in large numbers, namely on rocky slopes W of the main road, 2 miles and 6 miles SW of Debre Berhan which is 80 miles and 76 miles NE of Addis Ababa, on the road to Dessie, at 8,900 ft. Plants observed 27 miles from Debre Berhan (9,300 ft.), and 10 miles further SW (8,700 ft.) were not flowering but appear to belong here. He subsequently found several plants in flower 36km. (22 miles) N of Addis Ababa, on the road to the Blue Nile and Debra Markos, at 8,100 ft., and also further N above Boli Gorge on Brigadier Sandford's farm "Mulu" which is 34 miles N of Addis Ababa. These had slightly longer racemes with shorter (30mm.) flowers, and are outlying forms of *A. berhana*, not of *A. percrassa* Tod.

A. berhana is nearest allied to *A. percrassa* Tod. which the author has seen in large numbers near Dessie, near Mai Chau, on Amba Alaji, west of Adigrat, and further north on the Kohaito Plateau between Senafe and Adi Caieh in Eritrea – but not below 8,000 ft. *A. berhana* is a slightly smaller plant with little or no stem, and subcapitate racemes with curved-cylindric flowers 30—35mm. long. *A. percrassa* is a larger plant with thick decumbent stems, longer, narrower racemes and short cylindric flowers averaging only 20mm. long, and not curved.

A. debrana Christian in *Fl. Plants S. Afr.* 26: Plate 1016 (1947) was described from west of the main road SW of Debre Berhan, but the author found no plants fitting the description at that locality. All plants still in flower on 30 April 1956 bore subcapitate racemes with 35mm. curved-cylindric flowers. *A. debrana* as described with 11cm. cylindric-acuminate racemes, and red perianth only 22mm. long, is clearly a form of *A. percrassa* Tod. and should be reduced to synonymy.

The main flowering period of *A. berhana* is February—March.

109. **A. monticola** Reynolds in *Journ. S.A. Bot.* 23: 7 (1957).

DESCRIPTION. *Plant* succulent, large, with little or no stem, usually growing singly.

Leaves 24 or more, densely rosulate, lanceolate-attenuate, spreading, slightly recurved near apex, 60—70cm. long, 14—16cm. broad at base; *upper surface* olive-green and somewhat glossy, unicoloured, flat low down, slightly canaliculate upwards; *lower surface* convex, unicoloured olive-green, rather glossy; *margins* sinuate-dentate, with very prominent brown horny edge armed with paler brown teeth that are deltoid, pungent, 6mm. long at middle of leaf, smaller towards apex and base, 10—15mm. distant. *Sap* dries brownish.

Inflorescence a branched panicle 1m. high, 2—4 simultaneously.

Peduncle basally plano-convex and up to 3cm. broad, rather compactly about 8-branched from the middle or lower, the lowest branch sometimes 1—3 rebranched and subtended at base by a scarious many-nerved ovate-acute bract about 25mm. long, 20mm. broad.

Racemes subcapitate, at first slightly conical, becoming sub-corymbose, 6—8cm. long, 8cm. diam., youngest buds suberect and hidden by densely imbricate bracts, older buds spreading, open flowers nutant.

Bracts lanceolate, long-pointed, 15—20mm. long, 6—7mm. broad, thin, scarious, brownish, 5—7-nerved.

Pedicels 15—20mm. long.

Perianth mostly yellow, sometimes bright scarlet, averaging 38mm. long, cylindric-trigonous, basally flat to slightly rounded, 8mm. diam. across the ovary, exceedingly slightly constricted above the ovary thence trigonous, the mouth wide open; *outer segments* free for 14mm., obscurely 3-nerved; the nerves greenish, apices subacute, spreading to revolute; *inner segments* free but dorsally adnate to the outer for 22mm., broader than the outer and with 3 crowded nerves forming a keel, the apices more obtuse and more spreading than the outer.

Filaments pale lemon, the 3 inner narrower and lengthening before the 3 outer with their *anthers* in turn exserted 5—6mm.; *stigma* at length exserted 8mm.; *ovary* green, 7mm. long, 3mm. diam. (Plate 62, Figs. 283—285).

ETHIOPIA. *Tigre Prov.*, mountain slopes, 7km. north of Mai Chau, c. 12° 41′ N, 39° 47′ E, c. 2460m., 24 April 1945, yellow flowers, Reynolds 8118 holotype (PRE), isotype (K, EA); red flowers, Reynolds 8117 (PRE, K).

PLATE 62

ALOE MONTICOLA Reynolds.

Mountain slopes 7km. N of Mai Chau, Tigre Prov., N. Ethiopia.
Alt. c. 2,460m. Height 1·20m.

FIG. 283.

A. monticola Reynolds. Yellow flowered plant on mountain slopes 7km. N of Mai Chau, Tigre Prov. N. Ethiopia. Alt. 2460m. Height 1·30m.

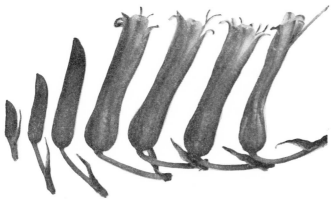

FIG. 284.

A. monticola Reynolds. Red flowers 1/1.

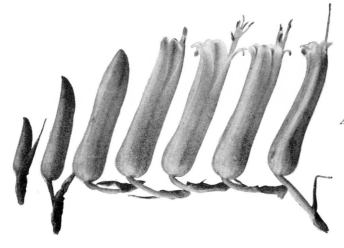

FIG. 285.

A. monticola Reynolds. Yellow flowers 1/1.

This very distinctive species occurs in the high mountains of northern Ethiopia from upper northern slopes of Amba Alaji to south of Adishew, and to about 3 miles south of Mai Chau (Mai Chew), a distance of about 45 miles (72km.). The largest numbers were found on mountain slopes of volcanic rock 4 miles north of Mai Chau at a point 112 km. (70 miles) S of Mekele and 268km. (165 miles) N of Dessie, at an elevation of 8,200 ft. (2360m.), with numbers of *A. percrassa* Tod. nearby.

The altitude range appears to be from 7,900 ft. to 8,500 ft. (2370—2550m.), while yellow flowers were more frequent than scarlet.

A. monticola is a most attractive and distinctive species characterized by having large olive-green, somewhat glossy, leaves with prominent horny, brown margins, and paler brown teeth that are longest (6mm.) at the middle of the leaf. The bracts are 15—20mm. long while the perianth averages 38mm. in length. Racemes are at first slightly conical with suberect buds covered by large densely imbricate bracts. With development, racemes become rather flat-topped, the young buds remaining suberect.

A. monticola seems to be nearest allied to *A. elegans* Tod. (which grows from the northern foot of Amba Alaji northwards to Eritrea where it is abundant) but the latter has grey-green leaves that are never glossy, shorter pedicels, bracts and flowers, while in racemes the young buds always spread horizontally to slightly downwards.

GROUP 17

Medium To Large Plants With Leaves Spreading To Recurved, Slightly To Deeply Canaliculate

Plants acaulescent or with erect or decumbent stems 50—80cm. long. *Leaves* up to 80cm. long, 16cm. broad at base, forming open (not compact) rosettes. *Inflorescence* rarely sparsely branched, mostly many-branched and about 1m. high. *Racemes* sublax to dense, sometimes slightly secund. *Bracts* small and inconspicuous. *Pedicels* mostly about 10mm. long. *Perianth* cylindric-trigonous, straight, yellow, orange or red, 22—36mm. long; *outer segments* free for 10—15mm., except in *A. macleayi* which is free to base.

Type species: *A. megalacantha* Bak.

KEY TO THE SPECIES

A. Inflorescence Simple or 1-Branched, 50cm. High:

1. *Leaves* 45cm. long, 10—12cm. broad. *Racemes* densely flowered, 6—9 cm. long. *Perianth* 28—30mm... .. .. 110 *A. schelpei*

B. Inflorescence 2—3-Branched, 1m. High:

(Becoming many-branched in cultivation after rains):
1. Acaulous, solitary. *Leaves* 50—60cm. long, 10—12cm. broad. *Racemes* 15—20cm. *long. Pedicels* 10—12mm. long. *Perianth* apricot-scarlet, 35mm. long .. .. 111 *A. keayi*

C. Inflorescence Rather Compactly Many-Branched, 90cm. High:

(a) *Racemes* narrowly cylindric-acuminate with slender tip, 15cm. long:
1. *Leaves* grey-green, sometimes spotted. *Pedicels* 13mm. long. *Perianth* 28mm. long, scarlet .. .. 112 *A. schweinfurthii*
(b) *Racemes* shorter, denser: *Inflorescence* more branched, flowers yellow .. .. 112a *var. labworana*
(c) *Leaves* 60cm. long, 14cm. broad, with thickened margins and large blunt teeth:
1. *Racemes* cylindric-conic, 6—8cm. long. *Pedicels* 10—15mm. long. *Perianth* yellow or scarlet, 28—30mm. long .. .. .. 113 *A. megalacantha*

(*d*) *Plants* acaulescent. *Leaves* 50cm. long, 12cm. broad. *Racemes* cylindric-conic, 22cm. long. *Perianth* 36mm. long, scarlet; *outer segments* free to base .. .. 114 *A. macleayi*
(*e*) *Perianth* clavate, scarlet, 22mm. long – see Group 13 .. .. 84 *A. calidophila*

D. Inflorescence Divaricately Many-Branched, Racemes Sub-secund:

(*a*) *Perianth* cylindric-trigonous; *outer segments* free for 10mm.:
  1. *Leaves* 50—70cm. long, 10cm. broad; *marginal teeth* only 1 (or 2)mm. long. *Pedicels* 5—6mm. long. *Perianth* scarlet, 23mm. long .. .. 115 *A. microdonta*
  2. *Leaves* 80cm. long, 17cm. broad; *teeth* 3mm. long. *Pedicels* 10mm. long. *Perianth* yellow, orange, red, 28mm. long .. .. 116 *A. marsabitensis*

110. A. schelpei Reynolds in *Journ. S.A. Bot.* 27: 1 (1961).

Description: *Plant* of low growth with decumbent stems that are short or up to 50cm. long, 5—6cm. thick, with shoots from base or at random along the stem, forming dense groups.

Leaves 16—20, rosulate, lanceolate-attenuate, averaging 45cm. long, 10—12cm. broad at base, the youngest erectly spreading, the oldest spreading to recurved; *upper surface* glaucous with bluish tinge, unicoloured or sometimes with several pale-green to creamy lenticular spots near base, slightly concave at base, rather deeply canaliculate upwards; *lower surface* rounded, slightly deeper green than upper surface, usually with several spots in lowest quarter; *margins* with prominent reddish-pink edge armed with teeth of the same colour at base, paler at apex, firm to subpungent, 2—3mm. long, about 15mm. apart. *Sap* dries dark brown.

Inflorescence consistently simple or 1-branched, averaging 50cm. high, with the peduncle basally plano-convex and 16—18mm. broad.

Raceme cylindric-conic, 6—9cm. long, 6—7cm. diam., rather densely flowered, the youngest buds spreading horizontally to slightly downwards, open flowers nutant to subpendulous.

Bracts ovate-acute, thin, dry, dirty-white, 5mm. long, 3mm. broad, 3—5-nerved.

Pedicels pink, slender, the lowest 13—15mm. long.

Perianth orange-red, paler at mouth, 28—30mm. long, cylindric-trigonous, 7mm. diam. across the ovary, very slightly narrowed above the ovary on the underside, thence very slightly curved and enlarging trigonously towards the throat and slightly compressed laterally; *outer segments* free for 12mm., paler and thinner at the margin, 3-nerved, the apices subacute and slightly spreading; *inner segments* broader than the outer and with 3 crowded nerves forming an orange-red keel, the apices brownish and more obtuse than the outer.

Filaments pale yellow, the 3 inner narrower and lengthening before the 3 outer; *anthers* brown, in turn exserted 2—3mm.; *style* greenish yellow, with the *stigma* at length exserted 3—4mm.; *ovary* yellowish green, 6mm. long, 3mm. diam. (Figs. 286–289).

Ethiopia. *Shoa Prov.:* Boli Gorge, Mulu Sayu, alt. 7,000 ft., 13 Sept. 1952, Curle et Schelpe 61, holotype (BM); ex Mulu Sayu, cult. Greendale, Salisbury, Rhodesia, fl. 10 April 1960, L. C. Leach 9838 (PRE, K).

Fig. 286.

A. schelpei Reynolds. Flowering plants photographed by Dr. E. A. Schelpe in September 1952, at Mulu Sayu, Boli Gorge, 54km. N of Addis Ababa, Shoa Prov., Ethiopia. Height 60cm.

Fig. 287.

A. schelpei Reynolds. Plants at the Fig. 286 locality photographed by the author.

Fig. 288.

A. schelpei Reynolds. Raceme × 9/10. Photo: Mr. L. C. Leach.

Fig. 289.

A. schelpei Reynolds. Flowers natural size.

A. schelpei was named after Dr. E. A. Schelpe (Dept. of Botany, University of Cape Town), who discovered it in September 1952, on steep grassland slopes of the Boli Gorge, Mulu Sayu, Shoa Province, Ethiopia. Mulu Sayu is the name of Brigadier D. A. Sandford's farm, lying to the west of the road to the Blue Nile and Debra Marcos, 54km. N of Addis Ababa.

In May 1956 the author visited Mulu Sayo expressly to investigate this species, and found large numbers of plants on steep north-east slopes of the Boli Gorge, facing the 700 ft. waterfall of the Mugur River (a tributary of the Blue Nile), at c. 9° 14′ N, 38° 40′ E, and at an altitude of 7,700 ft. Unfortunately no plants were then in flower, but a description of the available material was prepared. Dry spikes lying about were consistently simple or only 1-branched, and averaged 50cm. in height.

Three large plants brought back to Johannesburg had shown no sign of flowering in five years, but a plant given to Mr. L. C. Leach, and cultivated by him at Greendale (near Salisbury, Rhodesia), flowered there in April 1960, when the description was completed.

A. schelpei appears to be nearest allied to the Somaliland species *A. megalacantha* Bak. from which it differs chiefly in having much shorter, decumbent stems, smaller rosettes and leaves, an inflorescence only 50cm. in height which is simple or only 1-branched.

The cylindric-conic racemes of *A. schelpei* with the youngest buds spreading horizontally to slightly downwards suggests an affinity with *A. elegans* Tod., but the latter is acaulescent, is not of shrubby growth and has a much taller, very much more branched inflorescence.

111. A. keayi Reynolds in *Journ. S.A. Bot.* 29: 43 (1963).

DESCRIPTION: *Plant* succulent, acaulescent or with very short stem, sometimes with 1—2 suckers.

Leaves 20—30, densely rosulate, the youngest suberectly spreading, the oldest up to 60cm. long, 10—12cm. broad at base, gradually narrowing to an acute apex; *upper surface* green, with or without a few scattered pale green elliptic spots, flat low down, slightly canaliculate upwards; *lower surface* rounded, green, mostly without spots or markings; *margins* armed with deltoid, pungent teeth, 5—6mm. long, irregularly 10—15mm. apart.

Inflorescence usually 2—3-branched, 1m. high, but 1·20m., and developing 10 branches in cultivation at the end of the rains.

Peduncle green with a slight bloom.

Racemes subdensely flowered, cylindric-conic, 15—20cm. long, about 9cm. diam., the buds suberect, dull scarlet with dull green tips, open flowers nutant, pale scarlet to pinkish-apricot, paler at mouth.

Bracts deltoid-acute, 5—7mm. long, 2mm. broad at base, 3-nerved.

Pedicels the lowest arcuate-ascending, 10—12mm. long, slightly shorter upwards.

Perianth pale apricot-scarlet to pinkish-apricot, 35mm. long, basally obtuse and shortly stipitate, 8mm. diam. across the ovary, very slightly constricted above the ovary thence slightly enlarging trigonously to an open mouth; *outer segments* free for 14mm., 3-nerved to base, the nerves greenish at apex; *inner segments* broader, dorsally adnate to the outer for half their length, the upper free portion with 3 crowded nerves forming a slight keel extending to base and giving the whole perianth a somewhat striped effect.

Filaments lemon, filiform-flattened, the 3 inner narrower and lengthening before the 3 outer with their *anthers* in turn exserted 2—3mm.; *stigma* at length exserted 3—4mm.; *ovary* light green, 7mm. long, 3mm. diam. (Figs. 290–292).

GHANA. Accra Plains, Nyanyana to Odupoukpeehe, near main Accra–Winneba road, fl. 5 April 1959, R. W. J. Keay et C. D. Adams, FHI 37757 (FHI); plant coll. Keay et Adams at type loc. cult. Idaban (Nigeria), fl. 24 August 1962, FHI 37757A, holotype (K), isotype (BM, PRE, EA, FHI, GC).

Fig. 290.

A. keayi Reynolds. Plant on the Accra Plains, Nyanyanu to Odupoukpeehe, near the main Accra-Winneba road, Ghana; flowering 5 April 1959, at the commencement of the rainy season. Height 1m.
Photograph: Mr. R. W. J. Keay.

Fig. 291.

A. keayi Reynolds. Plant from Accra Plains, Ghana, cult. Ibadan, Nigeria, flowering Sept. 1960 at end of rainy season. Height 1·20m.

Fig. 292.

A. keayi Reynolds. Flowers 1/1.

A. keayi was named after Mr. R. W. J. Keay, at that time Director of Forest Research, Ibadan, Nigeria, who has contributed considerably to the advancement of botanical knowledge of the Nigerian flora and elsewhere.

A. keayi appears to be nearest allied to *A. schweinfurthii* Bak. which grows in the same area (and eastwards to the Congo–Sudan and Congo–Uganda borders) but differs in having little or no stem, broader, less recurved leaves, racemes that are denser and less acuminate, and in the shape of the flowers.

Plants flowering on the Accra Plains in April – at the commencement of the rains – usually have 2—3-branched inflorescences about 1m. high, whereas the same plants cultivated in Ibadan, Nigeria, flowering in September at the end of the rainy season, are considerably more robust and produce an inflorescence 120cm. high, with up to 10 branches, the lowest of which having 1—2 branchlets.

The perianth of *A. keayi* is slightly constricted above the ovary, thence slightly enlarging, whereas in *A. schweinfurthii* it is more cylindric-trigonous. In the latter the leaves are more grey-green, narrower, and more recurved, and racemes narrow to a slender tip.

112. **A. schweinfurthii** Baker in *Journ. Linn. Soc.* 18: 175 (1880), in Th. Dyer *Fl. Trop. Afr.* 7: 467 (1898); Durand et Schinz *Consp. Fl. Afr.* 312 (1893); *non Gard. Chron.* 23: ser. 3, 197, fig. 76 (1898) – this is *A. elegans* Tod. (= *A. aethiopica* (Schw.) Berger); *non* Hooker in *Bot. Mag. t.* 7667 (1899) – this is also *A. elegans* Tod.; Berger in Engler's *Pflanzenr.* Liliac.–Aloin. 246 (1908); Reynolds in *Journ. S.A. Bot.* 20: 165–8 (1954).

The following synonymy according to R. W. J. Keay in *The Nigerian Species of Aloe*, in *Kew Bull.* 17: No. 1, 65 (1963):

—— *A. barteri* Bak. in *Journ. Linn. Soc.* 18: 168 (1880) *pro parte*, *Fl. Trop. Afr.* 7: 464 (1898) *pro parte*; *Fl. W. Trop. Afr.* 2: 345 (1936) *pro parte*.

—— *A. barteri* Bak. var. *lutea* A. Chev. in *Etudes Fl. l'Afr. Cent. Franc.* 1: 313 (1913).

—— *A. trivialis* A. Chev. in *Rev. Bot. Appliq.* 31: 594 *t.* 32B (1952) *desc. gall. tant.*

DESCRIPTION based on flowering plants at the type locality; Jebel Bangenze, Equatoria Prov., Sudan.

Stem none or short, with shoots forming small to large dense groups.

Leaves 16—20, densely rosulate, the younger erectly spreading, older spreading and recurved in upper quarter, averaging 45cm. long (sometimes reaching 50—60cm.), 6—7cm. broad at base, gradually tapering to the apex; *upper surface* grey-green, with bluish tinge, sometimes reddish-tinged, flat low down, canaliculate upwards, usually with several elongated dull whitish spots in lower third; *lower surface* convex, greyer-green than upper surface, usually with a few dull spots near base; *margins* sinuate-dentate, armed with pungent deltoid teeth which are reddish-brown at apices and paler near base, averaging 4mm. long, 10—12mm. distant, slightly hooked forward. *Sap* dries purplish.

Inflorescence a branched panicle averaging 90cm. high.

Peduncle brown, slender, plano-convex and 15mm. broad at base, terete upwards, 8—9mm. thick at the middle, 8—10-branched from the middle or higher, the 1—2 lowest branches sometimes with 1—2 branchlets.

Racemes subdensely to sublaxly flowered, rather narrowly cylindric-acuminate, the terminal usually the longest and averaging 15cm. long, 7cm. diam., the buds suberect, scarlet and slightly grey-tipped, open flowers at first spreading, becoming subpendulous.

Bracts small, ovate-acute, averaging 5mm. long, 2—3mm. broad at base, subscarious, dirty-white, rather thin, mostly 1-nerved.

Pedicels averaging 13mm. long, lengthening in the fruit.

Perianth cylindric-trigonous, straight, averaging 28mm. long, scarlet, turning orange at mouth or throughout, basally very slightly obtusely tapering to the pedicel, cylindric and 7mm. diam. across the ovary, thence very slightly narrowed on underside only, cylindric-trigonous above the ovary, the mouth open; *outer segments* free for 12mm., paler at the edges, 3-nerved to base, the apices acute, spreading; *inner segments* free but dorsally adnate to the outer for half their length, broader than the outer and with 3 crowded nerves forming an orange keel throughout, the apices more obtuse, and more spreading to revolute.

Filaments pale lemon, filiform-flattened, the 3 inner narrower and lengthening before the 3 outer, with their *anthers* in turn exserted 2—3mm.; *style* yellow, with *stigma* at length exserted 4—5mm.; *ovary* brownish olive, 5mm. long, 2·5mm. diam. (Plate 63, Figs. 293–294)

"Central Africa, Niamniam, at Makporru Hill", Schweinfurth, ser. iii, 167!, May 1870 (K, holotype).

Fig. 293.

A. schweinfurthii Bak. Plants between Aba and the Sudan border, Kibali-Ituri Dist., Oriental Province, Congo (Leo), flowering in July. Height 85cm.

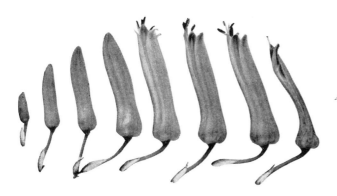

Fig. 294.

A. schweinfurthii Bak. Buds and Flowers 1/1 from the Plate 63 plant.

PLATE 63

ALOE SCHWEINFURTHII   Baker.

On Jebel Bangenze (type locality), Zande Dist., Equatoria Province,
Sudan. Alt. 2,600 ft. Height 3 ft.

SUDAN REPUBLIC. *Equatoria Prov.:* Kindi-Kare (Zande), Mt. Bangenze, abundant on rocky slopes, 16 May 1937, J. G. Meyer 6634! (K). *Zande Dist.*, Mt. Bangenze, on greiss slopes, 30 May 1953, R. K. M. Anthony A701! (PRE); Jebel (Mt.) Bangenze, near the Congo border at c. 4° 28′ N, 29° E, alt. 2,600 ft., fl. 10 July 1954, Reynolds 7284 (PRE, K, BR, EA, KHARTOUM). *Mongalla,* Kendi Hill, near source of River Yei, c. 1100—1200m., 27 Feb. 1934, J. E. Dandy 509! (BM). *Kordofan,* Nuba Mountains, c. 12° N, 30° E, 600m., among rocks on sides of Jebels, common, July 1952, R. du Bois s.n. (PRE, KHARTOUM).

CONGO (late Belgian). *Oriental Prov.:* Kibali–Ituri Dist., Faradje Territory, 6 miles E of Aba (= 5 miles W of Sudan border), 3,200 ft., 13 July 1954, Reynolds 7489 (PRE, K, BR, EA); 9 miles W of Adranga, 68 miles E of Watsa, 5 July 1954, Reynolds 7283 (BR).

GHANA. Accra Plains, 20 Feb. 1901, T. W. Brown 928! (K).

W. NIGERIA. Lagos, Feb. 1895, Millen 172! (K); Okekpologon (between Olokomeji and Iseyin), 7° 54′ N, 3° 30′ E, 11 Nov. 1959, Hambler 776! (FHI, PRE); Idanre Hills, 24 Oct. 1948, Keay in F.H.I. 22582! (FHI, K). *Ondo Prov,.* Idanre Hills, cult. Ibadan, fl. Oct. 1948, Keay in F.H.I. 22716 (FHI, SRGH, K).

N. NIGERIA. Jos Plateau, Sara Hills, Dutsen Adari, above Badni, 23 Oct. 1957, Hepper 1131! (K).

W. CAMEROONS. *Adamawa Prov.:* Mapeo Dist., Atlantika Mountains, 18 Dec. 1957, Hepper 1603! (K).

SHARI. Banda, Kaga Balidja, 8 Dec. 1902, *Chevalier* 6732 (P, holotype of *A. trivialis*); same locality and date, *Chevalier* 6733 (P, possibly the type of *A. trivialis* var. *lutea* which is quoted in *Rev. Bot. Appliq.* 31: 597 as *Chevalier* (6783)—*fide* R. W. J. Keay.

UBANGI. Bangui, 18 Aug. 1902, *Chevalier* 5245 (K)—*fide* R. W. J. Keay.

NATIVE NAME

Ranga or *Rangambia* in the Azande tongue of the Zande District, Equatoria Province, Sudan.

TYPE LOCALITY

Baker founded this species on Schweinfurth's gathering Ser. iii No. 167, the type locality being "Niamniam, at Makporru Hill, May 1870", but the identity of *A. schweinfurthii* and its precise locality of origin have remained in doubt until recently.

In the third publication, Hooker in *Bot. Mag. t.* 7667 records that the granite hill of Makporru is at lat. 4° 45′ N, long. 28° 30′ E, while Berger stated that Schweinfurth told him that this species had not been introduced alive into Europe.

Schweinfurth's herbarium was destroyed during the war, it appears, but Baker's holotype is at Kew.

Two figures of "*A. schweinfurthii*" have been published, one in *Gard. Chron.* 23: ser. 3, 197, fig. 16 (1898), the other in *Bot. Mag. t.* 7667 (1899), but these far from represent *A. schweinfurthii* – they are both *A. elegans* Tod.

It was clear that nothing less than a personal visit to the type locality would ever enable the author to establish the identity of this long "lost" species, but the problem was to find the type locality. Where was Makporru Hill?

Professor K. N. G. MacLeay, Department of Botany of the University College of Khartoum, made exhaustive enquiries in the Zande area of the Equatoria Province of the Sudan (the Niamniam-land of Schweinfurth), and also examined various maps, but was unsuccessful in locating any hill bearing the name of Makporru, although there was a small river of that name shown at 4° 50′ N, 28° 40′ E.

The solution was eventually found in Schweinfurth's book *The Heart of Africa*, English translation, 2 vols., London 1873. On 27 May 1870, Schweinfurth had reached "Mount Baginze", and he records "Masses of brilliant Aloes, with their scarlet and yellow blossoms, grew luxuriantly upon the slopes of gneiss". (Vol. 2, p. 214).

Mt. (Jebel) Bangenze can safely be accepted as the type locality. It is situated on the Sudan–Congo border, at c. 4° 28′ N, 29° E, at 2,600 ft. alt.

On 9 July 1954, Mr. E. M. McDermid, Entomologist at Yambio, and Mrs. McDermid, conducted the present author to Mt. Bangenze.

For record purposes, the route from Yambio (320 miles W of Juba) led eastwards along the Maridi and Juba road for 50 miles, thence turn off 17 miles southwards to near a small Zande village called Gbuo, and then along a track for 5 miles to the south-west. From that point, after a walk of two miles through tall grass woodland, including a few hundred yards struggling through marshy ground densely filled with 15 ft. elephant-grass (and keeping well down-wind from several elephants), Bangenze was reached, near the Congo border. Considerable numbers of only one species of Aloe were found there, many in flower, growing in scanty soil on granite, in shallow pockets or in crevices on slopes. They were *A. schweinfurthii*, without doubt.

DISTRIBUTION

A. schweinfurthii is widely distributed from the SW parts of the Sudan, and the NE corner of the (formerly Belgian) Congo, westwards to the Ubangi basin and Upper Shari (on rocky hills called "Kaga"), westwards to the W. Cameroons, Nigeria (Jos Plateau and Panshanu, E of Jos to the Idanre Hills, Ado Rock, S of Iseyin near Ibadan, Lagos), across to the Accra Plains in Ghana.

AFFINITIES

A. sereti De Wild., from 6 miles N of Irumu, Oriental Province, Congo, is a near ally, but differs in having mostly 3-branched inflorescences. *A. mubendiensis* Christian, from the Toro District of the Western Province of Uganda, is another close ally, but is distinguished by having a more branched inflorescence with more divaricate branching, and denser racemes with the flowers sometimes slightly secund.

IDENTITY OF *A. BARTERI* BAK.

At Kew there are two sheets of Aloe collected by C. Barter in Nigeria. The first comprises an inflorescence only (no leaf) of what is clearly *A. schweinfurthii*, but it has no number and is not named or annotated by Baker.

The second sheet is named *A. barteri* in Baker's handwriting, and is also marked holotype. It is Barter 1502! from Nupe (which includes the area between Kaduna and the Niger confluence in the southern part of Niger Province). This sheet comprises two detached racemes and one long-attenuate leaf. Mr. R. W. J. Keay has also found that the leaf is that of *A. schweinfurthii*, but the racemes, with perianths showing the typical subglobose basal swelling, clearly belong to a totally different species, which was subsequently described as *A. buettneri* by Berger in 1905. *A. barteri*, therefore, proves to be a mixture of species, and cannot be upheld.

Both species were published in the same paper (1880). *A. schweinfurthii* is a good species with a wide distribution, and *A. barteri* is now relegated *pro parte* (leaf only) as a synonym of it.

112A Var. 1. **A. schweinfurthii** Bak. var. **labworana** Reynolds in *Journ. S.A. Bot.* 20: 140 (1956).

DESCRIPTION: *Plant* succulent, of medium size, acaulescent, suckering at ground level and forming groups.

Leaves 12—16, rosulate, erectly spreading, narrowly lanceolate-attenuate, recurved in upper quarter, 60—80cm. long, 7—8cm. broad at base, 2cm. thick low down; *upper surface* flat to slightly canaliculate, bluish-green with a grey powdery bloom, with numerous very pale-greenish spots throughout, the spots lenticular, 3—6mm. long, 1—2mm. broad at the middle; *lower surface* convex, greyer-green than upper surface, more copiously spotted throughout, the spots smaller and more crowded; *margins* sinuate-dentate, armed with pungent, deltoid, reddish-tipped teeth which are 5—6mm. long, 12—20mm. distant, with rounded interspaces. *Sap* dries yellowish.

Inflorescence a divaricately many-branched panicle up to 90cm. high.

Peduncle brown, basally plano-convex and 20—25mm. broad, divaricately branched from the middle or lower, with 10—12 arcuate-ascending branches, the 1—2 lowest with 3—4 branchlets.

Racemes cylindric, slightly conical, 8—9cm. long, 5cm. diam., youngest buds suberect, denser, open flowers laxer, nutant to subpendulous, the whole raceme (axis, pedicels and flowers) uniformly yellow.

Bracts ovate-acute, about 2mm. long and broad, clasping the pedicel, thin, scarious, 1-nerved.

Pedicels yellow, 10mm. long.

Perianth yellow, 28mm. long, cylindric, slightly trigonous, basally obtuse, 6—7mm. diam. across the ovary, thence very slightly narrowed on the underside and enlarging slightly to a wide open mouth; *outer segments* free for 9mm. (definite tube of 19mm.), with 3 greenish nerves throughout, the apices subacute, slightly spreading; *inner segments* themselves free but dorsally adnate to the outer to beyond the middle, broader than the outer, keeled, the apices more obtuse and more spreading than the outer.

Filaments very pale lemon, filiform-flattened, the 3 inner narrower and lengthening before the 3 outer with their *anthers* in turn exserted 3—4mm.; *style* pale yellow; *stigma* at length exserted 5mm.; *ovary* pale green, 5mm. long, 2·5mm. diam. (Plate 64, Fig. 295).

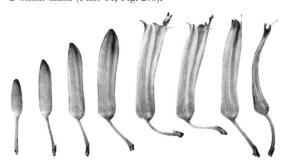

FIG. 295.

A. schweinfurthii Bak. var. *labworana* Reynolds. Flowers 1/1 from a plant from the Labwor Hills, Karamoja, Uganda.

PLATE 64

ALOE SCHWEINFURTHII   Baker.
var. LABWORANA   Reynolds.

Plant from Abim, Labwor, Uganda, flowering in Johannesburg. Height
85cm.

UGANDA. *Northern Prov.:* Karamoja, Labwor Hills, at Abim, 6 miles SW of Rwot, 41 miles SW of Kotido, c. 2° 47′ N, 33° 38′ E, c. 4,500 ft. (coll. T. H. E. Jackson), fl. 15 Oct. 1955, Reynolds 7980 holotype (PRE), isotype (K, EA); Labwor Hills, Aremo, 58 miles SW of Kotido, c. 2° 30′ N, 33° 53′ E. (coll. T. H. E. Jackson), cult. Kitale, fl. 25 Oct. 1955, Reynolds 8006 (PRE, EA, K); Labwor Hills, Loyoroit, 30 miles SW of Kotido, c. 2° 46′ N, 33° 41′ E. (coll. H. Wreford Smith), cult. Johannesburg, fl. 27 March 1955, Reynolds 6274 (PRE, K); Labwor Hills, Dec. 1962, Tweedie 2528 (EA)—excellent material.

The var. *labworana* closely resembles typical *A. schweinfurthii* in habit of growth, leaves and markings, small 1-nerved bracts, pedicels and shape and size of flowers, but differs in having comparatively longer leaves with larger marginal teeth, and a more branched inflorescence with shorter, denser, not acuminate racemes of yellow flowers. The most striking difference is that the rachis, pedicels and flowers are all of a uniform yellow colour.

113. **A. megalacantha** Bak. in Th. Dyer *Fl. Trop. Afr.* 7: 469 (1898); Berger in Engler's *Pflanzenr.* Liliac.–Aloin. 252 (1908); Reynolds in *Journ. S.A. Bot.* 24: 169 (1958).

—— *A. magnidentata* Verdoorn et Christian in *Fl. Plants Afr.* 26: Plate 1015 (1947).

Note: Baker described *A. megalacantha* as an *Imperfectly known species*, citing Riva 905 as his type. Berger stated *Habitus ignotus*. Riva 905 was collected on 2 Jan. 1893 at Mil Mil in the Ogaden, Ethiopia, which is about 100 miles S of Hargeisa, the capital of Somalia North, formerly Somaliland Protectorate.

It was Mr. Peter Bally who specially journeyed from Hargeisa down to Mil Mil to investigate the identity of the species there, and he found that plants were clearly conspecific with the species found in considerable numbers all around Hargeisa.

A. magnidentata was described from Dire Dawa, in Harar Province, Ethiopia, but plants at that locality also proved to be conspecific with *A. megalacantha*.

The description is based on personal observations of many plants near Hargeisa and near Dire Dawa.

DESCRIPTION: *Plants* usually growing in groups, with *stems* 50—100cm. tall, the apical 50cm. subdensely foliate, with old dried leaf remains persistent.

Leaves rosulate, 24 or more, averaging 60cm. long (sometimes 80cm.), 13—15cm. broad at base and 10—15mm. thick, gradually attenuate, spreading to much recurved with the apices of leaves often pointing downwards; *upper surface* unicoloured dull light-green, deeply canaliculate; *lower surface* rounded, otherwise as the upper surface; *margins* with thickened, pinkish, horny edge armed with large,somewhat blunt, pinkish teeth that are reddish-brown tipped, 5—6mm. long, about 20mm. apart.

Inflorescence a many-branched panicle about 1m. high, sometimes 2—3 simultaneously from a rosette.

Peduncle basally plano-convex and 30mm. broad, branched below the middle with 12 or more arcuate-ascending branches, the lowest 2—3 sometimes with 2—3 branchlets.

Racemes cylindric-conic, 6—8cm. long, about 7cm. diam., subdensely flowered, the buds denser and suberect, open flowers a little laxer and nutant.

Bracts small, ovate-deltoid, 5mm. long, 2—3mm. broad, thin, dry, dirty-white, 3—5-nerved.

Pedicels green, 10—15mm. long.

Perianth yellow, orange or scarlet, cylindric-trigonous, straight, 28—30mm. long, basally flat or slightly rounded, 8mm. diam. across the ovary, thence very slightly narrowed on underside only, slightly widened upwards with wide open mouth; *outer segments* free for 15mm., paler at the edges, 3-nerved, with subacute slightly spreading apices; *inner segments* broader than the outer, with 3 crowded nerves forming a keel, the apices more obtuse and more spreading than the outer.

Filaments filiform-flattened, the 3 inner narrower and lengthening before the 3 outer with their *anthers* in turn exserted 3mm.; *stigma* at length exserted 4mm.; *ovary* pale green, 6mm. long, 3mm. diam. (Plates 65, 66, Figs. 296–298).

ETHIOPIA. *Ogaden,* Mil Mil, 2 Jan. 1893, Riva 905 (FI, holotype). *Harar Prov.* ex Dire Dawa, coll. McLoughlin 825, cult. Pretoria, fl. 10 Feb. 1943, No. 27206 in Nat. Herb.—type of *Fl. Pl. Afr.,* Plate 1015 (PRE); ex Dire Dawa, coll. A. G. McLoughlin 824, cult. Ewanrigg, fl. 20 Oct. 1944, Christian 1167, No. 27281 in Nat. Herb. as type of *A. magnidentata* (PRE, SRGH); cult. Pretoria, fl. 26 Feb. 1945, A. G. McLoughlin 824 (PRE); in large numbers 3—6 miles W of Dire Dawa on road to Awash, 3,800 ft., 8 May 1956, Reynolds 8155 (PRE, K, EA).

SOMALIA NORTH (formerly Somaliland Prot.). Hargeisa, 2 Oct. 1954, Bally 9915 (K, EA); ex Hargeisa Township, cult. Johannesburg, fl. 26 April 1953, flowers orange, Reynolds 6244 (PRE, EA, SRGH); 30 miles E of Hargeisa, 27 Aug. 1956, flowers red, Reynolds 8332 (K, PRE), flowers yellow, Reynolds 8333 (PRE).

A. megalacantha grows in considerable numbers for many miles around Hargeisa, and it is surprising that all the early botanists travelling that way had mistaken it for *A. abyssinica* Lam., a species brought back to Paris by Bruce, presumably from Northern Eritrea or Ethiopia. *A. abyssinica* remains an unknown species – see *Species imperfectly known* for discussion and photograph of the type in Paris.

PLATE 65

ALOE MEGALACANTHA Baker.

Red-flowered form, 30 miles E of Hargeisa, Somalia North. Flowering
in August 1957. Height 1·30m.

PLATE 66

ALOE MEGALACANTHA Baker.

Yellow-flowered form, 30 miles E of Hargeisa, Somalia North.
Flowering in August 1957. Height 1·30m.

Fig. 296.

A. megalacantha Bak. Yellow-flowered plants 4 miles SE of Diredawa, Harar Province, Ethiopia, alt. 4,400 feet. Height 7 feet.

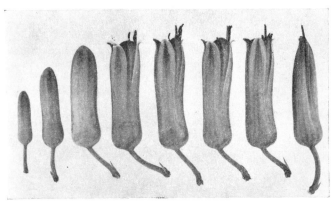

Fig. 297.

A. megalacantha Bak. Yellow flowers 1/1, from a plant 4 miles SE of Diredawa, Harar Prov., Ethiopia.

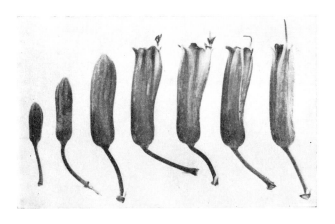

Fig. 298.

A. megalacantha Bak. Red flowers 1/1 from a plant 30 miles E of Hargeisa, Somalia North.

DISTRIBUTION

A. megalacantha is widespread through central and western Somalia North, especially around Hargeisa and for 40 miles NW of Borama near Kolujet and Bawn. In Ethiopia, large numbers occur around Dire Dawa; also W of Lake Zwai, 216km. S of Addis Ababa; at Mil Mil, 100 miles S of Hargeisa. Does *A. megalacantha* grow in Arabia?

In "Birds of Arabia" by Colonel R. Meinertzhagen, D.S.O. (Edinburgh 1954), there is a photographic plate (number 6) of a termite mound near Lodar, Aden Protectorate. In the foreground are numerous plants of a species of Aloe. In the left lower corner is a plant with an indistinct inflorescence. These plants with channelled, recurved leaves and stems about 50cm. tall, bear a most striking resemblance indeed to *A. megalacantha* Bak. which occurs in considerable numbers all around Hargeisa, etc. It may be that *A. megalacantha* grows in Aden Protectorate also.

DYE MAKING

The author was told in Hargeisa that the leaves of *A. megalacantha* are used by the Somalis for making a permanent black dye.

Leaves are buried in the ground for about a week. They are then removed and burnt. The ash is mixed with sisal fibre, matting, etc. and buried again for two or three days. The material has then been dyed black permanently.

Later, in Erigavo, the Forester, Ahmed Sheikh Mohamed, told of another method. The Somalis collect dried leaf remains of other aloes and put them thickly in a pot of boiling water. The mixture is kept at the boil for 48 hours and turns black. Bark, fibre, matting, etc. soaked in this mixture is permanently dyed black.

NATURAL HYBRIDS

Crosses of *A. megalacantha* with *A. rigens* Reynolds et Bally, and also with *A. hildebrandtii* Bak., occur on the Gaan Libah Plateau 12 miles NW of Ghor, off the Hargeisa–Burao road, in Somalia North.

Crosses with *A. mcloughlinii* Christian were observed among both parents about 3 miles W of Dire Dawa, Harar Province, Ethiopia.

114. **A. macleayi** Reynolds in *Journ. S.A. Bot.* 21: 55 (1955).

DESCRIPTION: A large acaulescent plant, apparently solitary and not suckering or forming groups.

Leaves about 24, densely rosulate, erectly spreading and gracefully recurved, lanceolate-attenuate, up to 50cm. long, 12cm. broad at base; *upper surface* deep-green to olive-green, obscurely lineate, without spots, rather flat near base, deeply canaliculate upwards; *lower surface* rounded, similar to the upper surface in colour; *margins* yellowish-white, armed with firm, white, uncinate, deltoid teeth which are 4mm. long, irregularly 8—15mm. distant. *Leaf sap* dries yellow.

Inflorescence a much-branched panicle, 90cm. high, produced at a slight angle but with all racemes erect.

Peduncle brown, flattened and 2cm. broad at base, dichotomously about 9-branched from below the middle.

Racemes cylindric-conical, the terminal 22cm. long, 5·5cm. diam., laterals a little shorter, buds minutely white-spotted, suberect, denser, open flowers laxer, subpendulous.

Bracts small, clasping the pedicel, broadly and shortly ovate-acute, 3mm. long, 4mm. broad, pale brown, thin, subscarious, 3-nerved, the central nerve raised, dark-brown.

Pedicels dull scarlet, lowest 10mm. long.

Perianth cylindric-trigonous, 36mm. long, scarlet at base and along the nerved part of the outer segments to the middle, the mouth orange to yellowish, slightly rounded at base and not stipitate, 7mm. diam. across the ovary, thence trigonous upwards; *outer segments* free to base, 6mm. broad at the middle, with pale thin edges, 3—5-nerved throughout, the apices subacute, spreading; *inner segments* free, longer and thinner than the outer, 7mm. broad at the middle, with a prominent orange keel throughout, the apices brown-tipped, more obtuse and more spreading to revolute.

Filaments very pale lemon, filiform-flattened, the 3 inner narrower and lengthening before the 3 outer, with their *anthers* in turn exserted 2—4mm.; *style* pale yellow; *stigma* at length exserted 3mm.; *ovary* olive-green, 7mm. long, 3mm. diam. (Plate 67, Fig. 299).

SUDAN. *Equatoria*, Imatong Mountains, near Gilo, c. 4° 10′ N, 32° 45′ E, 5,400 ft., coll. Dr. K. N. G. MacLeay, cult. Johannesburg, fl. 28 Feb. 1954, Reynolds 6773, holotype (PRE), fl. 27 March 1955, isotype (K, EA).

A. macleayi was named after Professor K. N. G. MacLeay (formerly Botany Dept., University of Khartoum), who first collected plants in June 1947, and again in January 1951, among rocks on a grassy bank above the road bridge over the River 'Ngairigi, near Gilo, in the Imatong Mountains, Equatoria Province of the Sudan. Prof. MacLeay found plants "frequent in secondary grassland, and from 5,000—8,000 ft., which roughly corresponds with the range of *Pteridium aquilinum* on the western side of the Imatongs".

PLATE 67

ALOE MACLEAYI   Reynolds.

Plant from the Imatong Mountains near Gilo, Equatoria Prov., Sudan;
flowering in the author's garden. Height 1m.

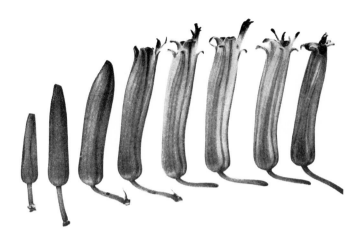

Fig. 299.

A. macleayi Reynolds. Flowers 1/1 from a plant from near Gilo Imatong Mtns., Equatoria Prov., Sudan.

A. macleayi is a most handsome acaulescent species with large deep-green unspotted leaves which are deeply channelled and gracefully recurved. The inflorescence is a large well-branched panicle 90cm. high, and bears striking racemes of 36mm. scarlet flowers.

The perianth segments are free to base, and clearly 3—5-nerved throughout. The buds are minutely spotted which is a character found in *A. secundiflora* Engler, but the latter has oblique racemes with flowers secund, segments free for only half of their length, and very different leaves.

115. **A. microdonta** Chiovenda in *Plantae novae vel Minus Notae ex Ethiopia* 1: 7 (1928), in *Fl. Somal.* 1: 315 (1929); Reynolds in *Journ. S.A. Bot.* 20: 31 (1954).

Note: A photograph by Scassellati et Muzzocchi as Tab. 24, Fig. D in Chiov. *Result. Sci. Miss. Stefani* 1: p. 222 (1916) depicts flowering plants of *A. microdonta* from Mugnica on the Juba River.

DESCRIPTION: The species was originally described *Habitus ignotus*. The subjoined description is based on personal observations at many localities in Somalia.

Stem slender, short or up to 1m. long, procumbent, with apical portion ascending, with shoots low down at random, and sometimes forming dense groups of low shrubs several metres across.

Leaves about 16, densely aggregated at apex of stems, 50—70cm. long, 9—11cm. broad near base when pressed flat, gradually tapering from base to apex, spreading and much recurved with apices of oldest leaves pointing to the ground; *upper surface* deeply canaliculate, dull green to olive-grey, sometimes with reddish tinge, of uniform colour or sometimes with a few dull white lenticular spots near base; *lower surface* much rounded, a little greener than the upper surface, with or without a few white lenticular spots low down; *margins* straight, armed with minute to small whitish teeth with pale-brown tips, 1mm. (rarely 2mm.) long, more crowded near base (5—8mm. apart), more distant (10—14mm.) upwards, obsolescent towards apex. *Sap* dries yellow.

Inflorescence a slender, much-branched erect panicle about 1·3m. high.

Peduncle brown with a powdery bloom, plano-convex and 15—18mm. broad at base, terete upwards, branched above the middle, with 8—12 spreading slender branches, the lowest of which sometimes with 2—4 branchlets.

Racemes oblique or slightly ascending, 10—15cm. long, rather laxly flowered, the pedicels 5—10mm. apart, the red flowers more or less secund.

Bracts minute, ovate-acute, 2—4mm. long, 2mm. broad at base, dirty-white, thin, scarious, with 3 congested nerves.

Pedicels 5—6mm. long.

Perianth scarlet, sometimes paler at mouth, 23mm. long, cylindric-trigonous, basally rounded or sometimes obtusely tapering into the pedicel, cylindric and 7mm. diam. across the ovary, thence trigonous with the mouth open; *outer segments* free for 10mm., with pale, almost white margins, 3-nerved, the apices subacute, straight to slightly spreading; *inner segments* themselves free but dorsally adnate to the outer for half their length, broader than the outer, with a prominent scarlet keel and broader white border, and more obtuse and slightly more spreading apices.

Filaments lemon, filiform-flattened, the 3 inner narrower and lengthening before the 3 outer, with their *anthers* in turn exserted 3mm.; *stigma* at length exserted 5mm. (Plate 68, Figs. 300, 301).

"SOMALIA MERIDIONALE". Between Genale and Audegle, in bush, 7 Feb. 1924, Puccioni et Stefanini n. 49 (FI).

SOMALIA SOUTH. Beles Cogani, 28 miles E of Liboi, 26 Jan. 1954, Bally 9500! (K, G, EA); at Margherita on the Juba River, alt. 50 ft., 3 Oct. 1953, Reynolds 7116 (K, PRE); same locality, 3 Oct. 1953, Bally 9350! (EA); red sandy flats, 116 miles N of Mogadishu (20 miles S of Bulo Burti), c. 3° 33' N, 45° 34' E, 400 ft., 8 Oct. 1953, Reynolds 7140 (K, PRE); 8 miles N of Mogadishu, 2° 06' N, 45° 25' E, alt. 100 ft., 8 Oct. 1953, Reynolds 7135 (K, PRE); on light soils in bush 62 miles SE of Lugh Ferrandi, 1,300 ft., leaf only, 26 Sept. 1953, Reynolds 7090 (PRE); near Anole, 24 miles S of Bardera, 250 ft., leaf only, 30 Sept. 1953, Reynolds 7103 (PRE).

PLATE 68

ALOE MICRODONTA   Chiov.

At Margherita, 43 miles N of Kismayo, Somalia.   8 miles N of Mogadishu, Somalia, Alt. 3,000 ft.
Height 1·4m.   Height 1·4m.

FIG. 300.

A. microdonta Chiov. A form 116 miles N of Mogadishu, 20 miles S of Bulu Burti, Somalia, c. 3° 33′ N., 45° 34′ E. Alt. 400 ft. Height 4 ft.

FIG. 301.

A. microdonta Chiov. Flowers natural size.

TYPE LOCALITY

Somalia meridionale refers to the original Southern Italian Somalia, and includes the country NW and SW of Mogadishu to the Juba River. Genale and Audegle are agricultural settlements on the Webi Shebeli River, SW of Afgoi on the road down to Brava and Kismayo, at approximately 1° 52′ N., 44° 47′ E.

Considerable quantities of plants fitting the description and matching photographs of the type material were found in this neighbourhood, in fact, it was eventually found that *A. microdonta* enjoyed the widest distribution, and occurred in the largest numbers, of all the Aloes seen in Somalia. It was frequently observed planted on Somali graves, and used for demarcating boundries of fields. It also appears to be confined within the boundaries of Somalia, and was found mostly on grey limestone rubble and soil in partial shade.

DISTRIBUTION

62, 64—67, 70—73 miles SE of Lugh Ferrandi; 50 miles SW of Iscia Baidoa; 14 miles NE of Bardera; repeatedly along the 200 miles southwards from Bardera to Gelib and Margherita at alt. 350 ft.—50 ft.; on the Gelib–Modun road (turn off for Brava) occurs at miles (from Gelib) 76, 80, 84, 95—102; Goluin 12 miles SW of Vittoria d'Africa; in considerable numbers, almost continuously from 30 miles SW of Afgoi up to Afgoi, the type locality being in this area; 3 miles W and N of Mogadishu; 7, 10—20 miles N of Villaggio Duca d'Abruzzi (65, 68—78 miles N of Mogadishu); 26 miles S of Bulo Burto (116 miles N of Mogadishu), alt. 400 ft. Probably also occurs further northeast. Trans Juba: 21, 76, 84 miles NW of Kismayu; at mile 89 (3 miles W of Beles Cogani Italian Customs). At mile 117 (25 miles W of Beles Cogani) *A. microdonta* meets and crosses with *A. rabaiensis* Rendle in large numbers. Western limit appears to be long. 41° 25′ E., with the southern limit about lat. 0° 05′ N.

A. microdonta is characterised by having large, deeply channelled, recurved leaves with minute marginal teeth about 1mm. long, a much-branched, paniculate inflorescence about 1·3m. high with obliquely spreading racemes of somewhat secund scarlet flowers. Bracts are exceedingly small.

116. **A. marsabitensis** Verdoorn et Christian in *Fl. Plants S. Afr.* 20: Plate 798 (1940).

DESCRIPTION based on many plants in Dodoth County, N. Karamoja, Uganda.

Plants large, solitary, or in small groups. *Stem* short, or decumbent and 50—80cm. long, with old dried leaf remains persistent.

Leaves about 20, densely rosulate, broadly lanceolate-attenuate, spreading and recurved, up to 80cm. long, 16—18cm. broad, about 2cm. thick near base; *upper surface* deeply canaliculate and U-shaped in cross sections, unicoloured grey-green with reddish tinge, unspotted; *lower surface* rounded, grey-green, without spots or markings; *margins* armed with pinkish-brown, deltoid, pungent teeth 2—3mm. long, 15—20mm. distant, joined by a pinkish-brown cartilaginous edge in lower half, the edge obsolescent upwards with the interspaces the colour of the leaf near apex.

Inflorescence a divaricately many-branched pyramidal panicle 1—1·20m. high, sometimes 2 simultaneously.

Peduncle basally plano-convex and 3cm. broad, divaricately branched from below the middle with 18—20 spreading ascending virgate branches, the lowest with 4—6 branchlets some of which rebranched and sometimes producing a total of 60 racemes.

Racemes subcylindric or somewhat secund, mostly suberect, sublaxly-flowered, the terminal raceme usually shorter, erect, with flowers evenly distributed, lateral racemes mostly oblique to oblique-ascending, terminal racemes of lowest branches usually but not always the longest and 10—15cm. long.

Bracts very small, ovate-acute, thin, white, scarious, 2—3mm. long and broad, 1—3-nerved.

Pedicels averaging 10mm. long.

Perianth light coral-red, yellowish at mouth, or yellow, greenish at mouth, averaging 28mm. long, cylindric-trigonous, or sometimes broader at base and narrower at mouth, 10—12mm. diam. across the ovary, very slightly narrowed above the ovary, the mouth straight and not upturned; *outer segments* free for 10mm., 3-nerved, the apices subacute, brownish, slightly spreading; *inner segments* free, but dorsally adnate to the outer for 20mm., broader than the outer, with broad pale borders and 3 crowded nerves forming a keel and the apices brownish-tipped, more obtuse and more spreading.

Filaments pale-lemon, filiform-flattened the 3 inner narrower and lengthening before the 3 outer with their *anthers* in turn exserted 3 mm.; *stigma* at length exserted 4—5mm.; *ovary* pale green, 8mm. long, 4mm. diam. (Plate 69, Figs. 302, 303).

KENYA. *Northern Prov.:* Mt. Marsabit, Gof Bongoli Crater, 4,500 ft., coll. 12 July 1938, Pole Evans et Erens 1275, cult. Div. of Bot., Pretoria, fl. 15 May 1940 (red flowers), Christian 990, type of *Fl. Pl. S. Afr.*, Plate 798 (holotype PRE, SRGH); fl. again 10 Sept. 1940, I. B. Pole Evans et J. Erens 1275 (PRE).

UGANDA. *Karamoja:* Loyoro, 5,000 ft., Mar. 1945, Tweedie 690 (K); coll. 7 miles W of Loyoro in Northern Karamoja, c. 3° 23′ N, 34° 07′ E, 4,500 ft., cult. Kangole, 15 miles W of Moroto, fl. 13 Oct. 1955 (yellow flowers), Reynolds 7951 (PRE, E, EA).

SUDAN. Collected by Mr. John G. Williams (Ornithologist, Coryndon Museum, Nairobi) at Kamathia Post in the SE corner of the Sudan, c. 4° 53′ N., 35° 21′ E, alt. 2,200 ft.—this is north of Todenyeng, N. Turkana, Kenya; flowers yellow, specimens not prepared.

A. marsabitensis was first collected in July 1938 by Dr. I. B. Pole Evans and Mr. J. Erens during their East African Expedition. Dr. Pole Evans wrote at the time, "Marsabit is a volcanic mountain rising up to 5,000 ft. in the desert country of the Northern Frontier of Kenya. The mountain contains a number of crater lakes, the largest of which measures about 1½ miles across."

Mr. Erens added: "This Aloe occurs in large numbers in arid country on the rim of Gof Bongole Crater, alt. 4,500 ft., both in shade and in the open. It has a decumbent habit, the stem creeping along the ground; it was not noticed suckering in the wild state as it does in cultivation. A somewhat unusual character of this species is that the terminal raceme is only about half the length of the lowest lateral raceme."

A. marsabitensis grows in abundance in the northern parts of Karamoja, especially in Dodoth County, from 4 miles NE of Kotido, and for 25 miles to Loroyo, and at 6 and 9 miles W of Loroyo, c. 3° 23′ N, 34° 06′ E, at 4,400 ft. alt.

The type at Marsabit is described as having red flowers. In Karamoja, only yellow flowers were noticed, and these differed in being sometimes slightly broader at base than at the mouth. The whole inflorescence is divaricately branched and pyramidal in shape. Terminal racemes are usually erect, cylindric, and with flowers evenly distributed around the rhachis; the lateral racemes are mostly suboblique with flowers subsecund to secund depending on the obliquity of the raceme. The apical terminal raceme is usually but not always shorter than the terminal racemes of lowest branches.

The nearest affinity appears to be *A. megalacantha* Bak. but this species differs in having very large marginal teeth, and much denser, more conical racemes.

NATIVE NAMES: *Achuka* and *Echuchukua*, the Karamojong words for Aloe in general.

PLATE 69

ALOE MARSABITENSIS   Verdoorn et Christian.
At Kangole, 15 miles W of Moroto, Karamoja, Uganda. Height 1·5m.

Fig. 302.

A. marsabitensis Verdoorn et Christian. Plants in very young bud 9 miles W of Loyoro, 35 miles N of Kotido, Dodoth County, Karamoja, Uganda, c. 3° 23′ N., 34° 06′ E., Alt. 4400 ft. Height 6 ft

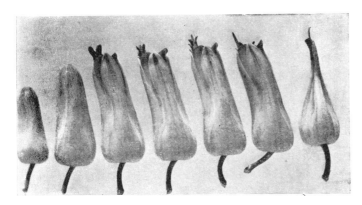

Fig. 303.

A. marsabitensis Verdoorn et Christian
Yellow flowers natural size.

GROUP 18

(Sect. *Pachydendron* Haw. *pro parte*)

PLANTS TALL-STEMMED, SIMPLE OR FEW-BRANCHED FROM BASE

Stems simple or few-branched from base, 2—6m. and more high, smooth or densely bearded with dried remains of old leaves. *Leaves* rosulate, mostly large, spreading to recurved, often canaliculate, smooth or partly aculeate. *Inflorescence* mostly a many-branched panicle with erect or oblique racemes. *Racemes* cylindric, conical or subcapitate, sublaxly to very densely flowered, mostly erect, sometimes suberect to oblique (*A. excelsa*) or oblique and with flowers slightly secund (*A. ballyi*). *Bracts* small to large. *Pedicels* short to long. *Perianth* cylindric, red, orange or yellow, short (18—19mm.) to long (42—45mm.).

Type species: *A. volkensii* Engler.

Tropical species: 10, including *A. gillilandii* Reynolds from Arabia.

Species included in this group are those which develop tall stems that are simple or few-branched from base, not higher. Stems may be smooth or densely bearded with the dried remains of old leaves. Only simple stems or few-branched, are included here; species with stems branched above ground level are included under shrubs. The imperfectly known *A. angolensis* Bak. appears to be related to *A. littoralis* Bak., and is very doubtfully included here.

A. volkensii is essentially a tall, simple-stemmed species, but in cultivation, and especially from injuries, it often branches freely and becomes shrubby.

KEY TO THE SPECIES

A. Perianth Less Than 20mm. Long:

Stems slender, smooth, simple or few-branched from base, 2—4m. tall. Marginal teeth white, 1mm. long, 10mm. apart. Inflorescence 50—60cm. tall, 6—10-branched, bracts very small:
1. *Leaves* 30 × 5·5cm., upper surface flat. *Racemes* cylindric, 8—10cm. long. *Pedicels* 9mm. long. *Perianth* 19mm. long, scarlet; *outer segments* free for 5—6mm.   .. ..   117 *A. medishiana*
2. *Leaves* 50—60cm. long, deeply canaliculate. *Racemes* 5—6cm. long. *Pedicels* 5—6mm. long. *Perianth* 18mm., yellow, *outer segments* free for 12mm.   .. ..   118 *A. gracilicaulis*

B. Perianth 20—24mm. Long:

Stem to 70cm. high. *Leaves* 60cm. long, 5cm. broad, thick and fleshy. *Inflorescence* simple or to 3-branched. *Racemes* densely flowered, 10cm. long. *Pedicels* 3—6mm. long. *Perianth* sulphur-yellow, 20—24mm. long (very doubtfully included here)   ..   ..   119 *A. angolensis*   ➤

C. Perianth 30—35mm. Long:

(*a*) *Pedicels 1mm. long:*
1. *Stem* always simple, 3m. and more tall. *Leaves* 80 × 15cm., recurved, canaliculate. *Inflorescence* many-branched, 80—100cm. high, lowest branches and racemes oblique. *Perianth* reddish-orange, 30mm.; *outer segments* free 22m.   ..   ..   121 *A. excelsa*
(*b*) *Pedicels 6—7mm. long:*
Stem simple, 3—4m. and more. *Inflorescence* 8—10-branched, 1·5m. high. *Racemes* narrowly cylindric, 30cm. long. *Perianth* rose-pink, 30—34mm. long   ..   ..   122 *A. littoralis*
(*c*) *Pedicels 10—15mm. long:*
Stem smooth, always simple, 2m. high. *Leaves* 65 × 15cm., recurved, canaliculate, *teeth* 1mm. long. *Inflorescence* 8-branched, 90cm. high. *Racemes* 15cm. long with buds at first hidden by imbricate bracts. *Perianth* scarlet, 30mm. long, thick and fleshy, *outer segments* free to base   ..   ..   120 *A. gillilandii*
Stem simple, smooth, 5—6m. high. *Leaves* 90 × 14cm., "smell strongly of mice". *Inflorescence* produced subobliquely, 60cm. high and broad, divaricately many-branched. *Racemes* slightly oblique with flowers slightly subsecund. *Perianth* reddish-orange, 33mm. long   ..   ..   125 *A. ballyi*
Stem simple up to 6—7m. high, densely bearded with old dried leaf remains. *Leaves* 60 × 9—10cm., *teeth* pungent, 4mm. long. *Inflorescence* divaricately many-branched, 70—80cm. high. *Racemes* capitate-conic, 8—12cm. long. *Perianth* reddish-orange, slightly curved, 35mm. long ..   ..   126 *A. volkensii*

D. Perianth 42—45mm. Long:

Stems simple or few-branched from base, 2—3m. tall:
1. *Leaves* 30—35 × 6cm., upper surface flat, teeth 4—5mm. long. *Inflorescence* 3—5-branched, 70—90cm. high. *Racemes* cylindric, 15—18cm. long. *Pedicels* 12mm. long. *Perianths* orange-scarlet, 42mm. long.   ..   ..   124 *A. rupicola*
2. *Leaves* 50 × 6—8cm., canaliculate, teeth 1—1·5mm. long. *Inflorescence* dichotomously 2—3-branched, 60cm. high. *Racemes* capitate, buds slightly deflexed. *Pedicels* 35—40mm. long. *Perianth* 45mm. long, scarlet or orange, mouth slightly upturned   123 *A. munchii*

PLATE 70

ALOE MEDISHIANA   Reynolds et Bally.

On rocky slope at Medishe, 24 miles NE of Erigavo, Somalia North.
Height 2·25m.

117. **A. medishiana** Reynolds et Bally in *Journ. S.A. Bot.* 24: 186 (1958).

DESCRIPTION: *Plants* sometimes with simple stems, sometimes with stems branched at base and of somewhat shrubby growth. *Stems* smooth, very slender up to 2m. high, 3—3·5cm. diam.

Leaves about 24, crowded along the apical 20cm. of stems, ensiform, spreading to decurved, up to 30cm. long, 5·5cm. broad at base, gradually narrowing to the apex; *upper surface* grey-green, without spots or markings, flat to slightly convex; *lower surface* rounded, otherwise as in upper surface; *margins* with a continuous narrow white cartilaginous edge armed with very small, firm white teeth that are about 1mm. long and more crowded (5mm. apart) low down, more distant (10mm. apart) to obsolescent upwards.

Inflorescence a branched panicle about 50cm. tall, sometimes 2 simultaneously.

Peduncle brown with a bloom, plano-convex and 15mm. broad at base, branched at the middle or higher with 6—8 branches, the lowest of which sometimes with 3—5 branchlets, the whole inflorescence producing about 15 racemes.

Racemes cylindric, averaging 8—10cm. long, 5cm. diam., sublaxly flowered, the buds spreading, the open flowers nutant.

Bracts ovate-acute, 2—3mm. long, 2mm. broad, thin, dry, white, 1-nerved, or with a faint nerve on each side appearing as 3-nerved.

Pedicels averaging 9mm. long.

Perianth dull scarlet, cylindric-trigonous, 19mm. long, 5mm. diam. across the ovary, thence very slightly curved and trigonous upwards; *outer segments* connate into a tube to beyond the middle (free for 5—6mm. only), obscurely 3-nerved, the apices subacute and slightly spreading; *inner segments* broader than the outer and with more obtuse, more spreading apices.

Filaments white, the 3 inner narrower and lengthening before the 3 outer with their *anthers* in turn exserted 1—2mm.; *stigma* at length exserted 3mm.; *ovary* pale brown 4mm. long, 2·5mm. diam. (Plate 70, Fig. 304).

SOMALIA NORTH (formerly Somaliland Prot.). Exposed rocky slopes at Medishe, 24 miles NE of Erigavo, c. 10° 36′ N, 47° 34′ E, c. 4,800 ft. alt., 10 Sept. 1957, Reynolds 8441 holotype (PRE), isotype (K, EA); 24 miles NE of Erigavo, 4,900 ft., 5 Oct. 1954, Bally 10342 (K, EA); Eastern Al Madu Range, 5,000 ft., flowers red, "smells of rats", 10 Oct. 1956, Bally 11006 (K, EA), appears to belong here.

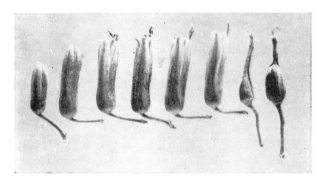

FIG. 304.

A. medishiana Reynolds et Bally. Flowers 1/1 from a plant at Medishe, 24 miles NE of Erigavo, Somalia North.

A. medishiana was found by Mr. P. R. O. Bally in November 1954, and by the author in Sept. 1957, in large numbers on exposed rocky slopes at Medishe, which is 24 miles NE of Erigavo at about 4,800 ft. altitude. In floral characters it is closely allied to *A. gracilicaulis* at mile 19 from Erigavo on the road down to Mait, but *A. medishiana* differs in having shorter more spindly stems, leaves narrower and half as long, with the upper surface flat to slightly convex (not deeply canaliculate), longer pedicels, and red perianths with outer segments free for only 6mm.

Near Geldin in the far-eastern Al Madu, Mr. Bally has found plants with leaves 6·5cm. broad, 38cm. long, and with more capitate racemes. This might belong here but further investigation is necessary.

The Somali name for *A. medishiana* is *Daar der,* the tall Aloe.

118. **A. gracilicaulis** Reynolds et Bally in *Journ. S.A. Bot.* 24: 184 (1958).

DESCRIPTION: *Plant* with slender stem, simple or branched at base, smooth. *Stem* 2—4m. tall, 8—10cm. diam. near ground level, about 6cm. diam. at the middle, with persistent dried leaf remains for 30—50cm. below the rosette of leaves.

Leaves about 20, rosulate, crowded at apex of stem, ensiform, basally sheathing, 8cm. broad at base, gradually narrowing to an acute apex, 50—60cm. long, youngest leaves erectly spreading, the oldest much recurved with their apices pointing downwards; *upper surface* unicoloured grey-green, flat at base, deeply canaliculate upwards; *lower surface* rounded; *margins* with 1mm. broad white cartilaginous border armed with white cartilaginous blunt teeth, 1mm. long, irregularly 2—10mm. apart, usually more crowded low down, more distant upwards.

Inflorescence a branched panicle averaging 60cm. high, 2—3 simultaneously.

Peduncle basally plano-convex and 15mm. broad, terete upwards, divaricately about 10-branched from below the middle, the 1—2 lowest branches with 3—5 branchlets, less rebranched upwards, the branches very slender (about 4mm. thick).

Racemes cylindric, subdensely flowered, 5—6cm. long, 5cm. diam., youngest buds sub-erect and denser, slightly laxer downwards, open flowers nutant, whole raceme yellow.

PLATE 71

ALOE GRACILICAULIS   Reynolds et Bally.

19 miles N of Erigavo, on Mait road, Somalia North; Alt. 3,800 ft.
Height 9 feet.

Bracts ovate-acute, 3mm. long, 2mm. broad, white, scarious, 1—3-nerved.
Pedicels averaging 5—6mm. long.
Perianth yellow, cylindric-trigonous, averaging 18mm. long, 5mm. diam. across the ovary, thence trigonous, the mouth open; *outer segments* free for 12mm. (tube 6mm.), thin at the margins, obscurely 3-nerved, apices sub-acute, slightly spreading; *inner segments* free but dorsally adnate to the outer for 6mm., broader than the outer, almost white with yellow keel, the apices more obtuse and more spreading.
Filaments white, the 3 inner narrower and lengthening before the 3 outer with their *anthers* in turn exserted 3—4mm.; *stigma* at length exserted 4—5mm.; *ovary* pale green, 5mm. long, 2mm. diam. (Plate 71, Fig. 305).

SOMALIA NORTH (formerly Somaliland Prot.). In dry bush country, 19 miles N of Erigavo on Mait road, alt., 3,800 ft., c. 10° 51′ N, 47° 14′ E, 9 Sept. 1957, Reynolds 8428 holotype (PRE), isotype (K, EA).

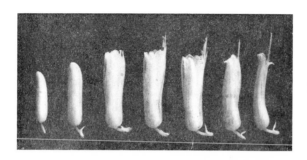

FIG. 305.

A. gracilicaulis Reynolds et Bally. Yellow flowers 1/1 from bud to post-anthesis stages, from a plant in dry bush country, 19 miles N of Erigavo, on road down to Mait (below the tunnel) Somalia North.

A. gracilicaulis grows in some numbers in dry bush country, on lower slopes of the Kol Hosis range, 19—20 miles northwards from Erigavo on the road down to Mait, between 3,800 ft. at mile 19, and 3,600 ft. at mile 20. Plants occur with stems simple or branched at base, the stems varying from 2—4m. in height. Leaves are rather deeply channelled and recurved, while apices of lowest leaves point downwards. The inflorescence is a much-branched panicle with yellow flowers only 18mm. long.

Certain plants found by Mr. Peter Bally, with short yellow flowers, at Agasur at the eastern end of the Al Madu Range, alt. 5,200 ft., might belong here.

A. gracilicaulis is allied to *A. retrospiciens* at Darburruk (on the Hargeisa–Berbera road), but the latter has shorter, slenderer stems, shorter, less channelled leaves, and denser, shorter capitate racemes with the flowers somewhat subsecund and pointing backwards.

A. medishiana Reynolds et Bally, at Medisha, 24 miles NE of Erigavo, is a close ally, but this species has much shorter, less recurved leaves, longer (9mm.) pedicels, and scarlet perianths with the outer segments free for only 6mm.

The Somali name for *A. gracilicaulis* is *Daar der*, the tall Aloe.

119. **A. angolensis** Baker in *Trans. Linn. Soc.* ser. 2, Bot. 1, 236 (1878), in *Journ. Linn. Soc.* 18: 162 (1880), in Th. Dyer *Fl. Trop. Afr.* 7: 466 (1898); Rendle in *Cat. Welwitsch. Afr. Pl.* 2: 1, 44 (1899); Berger in Engler's *Pflanz.* Liliac.–Aloin. 239 (1908).

DESCRIPTION: Based on Baker's, Welwitsch's and Berger's accounts, also on the type material at BM.

Plants subacaulescent (but a fine plant, and the most robust of all the Angola species except the arborescent – Welwitsch).

Leaves densely rosulate, suberect, lanceolate-ensiform, glaucous, not spotted below, very fleshy, 60cm. long, 4—5cm. broad in the type specimen, broader in others, basally amplexicaul, the apex subobtuse, toothed and twisted to the left; *margins* not sinuate-dentate, armed with teeth 2mm. long, 15—20mm. apart, the interspaces straight.
Inflorescence lateral, 90cm. high, simple or 1–3-branched, branches arcuate-erect.
Peduncle straight, shining green with a reddish bloom ("as thick as a finger"—Welwitsch).
Raceme densely flowered, cylindric slightly acuminate, about 10cm. long.
Bracts broadly ovate-acute, 10mm. long, scarious, white with many dark nerves.
Pedicels 3—6mm. long.
Perianth sulphur-yellow, pendulous, 20—24mm. long; *outer segments* connate to beyond the middle.
Genitalia scarcely exserted. (Fig. 306).

ANGOLA. *Loanda Dist.*: Barra do Bengo, on wooded hills between Quisoma and Cacuaco at Mutollo in the District Quicuxe—not plentiful, fl. 29 July 1858, Welwitsch 3728 (BM holotype!, LISU isotype).

The Latin version reads "In collinis sylvestribus inter Quisamas ex Quicuxe versus Mutollo et versus Cacuaco, rarior."

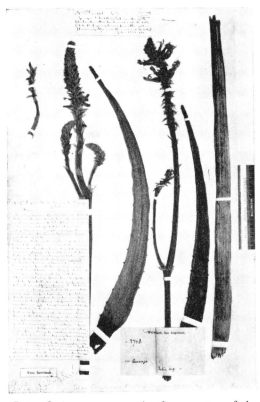

Fig. 306.

A. angolensis Bak. Photograph of Welwitsch 3728, holotype (BM). *By courtesy Mr. J. E. Dandy, Keeper of Botany, British Museum, (Natural History) London.*

Inter Quisamas means in the country of the Quisama people. Cacuaco is a village and Posto 12 miles NE of Luanda. Quicuxe is a district NE of Luanda. Mutollo is a native name for a type of xerophytic vegetation in which tree Euphorbias predominate, but Welwitsch used Mutollo as a place name. (Under his No. 1807 *Acacia farnsiana* he refers to "slopes of Mutollo above Quicuxe"). According to Welwitsch, *A. angolensis* is to be found between Quicuxe and Mutollo, and also between Quicuxe and Cacuaco. He also refers to it as the "Yellow flowering Aloe near Quicuxe and Mutollo."

Professor F. A. Mendonça states that Mutollo can safely be taken as being in the hills between Quicuxe and the Bengo River. According to other collectings by Welwitsch on the same date and area, Professor Mendonça has found that the type locality of *A. angolensis* is the low hills facing the Bengo valley not far from the sea coast near the so-called Barra do Bengo – mouth of the Bengo River, NE of Luanda.

In Welwitsch's day, the old road to the Bengo River went along the hills facing the sea – further west than the present inland road.

A. littoralis Bak. and *A. zebrina* Bak. occur abundantly between Loanda and the Bengo River, but the identity of *A. angolensis* remains in doubt.

Further north, beyond Caxito, on steep limestone slopes facing the sea near the mouth of the Dande River, Eng. Grandvaux Barbosa and Senhor R. Santos have found certain plants, "locally abundant in small colonies" which might prove to be the long-lost *A. angolensis*. Plants had very dry dehisced capsules, and kind of racemes, length and colour of flowers is not known (at the time of writing).

AFFINITY. Habit of growth is not stated, and its nearest affinity is not known to me. The thick leaves, and the kind of inflorescence suggests that *A. angolensis* might belong to the *A. littoralis* complex.

120. **A. gillilandii** Reynolds in *Journ. S.A. Bot.* 28: 287 (1962).

DESCRIPTION: *Plants* solitary with rather slender, simple stem up to 2m., 10cm. diam., smooth.

Leaves about 16, densely rosulate, 15cm. broad at base, gradually narrowing to an acute apex, about 65cm. long, the youngest leaves spreading, the oldest recurved with their apices pointing downwards; *upper surface* unicoloured grey-green, almost flat at base, rather deeply canaliculate upwards; *lower surface* grey-green, rounded; *margins* with continuous pale-pink cartilaginous edge armed with rather soft pale-pink cartilaginous teeth, 1—1·5mm. long, irregularly 5—10mm. apart.

Inflorescence a branched panicle, c. 90cm. high.

Peduncle basally plano-convex and 18mm. broad, about 8-branched from below the middle, the lowest branch sub-tended at base by a broadly ovate-acute, many-nerved, brown, scarious bract, 25mm. long, 20mm. broad.

Racemes cylindric-acuminate, c. 15cm. long, 6cm. broad, sublaxly-flowered, the buds suberect, open flowers cernuous to pendulous, the young buds at first hidden by large densely imbricate bracts.

Bracts broadly ovate-acute, basally clasping the pedicel, 10mm. long, 8mm. broad when pressed flat, brownish, scarious, 5—7-nerved.

Pedicels 12mm. long, inserted in base of perianth almost at right angles.

Perianth scarlet, paler at mouth, broadly cylindric-trigonous, 30mm. long, 10mm. diam. across the ovary, rather thick and fleshy, the mouth upturned; *outer segments* free to base, paler at margins, 5—7-nerved, apices obtuse; *inner segments* free to base, with 3 crowded nerves forming a slight keel, apices brownish-tipped, obtuse to almost rounded and slightly revolute.

Filaments lemon, flattened, the 3 inner narrower and lengthening before the 3 outer with their *anthers* in turn exserted 3—4mm.; *stigma* at length exserted 5mm; *ovary* green, 6mm. long, 4mm. diam. (Figs. 307–309).

ARABIA. Dathina Plain, c. 130 miles NE of Aden, coll. Prof. H. B. Gilliland, fl. Mbabane, Swaziland, 17 Sept. 1961, Reynolds 6364 holotype (PRE), isotype (K).

A. gillilandii was named after Professor H. B. Gilliland (University of Malaya, Singapore) who first discovered plants in February 1952, on the Dathina Plain, about 130 miles NE of Aden, Arabia, at an elevation of about 1300m.

When sending a plant in 1952, Professor Gilliland remarked that plants were solitary, with simple stems up to 6—8 ft. in height. When this plant eventually flowered in September 1961, the description was completed.

In his book *In the High Yemen* (1942) the late Dr. Hugh Scott records (p. 41): "Aloes of unusual form, with tall pole-stems rising among dense thickets of the lower gorge of Wadi Dareija, . . . a few miles SW of Dhala on the old track still used by camel caravans between Aden and Dhala" (Aden Protectorate, Arabia).

Scott identified it as *A. sabaea* Schweinfurth, but this was incorrect. *A. sabaea* is a much-branched tree 25 ft. and more high, whereas *A. gillilandii* has a simple stem only 6—8 ft. tall.

Scott's photograph of these plants most strongly suggests that they are conspecific with *A. gillilandii*.

On p. 98, Scott mentions having seen "the same tall pole-stemmed Aloes" in the Saiyani District, northwards from Taizz on the road to Sana, in the Yemen. The present known distribution therefore, is from the Dathina Plain westwards through Dhala to near Taizz in the Yemen.

Mr. John Lavranos, who has made a special study of the Aloes of Arabia, has communicated the following:

"This interesting species is rather conspicuous along the rugged escarpment which rises behind the coastal mountains of South-Western Arabia, in an area which has hitherto received scanty attention from Botanists.

"On the basis of my own observations and the information given by Scott in 'The High Yemen' as well as by Van der Meulen in 'Aden to the Hadhramaut', the distribution of *Aloe gillilandii* as at present known would extend from the Saiyani country NE of Taiz in the Yemen (approx. lat. 13° 40′ N, long. 44° 05′ E) in the west, to the Talh Pass (approx. lat. 14° 07′ N, long. 46° 16′ E) in the east. It may well be expected that the distribution of the species extends for some 40 miles eastwards of the Aqaba Talh, along the precipices of the Kor al Ud.

"I visited Scott's locality in Wadi Dareija (lat. 13° 41′ N, long. 44° 43′ E) on the 24th August, 1962 and found numbers of plants growing on rock faces and exposed talus slopes. All the plants seen were solitary with simple, erect stems.

"The species was also found and collected on the 16th August, 1962 at the base of the precipices crowning the Audhali Escarpment between the Aqaba Thirah (13° 53′ N, 45° 47′ E) and a point lying in lat. 14° 00′ N, long. 45° 53′ E in the Audhali country. In this area the plants appeared to have less robust but equally tall stems.

"Although I covered much ground on the Dathina plain, I saw not a single specimen of *Aloe gillilandii* in that very open country. The species might, however, occur on some of the higher isolated granite-gneiss domes arising therefrom. It may also be noted that the Dathina plain is not in the Hadhramaut either in the political or in the geographical sense. The latter region begins some 100 miles to the East.

"My observations leave no doubt in my mind that *Aloe gillilandii* is a species peculiar to dry, mountainous country and that it shows a definite predilection for extremely steep localities, ranging in altitude from 4,250 to 6,750 ft. The rainfall varies from some 350mm. in the west (Wadi Dareija) to 250mm. along the Audhali Escarpment."

Fig. 307.

Habitat of *A. gillilandii* Reynolds. Kor al Audilla. View W from top of Aqaba Thirah; Yafa'i Mountains in distance, Arabia.
Photo: Mr. C. Meintjes.

Fig. 308.

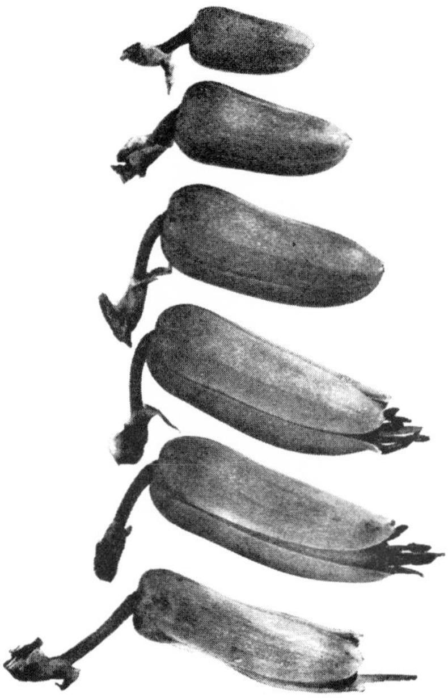

Fig. 309.

A. gillilandii Reynolds.

Fig. 308. Plant collected by Prof. H. B. Gilliland about 130 miles NE of Aden, Arabia, flowering at Mbabane, Swaziland. Height 6ft.

Fig. 309. Buds and flowers natural size.

The present author has not seen the tree *A. sabaea* Schweinfurth in the Yemen, but judging from Berger's description in *Pflanzenr*. Liliac.–Aloin. 320 (1908) it seems that *A. gillilandii* is a near ally in leaves, pedicels and flowers, but has a simple stem only 1—2m. high. *A. sabaea* is described *inter alia* as having a 3—4-branched inflorescence, triangular-ovate bracts 15mm. long, and perianth outer segments connate into a tube for 6mm. from base.

In *A. gillilandii* the inflorescence is 8-branched, the bracts are broadly ovate-acute, 10mm. long and 8mm. broad, while perianth outer segments are free to base.

121. **A. excelsa** Berger in *Notizblatt Berlin Bot. Gart. u Museums* 4: 247 (1906), in Engler's *Pflanzenr*. Liliac.–Aloin. 314 (1908); in *Fl. Plants S. Afr.* 2: Plate 62 (1922).

DESCRIPTION: *Plants* with simple stems averaging 2—4m. high, densely bearded with old dried leaf remains.

Leaves about 30, the youngest suberectly spreading, the oldest spreading to recurved, up to 80cm. and more long in old specimens, 15cm. broad at base, gradually narrowing to the apex; *upper surface* unicoloured, dull green, without spots or markings, usually not spiny, deeply canaliculate; *lower surface* rounded, usually rather tuberculate-aculeate; *margins* armed with reddish-brown, deltoid, pungent teeth, 5—6mm. long, 15—20mm. apart, sometimes forward uncinate, the interspaces the colour of the leaf.

Inflorescence a many-branched panicle about 80—100cm. high, the branches rather slender, the lowest 2—3-branches with the racemes suberect to slightly oblique.

Racemes very densely flowered, cylindric, 15—20—25cm. long.

Bracts reflexed, 4—6mm. long and broad, thin, dry, dirty-white.

Pedicels exceedingly short, about 1mm. long.

Perianth reddish or reddish-orange, cylindric, slightly ventricose, averaging 30mm. long, 5mm. diam. across the ovary, enlarging to 7mm. at the middle, and then narrowing a little to the wide open mouth; *outer segments* free for three-quarters their length, clearly 3-nerved, the apices subacute slightly spreading; *inner segments* free, broader than the outer.

Filaments flattened, the 3 inner narrower and lengthening before the 3 outer with their *anthers* in turn exserted 8—10mm.; *stigma* at length exserted 10mm. (Plate 72, Figs. 310, 311).

RHODESIA. *Bulawayo Dist.:* Matopos, in bush with large Euphorbias, Dec. 1903 (in fruit), R. Marloth 3888 (PRE)— the only specimen cited by Berger, hence presumably holotype. Matopos, coll. Eyles 1240, without date, is also labelled Marloth 3888 (PRE). Matopos, coll. J. Wickens, cult. Div. of Bot., Pretoria, fl. 11 Aug. 1915, no. 203 in Nat. Herb. (PRE), fl. 9 Sept. 1918 (PRE), fl. Aug. 1921, type of *Fl. Pl. S. Afr.* 2: Plate 62 (1922), no. 1453 in Nat. Herb. (PRE). *Bulawayo Dist.*, Matjesumphlope Farm, 19 Sept. 1919, C. R. Edmonds 226 (PRE). *Chibi Dist.*, 2 miles S of Chibi River, cult. Greendale, 6 Aug. 1962, L. C. Leach 11510 (SRGH). *Salisbury Dist.*, Chindamore Res. 20 miles N of Salisbury, cult. Greendale, fl. 9 Aug. 1962, L. C. Leach 11515 (SRGH).

MALAWI: *Southern Prov.* Plant ex Tuchilla Plain between Cholo and Mt. Mlanje, cult. Greendale, fl. 1 Sept. 1962, L. C. Leach 11519 (SRGH).

A. excelsa is a noble plant, with simple tall stem. Leaves may be smooth, or tuberculate-aculeate on lower surface, especially when young, the inflorescence is a many-branched, somewhat rounded panicle with the lowest racemes oblique to suberect, with the others erect. Flowers vary from red to reddish-orange.

A. excelsa is nearest related to *A. rupestris* Bak. in Zululand and Swaziland, but the latter differs in having simple or branched stems, smaller, smooth leaves, all racemes erect, shorter paler flowers with a distinct tube.

DISTRIBUTION

RHODESIA: Widespread in many parts of the country: Plumtree, Matopos, Bulawayo, Gwelo; Antelope Mine, Balabala, Stanhope, Filabusi, South of Shabani, Tokwe River, Lundi River (Mr. E. J. Bullock reports it on banks of the Lundi River, south of Hippo Valley Estates, in the south).

Hills near Lundi northwards to Zimbabwe and plentiful on hills eastwards along road to Birchenough Bridge. In the Biriwiri Valley, 18 miles NW of Melsetter (with *A. aculeata* and crosses); Rusape, Inyazana, north of Penhalonga; 57 miles NE of Salisbury on Mtoko road, beyond Chibakwe River, etc. Altitudes range from 1,500 ft. to 5,000 ft.

MOÇAMBIQUE: Manica and Sofala, on Mt. Zembe and neighbouring granite hills S of Vila Pery. Mr. L. C. Leach reports that orange-flowered plants predominate here. *A. excelsa* occurs socially with *A. cameroni* and *A. chabaudii* and crosses with these two species are not uncommon.

MALAWI: In the Tuchila Valley, W of Mlanje Mountain, and also seen by the author SE of Fort Johnstone.

ZAMBIA: About 30 miles SE of Lusaka on rocky outcrops on SW bank of the Kafue River, about 500 yards upstream from entrance to the gorge. – Mr. E. J. Bullock.

PLATE 72

ALOE EXCELSA Berger.

At the Matopos, S of Bulawayo, Rhodesia. Height 8 feet.
From a Kodachrome by Mr. D. C. H. Plowes.

FIG. 310.

A. excelsa Berger. In the Biri Wiri Valley, 6 miles from Skyline, 18 miles NW of Melsetter, Rhodesia. Alt. 4,100 ft. (*A.aculeata* and crosses grow nearby).

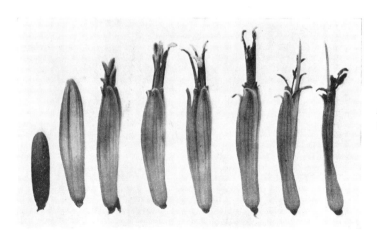

FIG. 311.

A. excelsa Berger. Flowers 1/1 from a plant at the Zimbabwe Ruins, SE of Fort Victoria, Rhodesia.

122. **A. littoralis** Baker in *Trans. Linn. Soc.* Ser. 2, Bot. 1, 263 (1878), in *Journ. Linn. Soc.* 18: 174 (1880), in Th. Dyer *Fl. Trop Afr.* 7: 467 (1898); Durand et Schinz *Consp. Fl. Afr.* 5: 308 (1893); Rendle in *Cat. Welwitsch Afr. Plants* 2: 1, 46 (1899); Berger in Englers' *Pflanzenr.* Liliac.– Aloin. 223 (1908); Reynolds in *Journ. S.A. Bot.* 26: 81 (1960).

—— *A. rubrolutea* Schinz in *Bull. Herb. Boiss.* 4: app. 3, 39 (1896); Bak. in Th. Dyer *Fl. Trop. Afr.* 7: 460 (1898); Berger *l.c.* 221 (1908); Engler et Drude *Veget. Erde* 9: 2, 329, Fig. 227 (1908); Berger in *Bot. Mag. t.* 8263 (1909) – a very young plant; *Fl. Pl. S. Afr.* 21: Plate 802 (1941); Reynolds in *Aloes S. Afr.* 327 (1950).

—— *A. schinzii* Bak. in Th. Dyer *Fl. Trop. Afr.* 7: 459 (1898).

DESCRIPTION: Based on large numbers of plants at and near Luanda, Angola.
Plant solitary. *Stem* simple, averaging 2m. high, sometimes 3—4m., usually densely bearded with the shrivelled remains of old dried leaves.
Leaves about 30—40, densely rosulate, averaging 60cm. long, 10—13cm. broad at base, gradually narrowing to an acute apex, mostly spreading to sometimes slightly recurved; *upper surface* grey-green, usually without spots or markings, flat low down, slightly canaliculate upwards; *lower surface* convex, same colour as upper surface, sometimes with a few small brown teeth from a white base in median line for 20—30cm.; *margins* somewhat sinuate-dentate, armed with pungent, brown, deltoid teeth, about 3—4mm. long, 10—15—20mm. apart.
Inflorescence 1—2 from a rosette, a many-branched panicle averaging 1·5m. tall.
Peduncle basally plano-convex and 4—5cm. broad, branched below the middle with 8—10 branches, the lowest 1—3 sometimes with 3—5 branches making a total of 20 or more racemes per inflorescence.
Racemes narrowly cylindric-acuminate, 30cm. long, 6cm. diam., lengthening to 50—60cm. in the fruit.
Bracts narrowly lanceolate, thin, scarious, very white, somewhat brittle, 12—18mm. long, 5—6mm. broad, 5—7-nerved, usually deflexed.
Pedicels 6—7mm. long.
Perianth rose-pink to deep pink-scarlet, cylindric-trigonous, 6mm. diam. across the ovary, 30—34mm. long, paler at mouth, becoming somewhat yellowish after anthesis; *outer segments* free to the middle (15—17mm.), with pale border giving the perianth a white-striped effect, the apices subacute; *inner segments* broader than the outer, with broader pale marginal border with 3 crowded nerves forming a deep pink keel, the apices more obtuse, more spreading.
Filaments very pale lemon, filiform-flattened, the 3 inner narrower and lengthening before the 3 outer with their *anthers* in turn exserted 1—2mm.; *stigma* at length exserted 2—3mm.; *ovary* olive-green, 6mm. long, 3mm. diam. (Plate 73, Figs. 312–314).

FIG. 312.　　　　　　　　　FIG. 313.
A. littoralis Bak.

FIG. 312. Plant with two inflorescences, 9 miles W of Bocoio, 49 miles E of Lobito, Benguela Dist., Angola, c. 12° 29′ S., 14° 09′ E. Alt. 2,800 ft. Height 10 feet.

FIG. 313. Plant near Nyanyadzi in the Sabie valley, Rhodesia.　*Photo: Mr. D. C. H. Plowes.*

PLATE 73

ALOE LITTORALIS   Baker.

At Vila Paiva Conceiro (Quipungu). 82 miles E of Sá da Bandeira,
Huila Dist., Angola. Height 9 feet.

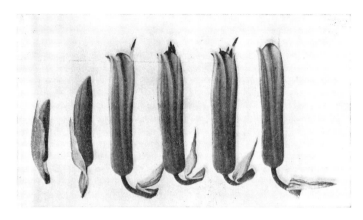

Fɪɢ. 314.

A. littoralis Bak. Buds and flowers 1/1 from a plant at Vila Conceiro, 82 miles E of Sá da Bandeira, Huila Dist., Angola.

Aɴɢᴏʟᴀ. *Luanda*, Barra do Bengo, very plentiful on dry hills in the whole littoral region of Luanda. In flower May—July 1854, Welwitsch 3727 holotype (BM!), isotypes (K! LISU). *Note:* The Bengo River enters the sea NE of Luanda. Cuanza Nort, Dondo, 60m., Gossweiler 12613! (LISC). *Benguela Dist.,* 9 miles W of Bocoio (Souza Lara), 49 miles E of Lobito, 2,800 ft., 3 July 1959, Reynolds 9317 (K, PRE, LUA). *Huila Dist.,* Humpata, Chela Mountains, Sept. 1893, Sir H. H. Johnston (K)—Humpata lies about 15 miles SW of Sá da Bandeira; at Vila Paiva Conceiro (Quipungo), 82 miles E of Sá da Bandeira, 14° 50′ S, 14° 33′ E, 25 June 1959, Reynolds 9267 (PRE, K, LUA). *Mossamedes*, Bilaba, Cacanda, 850m., 7 May 1960, E. J. Mendes 4003! (LISC).

Zᴀᴍʙɪᴀ (N. Rhodesia). Barotseland, 15 miles S of Nangweshi, 23 July 1952, L. E. Codd 7157 (PRE)—this is NNW of Katima Mulilo.

Rʜᴏᴅᴇsɪᴀ. Near Birchenough Bridge, July 1954, L. C. Leach 330! (no. 76965 in GHS (K, SRGH))—also occurs abou. 30 miles NNW of Bulawayo between Nyamandhlovu and the main road to the Victoria Falls.

Mᴏçᴀᴍʙɪǫᴜᴇ. Sol do Save, near Pafuri, a few miles from the Rhodesian border, 30 April 1961, R. B. Drummond 7636 (SRGH).

S.-W. Aғʀɪᴄᴀ, Bᴇᴄʜᴜᴀɴᴀʟᴀɴᴅ Pʀᴏᴛᴇᴄᴛᴏʀᴀᴛᴇ and N. Tʀᴀɴsᴠᴀᴀʟ.—See *Aloes of S. Africa* 327–330 (1950).

Dɪsᴛʀɪʙᴜᴛɪᴏɴ: From the western parts of Angola, especially along the coastal hills to about 100 miles inland; abundant in the Sá da Bandeira District; southwards to Windhoek in S.W. Africa; eastwards through parts of Barotseland and Bechuanaland to the southern parts of Rhodesia and the northern Transvaal to Moçambique near Pafuri, a few miles from the Rhodesian border.

Vᴀʀɪᴀᴛɪᴏɴ: From Loanda to Cacuaco plants are found with 1—2 inflorescences up to 2m. tall; 1—1·5m. is about the average. Young acaulescent plants have surprisingly large inflorescences.

In several parts of Angola the author ran across many plants that were acaulescent, or had procumbent stems (not erect) to 50cm. long; not one tall-stemmed plant was seen anywhere nearby, eg. Gabela, Quibala, Vila Nova de Seles, Conda, 8 miles E of Salazar, 20 miles W of Lucala, also on rocks near Pungo Andongo.

In some localities young plants have leaves rather copiously spotted both sides. Mr. L. C. Leach reports similar acaulescent plants with leaves large, white-spotted, and with bracts 20mm. long, in the Ondangua region, westwards towards Ohopoho, Ovamboland, S. W. Africa, S of the Angola border.

In his original description, Baker stated "A shrub 2—3m. high – trunk most frequently simple". In the neighbourhood of Luanda–Cacuaco, shrub-like plants can sometimes be seen but it seems that the branching of the stem at base was the result of injury. *A. littoralis* is essentially a simple-stemmed species.

Hʏʙʀɪᴅs. Crosses with *A. zebrina* occur on the Fortaleza São Filipe Hill which dominates Luanda; also not rare among both parents almost all round Sá da Bandeira.

123. **A. munchii** Christian in *Fl. Pl. Afr.* 28: Plate 1091 (1950).

Dᴇsᴄʀɪᴘᴛɪᴏɴ based on many plants along the Chimanimani mountains, east of Melsetter, Rhodesia.

Plants usually with simple or sparingly branched, very slender stems averaging 2—3m. high (sometimes 4—5m. in height), the old dried leaf remains usually not persistent.

Leaves densely rosulate, about 24—30, ensiform, erectly spreading to spreading and recurved in upper third, averaging 50cm. long, 6—8cm. broad; *upper surface* dull grey-green with reddish tinge, without spots or markings, rather flat near base, canaliculate upwards; *lower surface* rounded, without spots or markings; *margins* with pinkish cartilaginous edge armed with very small pinkish teeth 1—1·5mm. long, 10—15mm. apart, the interspaces straight.

Inflorescence dichotomously 2—3-branched, 60cm. high, sometimes 2 simultaneously.

Peduncle basally plano-convex and 20mm. broad, branched about the middle, finely sulcate, with a few broad sterile bracts, 15mm. long and broad below the racemes, which lie in the same plane.

Racemes 10—12cm. long, 14cm. diam., at first flatly conical, with the buds grey-green tipped and immature flowers spreading to slightly deflexed, at length becoming capitate and round- or flat-topped, with the lowest open flowers nutant to subpendulous.

Bracts ovate-cuspidate, thin, subscarious, 14mm. long, 10—12mm. broad when pressed flat, many-nerved.

Pedicels arcuate-oblique, 35—40mm. long, the apices cernuous.

Perianth cylindric-trigonous, scarlet or orange, 45mm. long, basally obconic, 7—8mm. diam. across the ovary, enlarging slightly to the mouth, the mouth slightly up-turned; *outer segments* free to base, 3—5-nerved, the apices slightly spreading; *inner segments* free, thin at the edges, with 3 crowded nerves forming a keel throughout, the apices brown-tipped, more obtuse and more spreading than the outer.

Filaments lemon, the 3 inner narrower and lengthening before the 3 outer with their *anthers* in turn exserted 2—3mm.; *stigma* at length exserted 4—5mm.; *ovary* green, 7mm. long, 3mm. diam. (Plate 74, Figs. 315–317).

RHODESIA. *Melsetter District*, from the Chimanimani Mtns., alt., 5,000—7,000 ft., coll. 3 Sept. 1945, cult. Rusape, fl. 14 July 1950, R. C. Munch No. 2 in Herb. Christian 1219, holotype (SRGH); cult. Rusape, fl. 14 July 1950, Verdoorn ex Munch, No. 28438 in Nat. Herb. (PRE)—type of *Fl. Pl. Afr.* 28: Plate 1091 (1950); Chimanimani Mtns., 7 Aug. 1950, Davis in G. H. 28848 (K, SRGH), Chimanimanis, 5,800 ft., 21 July 1956, Reynolds 8225 (K, PRE, SRGH); Chimanimani Mtns., 11 July 1958, L. C. Leach 112 (K, SRGH).

MOÇAMBIQUE. Manica et Sofala, Manica, Chimanimani Mountains, 1700m., 6 July 1949, Pedro et Pedrogaõ 7205!, with excellent photographs (PRE).

A. munchii was named after Mr. R. C. Munch of "Mona", Rusape, who discovered plants along the Chimanimani Mountains in the Melsetter District of Rhodesia, in September 1945.

It is a very distinctive species distinguished by having very slender smooth stems, a sparingly branched inflorescence, the racemes lying in the same plane. The racemes have been described as "like a pagoda" and are characterised by having the buds and youngest immature flowers horizontally disposed to slightly deflexed. The bracts are very large, while pedicels are 35—40mm. long, with the scarlet or orange flowers averaging 45mm. long.

FIG. 315.   FIG. 316.
A. munchii Christian.

FIG. 315. Eastern slopes of the Chimanimani Mountains, Manica and Sofala, Moçambique, 1,700m alt.—Part of stem hidden.   *Photo: Senhor J. Gomes Pedro.*

FIG. 316. Near the Rest Hut, Chimanimani Mtns., Melsetter Dist., Rhodesia, alt. 5,600 ft. Height 8 ft.

PLATE 74

ALOE MUNCHII Christian.

On the Chimanimani Mnts., Melsetter Dist., Rhodesia. Alt. 5,900 ft.
Height 12 ft.—With Mr. R. C. Munch.

FIG. 317.

A. munchii Christian. Flowers 1/1 from bud to post-anthesis stages, with bract 1/1.

A. munchii is nearest allied to *A. arborescens* Mill. which is essentially a many-branched shrub, whereas *A. munchii* is more a caulescent species, and rarely shrub-like. *Leaves* are similar, while *A. arborescens* differs in having longer pointed racemes with all buds at first covered by imbricate bracts, and at no stage deflexed.

DISTRIBUTION: *A. munchii* grows abundantly in many places along the Chimanimanis from 5,000—7,000 ft. Mr. J. A. Whellan and others, have found it extends as far east as Martin's Falls and the Valley of the Wizards, also in Skeleton Pass, across the border in Moçambique.

124. **A. rupicola** Reynolds in *Journ. S.A. Bot.* 26: 89 (1960).

DESCRIPTION: *Plant* with stems 2—3m. (sometimes 4—5m.) tall, about 10—12cm. thick, simple or branched from base.

Leaves about 40, densely rosulate, averaging 30—35cm. long, 6cm. broad, plus 10cm. of dried, brittle purplish apex, the youngest sub-erectly spreading, the oldest spreading; *upper surface* green, rather flat, obscurely lineate, without spots; *lower surface* slightly rounded, green, rather prominently lineate low down, the lines becoming more obscure upwards; *margins* sinuate-dentate, armed with pungent, reddish-brown teeth averaging 4—5mm. long and 10mm. apart at middle of leaf, the teeth smaller and more crowded near base. *Sap* dries pale yellow.

Inflorescence a branched panicle 70—90cm. high.

Peduncle plano-convex and 25mm. broad at base, mostly 3—5-branched (rarely 7—8) from the middle.

Racemes subdensely flowered, cylindric, 15—18cm. long, 8—9cm. diam., youngest buds grey-tipped suberect, older horizontally disposed, open flowers nutant to subpendulous.

Bracts ovate-acute, averaging 9mm. long, 5mm. broad, obscurely nerved, clasping the pedicel.

Pedicel lowest averaging 12mm. long.

Perianth orange-scarlet, averaging 42mm. long, cylindric-trigonous, very slightly clavate, 7mm. diam. across the ovary, thence trigonously enlarging upwards; *outer segments* free to the middle (free for 21mm., tube 21mm.), paler at margins, apices sub-acute, slightly spreading; *inner segments* themselves free but dorsally adnate to the outer to the middle, with broad white border and with orange-scarlet keel, the apices more obtuse and slightly more spreading than the outer.

Filaments very pale lemon, filiform-flattened, the 3 inner narrower and lengthening before the 3 outer with their *anthers* in turn exserted 2—3mm.; *stigma* at length exserted 3mm.; *ovary* pale green, 8mm. long, 4mm. diam. (Plate 75, Figs. 318, 319).

ANGOLA. *Bié Dist.:* On rocky hill 3 miles S of Chinguar, c. 12° 35′ S, 16° 20′ E, alt. 5,850 ft., fl. 19 June 1958, Reynolds 9243 holotype (PRE), isotype (K, LUA).

A. rupicola was discovered on Chimbango Hill, 3 miles S of Chinguar, which is about midway between Silva Porto and Nova Lisboa, Angola. Plants were found mostly along the top of the ridge, with *A. grata* a little lower down. Although both species flower at the same time, no hybrids were seen.

A. rupicola is a plant with stems averaging 2—3m. tall, but occasionally reaching 4—5m., and mostly simple or branched from base. Old dried leaf remains are not persistent. Leaves are obscurely lineate on upper surface, and more prominently lineate on lower surface, especially in lower half of leaf, while perianths are very slightly clavate.

Its nearest ally appears to be *A. volkensii* Engler from Tanzania, but the latter differs in having stems with old dried leaf remains persistent, leaves longer and not lineate, inflorescence much more copiously branched, longer pedicels, and shorter perianths that are not very slightly clavate.

PLATE 75

ALOE RUPICOLA   Reynolds.

On Chimbango hill near Chinguar, midway between Silva Porto and
Nova Lisboa, Bié Dist., Angola. Height 3—4m.

Fig. 318.

A. rupicola Reynolds. Plants on Chimbango Hill, 3 miles S of Chinguar, midway between Silva Porto and Nova Lisboa, Angola, c. 12° 35′ S., 16° 20′ E., alt. 5,850 ft. Fl. 19 June 1959. Height 2m.

Fig. 319.

A. rupicola Reynolds. Flowers 1/1 from bud to post-anthesis stages.

125. **A. ballyi** Reynolds in *Journ. S.A. Bot.* 19: 2 (1953).

DESCRIPTION: *Stem* slender, simple, up to 5—6m. high, 10—15cm. thick, glabrous, the old leaves not persistent.

Leaves about 25, densely rosulate at apex of stem, lanceolate-long attenuate, up to 90cm. long, 14cm. broad at base, the youngest leaves spreading, the oldest much recurved, deeply canaliculate, and U-shaped in cross-section; *both surfaces* grey-green, glabrous throughout without spots or lineation; *margins* armed with laterally compressed deltoid, pungent, white teeth averaging 4—5mm. long, 10—15mm. distant, more crowded nearer base of leaf, more distant upwards, the teeth sometimes forward-uncinate, the interspaces straight.

Inflorescence a much-branched panicle, about 60cm. long and broad, produced sub-obliquely.

Peduncle biconvex and 20mm. broad at base, terete upwards, with about 20 branches from low down, the lowest re-branched, and subtended at base by a thin, dry, white *bract* about 18mm. broad, 14mm. long, about 7-nerved, the branches mostly spreading with the racemes oblique.

Racemes up to 14cm. long, rather laxly about 20-flowered, the buds dull scarlet, tipped bluish-green, with a slight bloom, the open flowers carmine to reddish-orange, the pedicels upturned with the buds and flowers mostly subsecund to secund, depending on the degree of obliquity of the racemes.

Bracts clasping the pedicels, ovate-acute, 5mm. long, 5mm. broad at base, thin, scarious, dirty-white, about 5-nerved.

Pedicels lowest 10mm. long, mostly up-curved.

Perianth carmine to reddish-orange, greyish-tipped, 33mm. long, cylindric, 9mm. diam. near base, exceedingly slightly constricted on under-side above the ovary, very slightly curved, the mouth wide open; *outer segments* free for two-thirds their length (tube 11mm.), distinctly 3-nerved from base to apex, the nerves dull pale reddish, the apices subacute, slightly spreading; *inner segments* themselves free but dorsally adnate to the outer for one-third their length, broader than the outer, with their brownish-tipped apices more obtuse and more spreading than the outer, and with a prominent median nerve throughout.

Filaments pale lemon, filiform-flattened, the 3 inner narrower and lengthening before the 3 outer, with their *anthers* in turn exserted 4—5mm.; *style* pale yellow, filiform, with the *stigma* at length exserted 5mm.; *ovary* pale green, 6mm. long, 4mm. diam., finely 6-grooved; *capsule* for some time enwrapped with the dried remains of the perianth; mature fruits and seeds not seen. (Figs. 320—323).

KENYA. In dense bush, 2½ miles W of Mwatate (20 miles W of Voi), approx. 3° 30′ S, 38° 23′ E, alt. 3,000 ft., 31 March 1952, Reynolds 6378 holotype (PRE), isotype (K, EA). Mwatate, 20 miles W of Voi, 20 July 1960, L. C. Leach 10300 (SRGH). Thika, 20 miles beyond Athi River, Dec. 1938, Bally 11423 (G, EA).

TANZANIA. S. Pare Mountains, Mamba Track, 17 June 1942, P. J. Greenway 6470 (K, PRE, EA); S. Pare Mountains Kisiwani, 2 Feb. 1936, P. J. Greenway 4573 (K, EA)—"whole plant smells strongly of mice"; top of Manyara Escarpment, 1 July 1956, Bally 10607 (EA).

FIG. 320   FIG. 321.

A. ballyi Reynolds.

FIG. 320. Plant 2½ miles W of Mwatate, 20 miles W of Voi, Keyna, alt. 3,000 ft. Height 18 feet— With Mr. P. R. O. Bally.

FIG. 321. Near Oldonyo Sambu, N of Mt. Meru, Tanzania, (Tanganyika).

Photo: Mr. P. R. O. Bally.

Fig. 322.

A. ballyi Reynolds. Inflorescence with sunbird.
Photo: Mr. P. R. O. Bally.

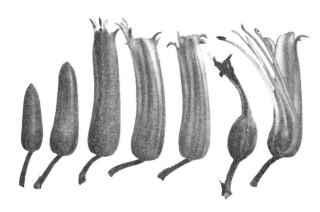

Fig. 323.

A. ballyi Reynolds. Buds and flowers 1/1, with
one flower partly laid bare.

A. ballyi was named after Mr. P. R. O. Bally, Botanist, Coryndon Museum, Nairobi, who first found plants near Makania on the western side of the S. Pare Mountains in September 1934, and again in December of that year near the top of the Manyara Escarpment beyond Lake Manyara and Mto-wa-Mbu, on the road westwards from Arusha via Makuyuni to Ngorongoro Crater, in Tanzania. He has also photographed plants on the Nguruman Escarpment near Oldonyo Sambu, north of Mt. Meru, in Tanzania. The author found it near Kisiwani, at the northern end of the S. Pare Mountains in dense bush and in almost impenetrable thickets of Sansevieria and Euphorbia, growing socially with *A. deserti* Berger, Kisiwani being the type locality of the latter. Dr. P. J. Greenway records that *A. ballyi* is "locally common all down the eastern side of the S. Pare Mountains, on the foot slopes, between 4,000—5,000 ft."

A. ballyi is a very distinctive species with a tall, slender, simple stem reaching 20 ft. and more in height. The leaves are deeply channelled and recurved, while old dried leaves fall, giving the stem a clean, smooth appearance. The leaves and sap give off a permeating, very decided odour of rats or mice, on which account this species has for some time been known as the "Rat Aloe".

The inflorescence is produced sub-obliquely, with the reddish-orange flowers sometimes more or less secund, depending on the angle of the raceme; the more horizontal the raceme, the more secund the flowers.

On Mr. H. A. Delap's estate, "Kayata", about 50 miles E of Nairobi and E of Donyo Sabuk in dense bush near the Athi River, the author noticed many tall, simple-stemmed plants, and also several which branched from the base and formed large shrubs; but this form is not typical of the species as a whole.

The flowering period appears to be from December to June, depending on the rains, and the locality.

126. **A. volkensii** Engler in *Pflanzenwelt Ost-Afr.* 171 (1895); Baker in Th. Dyer *Fl. Trop. Afr.* 7: 466 (1898); Berger in Engler's *Pflanzenr.* Liliac.–Aloin 249 (1908).

—— *A. stuhlmannii* Baker in *Fl. Trop. Afr.* 7: 457(1898); Berger in Engler's *Pflanzenr.* Liliac.– Aloin. 249 (1908) appears to belong here, in synonymy. Berger says it is probably the same species as *A. volkensii*.

DESCRIPTION: *Plants* with stems averaging 3—4m. high, 10—12cm. thick, usually simple, sometimes with 1—2 branches from base with all old dried leaf remains persistent.

Leaves densely rosulate at apex of stems, up to 60cm. long, 9—10cm. broad at base, gradually tapering from base to apex, spreading to sometimes slightly recurved; upper surface glaucous- to olive-green, sometimes sparingly spotted only when young, slightly concave low down, canaliculate upwards; *lower surface* convex to rounded, otherwise as the upper surface; *margins* sinuate-dentate, armed with horny, pungent, brown-tipped, deltoid teeth, 4mm. long, more crowded low down (8mm. apart), more distant upwards (15mm. apart). *Sap* dries yellow.

Inflorescence a many-branched, somewhat pyramidal panicle about 70—85cm. high.

Peduncle basally plano-convex and about 35mm. broad, divaricately about 10-branched from well below the middle, the lowest branches with 2—4 branchlets and somewhat arcuate-ascending with all racemes erect.

Racemes at first somewhat capitate and flat-topped with youngest buds erect and densely grouped, with development becoming more cylindric-conical and 8—12cm. long, 8—9cm. diam., the youngest buds yellowish-green tipped, denser and not hidden by imbricate bracts, open flowers paler, a little laxer and nutant to subpendulous.

Bracts ovate-acute, thin, scarious, about 5mm. long and broad, 5-nerved.

Pedicels averaging 15mm. long.

Perianth reddish-orange to pale scarlet, sometimes slightly glossy, paler at mouth, cylindric, slightly curved, averaging 35mm. long, basally obtuse and broadly obconic, 7—8mm. diam. across the ovary, very slightly narrowed above the ovary, thence slightly enlarging, the mouth open; *outer segments* free for 15mm., obscurely 3-nerved to base, the apices spreading; *inner segments* free, broader than the outer, with more obtuse, more spreading brownish-tipped apices.

Filaments lemon-yellow within, the 3 inner narrower and lengthening, before the 3 outer with the exserted portion orange, and with their anthers in turn exserted 4—5mm.; *stigma* at length exserted 5—6mm.; *ovary* pale-green, 8mm. long, 3·5mm. diam. (Plate 76, Figs. 324—326).

TANZANIA. *Northern Prov.:* Plentiful E of Marangu, alt. 1550m., 19 June 1893, height 4—5m., Volkens 406 (B, holotype). (*Note:* Maranga lies on the lower foothills of Mawenzi, E of Kilimanjaro, 8 miles N of Himo, which village is 17 miles E of Moshi on road to Taveta and Voi; also grows near Rombo, 10 miles beyond Marangu); Western foot of Kilimanjaro, in riverine forest gorge of Engare Nairobi North River, 11 miles N of Sanya Juu, 45 miles W of Moshi, 5,100 ft., fl. 6 July 1958, Reynolds 8792 (K, EA, PRE); top of Mto-Wa-Mbu escarpment, overlooking NW end of Lake Manyara, 75 miles SW of Arusha, 23 miles W of Makayuni turn-off, 3,900 ft., 9 July 1958, Reynolds 8805 (K, EA, PRE); Manyara escarpment, 3,500 ft., 1 July 1956, Bally 10605 (K); Seronera, Serengeti, 2 June 1961, Greenway 10351 (EA). *Tanga Prov.:* S. Pare Mountains, Vudea, common on steep slopes, 4,200 ft., 1 July 1942, P. J. Greenway 6516 (PRE, EA); SE Umba Steppe, cult. Amani, 31 Dec. 1941, P. J. Greenway 6427 (PRE, EA, SRGH), also Greenway 6424, 6428 (SRGH). *Lake Prov.:* Ex Shinyanga, cult. Ewanrigg (near Salisbury, Rhodesia), 16 June 1939, B. D. Burtt 6559, Christian 778 (K, BM, SRGH).

UGANDA. *Ankole*, along the Ruizi River near Mbarara, 4,500 ft., 30 July 1954, Reynolds 7500 (K, PRE, EA).

KENYA. Emali Hill, coll. van Someren, April 1940, Bally 11448 (K).

RWANDA. Dr. G. Troupin records: Parc National de la Kagera, between Uruwita and Kamakaba, Jan. 1938, Lebrun 9700 (BR); Mutara Region, near Kakitumba, Kayonza Hill, Feb. 1958, Troupin 5901 (BR, YBI); same loc. Kakole Hill, alt. 1350m., Feb. 1958, Troupin 6176 (BR, LWO, YBI, NY).

ZANZIBAR: Photographed by Mr. P. G. Archer in December 1954, in bush near Potoa, in the NE corner of the Island at approx. 5° 52′ S, 39° 17′ E. It is not known whether *A. volkensii* grows wild on Zanzibar, or whether it was introduced from the mainland.

A. volkensii is essentially a species with tall, simple stems averaging 3—4m. high; stems of 6—7m. are also met with when plants grow in tall dense bush. Stems may be sparingly branched at ground level but not higher. In cultivation plants often become much more branched and shrub-like. In young plants, the leaves may be spotted and spaced along the apical part of the stem. With age leaves become more densely rosulate, and the spots disappear.

Racemes are at first somewhat flat-topped with the buds denser and open flowers laxer. With development, the raceme elongates a little and becomes cylindric-conic.

DISTRIBUTION: Occurs in the N. Pare Mountains, along the east, south and west foot slopes of Kilimanjaro, westwards to the Serengeti, Manyara Escarpment, Mbulu highlands, Shinyanga and generally along the south-east, south and west shores of Lake Victoria, northwards to the Kagera River Valley, NW of Bukoba, westwards into Ruanda, and northwards to the Ruizi River, near Mbarara.

PLATE 76

ALOE VOLKENSII   Engler.
Along the Ruizi River, near Mbarara, Ankole, Uganda. Height 10 ft.

Fɪɢ. 324.   Fɪɢ. 325.

A. volkensii Engler.

Fɪɢ. 324. Top of Mto-Wa-Mba escarpment, 75 miles W of Arusha Tanzania (Tanganyika). Height 6—7m.

Fɪɢ. 325. Near Potoa, in the NE corner of Zanzibar Island, c. 5° 52′ S., 39° 17′ E.

Photo: Mr. P. G. Arthur.

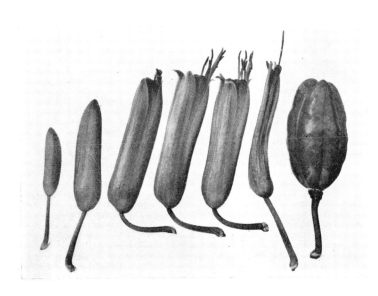

Fɪɢ. 326.

A. volkensii Engler. Flowers with buds and fruit 1/1.

GROUP 19

PLANTS OF SHRUBBY GROWTH

Plants of shrubby growth, varying from low undershrubs with short stems, to large shrubs, 3—4m. high, which sometimes form dense thickets several metres across.

These plants comprise a difficult, exceedingly complex, and often exasperating group. Species vary much in different localities, and it is not possible to devise any key whereby the student can "run" the various forms of species to a satisfactory identification.

One character common to all the African Aloe shrubs – irrespective of size – is their *prolongate* type of stem. That is, the apical quarter to half of stems is sublaxly to subdensely foliate. In younger stems the basal leaf sheaths are longer and clearly visible; in old well-developed stems the leaves are more densely crowded for about 30—50cm. along the apical portion of stems, with the old dried leaf remains usually persistent to base.

Racemes vary from shortly capitate and only 3cm. long (*A. yavellana*) to 25cm. long and narrowly cylindric (*A. cameronii* var. *dedzana*). *Pedicels* vary from 3–5mm. to 35mm. long. *Bracts* from minute to very large. *Perianth* from 20mm. yellow (*A. retrospiciens*) to slender, slightly curved and up to 48mm. long as in some forms of *A. cameronii*.

Plants of low growth and undershrubs, treated elsewhere include *A. jacksonii* (Group 4, and *A. cremnophila* (Group 10).

Shrubs characterised by having distinctly clavate perianths will be found under Group 13.

Typical species: *A. dawei*, *A. nyeriensis*.

Tropical species: 22, of which *A. arborescens* occurs very abundantly in South Africa.

KEY TO THE SPECIES

A. Low Undershrubs

(a) *Inflorescence simple, 10—15cm. high:*
   Stems 15—20cm. *Leaves* 8cm. long, spotted, "conspicuously squarrose". *Raceme* subdense, 4—5cm. *Pedicels* 10mm. *Perianth* 20mm. long .. .. 127 *A. squarrosa*

(b) *Inflorescence simple, 20cm. high:*
   Stems to 30cm., thicker upwards. *Leaves* 10cm. long, 2·5cm. broad, copiously spotted both sides, *Pedicels* 7mm. *Perianth* 24mm., scarlet .. .. 128 *A. zanzibarica*

(c) *Inflorescence simple or 1—2-branched, 40cm. high:*
   Stems 20cm. *Leaves* 15cm. long, 3·5cm. broad, spotted both sides. *Perianth* pale coral-red, greenish-tipped, 20—22mm. long.. .. 129 *A. tororoana*

(d) *Inflorescence 3—5-branched, 40—50cm. high:*
   Stems very short. *Leaves* 22cm. long, 4cm. broad. *Pedicels* 13mm. *Perianth* 30mm., *outer segments* free, markedly revolute at apex 130 *A. hendrickxii*

(e) *Inflorescence 120—150cm. high, 6-branched; racemes at first limp and drooping, becoming stiff and erect when flowers open:*
   Leaves about 40cm. long, 7cm. broad. *Bracts* conspicuously white. *Perianth* dull rose-pink, 32—35mm. .. .. 131 *A. deserti*

B. Larger Plants with Stems 50cm.—1m. Long:

(a) *Stems mostly sprawling over rocks:*
   Leaves 25cm. long, 5cm. broad. *Inflorescence* pyramidal, divaricately 8—12-branched, 50cm. high. *Perianth* 28m. yellow, orange, red; *outer segments free* .. .. 132 *A. hildebrandtii*

(b) *Stems at first erect then falling, with apices ascending:*
   Leaves bronze-brown, 40cm. long, 5cm. broad. *Inflorescence* 8—10-branched, 60—90cm. high. *Racemes* capitate, 2—3cm. long. *Perianth* 27mm. .. .. 133 *A. yavellana*

(c) *Plants of denser growth, stems erect:*
   Leaves 20cm. long, 6cm. broad. *Inflorescence* dichotomously 2—3-branched, 35cm. high. *Racemes* capitate, 6—8cm. long. *Pedicels* 16mm. *Perianth* pale orange-scarlet, 25mm. .. .. 134 *A. andongensis*

(d) *Stems few, simple or sparingly branched:*

    1. *Leaves* 45cm. long, 6cm. broad, often turning copper-red in winter. *Inflorescence* 2—3-branched, 70cm. high. *Racemes* subdense, 10—15cm. long. *Bracts* minute. *Pedicels* 3—5mm. long. *Perianth* slightly curved, 45mm. long .. ..   135 *A. cameronii*

    2. *Plants* more densely shrubby. *Racemes* narrowly cylindric, 20—25cm. long, only 5cm. diam. .. ..   135a var. *dedzana*

    3. *Racemes* dense. *Perianth* more fleshy, more clavate. Anthers and style exserted 8—10mm.   .. ..   135b var. *bondana*

C. STEMS SPARINGLY BRANCHED, 1—1·5M. HIGH:

(a) *Inflorescence 2—3-branched, 40—50cm. high:*
    Leaves 30cm. long, 5cm. broad. *Racemes* 10—20cm., sub-lax. *Pedicels* 14mm. *Perianth* rose-scarlet, 30mm. .. ..   136 *A. palmiformis*

(b) *Inflorescence divaricately many-branched, 45cm. high:*
    Leaves 25cm. long; *teeth* minute. *Pedicels* 5—6mm. *Perianth* yellow, only 20mm. long .. ..   137 *A. retrospiciens*

D. PLANTS OF MUCH MORE SHRUBBY GROWTH, STEMS 1—1·5M. HIGH:

(a) *Inflorescence 2—4-branched, 50—70cm. high; Pedicels 20—25mm. long. Perianth 38—40mm. long:*
    1. *Leaves* dark olive-green, 25cm. long, 8cm. broad. *Racemes* densely flowered, 20—25cm. long. *Bracts* 30mm. long, 15mm. broad. *Outer segments* free for 10mm. .. ..   138 *A. babatiensis*

    2. *Leaves* 40cm. long, 9cm. broad, with conspicuously large 8—9mm.-long teeth. *Racemes* 18cm. *Outer segments* free   ..   139 *A. elgonica*

(b) *Inflorescence 5—8-branched, 60—80cm. high:*
    1. *Leaves* 50cm. long, 6cm. broad, sometimes deflexed and with a few transverse folds dorsally near base. *Racemes* 12cm. *Pedicels* 13mm. long. *Perianth* 34mm. long   .. ..   140 *A. flexilifolia*

    2. *Leaves* 45cm. long, 8cm. broad, channelled and sometimes striate. *Racemes* cylindric with rounded apex, 10—12cm. long. *Perianth* yellow, 30mm. long .. ..   141 *A. boscawenii*

(c) *Perianth minutely white-speckled, 32—34mm. long:*
    1. *Leaves* 45cm. long, 8cm. broad. *Racemes* capitate, round-topped, 9cm. long, 8cm. broad. *Pedicels* 18mm. long .. ..   142 *A. rabaiensis*

    2. *Leaves* 50cm. long, 8cm. broad. *Racemes* cylindric-acuminate, 10—15cm. long. *Perianth* rather thick and fleshy. *Pedicels* 14mm.   143 *A. dawei*

(d) *Plants forming thickets some metres across, Stems slender. Inflorescence 6—8-branched, 40—50cm. tall. Pedicels 10mm. Perianth 28—30mm.:*
    1. *Leaves* 30cm. long, 5cm. broad. *Inflorescence* pyramidal, divaricately branched, the branches and *racemes* almost horizontal with flowers sub-secund .. ..   144 *A. gossweileri*

    2. *Leaves* 30cm. long, 3·5cm. broad. *Inflorescence* less branched, more compact, when racemes sub-oblique flowers slightly subsecund   .. ..   145 *A. catengiana*

E. LARGE SHRUBS, 2—3M. HIGH, OFTEN FORMING LARGE DENSE THICKETS:

(a) *Stems slender, somewhat spindly, 4cm. thick, Leaves only 3·5cm. broad:*
    1. *Inflorescence* 2—4-branched, 50cm. high. *Racemes* broadly cylindric-acuminate, 10—12cm. long. *Pedicels* 20—25mm. *Perianth* 35mm. long   .. ..   146 *A. kedongensis*

(*b*) *Stems thicker, leaves larger:*
    1. *Leaves* 35cm. long, 5cm. broad. *Inflorescence* 3—5-branched,
80cm. high. *Racemes* 15cm. *Pedicels* 20mm. *Perianth* bright
sheeny orange-scarlet, 36mm. long .. .. 147 *A. ngobitensis*
    2. *Stems* gradually thickening from base upwards. *Leaves* 55cm.
long, 7cm. broad. *Inflorescence* 5—8-branched, 60cm. high.
Perianth scarlet, 40mm. long .. .. 148 *A. nyeriensis*
(*c*) *Stems* much branched and rebranched. *Leaves* 50cm. long, 6cm.
broad, teeth pale. *Inflorescence* mostly simple, 60cm. long. *Bracts*
large, at first imbricate and covering the apical buds. *Pedicels* 35—
40mm. long. *Perianth* 40mm. .. .. 149 *A. arborescens*

127. **A. squarrosa** Baker in Balf. *f.* in *Proc. Roy. Soc. Edin.* 12: 97 (1883); Balf. *f. Bot. of Socotra*
in *Trans. Roy. Soc. Edin.* 31: 292 (1888); Durand et Schinz *Consp. Fl. Afr.* 5: 312 (1893); Berger
in Engler's *Pflanzenreich* Liliac.–Aloin. 265 (1908).

DESCRIPTION based on Baker's and Berger's account, and the type at Kew.
    Stem simple (when originally described), 15—20cm. long, 7—8mm. thick, the apical 9cm. sublaxly foliate.
    Leaves basally sheathing, about 14, spreading to much recurved at the apex, deltoid-lanceolate attenuate, 8cm. long,
2cm. broad at base, "conspicuously squarrose" (rough or scurfy), green with transversely arranged whitish spots;
margins with spreading, crowded, uncinate-curved teeth, 2—3mm. long, 4mm. apart.
    Inflorescence simple, always curved?, 10—15cm. long, with a few sterile-bracts.
    Raceme subdensely flowered, 4—5cm. long.
    Bracts narrowly triangular, subulate-cuspidate, scariose, white, 6mm. long.
    Pedicels ascending, 10mm. long.
    Perianth red, cylindric, 20mm. long; *outer segments* free for 6mm.
    Anthers very shortly exserted. (Fig. 327.)

SOCOTRA. At base of limestone cliffs, SW of Galonsir, 1,000 ft., fl. Feb.–March 1880, Bayley Balfour 282! (K).

Balfour states: "A very distinct spotted-leafed species. We found only two plants of this species
at one locality in Socotra – south-west of Galonsir". This locality, according to his map, is at the
far western end of the Island of Socotra.
    The stem was described as simple when originally described from the material sent to Kew by
Balfour.

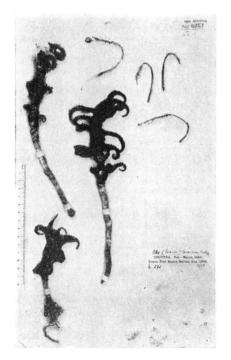

FIG. 327.

A. squarrosa Bak. Photo of the type material at Kew – on limestone
cliffs SW of Galonsir Socotra, 1,000 ft., Feb.—March 1880, Bayley
Balfour 282.

Photo: By courtesy The Director, Royal Botanic Gardens, Kew.

The type material has stems 15—20cm. long, of which the apical 9cm. is rather laxly foliate. This kind of *prolongate* stem in the present author's experience invariably branches from base and forms small, low undershrubs. On the assumption that *A. squarrosa* does form very low undershrubs in the wild state, this species is included here.

It seems that *A. zanzibarica* Milne-Redhead is a near ally, but differs in having longer, thicker stems that become thicker upwards, with larger leaves, a taller inflorescence, shorter pedicels, and longer (24mm.) flowers.

128. **A. zanzibarica** Milne-Redhead in *Kew Bull.* 33 (1947).
—— *A. concinna* Baker in *Fl. Trop. Afr.* 7: 461 (1898); Berger in Engler's *Pflanzenr.* Liliac.–Aloin. 265 (1908); C. H. Wright in *Bot. Mag. t.* 8790 (1919) – *non* (Haw.) R. & S. (1829).

DESCRIPTION based partly on Baker's original description and Wright's in *Bot. Mag.*, but mostly on a cutting from the original Kew stock when it flowered in Johannesburg.
Plant a low undershrub with several stems branched from base, the stems sublaxly foliate in apical portion, 30cm. and more high, 1 cm. thick near base, becoming noticeably thicker upwards and 20mm. thick near apex.
Leaves about 12—16, grouped along the apical 7cm. of the stem, lanceolate-acute, spreading to recurved, 10cm. long, 25mm. broad at base, gradually narrowing to the acute apex; *upper surface* flat low down, canaliculate upwards, light green with numerous very pale-green almost white small lenticular spots throughout; *lower surface* convex to rounded, similar to upper surface; *margins* rather deeply sinuate-dentate, armed with firm deltoid teeth that are the colour of the leaf at base, white at apex, smaller and more crowded low down, 4—5mm. long, 5—7mm. apart at middle of leaf, thence smaller upwards.
Inflorescence ascending, simple (always ?), 20cm. high.
Peduncle basally plano-convex and 5mm. broad, clothed with a few sterile-bracts that are narrowly lanceolate, 7mm. long, 3mm. broad, thin, dry, white, 3-nerved.
Raceme sublaxly flowered, cylindric, 6cm. long, 4·5cm. diam., the buds spreading, open flowers nutant.
Bracts narrowly lanceolate, long-pointed, 5mm. long, 2mm. broad, thin, scarious, white, 3-nerved.
Pedicels 7mm. long.
Perianth light-scarlet, greenish at mouth, 24mm. long, cylindric and 6mm. diam. across the ovary, slightly trigonous upwards; *outer segments* free for 7mm., 3-nerved, apices subacute, slightly spreading; *inner segments* broader than the outer, themselves free but dorsally adnate to the outer for 17mm., with broad white marginal border and 3 crowded nerves forming a keel that is greenish near apex, the apices more obtuse and more spreading than the outer.
Filaments pale-lemon, the 3 inner narrower and lengthening before the 3 outer with their *anthers* in turn exserted 2—3mm.; *stigma* at length exserted 3mm.; *ovary* green, 4mm. long, 2mm. diam. (Figs. 328—330).

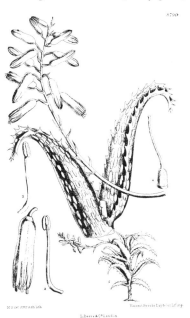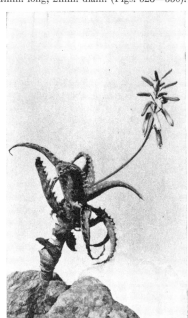

FIG. 328.   FIG. 329.
A. zanzibarica Milne-Redhead.
FIG. 328. An uncoloured plate at Kew, of *A. zanzibarica*, then known as *A. concinna*
Bak. in *Bot. Mag. t.* 8790 (1919).
Photo: By courtesy The Director, Royal Botanic Gardens, Kew.
FIG. 329. A branch (flowering in Johannesburg) from the original plant at Kew
from which the *Bot. Mag. t.* 8790 was prepared.

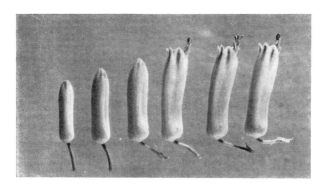

Fig. 330.

A. zanzibarica Milne-Redhead. Flowers natural size.

ZANZIBAR. Cultivated specimen, Kirk!; described from a plant that fl. at Kew, April 1895 (K)—as *A. concinna* Baker. Cutting from original stock at Kew, cult. Johannesburg, fl. 30 March 1959, Reynolds 9077 (PRE).

In the third publication of *A. concinna*, C. H. Wright in *Bot. Mag. t.* 8790 (1919) states: "The Aloe now figured was first discovered at Zanzibar by Sir John Kirk by whom it was presented to Kew. It has grown satisfactorily . . . and suckers rather freely. The original plant flowered at Kew for the first time in April 1895, and when it was then described by Mr. Baker it had "laxly rosulate" leaves. But by 1901 it had developed a stem thirteen inches high with scattered foliage. From the suckers several independent plants have been raised, and one of these, which forms the subject of our plate, flowered at Kew in October 1916."

The *Bot. Mag.* plant is shown with the inflorescence horizontally disposed, which is the result of growing under unnatural heated conditions under glass. When a cutting from the same stock, sent out from Kew, flowered in Johannesburg, it produced the usual ascending type of inflorescence.

A new name, *A. zanzibarica* Milne-Redhead, was necessary for this distinct little Aloe, since Baker's name was invalid, the epithet having been used earlier for a plant now known as *Haworthia viscosa* (L.) Haw., var. *concinna* (Haw.) Bak.

TYPE LOCALITY: Unknown. It is most highly improbable that this species was ever collected by Kirk on Zanzibar. Modern botanists have searched the Island for plants of *A. zanzibarica* without success. Most, if not all, of the Aloe species sent by Kirk to Kew were wrongly attributed to the Island of Zanzibar, when they had been collected somewhere on the mainland, Zanzibar merely being the point of dispatch.

It is remarkable that this most distinctive little species has never been collected again. Its locality of origin remains a mystery.

129. A. tororoana Reynolds in *Fl. Plants Afr.* 29: Plate 1144 (1952).

Plant succulent, a low undershrub with slender stems about 20cm. long, 15mm. thick, with rosettes of leaves about 25cm. diam.

Leaves about 12, densely rosulate, lanceolate-attenuate, the youngest erectly-spreading, the oldest spreading-recurved, up to 15cm. long, 3—5cm. broad at base, 10mm. thick; *upper surface* almost flat, dull milky-green, with few to many small, oblong, dull white spots throughout; *lower surface* convex, with more numerous more crowded spotting than upper surface; *margins* sinuate-dentate, armed with pale, almost white, brown-tipped, pungent teeth, 2—3mm. long, 5—10mm. apart, slightly hooked forward.

Inflorescence simple, or with 1—2 slender, very short branches from about the middle, up to 40cm. tall.

Peduncle slender, basally flattened and 6mm. broad, terete and 4mm. thick upwards, with a few sterile-bracts that are 3mm. long, 3mm. broad at base, apiculate, subscarious, 3-nerved.

Raceme cylindric-acuminate, the terminal the longest, 8—10cm. long, sublaxly flowered; the buds somewhat imbricate and erectly pressed against the axis.

Bracts small, ovate-deltoid, 3mm. long, 2mm. broad at base, thin, scarious, 3-nerved.

Pedicels 8—10mm. long, the coral-red colour of the base of the perianth.

Perianth 20—22mm. long, coral-red to scarlet, greenish-tipped, 5mm. diam. across the ovary, thence narrowed to 4 mm. diam., and slightly enlarging to the throat; *outer segments* free for 7mm., paler at the edges, obscurely 3-nerved; *inner segments* free, but dorsally adnate to the outer for two-thirds their length, broader than the outer and with broader, more spreading apices.

Filaments pale-lemon, filiform-flattened, the 3 inner narrower and lengthening before the 3 outer with their *anthers* in turn exserted 1mm.; *stigma* at length exserted 1—2mm.; *ovary* lemon-yellow, 3mm. long, 2mm. diam. (Figs. 331–333).

UGANDA. On sheer rock faces near the NE summit of Tororo Rock, Tororo, c. 0° 42′ N, 34° 12′ E, 4,400 ft., 25 April 1952, Bally et Reynolds 6594, holotype (PRE); Tororo Rock, cult. Pretoria, H. C. Dawkins in Nat. Herb. no. 28427 (PRE); plant ex Tororo Rock, cult. Johannesburg, fl. 8 May 1960, Reynolds 6594A (K); Tororo Rock, 4,800 ft., Dec. 1959, Tweedie 1937 (K).

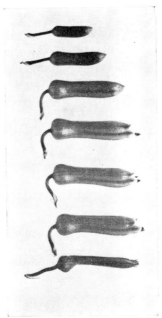

Fig. 331.

A. tororoana Reynolds. Plant photographed at Tororo Rock, near Kenya Border, Uganda; c. 0° 42′ N., 34° 12′ E. Height 50cm.

Fig. 332.
A. tororoana Reynolds.

Fig. 332. Plants from Tororo Type locality flowering at Johannesburg. Height 45cm.

Fig. 333.

Fig. 333. Flowers natural size.

This very distinctive species was discovered in 1946 by Mr. H. C. Dawkins, at that time forest ecologist at Kampala.

In April 1952, Mr. P. R. O. Bally collected plants on sheer rock faces near the NE summit of Tororo Rock, which is behind Tororo Village, across the border in Uganda. Mr. Bally brought down several flowering specimens which enabled the description to be drawn up.

It seems that *A. tororoana* could best be regarded as a small low undershrub with stems about 20cm. long. A striking feature of the slender inflorescence which is simple in young plants, and with 1—2 short branches in adult plants, is the colour of the buds which are coral-red for four-fifths of their length, the apical fifth being green. The pedicels are also coral-red.

139. A hendrickxii Reynolds in *Journ. S.A. Bot.* 21: 51 (1955).

DESCRIPTION: A small shrub of low, compact growth.

Stem none or very short, with numerous off-shoots forming small dense groups.

Leaves about 16, rosulate, narrowly lanceolate-attenuate, spreading, slightly recurved near apex, basally amplexicaul, 22cm. long, 4cm. broad; *upper surface* dull green with a greyish bloom, without spots or markings, slightly concave low down, a little channelled upwards; *lower surface* greyer-green than upper surface, rounded, mostly without spots or lines but sometimes with a few obscure dull-greyish elongated spots; *margins* armed with firm greenish-white teeth in lower half of leaf, the teeth brownish-tipped in upper half of leaf and averaging 3mm. long, 5—8mm. distant. *Sap* dries yellow.

Inflorescence a branched panicle about 40—50cm. high, 4—5-branched, the terminal raceme the highest.

Peduncle flattened and 7mm. broad at base, about 5mm. thick at the middle, clothed with 4—6 sterile-bracts, the lowest up to 18mm. long, 5mm. broad, thin, dry, 5—7-nerved, smaller upwards.

Raceme cylindric-conic, the terminal the longest and 12—15cm. long, the lateral shorter, subdensely flowered, uni-coloured, dull-scarlet, the apex a small tuft of wilted bracts, youngest buds suberect and greyish-tipped, open flowers subpendulous.

Bracts long-deltoid, lowest 14mm. long, 3—4mm. broad, subscarious, 5—7-nerved, slightly longer than the pedicels.

Pedicels lowest 13mm. long, lengthening in the fruit.

Perianth dull-scarlet, 30mm. long, cylindric, 4·5mm. diam. across the ovary, slightly decurved, the mouth wide open; *outer segments* free for 10mm., obscurely 3-nerved, thinner at the edges, the apices subacute and much recurved to revolute; *inner segments* free but dorsally adnate to the outer for two-thirds their length, longer and broader than the outer, with thin white edges and a scarlet keel, distinctly brown-nerved on inside near apex, the apices markedly recurved to revolute.

Filaments pale lemon, filiform-flattened, the 3 inner narrower and lengthening before the 3 outer with their *anthers* in turn exserted 2—3mm.; *stigma* at length exserted 3mm.; *ovary* pale yellow-green, 5mm. long, 2mm. diam. (Figs. 334, 335).

CONGO (formerly Belgian). *Oriental Prov.:* Kibali—Ituri Dist., Mont Aboro, alt. 2,450m., 2° N, 30° 52′ E, coll. F. L. Hendrickx (n. 6401 Bot.), cult. Johannesburg, fl. 12 March 1955, Reynolds 6300 holotype (PRE), isotype (BR).

FIG. 334.

A. hendrickxii Reynolds. Plant collected by Mr. Fred L. Hendrickx on Mount Aboro, Kibale-Iruti Dist., W of Lake Albert, Congo (Leo), flowering in the author's garden in Johannesburg. Height 50cm.

FIG. 335.

A. hendrickxii Reynolds. Flowers 1/1 from bud
to post-anthesis stage.

This distinctive new species was first collected by Mr. Fred L. Hendrickx, at that time Director of the I.N.E.A.C. Station de Mulungu – Tshibinda, which is near Bukavu, in the Kivu Province of the then Belgian Congo.

Mr. Hendrickx discovered this species in October 1951 on the summit of Mont Aboro which is the highest point of the ridge bordering the western side of the Great Rift in which Lake Albert lies. Mont Aboro is situated to the N of Kwandruma, at 2° 00′ N, 30° 52′ E. Plants were found at an altitude of 2450m., growing in small groups in fissures of granite outcrops.

A. hendrickxii is a small undershrub of low growth, and appears to be related to *A. sereti* De Wild., which grows near Irumu, and between Fataki and Nioka. It differs from *A. sereti* in being a much smaller plant with smaller leaves and rosettes, and in having a lower inflorescence, longer bracts, and perianths with markedly recurved outer segment apices.

131. **A. deserti** Berger in Engler's *Bot. Jahrb.* 36: 61 (1905), in Engler's *Pflanzenr.* Liliac.–Aloin. 225 (1908); Pole Evans in *Bot. Survey Mem.* 22: 226, Pl. 378–9 (1948); Reynolds in *Fl. Pl. Afr.* 29: Pl. 1151 (1953).

DESCRIPTION based on many flowering plants at the type locality, Kisiwani, Tanzania (Tanganyika).

Plants of somewhat low shrubby growth, growing in thickets or out in the open. *Stems* 30—50cm. long, 4—5cm. diam., ascending or to 1m. long, and divergent or decumbent, branched from base, with the apical 20—30cm. subdensely foliate.

Leaves about 16—20, narrowly lanceolate-attenuate, averaging 40cm. long, 7cm. broad at base, basally sheathing, the younger spreading, the older recurved; *upper surface* flat low down, slightly canaliculate upwards, dull green with brownish tinge, varying from unspotted or sparingly spotted to more copiously spotted, the spots elliptic, dirty-white;. *lower surface* convex, dull green, with or without spots; *margins* armed with pungent, deltoid, pale-brown teeth, 2—3mm long, 15mm. apart.

Inflorescence a branched panicle, 120—140cm. high.

Peduncle basally plano-convex and 15—20mm. broad, averaging 6-branched from above the middle, with large, conspicuously white, thin, sterile-bracts subtending base of branches, and with smaller sterile-bracts below the racemes; young racemes at first limp and drooping downwards with all buds covered by densely imbricate bracts, becoming stiff and erect when lowest flowers commence opening.

Racemes sublaxly flowered, cylindric, slightly acuminate, the terminal 20—25cm. long (laterals shorter), 7cm. diam., the buds spreading horizontally to slightly downwards.

Bracts conspicuously white, ovate-acute, 12mm. long, 6mm. broad, thin, very dry, brittle, 5—7-nerved, deflexed.

Pedicels 7—8mm. long.

Perianth dull deep rose-pink or coral-red with a bloom, 32—35mm. long, basally obtuse and shortly stipitate, cylindric and about 8mm. diam., thence exceedingly slightly narrower and trigonously slightly enlarging to an open mouth; *outer segments* free for 15mm., paler at the margins, obscurely 3-nerved, apices subacute, slightly spreading; *inner segments* adnate to the outer for half their length, with broader pale border, with 3 crowded nerves forming a deep-pink keel, the apices more obtuse and more spreading than the outer.

Filaments filiform-flattened, with their *anthers* in turn exserted 2—3mm.; *stigma* at length exserted 3—4mm.; *ovary* green, 6—7mm. long, 3·5mm. diam. (Plate 77, Figs. 336–339).

TANZANIA (TANGANYIKA). *Tanga Prov..*, Pare Dist.: Kisiwani, at the foot of the Pare Mountains, in flower and fruit, end June 1894, Volkens 2378 (B). — *Note:* Kisiwani is at the north-eastern tip of the South Pare Hills, 17 miles ENE of Same, at about 4° 10′ S, 38° E.;Kisiwani, fl. 24 June 1942, Greenway 6490! (K, EA, PRE); Kisiwani, 4 July 1958, alt. 2,400 ft., Reynolds 8772! (K, PRE, EA); S. Pare Hills, north of Gonja, 2,500 ft., July 1958, Tweedie 1684! (K); Ndungu, cult. Pretoria, 4 June 1946, A. G. McLoughlin 666! (PRE).

KENYA. Wakamba Reserve, between Machakos and Yatta Plains, cult. Pretoria, fl. 10 May 1940, I. B. Pole Evans et J. Erens 1108! (PRE, SRGH); near Voi, 1 Feb. 1953, Bally 8652 (EA); Bamba, 25 miles W of Kilifi, March 1953 (G, EA); 50 miles E of Nairobi, cult. Johannesburg, fl. 24 May 1953, Reynolds 6000! (PRE).

A. deserti is not an acaulescent species as has been thought. At the type locality it is a species of low shrubby growth, with stems branched at base and reaching 60cm. long when supported, or up to 1m. long when sprawling and decumbent, with the apical 20—30cm. sub-laxly foliate, as found in *Prolongatae*. The flowers are 30—35mm. long. This species is hardly a near ally of

PLATE 77

ALOE DESERTI   Engler.

Plants from Kisiwani (type locality), N. Pare Mountains, Tanga Dist.,
Tanzania, flowering in the author's gardens. Height 5 ft.

F<small>IG</small>. 336.   F<small>IG</small>. 337.

A. deserti Engler. Plants from 50 miles E of Nairobi, Kenya.

F<small>IG</small>. 336. Showing young developing inflorescence with limp, drooping racemes.

F<small>IG</small>. 337. The same plants three weeks later with racemes erect.

F<small>IG</small>. 338.

A. deserti Engler. Plants at type locality, Kisiwani at NE end of the South Pares, Tanzania. Plant on right with drooping racemes.

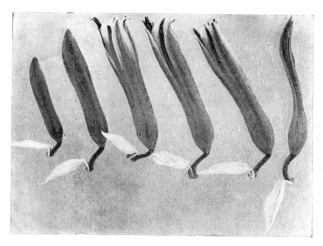

FIG. 339.

A. deserti Engler. Flowers 1/1. Note large
white bracts.

A. trichosantha and *A. tomentosa* in Berger's Series *Verae*, and it is now treated as a small shrub
of low growth.

A striking character of *A. deserti* is the remarkably large white bracts. Young racemes have
densely-imbricate bracts covering all the buds. At first all racemes are limp and drooping, and
only become stiff and erect when the lowest flowers commence opening.

When growing in shade of thickets at Kisiwani, *A. deserti* develops longer stems, that are erect
or decumbent, with shoots at random. Out in the open, and in cultivation, stems are shorter,
erect, and of less shrubby growth.

A near ally is *A. otallensis* Baker from Southern Ethiopia, but the latter is not of shrubby
growth, and also differs in having racemes which are erect at all stages of development.

132. **A. hildebrandtii** Bak. in *Bot. Mag. t.* 6981 (1888), in Th. Dyer *Fl. Trop. Afr.* 7: 468 (1898);
Berger in Engler's *Pflanzenr.* Liliac.–Aloin. 267 (1908).
—— *A. gloveri* Reynolds et Bally in *Journ. S.A. Bot.* 24: 180 (1958).

DESCRIPTION: *Plant* of shrubby growth, branched at base, with stems divergent, lying along the ground, or rambling
over rocks. *Stems* 3—4cm. diam., usually 50cm.—1m. long, the apical 30cm. subdensely foliate.
  Leaves lanceolate-attenuate, 20—30cm. long, 4—6cm. broad at base, spreading to slightly recurved; *upper surface*
dull green, with or without a few white lenticular spots, flat low down, slightly canaliculate upwards; *lower surface*
convex, similar to upper surface; *margins* armed with isolated, pungent, deltoid, reddish-brown teeth that are 2—3mm.
long, 8—10mm. apart, the interspaces the colour of the leaf, the teeth usually more crowded low down, more spaced
upwards; *sap* dries orange-brown.
  Inflorescence a branched panicle about 50cm. long, usually produced obliquely, sometimes 2—4 simultaneously in
very robust growth forms.
  Peduncle plano-convex and 12mm. broad at base, branched at the middle or lower, with 8—12 divaricate virgate
branches, the lowest 1—2 branches sometimes with 2—4 branchlets.
  Racemes cylindric, slightly conical, the terminal 10—18cm. long, 5cm. diam., rather laxly flowered, the flowers
evenly distributed in erect racemes, somewhat subsecund in oblique racemes, lateral racemes slightly shorter than the
terminal.
  Bracts very small, ovate-acute, averaging 3mm. long, 2mm. broad, white, thin, scarious, 1-nerved.
  Pedicels 10—15mm. long.
  Perianth yellow, orange, or dull scarlet with a bloom, cylindric-trigonous, 26—30mm. long, basally obtuse, 8mm.
diam. across the ovary, thence trigonous and narrowing slightly to the mouth; *outer segments* free for 12mm., obscurely
3-nerved, the apices subacute, slightly spreading; *inner segments* free but dorsally adnate to the outer to the middle,
broader than the outer and with broader, more obtuse apices.
  Filaments lemon, the 3 inner narrower and lengthening before the 3 outer with their *anthers* in turn exserted 3mm.;
stigma at length exserted 4mm.; *ovary* pale green, 6mm. long, 3mm. diam. (Plate 78, Figs. 340-343).

MATERIAL

"*East Tropical Africa.* Without locality. Plant coll. by Hildebrandt received from Berlin Bot. Garden in 1882, flowered
at Kew in July 1887, cult. specimen, Hildebrandt!" holotype (K).
SOMALIA NORTH (formerly Somaliland Prot.). N. slopes of Sheikh Pass, coll. P. Glover 1945, cult. Johannesburg, fl.
9 Feb. 1958, Reynolds 6233 (PRE, K); rocky slopes, Sheikh Pass, 4,000 ft., red flowers, 12 Feb. 1954, Bally 9659 (K,
EA); yellow flowers, 12 Feb. 1954, Bally 9660 (K, EA); Sheikh Pass, 12 Jan. 1947, yellow flowers, Bally 5709 (G, K,
EA); Sheikh Pass, cult. Hort. Bally, Nairobi, 14 April 1952, Reynolds 6543 (K, PRE); Gaan Libah, 12 miles NW of
Ghor, c. 9° 53′ N, 44° 47′ E, 5,300 ft., 29 Aug. 1957, yellow flowers, Reynolds 8358 (PRE, K, EA); same loc., red flowers,
Reynolds 8359 (PRE); N slopes of Sheikh Pass, 9° 53′ N, 45° 12′ E, 3,700—4,600 ft., 28 Aug. 1957, Reynolds 8340
(PRE); 17 miles N of Erigavo on road to Mait in dry bush country, c. 10° 50′ N, 47° 13′ E, 3,600 ft., 8 Sept. 1957,
Reynolds 8426 (PRE, K, EA).—This is the locality where Hildebrandt probably collected his type specimen.

ALOE HILDEBRANDTII   Baker.
A young plant, on Gaan Libah, 12 miles NW of Ghor, Somalia North.

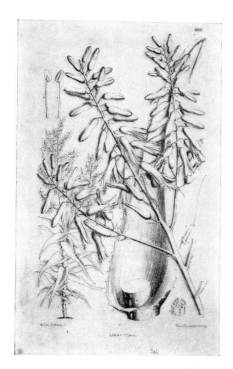

Fig. 340.

A. hildebrandtii Bak. From an uncoloured plate of the *Bot. Mag.*
t. 6981 (1888) much reduced.
By courtesy The Director, Royal Botanic Gardens, Kew.

Fig. 341.

A. hildebrandtii Bak. Yellow-flowered plant from near the top of Sheikh Pass, South of Berbera,
Somalia North – flowering in the author's garden. × 1/8 approx.

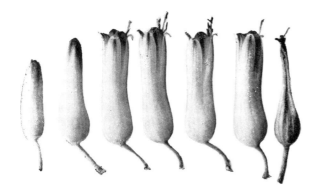

FIG. 342.

A. hildebrandtii Baker. Flowers 1/1 from **a** yellow-flowered plant.

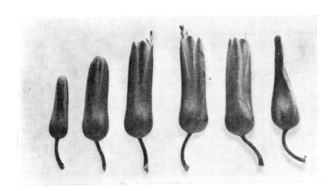

FIG. 343.

A. hildebrandtii Bak. Red flowers 1/1 from **a** plant 17 miles North of Erigavo, Somalia North.

TYPE LOCALITY

Type locality is not known. Baker (*Bot. Mag. t.* 6981) refers to Dr. Hildebrandt's "adventurous explorations of East Tropical Africa from 1872 to 1877" and he states, "Dr. Hildebrandt's explorations extended from Abyssinia and Somaliland southwards to the mountains of the interior opposite Zanzibar, and we do not know the exact country whence it came." Baker also stated that the *Bot. Mag.* drawing "was made from a plant that flowered at Kew for the first time in July 1889, which was received in 1882 from the Botanic Garden of Berlin." The author's problem was to try and ascertain where Hildebrandt could have collected the plants sent to Berlin and from there to Kew.

HISTORY

An account of *Hildebrandt's African Travels* appeared in *Journal of Botany* 17: 86 (1879), where it is recorded that Hildebrandt left Berlin in June 1872 for Aden, and arrived at Massawa (Red Sea port for Eritrea) in July. After travelling in the interior until October, he returned to Massawa and went to Aden.

From Aden, Hildebrandt undertook two excursions to the Somali coast – one to Berbera and Bulhar, the other a much longer one to "Lasgori" (Las Koreh on the coast) from which place he visited the Ahl mountains (which lie due south).

Note: The Ahl, or Al Madu range runs W to E from NE of Erigavo to near the eastern border of what is now Somalia North. There is a remote possibility that *A. hildebrandtii* might have been collected somewhere between the Al Madu and the coast.

Hildebrandt went to Zanzibar in July 1873, and returned to Europe in August 1874 to organise an expedition to Mt. Kenya.

In February 1875 he returned to Aden and arrived at "Meith" (Mait, now a ruin on the Somalia North coast). From here he visited the "Serrut" (Surud) mountains, and returned to Aden. From this point we are not concerned with Hildebrandt's further travels to Zanzibar, the Comoro Islands,

Madagascar, Pangani (Tanzanian coast), Lamu (Kenya coast) and his expedition from Mombasa on 10 January 1877, through the Taita, Wakamba and Kitui districts in the hopes of reaching Mt. Kenya. The reason is that *A. gloveri* Reynolds and Bally, known only in Somalia North, has now been found to be the same species as *A. hildebrandtii* hence the latter could have been collected only in Somalia North, the most likely place being between Mait and the Surud, N of Erigavo.

The *Bot. Mag.* figure is misleading because plants in nature never develop a slender erect simple stem incapable of supporting the weight of the plant depicted.

DISTRIBUTION

The Surud Madu lies about 13 miles NNW of Erigavo, the road down to Mait passing through the Tabah Gap at 6,000 ft. Forms of *A. hildebrandtii* occur from the north end of this Pass down the spectacular Kol Hosis escarpment to mile 7, and further down in dry bush country 17 miles from Erigavo, at 3,600 ft. This might well be the very locality where Hildebrandt originally collected his specimens. It is on his route from Mait to the Surud.

A. hildebrandtii occurs abundantly on Gaan Libar near the edge of the scarp, 12 miles NW of Ghor, at 5,200 ft., rainfall averaging 25—30 in. It is plentiful near the top of Sheikh Pass on the Berbera–Burao road, while Mr. Bally found it on the Fodjor Escarpment W of Sheikh, and on Wager Mountain to the east. Much further east it grows from the Surud down to 17 miles N of Erigavo.

VARIATION

A. hildebrandtii is essentially a shrubby species with a sprawling habit of growth, with stems 50cm.—1m. long and never erect except when growing in dense groups, the centre ones being supported. When stems are decumbent, the 30—50cm. foliate portion sometimes rests sideways on the tips of the leaves.

Length of stems and size of leaves is variable, while flowers may be scarlet, orange or yellow.

A. hildebrandtii is the only species in Somalia North with a sprawling habit of growth. It is nearest allied to *A. megalacantha* Bak. which is abundant around Hargeisa, but the latter is a much larger plant with stouter, erect stems, and much larger, deeply canaliculate leaves and different flowers.

HYBRID: Many crosses with *A. megalacantha* occur among both parents near the edge of the scarp on Gaan Libah.

133. **A. yavellana** Reynolds in *Journ. S.A. Bot.* 20: 28 (1954).

DESCRIPTION: *Plant* succulent, a shrub with erect or sprawling stems. *Stems* 3—4cm. diam., erect up to 1m., then falling, and sprawling and 2—3m. and more long, branching from the base, with the apical 20cm. ascending and subdensely foliate.

Leaves about 16—20, basally sheathing with the visible portion of sheaths striate, ensiform, spreading to suberect with the apical third recurved, 6—8cm. broad at base, gradually attenuate, up to 40cm. long, about 5mm. thick; *upper surface* bronze-brown in the sun, paler in the shade, usually without markings, flat near base, slightly canaliculate towards apex; *lower surface* rounded, paler bronze-brown to dull brownish-green, rather clearly green-lineate near base, more obscurely lineate upwards, not spotted; *margins* sinuate-dentate, armed with pungent, deltoid teeth which are pale reddish-brown tipped, 2—3mm. long, more crowded near base (5—8mm.), more distant (10—15mm.) upwards, obsolescent near apex, the interspaces rounded and the colour of the leaf. *Sap* dries yellow.

Inflorescence a branched panicle 60—90cm. high.

Peduncle plano-convex and 12—15mm. broad at base, terete upwards, branched about the middle, with 8—10 slender branches, the lowest with 2—3 branchlets high up, branches compact to arcuate-ascending.

Racemes erect, capitate or almost so, rounded at apex, the pedicellate part 2—3cm. long, the buds suberect, dark scarlet, clearly minutely white-flecked throughout and with grey stripes longitudinally in upper third, open flowers cernuous to subpendulous, scarcely white-flecked.

Bracts minute, deltoid, 3mm. long, 2mm. broad at base, thin, scarious, reflexed, with 3 crowded nerves sometimes appearing as 1-nerved.

Pedicels 10mm. long, the colour of the buds.

Perianth 27mm. long, cylindric-trigonous, dull scarlet at base, paler to orange upwards, basally obtusely tapering into the pedicel, cylindric and 5—6mm. diam. across the ovary, thence trigonous and narrowing on the underside, with the mouth very slightly upturned; *outer segments* free for 9mm., thinner at the margins, 3-nerved, the apices acute, straight or slightly spreading; *inner segments* themselves free but dorsally adnate to the outer for half their length, broader than the outer, with a reddish-orange keel, the apices more obtuse and more spreading than the outer.

Filaments pale orange, filiform-flattened, the 3 inner narrower and lengthening before the 3 outer with their *anthers* in turn exserted 1mm.; *style* pale orange, with *stigma* exserted 2mm.; *ovary* pale brown, 4mm. long, 2mm. diam. (Figs. 344, 345).

Fig. 344.

A. yavellana Reynolds. Plants near Yavello, Borana, S. Ethiopia. Height 1·20m.

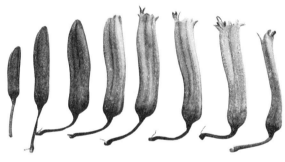

Fig. 345.

A. yavellana Reynolds. Flowers natural size.

S. Ethiopia. Sidamo, Borana, 1 mile W of Yavello, c. 4° 55′ N, 38° 06′ E, 5,600 ft., 18 Sept. 1953, Reynolds 7063 holotype (PRE), isotype (K); NE slopes of Mega Mountain, c. 4° 05′ N, 38° 20′ E, 6,400 ft., fruiting 9 Sept. 1953, Reynolds 7041 (PRE).

A. yavellana is allied to the five East African shrubby Aloes, *A. dawei* Berger from Entebbe and Kisumu, *A. kedongensis* Reynolds from the Rift Valley, *A. ngobitensis* Reynolds from north of the Aberdares, *A. nyeriensis* Christian from between Nyeri and Nanyuki, and *A. rabaiensis* from near Mombasa, but is immediately separated from them all by having bronze-brown leaves and capitate racemes with pedicels only 10mm. long and flowers only 27mm. in length, which are the smallest in this group. Another distinguishing character is that in *A. yavellana*, the dark scarlet buds are grey-striped in upper third, and are minutely white-flecked throughout. With its capitate racemes, *A. rabaiensis* is its nearest ally, but differs in having different leaves, and longer pedicels and flowers. The remaining four species all have longer racemes and longer pedicels and flowers.

A. yavellana occurs in numbers for a mile or more along north-eastern slopes of Mega mountain, in forest, in clearings, or on rocks, in places very difficult to find. The species was therefore named after a locality where it can easily be seen from the "road".

Another peculiarity of *A. yavellana* is that it forms fairly compact shrubs when stems are erect and not exceeding 1m. in length, but with development, stems topple over and form sprawling shrubs with stems 2—3m. long, especially on steep slopes, with the foliate portion ascending.

134. A. andongensis Bak. in *Trans. Linn. Soc.* ser. 2, Bot. 1, 263 (1878), in *Journ. Linn. Soc.* 18: 173 (1880), in Th. Dyer *Fl. Trop. Afr.* 7: 457 (1898); Rendle in *Cat. Welwitsch. Afr. Pl.* 2: 1, 46 (1899); Durand et Schinz *Consp. Fl. Afr.* 5: 303 (1893); Berger in Engler's *Pflanzenr.* Liliac.–Aloin. 241 (1908); Reynolds in *Journ. S.A. Bot.* 26: 82 (1960).

DESCRIPTION based on plants at the type locality Pungo Andongo, and elsewhere in Angola.

Plants of shrubby growth, with few to several stems short or 30—60cm. high, ascending, oblique, or sometimes fallen and re-rooting, usually with the apical 30cm. subdensely foliate, with old dried leaf remains persistent.

Leaves rosulate, about 14, lanceolate-attenuate, varying from spreading and slightly recurved to suberectly spreading and more compact, averaging 20—25cm. long, 6—7cm. broad at base; *upper surface* dull grey-green, mostly without spots, sometimes sparingly spotted, flat low down, slightly channelled upwards; *lower surface* convex, dull grey-green, usually with numerous crowded white spots near base; *margins* sinuate-dentate with slight cartilaginous edge armed with brownish deltoid teeth, 2—3mm. long, 5—7mm. apart, smaller and more crowded low down; larger and more spaced upwards.

Inflorescence 2—3-branched, 30—40cm. high.

Peduncle basally plano-convex and 10—14mm. broad, branched from the middle or lower.

Racemes varying from subcapitate with the pedicellate portion 6—8cm. long, to cylindric-acuminate and 10—12cm. long, 6—8cm. diam., in all forms the apical buds spreading horizontally to slightly deflexed, open flowers nutant.

Bracts lanceolate-acute, 5—8mm. long, 3mm. broad, thin, scarious, 3—5-nerved, somewhat clasping the pedicel.

Pedicels 14—18mm. long, suberectly spreading, the apex cernuous, the colour of the perianth.

Perianth pale orange-scarlet, paler at mouth, cylindric and very slightly decurved, averaging 25mm. long, basally obtuse and shortly stipitate, cylindric and 5—6mm. diam. across the ovary, narrowed to 4—5mm. above the ovary, thence enlarging to 6—7mm. diam. near the mouth and giving the perianth a slightly clavate appearance; *outer segments* free for 8mm., paler at the margins, obscurely 3—5-nerved, the apices subacute, slightly spreading; *inner segments* broader than the outer, keeled, with more obtuse, more spreading apices.

Filaments lemon, filiform-flattened, the 3 inner narrower and lengthening before the 3 outer with their *anthers* in turn exserted 1—2mm.; *ovary* pale-green, 3·5mm. long, 2mm. diam. (Figs. 346–350).

ANGOLA. *Cuanza Norte Dist.*: Pungo Andongo, frequent in rocky places, Welwitsch 3729 without date, holotype (BM), syntypes (K, LISU); coll. Pungo Andongo, cult. Johannesburg, fl. 14 May 1960, Reynolds 9585 (BM, K, PRE). *Cuanza Sul*, 4 miles NW of Cassongue, c. 11° 52′ S, 15° E, 5,000 ft., cult. Johannesburg, fl. 26 May 1960, Reynolds 9335 (PRE, SRGH).

FIG. 346.

Type locality of *A. andongensis* Bak. The road leading through the fabulous Pedras Negras to Pungo Andongo in the South-East corner of Cuanza Norte, Angola.

Fig. 347. Fig. 348.

A. andongensis Bak.

Fig. 347. Plant collected at Pungo Andongo, Angola (type locality), flowering in Johannesburg.

Fig. 348. Plants collected 14 miles south of Quibala, Cuanza Sul, Benguela Dist., Angola, c. 10° 55′ S., 15° 02′ N., flowering in the author's garden in Johannesburg.

Fig. 349.

A. andongensis Bak. Plants on rock pavement, and on top of tombs 14 miles W of Amboiva, Seles, Cuanza Sul, Angola. Note chevron pattern near top of tomb – reminiscent of the top of the east wall of Zimbabwe Ruins, SE of Fort Victoria, Rhodesia.

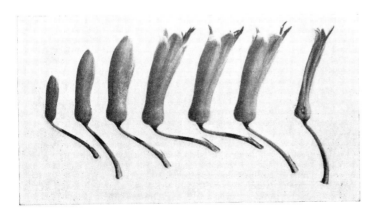

Fig. 350.

A. andongensis Bak. Flowers 1/1 from a plant collected at type locality, Pungo Andongo.

Type locality: Pungo Andongo is a small post in the midst of the fantastic rock formations known as the *Pedras Negras* in the far south-eastern parts of the Cuanza Norte District, 24 miles SE of Quizenga, 23 miles SW of Cacuso, 78 miles WSW of Malange, at approx. 9° 42' S, 15° 34'E, the road being at 3,500 ft. alt. The vast majority of plants are impossible to reach (except by helicopter) but there are a few sloping approaches leading up to some plants.

DISTRIBUTION AND VARIATION

A. andongensis is a most variable species. At Pungo Andongo, type locality, plants are of more robust growth, stems reach 60—80cm. long and are less branched than elsewhere. They may be erect, divergent, or fallen and re-rooted. Leaves are spreading to recurved, forming open rosettes.

When a species ranges over a wide area, there is often a gradual transition from one form to another. At the southern end of the distribution range, at a point four miles NW of Cassongue which is 47 miles NW of Luimbale (Luimbale being 160 miles E of Lobito on main road to Nova Lisboa), plants of *A. andongensis* have short stems and form patches sometimes a few metres across, the rosettes of leaves being more compact. This form is found for 20 miles along the road from Cassongue towards Amboiva (3,400 ft.) and westwards to near Vila Nova de Seles. From Amboiva to Cela and northwards, plants are found in large numbers all round Quibala (4,200 ft.) and westwards to Gabela. They have slenderer stems, are much more branched from base, and form compact shrubs, the apical 30cm. of stems being sublaxly foliate.

Leaves are mostly dull grey-green and unspotted, occasionally there are several crowded white spots dorsally near base. Twelve miles W of Quibala some plants were found with leaves copiously spotted on both sides.

Racemes vary from shorter and subcapitate (6—8cm. long), to longer and more cylindric-conic (10—12cm. long), but one fixed character which characterizes all forms of *A. andongensis* is the racemes in which the buds all spread somewhat horizontally, or are slightly deflexed.

HYBRIDS

Seven miles SE of Vila Nova de Seles, Cuanza Sul (type locality of *A. gossweileri* Reynolds), that species and *A. andongensis* grow socially and cross rather freely. The cross is very attractive.

135. **A. cameronii** Hemsley in *Bot. Mag. t.* 7915 (1903); Berger in Engler's *Pflanzenr.* Liliac.-Aloin. 263 (1908); Reynolds in *Aloes of Nyasaland* 34 (1954).
—— *A. macrosiphon* in *Kew Handlist of Tender Monocot.* 173 (1897) *non* Baker.

Description based on the various forms of the species as a whole as it occurs wild from Gt. Zimbabwe in Rhodesia, through Moçambique to Lilongwe and Mzimba in Malawi.

Plants of shrubby growth. *Stems* ascending, branched from base, short or up to 1m. and more high, varying from slenderer and somewhat spindly to thicker and more rigidly erect, 3—4cm. thick, the apical 30—50cm., subdensely foliate with all old dried leaf remains usually persistent.

Leaves basally sheathing-amplexicaul, suberectly spreading, varying from 5—7cm. broad at base, gradually narrowing to an acute pointed apex and 40—50cm. long; *upper surface* green in the rainy season, mostly turning copper-red in the winter months, mostly slightly canaliculate; *lower surface* convex to rounded, otherwise as in the upper surface; *both surfaces* usually without spots or markings; *margins* armed with pale-brown, pungent teeth, 2—3mm. long, 10—15mm. apart, the interspaces the colour of the leaf.

Inflorescence 2—3 simultaneously, dichotomously 2—3-branched from about the middle, averaging 60—90cm. high.

Peduncle basally plano-convex and 15—20mm. broad, lowest branch subtended at base by a broadly ovate, thin, scarious, many-nerved bract about 8mm. long, 5mm. broad.

Racemes cylindric, slightly acuminate, subdensely many-flowered, averaging 10—15cm. long and 7—8cm. diam., the buds spreading obliquely to horizontally, open flowers nutant.

Bracts broadly and shortly ovate-acute, about 2mm. long, 3mm. broad.

Pedicels 3—5mm. long, reddish-brown.

Perianth bright deep-scarlet, slenderly cylindric-curved, sometimes slightly clavate, averaging 45mm. long, 5—7mm. diam. across the ovary, slightly enlarging to the throat, and slightly contracted to the mouth; *outer segments* free for about 12—15mm., the apices subacute, slightly spreading; *inner segments* themselves free but dorsally adnate to the outer for their greater length, the apices more obtuse more spreading than the outer.

Filaments lemon, filiform-flattened, the 3 inner narrower and lengthening before the 3 outer with their *anthers* in turn exserted 3—4mm.; *stigma* at length exserted 5—6mm.; *ovary* green, 7mm. long, 2·5mm. diam. (Plate 79, Figs. 351-356).

PLATE 79

ALOE CAMERONII Hemsl.
A form 9 miles W of Dowa, Central Malawi.
Height 2m.

ALOE CAMERONII Hemsl.
var. DEDZANA Reynolds.
Plants from Dedza Mtn., Central Prov., Malawi,
growing at Nasonia, Cholo, S. Malawi. Height 1·5m.

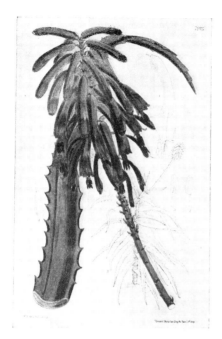

Fig. 351.

A. cameronii Hemsl. The figure in *Bot. Mag. t.* 7915 (1903).
Photo: By courtesy, The Chief, Botanic Research Institute Pretoria.

Fig. 352.   Fig. 353.

A. cameronii Hemsl.

Fig. 352. The form near Dambashawa, Salisbury District, Rhodesia. Height 3 ft. 6 ins.

Fig. 353. Growing in shallow pockets of soil on granite between Zimbabwe Ruins and Morgenster, Rhodesia. Height 3 ft. 6 ins.

FIG. 354. *A. cameronii* Hemsl. On rocks a few miles SW of Mrewa, on the Salisbury–Tete road, Rhodesia. Height 5 feet.

FIG. 355. *A. cameronii* Hemsl. var. *bondana* Reynolds. Between Bonda Mission and Nyamazi, Inyanga Dist., Rhodesia. Height 6 feet.

FIG. 355A.

A. cameronii Hemsl. var. *bondana* Reynolds. Buds and flowers 1/1.

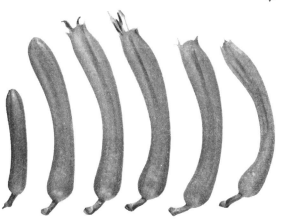

FIG. 356.

A. cameronii Hemsl. Flowers 1/1 from the plants depicted on Plate 79 (left) – a form in Central Malawi.

MALAWI (formerly Nyasaland). Plant sent to the Royal Botanic Gardens, Kew, in 1894 by Mr. K. J. Cameron of the African Lakes Corporation, fl. at Kew in Feb. 1903 (K, holotype), the type of *Bot. Mag. t.* 7915. *Central Prov.:* 53 miles N of Lilongwe on Kasungu Road, 7 June 1938, I. B. Pole Evans et J. Erens 606 (PRE); Rocky ridge, 26 miles NE of Lilongwe on Dowa road, 4,500 ft., stems 1m., old dried leaves persistent, 22 July 1952, Reynolds 6696 (K, PRE, SRGH) —see colour plate; on Nchisi Mountain, Kota Kota Dist., 27 July 1946, shrub 1—1·5m. high, L. J. Brass 16991 (SRGH).

ZAMBIA. Seen but not collected, on immense rocks, 98 miles W of Fort Jameson, 276 miles E of Lusaka, on Great East Road.

RHODESIA. *Victoria Dist.:* Between Zimbabwe and Morgenster Mission, on granite in shallow pockets of soil, cult. Greendale, fl. 17 June 1958, L. C. Leach 361 (SRGH). *Salisbury Dist.:* Domboshawa, cult. Greendale, fl. 16 June 1957, Leach 130 (PRE); Domboshawa, 30 May 1933, Eyles 4967 (SRGH); Chindamora Res., granite koppie, shortly caulescent, cult. Greendale, fl. 3 June 1961, L. C. Leach 11099 (SRGH); on granite hill at Ewanrigg, 4,200 ft., leaves copper-red in winter, 1914, F. B. Parkinson, in Herb. Christian No. 218 (SRGH). *Mrewa Dist.:* Granite koppie just W of Maramba Mission, height 3 ft. 6 in., cult. Greendale, fl. 4 June 1961, L. C. Leach 11101 (SRGH); *Inyanga Dist:* 3 miles W of Troutbeck, 6,800 ft., weak form, fl. 29 May 1954, N. C. Chase 5277 (SRGH); top of World's View, 6,800 ft., compact rosettes, racemes 15cm. long, 4 June 1959, L. C. Leach 9064 (SRGH). *Umtali Dist.:* Farm Cloudlands, Vumba, 1920, H. B. Christian 450 (SRGH); cult. Ewanrigg, fl. 20 July 1942, H. B. Christian 450 (PRE), fl. again July 1946, Christian 450 (SRGH).

MOÇAMBIQUE. *Manica and Sofala:* Mafura Mountain, coll. G. B. de Graca 13, cult. Ewanrigg, fl. 2 Aug. 1946, Herb. Christian No. 1272 (SRGH, PRE); Nharijara, coll. G. B. de Graca, cult. Ewanrigg, fl. 23 July 1952, No. 1251 in Herb. Christian (SRGH, PRE); 10 miles S of Vila Pery, 6 July 1959, L. C. Leach 9214 (SRGH).

Also occurs on southern foothills of Gorongosa Mountain, and on Zembe Mountain, 19 miles S of Vila Pery.

HISTORY

TYPE LOCALITY: Malawi, Blantyre. Hemsley in *Bot. Mag. t.* 7915 stated: "The plant from which our drawing was made was sent to the Royal Botanic Gardens, Kew, in 1894, by Mr. K. J. Cameron of the African Lakes Corporation, and flowered in February 1903." In a letter to the Director, Mr. Cameron said: "At the request and with the assistance of Mr. Scott Elliot, I have selected the following plants from our garden at Mandala. Then follows a list."

Concerning Mr. Cameron, the Secretary of the African Lakes Corporation, Glasgow, informed the present author that Mr. Cameron sailed for Nyasaland in March 1890 on a five-year contract as a planter. He signed a further agreement in February 1898 and arrived at Chinde on 27 April. He was then 36 years of age.

In response to a request, Mr. Arthur J. Stent – who joined the Corporation in 1902 and retired in 1947, communicated the following: "I met the late Mr. Kenneth J. Cameron at Namadzi Estate in 1903. There never was a botanical gardens in Mandala; our gardens were rather experimental plots than for show purposes. I think Mr. Cameron would have found *Aloe cameronii* growing on Mandala Estate on the sides of a ravine between the present Mandala house and the Blantyre– Limbe road. If he did not find his original plants within a hundred yards of the old Mandala house (now used as offices) I think he would find them within 400 yards." Hence, Blantyre might be the type locality. But it is possible that the type could have come from hills between Blantyre and Zomba, perhaps from Namasi Estate, near Zomba.

DISTRIBUTION

RHODESIA. In its numerous forms *A. cameronii* is found near the Great Zimbabwe ruins and on granite hills of the eastern arm of Kyle Dam in the south, to the Matopos, to Salisbury District, and between Horseshoe Block and Sipolilo in the Northern Umvukwes; Inyanga, Vumba Mountains, Umtali to various localities in Manica and Sofala in Moçambique.

MALAWI. Blantyre, Malombe Estate, Fort Lister, Namadidi near Zomba, and on top of Zomba Mountain. North and west of Fort Johnston, to Dedza Mountain, Chenje Hill in Kota Kota District, and near Dowa, northwards to near Kasungulu and Mzimba, which appears to be its northern limit.

VARIATION

Over a wide range of geographical stations from 3,500—7,000 ft. in altitude, *A. cameronii* is not only a species of remarkable beauty, especially with leaves turning shiny bronze-red in winter, but it is also an exceptionally variable species. In some localities stems are short and rosettes small, while at Dowa (Malawi) stems reach 3—4 ft. in height with all old dried leaf remains persistent.

Racemes of the typical form average 10—15cm. long, 7—8cm. diam. The inflorescence is dichotomously 2—3-branched.

In the furthest south localities (Zimbabwe) racemes are almost capitate. Flowers are rather slender, slightly curved, and average 45mm. long. Yellow flowers from the Vumba Mountains E of Umtali have been reported. A variety found between Bonda Mission and Nyamazi, 11 miles S of London Garage, NE of Rusape, has flowers with genitals exserted 10mm.

NATURAL HYBRIDS

Mr. L. C. Leach has found the following crosses with *A. cameronii* one parent:
1. × *A. arborescens*, about 10 miles SE of London Garage, Inyanga, Rhodesia.
2. × *A. chabaudii*, Zembe Mountain, 19 miles S of Vila Pery, Manica and Sofala, Moçambique. The author has observed the same cross near Zimbabwe, Victoria, Rhodesia.
3. × *A. christianii*, Chibakwe River, Salisbury–Mrewa Road, Rhodesia.
4. × *A. excelsa*, Mt. Zembe, Moçambique.
5. × *A. greatheadii*, near Domboshawa, N of Salisbury.

135A. **A. cameronii** var. **dedzana** Reynolds in *Journ. S.A. Bot.* 31: 167 (1965).

The var. *dedzana* differs from the typical form chiefly in having very long racemes which are 20—25cm. long, and only 5cm. diam. Plants form dense shrubs with stems about 50—80cm. long, the apical half subdensely foliate. (Plate 79, Fig. 357).

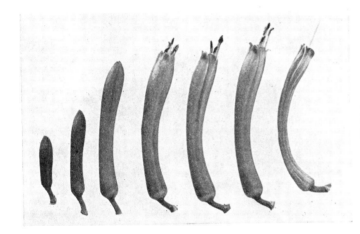

FIG. 357.

A. cameronii Hemsl. var. *dedzana* Reynolds. Buds and flowers 1/1 from a plant from Dedza Mtn., Central Malawi.

It seems that the late Mr. Basil Christian was the first to discover this striking variety on Dedza Mountain, Central Province, Malawi, when he and Mr. Fred Holland visited there in August 1938. It seems that Dedza Mountain and nearby hills is the headquarters of this variety. It has also been collected by Mr. L. C. Leach 15 miles S of Monkey Bay, N of Fort Johnston, in Southern Province.

MALAWI. *Central Prov.:* Ex Dedza Mountain, fl. 20 July 1942, raceme 20cm. long, Christian 459, holotype (SRGH), isotype (PRE); rocky hill near Dedza, racemes 25cm. long, 5cm. diam., leaves 50cm. long, 6cm. broad, Christian 952 (SRGH); ex Dedza Mountain, cult. Nasonia, Cholo, 10 July 1952, Reynolds 6662 (PRE, K)—see colour plate. *Southern Prov.:* On Monkey Bay–Fort Johnston Road, Aug. 1938, H. B. Christian 951 (SRGH); 15 miles S of Monkey Bay on Fort Johnston Road, cult. Greendale, racemes 20cm. long, 23 June 1958, Leach 382 (SRGH).

MOÇAMBIQUE. Manica and Sofala, near Garuso (40 miles E of Umtali), cult. Greendale, fl. 21 July 1958, raceme 18cm. long, 5cm. diam., L. C. Leach 415 (SRGH) appears to belong here.

135B. Var. 2. **A. cameronii** Hemsl. var. **bondana** Reynolds.

Varietas nova, a forma typica perianthio breviore, crassiore, clavatiore, genitaliis usque 10mm. exsertis differt.

RHODESIA. *Inyanga Dist.:* 10 miles SE of London Garage, Juliasdale, July 1956, anthers exserted 8—10mm., Leach 367 (SRGH); coll. 11 miles S of London Garage, between Bonda Mission and Nyamanze, cult. Mbabane, fl. 4 July 1964, Reynolds 8585 holotype (SRGH), isotype (PRE).

The var. *bondana* chiefly differs from the typical and other forms in having shorter, thicker, more clavate perianths, with anthers and style exserted up to 9—10mm. (Figs. 355, 355A).

Considerable numbers of plants occur on a granite hill between Bonda Mission and Nyamanzi, in a number of attractive colour forms. *Stems* mostly simple up to 60cm. tall, 4 cm. thick. *Leaves* average 35cm. long, 7cm. broad, and are dark-green tinged copper-red. *Inflorescence* 2—3 simultaneously, 60cm. tall, and mostly 2—3-branched from the middle. *Perianth* 38—40mm. long, mostly yellowish to orange, more fleshy than usual and somewhat clavate, with *anthers* and *style* exserted 9—10mm. This very handsome plant is well worth cultivating.

136. A. palmiformis Baker in *Trans. Linn. Soc.* ser. 2, Bot. 263 (1878), in *Journ. Linn. Soc.* 18: 173 (1880), in *Fl. Trop. Afr.* 7: 466 (1898); Rendle in *Cat. Welwitsch. Afr. Pl.* 2: 1, 45 (1899); Berger in Engler's *Pflanzenr. Liliac.-Aloin.* 248 (1908).

DESCRIPTION based on many plants along the top of a spur of the Serra da Chela, among sandstone rocks at 6,400 ft. alt., 8 miles SW of Sá da Bandeira, Huila Dist., Angola.

Plants of shrubby growth, with rather spindly *stems* branched mostly from base, 1—1·5m. high, 3—4cm. thick, the apical 30cm. subdensely foliate.

Leaves about 14, crowded at apex of stems, arcuate-ascending-recurved, or spreading-recurved, basally sheathing, the sheaths lineate and 10mm. apart, narrowly lanceolate-attenuate, up to 30cm. long, 5cm. broad; *upper surface* dull-green with reddish tinge, flat low down, shallowly canaliculate upwards, without spots or markings; *lower surface* deeper green, convex, usually with numerous crowded small pale-green almost white spots in lowest quarter of leaf, fewer or none upwards; *margins* sinuate-dentate, armed with pale-brown pungent, deltoid teeth about 4—5mm. long, 10mm. apart.

Inflorescence simple or forked in young plants, 3—4-branched in older, 2—3 the average, 40—50cm. high.

Peduncle basally flattened and up to 20mm. broad, 2—3-branched from the middle or lower.

Racemes sublaxly flowered, cylindric, slightly acuminate, 10—15—20cm. long, 7cm. diam., the youngest buds grey-green tipped and spreading more or less horizontally, open flowers nutant to subpendulous.

FIG. 358.   FIG. 359.

A. palmiformis Bak.

FIG. 358. Photo of Welwitsch 3726, holotype (BM).

Photo by courtesy Mr. J. E. Dandy, British Museum (Natural History), London.

FIG. 359. Collected on the Serra da Chela, 8 miles SW of Sá da Bandeira, Huila Dist., Angola, c 14° 59′ S., 13° 28′ E., alt. 6,400 ft.; flowering at Johannesburg.

Bracts very small, 2—3mm. long, 2mm. broad, 1-nerved.

Pedicels 13—15mm. long, obliquely spreading, the colour of the perianth.

Perianth rose-scarlet, cylindric-trigonous, 30mm. long, basally obtuse and very shortly stipitate, cylindric and 5·5 mm. diam. across the ovary, very slightly enlarging to the mouth; *outer segments* free for 10mm., the free portion almost white at the margins, obscurely 3-nerved, the apices slightly spreading; *inner segments* themselves free but dorsally adnate to the outer for 20mm., broader than the outer, keeled, with more obtuse, more spreading apices.

Filaments pale lemon, the 3 inner narrower and lengthening before the 3 outer with their *anthers* in turn exserted 1mm.; *stigma* at length exserted 2mm.; *ovary* green, 6mm. long, 2·5mm. diam. (Figs. 358–361).

ANGOLA. *Huila Dist.:* "Huila, plentiful in the higher rocky woods of Morro de Lopollo, of the subtemperate region at 1250—1500m., fl. in April 1860, Welwitsch 3726" holotype (BM), syntypes (K, LISU); Same loc., May 1860, Welwitsch 3731! (BM). *Note:* The village of Huila is 16km. (10 miles) SE of Sá da Bandeira, in Huila District. The Lopollo is a stream with a small waterfall (called *cascade* locally); Morro = hill, hence Morro de Lopollo is the hill where the Lopollo rises. This is the type locality. *Huila Dist.:* 8 miles SW of Sá da Bandeira, along the top of a spur of the Serra da Chela, c. 14° 59′ S, 13° 28′ E, 6,400 ft., cult. Johannesburg, fl. 29 June 1959, Reynolds 9292 (K, SRGH, PRE); Lubango, Humpata, near Perfmetro Forestry, 1970m., fl. 15 April 1950, E. J. Mendes 3604! (LISC).

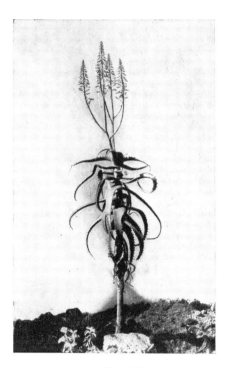 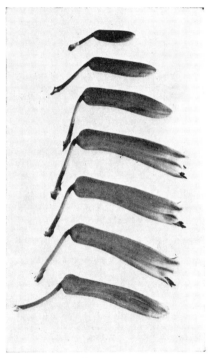

FIG. 360.　　　　　　　　　　　　　　FIG. 361.

A. palmiformis Bak.

FIG. 360. Plant collected on the Morro do Lopollo, above the Falls, near Huila Village. 16km. SE of Sá da Bandeira, Angola, (type locality) flowering at Mbabane, Swaziland. Height 2m.

FIG. 361. Flowers 1/1 from bud to post-anthesis.

Numbers of plants are found among sandstone rocks at the locality, 8 miles SW of Sá da Bandeira, and 7 miles NE of Humpata, which locality is about 8 miles NW of the type locality, Morro de Lopollo, and 1,500 ft. higher.

Stems are very slender and usually sparingly branched. Leaves are sometimes unspotted on both sides, but usually they are copiously spotted on lower surface near base. Marginal teeth are prominent. The inflorescence is mostly 2—3-branched and 50—60cm. high.

In his *Carta Fitogeografica*, p. 119 (1939), Gossweiler stated that *A. palmiformis* with stems up to 5m. occurs in the Catenge area. Catenge is a railway station 60 miles SE of Benguela at 1,700 ft. The species found there was in all ways distinct – see under *A. catengiana*.

137. **A. retrospiciens** Reynolds et Bally in *Journ. S.A. Bot.* 24: 182 (1958).

DESCRIPTION: *Plant* of shrubby growth, with stem sometimes simple, but mostly 2—6-branched at base and forming compact shrubs. *Stem* 1—1·25m. high, about 3cm. thick, the apical 10—20cm. subdensely foliate.

Leaves c. 12, crowded at apex of stem, rosulate, spreading to recurved, averaging 25cm. long, 5—6cm. broad at base, gradually narrowing to an obtuse apex, the apex with a few very small cartilaginous firm white teeth; *upper surface* bluish-grey with reddish tinge, flat low down, slightly canaliculate upwards, usually unicoloured but occasionally with a few scattered small white spots low down; *lower surface* convex, otherwise as upper surface; *margins* with a continuous white cartilaginous edge armed with firm white teeth that are 1mm. long and 5mm. apart, low down, and gradually smaller and more distant upwards, sometimes obsolete near apex.

Inflorescence a divaricately-branched panicle averaging 45cm. long.

Peduncle plano-convex and 12—15mm. broad at base, terete upwards, about 10-branched from the middle or lower, the lowest branches obliquely to almost horizontally disposed and up to 20cm. long, including the raceme.

Racemes subdensely flowered, the terminal usually erect and about 3cm. long, 5cm. diam., with the flowers evenly distributed around the axis, in racemes of oblique to horizontal branches the buds and flowers mostly secund, lying along the top of the axis and all pointing backwards.

Bracts narrowly ovate-deltoid, thin, scarious, white, 5mm. long, 2·5mm. broad, obscurely 3-nerved.

Pedicels 5—6mm. long.

Perianth yellow with greenish tips, cylindric-trigonous, averaging 20mm. long, 6mm. diam. across the ovary, thence slightly trigonous; *outer segments* free for 10mm. (tube 10mm.), obscurely 3-nerved, the nerves greenish, the apices subacute, slightly spreading; *inner segments* broader than the outer and with more obtuse more spreading apices.

Filaments pale lemon, the 3 inner narrower and lengthening before the 3 outer with their *anthers* in turn exserted 3mm.; *stigma* at length exserted 4mm.; *ovary* light green, 3mm. long, 2mm. diam. (Plate 80, Figs. 362, 363).

FIG. 362.

A. retrospiciens Reynolds et Bally. Plant on north side of Darburruk Tug, 55 miles NE of Hargeisa, on road to Berbera, Somalia North. Height 2m.

FIG. 363.

A. retrospiciens Reynolds et Bally. Flowers natural size.

PLATE 80

ALOE RETROSPICIENS   Reynolds et Bally.

At Darburruk, 55 miles NE of Hargeisa on Berbera road, Somalia North.
Height 5 feet.

SOMALIA NORTH (formerly Somaliland Prot.). At Darburruk, 55 miles NE of Hargeisa on Berbera road, c. 9° 52′ N, 44° 30′ E, alt. 2,700 ft., 21 Sept. 1957, Reynolds 8482 holotype (PRE), isotype (K, EA); north of Borama, 43° 16′ E, 10° 05′ N, 3,450—3,800 ft., 8 Nov. 1932, J. B. Gillett 4597! (K).

This distinctive species grows on both sides of Darburruk Tug (watercourse) near Darburruk Village, about 55 miles NE of Hargeisa on the road to Berbera, mostly among boulders in sandy soil, and under very arid conditions. The village is named after this Aloe, which the Somalis call *Daar buruk*.

A. retrospiciens rarely has a simple stem, plants are usually 2—6-branched (and more) at ground level. The leaves are bluish-grey with a bloom and have a reddish tinge. The inflorescence is divaricately branched, the slender branches being obliquely to horizontally disposed. The terminal raceme is erect with the flowers evenly distributed around the axis, but in horizontal racemes the flowers are more or less secund, lying along the upper side of the axis, with all buds and flowers pointing backwards. It was this character that suggested the specific epithet.

The 20mm. cylindric-trigonous flowers are closely allied to those of *A. gracilicaulis* and *A. medishiana*, both of which occur much further east in the Erigavo District, but the three could scarcely be confused. *A. gracilicaulis* has much longer, deeply channelled leaves, while *A medishiana* has longer pedicels and outer segments free for only 6mm. Neither has flowers secund and pointing backwards.

Mr. P. R. O. Bally has found plants – not flowering at the time – near Elan Gubato (near Hudiso at the foot of Sheikh Pass), which appear to belong to *A. retrospiciens*.

138. **A. babatiensis** Christian et Verdoorn in *Bothalia* 6: 2, 440 (1954).

DESCRIPTION based on large numbers of plants near Endalaghanet, 34 miles W of Babati on road to Mbulu, Tanzania (Tanganyika).

Plants dense shrubs. *Stems* up to 1m. and more long, with the apical 30cm. densely foliate, 5cm. diam., erect or divergent, sometimes procumbent with shoots at random forming dense groups of up to 2—4m. across.

Leaves about 24, densely rosulate, lanceolate-attenuate, spreading to recurved, averaging 25cm. long, 8—9cm. broad near base; *upper surface* unicoloured olive-green with reddish tinge, slightly glossy, flat low down, slightly channelled upwards, without spots or markings; *lower surface* convex, otherwise as the upper surface; *margins* sinuate-dentate, armed with firm to horny, pungent, reddish-brown, deltoid teeth, 4—5mm. long, about 10mm. distant.

Inflorescence a 2—4-branched panicle, usually produced laterally, sometimes 2 consecutively, averaging 65cm. high.

Peduncle basally flattened and 20—25mm. broad, arising laterally about 15cm. below the centre of the rosette, arcuate-ascending, averaging 2—4-branched from the middle or lower, the lowest branch subtended at base by a large ovate-acute, thin, subscarious, many-nerved bract about 40mm. long, 35mm. broad, the main axis below the terminal raceme

FIG. 364.

A. babatiensis Christian et Verdoorn. On the Mbulu Highlands, 1 mile S of Endalaghanet, 34 miles W of Babati, Northern Prov., Tanzania (Tanganyika), at approx. 4° 04′ S., 35° 23′ E., alt. 6,900 ft. Height 7 feet.

clothed with several conspicuous broadly ovate-acute, somewhat fleshy, many-nerved sterile bracts, up to 25mm. long, 18mm. broad at base.

Racemes cylindric-acuminate, subdensely flowered, the terminal averaging 20—25cm. long, 10cm. diam., the buds greenish tipped and hidden by large, fleshy, densely imbricate bracts, gradually slightly laxer downwards with the open flowers nutant to subpendulous.

Bracts rather pinkish, broadly ovate-acute, the lowest up to 30mm. long, 15mm. broad, fleshy, thinner at the edges, about 7—9-nerved.

Pedicels 20—25mm. long.

Perianth cylindric, very slightly clavate, salmon-pink, 38—40mm. long, 7—8mm. diam. across the ovary, thence exceedingly slightly narrowed above the ovary, a little decurved and enlarging to the throat, the mouth open; *outer segments* free for 8—10mm., very obscurely nerved, pale-brownish at the subacute slightly spreading apices; *inner segments* broader than the outer, with thinner paler edges and more obtuse, more spreading apices.

Filaments palelemon, filiform-flattened, with the 3 inner and 3 outer *anthers* in turn exserted 0—1mm.; *stigma* at length exserted 1—2mm.; *ovary* green, 7mm. long, 3mm. broad. (Figs. 364, 365).

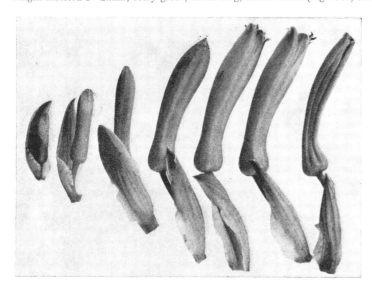

FIG. 365.

A. babatiensis Christian et Verdoorn. Flowers 1/1 from bud to post-pollination stages.

TANZANIA (TANGANYIKA). *Northern Prov.*: Coll. Pole Evans & Erens, Sept. 1938, about 35 miles NW of Babati on road to Ngorongoro Crater, cult. Ewanrigg, fl. 16 Sept. 1946, Pole Evans & Erens 872, Christian 985 in Nat. Herb. No. 28489 holotype (PRE), isotype (SRGH); 1 mile S of Endalaghanet, 34 miles W of Babati on road to Dongobesh and Mbulu, c. 4° 04′ S, 35° 23′ E, alt. 6900 ft., fl. 22 Sept. 1954, Reynolds 7523 (PRE, K, EA); plant ex Ewanrigg, fl. 30 Sept. 1950, R. C. Munch, 32420 in GHS (SRGH).

TYPE LOCALITY: *A. babatiensis* is not known anywhere near Babati, which is between Dodoma and Arusha, on the main north road to Kenya. Plants were first collected by Dr. I. B. Pole Evans and Mr. J. Erens in 1938, about 35 miles W of Babati on the track leading up to Mbulu and the Ngorongoro Crater. This is N of Mt. Hanang on the Mbulu highlands, at about 6,800—7,000 ft.

DISTRIBUTION: As far as is known, *A. babatiensis* appears to be restricted to the Mbulu highlands. It occurs at the northern end of the Mbulu highlands, 24 miles N of Mbulu, at 5,600 ft.; it grows abundantly 5 miles N to 1 mile S of Endalaghanet (Nar, Bashanet), about 35 miles W of Babati, and along the road southwestwards from Nar towards Ufana on the track to Singida.

NATIVE NAME: *Karangheri* in the Mbulu tongue of the Mbulu tribe.

A. babatiensis is a shrub with stem 1m. and more long forming dense patches 2—4m. across. The leaves are olive-green and somewhat glossy. The inflorescence is characterized by having remarkably large bracts which reach 30mm. long, 15mm. broad and hide the pedicels. The apical buds are at first hidden by densely imbricate bracts, while the axis below the racemes is clothed with several conspicuous sterile-bracts.

139. **A. elgonica** Bullock in *Kew Bull.* 503 (1932).

DESCRIPTION based on many flowering plants beyond Endebess, on Mt. Elgon, Kenya.

Plants of shrubby growth, forming small to large patches, sometimes a few metres across. *Stems* erect, short or up to 1m. or more long, the apical 30cm. usually densely foliate.

Leaves 20—24, rosulate, compactly arcuate-ascending, recurved near apex, up to 40cm. long, 9cm. broad at base; *upper surface* flat to slightly canaliculate, deep green, sometimes reddish-tinged, usually without spots; *lower surface* convex, of similar colour to upper surface; *margins* sinuate-dentate, armed with stout, pungent, prominent, deltoid teeth which reach 8—9mm. long, 10—15mm. apart at middle of leaf, smaller towards base and apex. *Sap* dries yellow.

Inflorescence 50—70cm. tall, varying from simple to 3—4-branched.

Peduncle basally plano-convex and 15mm. broad, terete upwards, brown and very minutely white-speckled, usually compactly 3—4-branched from the middle.

Racemes cylindric-conic, the terminal up to 18cm. long, 8—9cm. diam., the laterals shorter, densely flowered, youngest buds greenish-tipped, suberect, older buds spreading, open flowers subpendulous.

Bracts small, ovate-acute, 5mm. long, 4mm. broad, thin, scarious, dirty-white, 3-nerved.

Pedicels 20—25mm. long, suberect, nutant at apex.

Perianth orange-scarlet, paler at mouth, averaging 40mm. long, cylindric-trigonous, slightly obtusely tapering to the pedicel and shortly stipitate, cylindric and 7—8mm. diam. across the ovary, thence slightly narrowed on the underside and trigonous upwards, the mouth wide open; *outer segments* free for 15mm. (a definite tube to beyond the middle), obscurely 3-nerved, the apices subacute, spreading; *inner segments* free but dorsally adnate to the outer to the middle, broader than the outer, with broad white border, orange keeled, apices more obtuse and more spreading than the outer.

Filaments pale lemon, the 3 inner narrower and lengthening before the 3 outer with their *anthers* in turn exserted 2—3mm.; *style* lemon-yellow, with *stigma* at length exserted 4—5mm.; *ovary* yellow-green, 5mm. long, 3mm. diam.; *capsule* 19mm. long, 10mm. diam. (Plate 81, Figs. 366–367).

FIG. 366.

A. elgonica Bullock. Typical rosette showing size of marginal teeth. – From a plant on Mt. Elgon, Kenya.

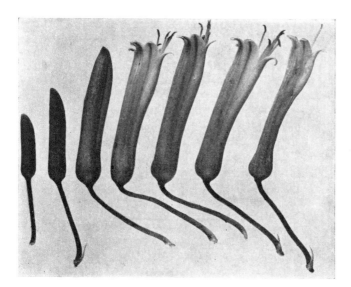

FIG. 367.

A. elgonica Bullock. Flowers natural size.

PLATE 81

ALOE ELGONICA   Bullock.

On slopes of Mount Elgon, above "Mutamayo", near Endebess, Kenya.
Alt. 7,800 ft. Height 1·20m.

KENYA. Mt. Elgon, 6,500,—7,500 ft., erect to 4 ft., flowers orange-scarlet, Dec. 1930, Major E. J. Lugard, n. 299, holotype (K); NE slopes of Mt. Elgon, above "Mutamayo", c. 1° 10′ N, 34° 44′ E, alt. 7,800 ft., 25 Oct. 1955, Reynolds 8003 (K, PRE, EA); Mt. Elgon, Aug. 1962, Tweedie 2406 (EA)—an excellent specimen; Turbo, Mrs. Boyds Hill (27 miles S of Kitale), 11 April 1943, Bally 5024 (G, EA); on rocks near Kipkarren River Bridge, 11 miles SE of Eldoret on road to Kapsabet, 11 Aug. 1954, Reynolds 7522 (K, PRE).

A. elgonica is a striking species with arcuate-ascending leaves forming compact rosettes, sometimes in patches a few yards again. A striking character is the remarkably large marginal teeth which often reach 9mm. long at the middle of the leaf, and 10—15mm. apart, becoming smaller towards base and apex. This is by far the largest marginal teeth of all the shrubs.

Plants vary from groups with shorter stems to others with stems 1m. and more long. Sometimes stems are slender, creeping and rooting with shoots at random forming hemispherical groups, the central plants being supported and with stems 2—3 ft. high, the outer plants smaller and more or less with short procumbent stems.

DISTRIBUTION: Slopes of Mt. Elgon, 6 miles NW of Eldoret, 20 miles NW of Eldoret, 11 miles SW of Eldoret on Kapsabet road.

HYBRID: Crosses of *A. elgonica* with *A. lateritia* were seen near the Kipuyon River road bridge on the Elgon link road, near Kitale.

140. **A. flexilifolia** Christian in *Journ. S.A. Bot.* 8: 167 (1942).

DESCRIPTION based on many plants flowering at the type locality, Kongei, W. Usambaras, Tanzania (Tanganyika).

Plant shrubby, much branched from base, forming groups sometimes 2m. across. *Stems* 60—100cm. long, 6—7cm. diam. when erect or suberect in deep soils, slender (5cm.) and 1—2m. long when in scanty soils and overhanging rock faces, the stems sublaxly foliate in apical 30cm.

Leaves rosulate, ensiform, long-pointed, the youngest suberectly spreading, the oldest spreading to recurved or somewhat falcately decurved when stems hang downwards, averaging 50cm. long, 6—7cm. broad, about 10mm. thick; *upper surface* flat low down, slightly canaliculate upwards, unicoloured glaucous-green with slight bluish tinge, without spots except sometimes when young, the spots disappearing with age; *lower surface* convex, sometimes (not always) with a few transverse folds or grooves near base; *margins* with narrow, pale, cartilaginous edge armed with small, brownish deltoid teeth, 1—2mm. long, and 10—20mm. apart, the interspaces straight. *Sap* dries brownish.

Inflorescence a branched panicle, 50—65cm. tall, usually produced sub-obliquely.

Peduncle basally plano-convex and 12mm. broad, rather divaricately 6—8-branched from below the middle, when suberect the branches arcuate-ascending, when on a hanging stem the peduncle at first somewhat recurved then arcuate-ascending.

Racemes cylindric, subdensely flowered, the terminal about 12cm. long, 7—8cm. diam., the lateral shorter and more capitate, youngest buds grey-green tipped, suberectly spreading, open flowers nutant.

Bracts ovate-deltoid, the lowest 5—6mm. long, 3mm. broad, thin, dry, whitish, 5-nerved.

Pedicels 12—14mm. long, obliquely spreading.

Perianth scarlet or brownish-red, paler at mouth, cylindric, 33—35mm. long, 9mm. diam. across the ovary, slightly constricted above the ovary and again slightly enlarging, the mouth open; *outer segments* free for 10mm., obscurely 3-nerved, apices subacute slightly spreading; *inner segments* broader than the outer and with more obtuse, more spread-apices.

Anthers the 3 inner and 3 outer in turn exserted 2—3mm.; *stigma* at length exserted 4mm.; *ovary* pale green, 6mm, long, 3mm. diam. (Plate 82, Figs. 368, 369).

TANZANIA (TANGANYIKA). Western Usambaras, Soni Dist.: Kongei, coll. Col. M. T. Boscawen, cult. Ewanrigg, fl. May 1940, Christian 897 holotype (SRGH), isotype (PRE, EA); rocky cliffs, Kongei–Gare road, 5,500 ft., panicle geotropic, 6 June 1942, P. J. Greenway 6464 (PRE, EA); above Soni, 4 April 1942, Bally 10577 (G, EA); half-mile NE of Vuga turn-off, 1000m., 14 June 1953, Drummond et Hemseley 2909 (K, EA, PRE); Zevingambo, 2 miles NW of Mlab, 1800m., on top of outcropping rocks and ledges on large cliff faces, 18 June 1953, Drummond et Hemsley 2944 (K, PRE); on rocks at Kongei, 5 miles NE of Soni on Gare road (type locality), 4,000 ft., 2 July 1958, Reynolds 8756 (PRE, K, EA).

A. flexilifolia is not known away from the Western Usambaras where it is found in several localities where outcropping rocky ledges and sheer faces occur. The species was so named because, in the type plant cultivated at Mr. Christian's magnificent gardens at Ewanrigg near Salisbury, the lower leaves were deflexed near base causing some transverse folds on lower surface near base.

When the present author visited the type locality he found that this leaf-folding occurred in some plants but not in all, and it is not a fixed character.

There are two noteworthy forms of *A. flexilifolia*:

1. Well-branched plants in scanty soil, overhanging sheer faces or rock ledges produce more slender stems 1m. and more long; leaves are more falcately decurved, and the inflorescence may be somewhat so-called geotropic, i.e. the peduncle at first points downwards with the branches arcuate-ascending.

2. Plants growing in flatter places in deeper soils produce thicker, shorter, erect or suberect stems supporting the weight of the leaves without falling over; leaves are more spreading and slightly recurved; the divaricately-branched inflorescence is produced somewhat obliquely, with the branches arcuate-ascending.

PLATE 82

ALOE FLEXILIFOLIA   Christian.

At the type locality Kongei, Soni Dist., W. Usambaras, Tanzania
(Tanganyika).—A small plant, height 1m.

FIG. 368.

A. flexilifolia Christian. Overhanging rocky ledges at Kongei, 5 miles NE of Soni on road to Gare, Lushoto District, Western Usambaras, Tanga Prov., Tanzania (Tanganyika). Alt. 4,000 ft.

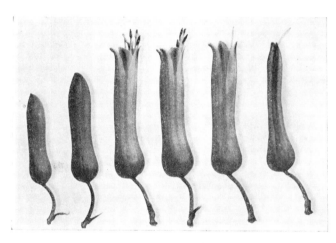

FIG. 369.

A. flexilifolia Christian. Flowers natural size.

141. **A. boscawenii** Christian in *Journn. S.A. Bot.* 8: 165 (1942).

DESCRIPTION by the late Mr. H. B. Christian.

Plants fruticose, branched from the base. *Stems* up to 1m. high and 5—7cm. diam., laxly foliate.

Leaves light green, immaculate, the younger erect-spreading, slightly recurved, the older spreading-recurved, ovate-lanceolate, 44 to 50cm. long, 8cm. broad at the base, the upper surface channelled, striate, the lower surface rounded; *margins* with a narrow cartilaginous line armed with brown-tipped, deltoid, spreading, pungent teeth, 2mm. long low down, 3mm. long above, 7mm. apart above the base, 18mm. apart towards the apex, interspaces straight, the teeth occasionally bifid.

Inflorescence erect, branched from above the middle, c. 90cm. high.

Peduncle brownish-green, laterally compressed, with a distinct rib on each side, 2cm. diam. on the long axis low down.

Bracts subtending the lowest branch deltoid-acute, 10mm. long, 10mm. broad at the base, 10-nerved, scarious.

Branches 5—7, the lower erect-spreading, usually sub-branched, 7mm. diam., the upper arcuate-spreading, shorter than the terminal, usually with one sterile bract.

Racemes cylindric, rounded at the apex, 10—12cm. long, 7cm. diam. rather lax below dense above usually with 2—3 flowers at some distance below the raceme, the buds erect-spreading, dull soft green gradually changing to yellow the mature flowers sub-pendulous.

Floral bracts long-acuminate, 7mm. long, 3mm. broad at the base, 3-nerved, scarious.

Pedicels green, erect-spreading, those of the mature flowers sub-cernuous, 18mm. long.

Perianth cylindric, straight, yellow shading to brownish at the apex, stipitate, 30m. long, 9mm. diam. over the ovary, hardly constricted towards the middle, slightly contracted towards the throat, laterally compressed to 7mm. diam.;

outer segments free for 18m., yellow shading to brownish at the apex, 3-nerved, the upper segments straight, the apices sub-acute, slightly spreading, the lower segment curved upwards, hardly spreading at the apices; *inner segments* the same colour as the outer, free to the base, 3-nerved, the apices slightly spreading, sub-obtuse.

Filaments pale yellow, just exserted; *anthers* brown, 3mm. long, at length withdrawn into the perianth; *style* yellow, included or, sometimes, at length exserted; *ovary* pale green, slightly elliptical in outline, 5mm. long, 3mm. diam. (Figs. 370, 371).

TANZANIA (TANGANYIKA). *Tanga Coast:* coll. Col. M. T. Boscawen, fl. Ewanrigg 2 Feb. 1939, Christian 902 holotype (SRGH), isotype (EA, PRE); 8 miles S of Moa, coast near Bomandani, 9 Aug. 1953, Drummond et Hemsley 3679 (EA). *Tanga Dist.,* N of Ngola (sea level), 9 June 1937, Greenway 4956 (EA)—"Leaves ensiform, grey-green, with paler marginal spines. Panicle 3—6-branched, fls. lemon yellow with green tips." Mtotohovu–Makajambi, 200 ft., 8 Dec. 1955, P. J. Greenway 4253 (SRGH). *Tanga Coast:* Greenway 3431, no. 1202 in Herb. Christian (SRGH).

FIG. 370.

A. boscawenii Christian. Plant from the Tanga Coast (without precise locality) Tanzania (Tanganyika), flowering at Ewanrigg, Salisbury Dist., Rhodesia.
Photo: The late Mr. H. B. Christian.

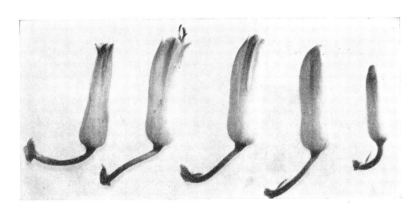

FIG. 371.

A. boscawenii Christian. Flowers natural size.
Photo: The late Mr. H. B. Christian.

"This Aloe is one of a fine collection of Aloes kindly sent to me in 1937 by Col. The Hon. M. T. Boscawen, D.S.O., M.C., of Mtotohovu, Tanga, in whose honour I have much pleasure in naming it. With its striking looking racemes, soft green above, gradually changing to yellow below, as the flowers develop, it is an addition to any Aloe garden and has the further advantage of a long flowering period, throwing up inflorescences at short intervals from early in February into May.

"In habit of growth it is much akin to *A. cameronii* Hemsl., but the leaves are more channelled, not at all glossy, and never change their colour to red or copper in the dry season. The inflorescence bears no resemblance to that of *A. cameronii* which is usually simple, bifurcate, or with 3—4 ascending branches, and the floral characters are entirely different in the two species. The inflorescence of our new sp. is perhaps nearest to that of *A. volkensii* Engl.; the habit is very similar and apart from the difference in colour of the flowers which in *A. volkensii* is red, and the shorter perianth tubes, there is very little difference between the flowers of the two spp. *A. cameronii* and *A. volkensii* only flower once during the season.

"The photograph is of a young plant which was in flower in the garden at Ewanrigg, S. Rhodesia, on 2.2.39." – H. B. Christian.

When the present author visited Col. Boscawen at Mtotohovu (north of Tanga and south of the Kenya border) in 1952, Col. Boscawen said "I sent a lot of different Aloe plants to Basil Christian from along the coast between Tanga and my home, Mtotohovu. I have no idea where I got *A. boscawenii* from, it was somewhere along the coast. I don't even know what my Aloe looks like," he said.

The author did not succeed in finding plants of *A. boscawenii*, but Drummond and Hemsley found it at Bomandani, 8 miles S of Moa, and Dr. Greenway at sea level N of Ngola, both on the Tanga Coast N of Tanga.

The author has no record as to what size mature specimens reach.

142. **A. rabaiensis** Rendle in *Journ. Linn. Soc.* 30: 410 (1895); Baker in Th. Dyer *Fl. Trop. Afr.* 7: 458 (1898); Berger in Engler's *Pflanzenr.* Liliac.–Aloin. 245 (1908).
—— *A. ngongensis* Christian in *Journ. S.A. Bot.* 8: 170 (1942).

Plants forming small to large shrubs with shorter stems when at edge of bush, reaching 1—2m. tall when supported in bush, the apical 30cm. of stems subdensely foliate.

Leaves suberectly spreading to slightly recurved, narrowly lanceolate-attenuate, up to 45cm. long, 8cm. broad; *upper surface* grey-green, mostly unspotted, flat low down, slightly channelled upwards; *lower surface* convex, same colour as upper surface; *margins* armed with brownish deltoid teeth, 4mm. long, more crowded low down (5—10mm. distant), more distant upwards (10—15mm. apart).

Inflorescence a branched panicle 60cm. high.

Peduncle basally plano-convex and 14mm. broad, about 6-branched from the middle upwards, the lowest branch subtended at base by a shortly-ovate thin, dry, 7-nerved bract, 10mm. long, 5mm. broad.

Racemes capitate, round-topped, the terminal 8cm. long, 8cm. diam., subdensely many-flowered.

Bracts deltoid, long-pointed, 7mm. long, 3mm. broad at base, thin, dry, 3—5-nerved.

Pedicels slender, 18mm. long, the colour of the perianth.

Perianth scarlet, sometimes slightly glossy, and sometimes minutely white-spotted, 32mm. long, basally obconic, 8mm. across the ovary, thence somewhat narrowed on the underside and slightly decurved, thence trigonal to the mouth; *outer segments* free for 9mm., paler at the margins, 3-nerved to base, the apices slightly spreading; *inner segments* themselves free but dorsally adnate to the outer for about 22mm., broader than the outer, with broad whitish border, with a keel in median line, and with more obtuse, more spreading apices.

Filaments filiform-flattened, the 3 inner narrower and lengthening before the 3 outer, with their *anthers* in turn exserted 2—3mm.; *stigma* at length exserted 4—5mm.; *ovary* pale olive-green, 6—7mm. long, 3mm. diam., finely 6-grooved. (Plate 83, Fig. 372).

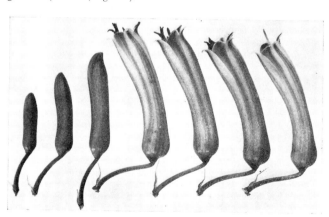

Fig. 372.

A. rabaiensis Rendle. Flowers 1/1 from the Plate 83 plant.

PLATE 83

ALOE RABAIENSIS   Rendle.

Near Langata, 6 miles SW of Nairobi, Kenya. Alt. 5,300 ft.

(*Note:* The brownish tinge on some leaves is road dust.)

KENYA. Mgandini, Rabai Hills, Mombasa, Sept. 1885, Rev. W. E. Taylor! holotype (BM); Ngong, 12 miles SW of Nairobi, coll. I. B. Pole Evans et J. Erens, Sept. 1938, fl. at Ewanrigg, 14 April 1941, Pole Evans et Erens 1129, (SRGH, PRE); near Langata entrance to R.N.N. Park, in bush, 6 miles S of Nairobi, 6 May 1952, Reynolds 6619 (PRE); same loc. fl. 9 Oct. 1955, Reynolds 7930 (K, PRE, EA); near Tiwi, 20 miles S of Mombasa, 12 July 1960, Leach et Bayliss 10230 (SRGH).

TANZANIA (TANGANYIKA). Between Oldeani and Lake Eyasi, 4,800 ft., 23 July 1957, Bally 11582 (K, EA), might belong here.

SOMALIA SOUTH. 3 miles W of Beles Cogani, alt. 400 ft., 26 Jan. 1954, Bally 9501 (K, EA). *Note:* This locality is 89 miles NW of Kismayu on road to Garissa in Kenya.

DISTRIBUTION

The type locality Mgandini (now a native school) is 3 miles beyond Rabai which was an old Mission Station 15 miles westwards from Nairobi on the old road, not far from the present Mariakani railway station.

A. rabaiensis occurs 10 miles WNW of Mariakani to near Mackinnon Road, near Voi, on the Lukenya Hills, near Nairobi and Ngong. Up the coast N of Mombasa it grows at Bamba, 25 miles W of Kilifi, and 45—55 miles N of Malindi, between Garsen Ferry (Tana River) and Witu. On the Nairobi–Fort Hall–Carissa road what appears to be *A. rabaiensis* was seen (not flowering – hence uncertain) at Molo, 87 miles E of Thika, and at another locality about 100 miles W of Garissa.

Much further on, across the border in Somalia South, *A. rabaiensis* grows 3 miles W of Beles Cogani (89 miles NW of Kismayu) in association with *A. microdonta* Chiov., and crosses are not infrequent; also grows 47 miles E of Liboi.

On the road from Mombasa down to Tanga, *A. rabaiensis* is found at mile 75.

In Tanzania, Mr. P. R. O. Bally reports it between Oldeani and Lake Eyasi, which lies S of the Ngorongoro Crater.

DISTINGUISHING CHARACTERS

From all the East African shrubby Aloes, *A. rabaiensis* is distinguished by having capitate round-topped, somewhat subglobose, rather densely-flowered racemes. The inflorescence averages 6-branched and 60cm. high. Stems are shorter when plants grow at the edge of bush, but reach 2m. when supported in dense bush. Stems may be erect, oblique, or fallen and re-rooted with shoots at random forming small to large dense patches.

A. yavellana Reynolds near Mega and Yavello in Borana, S. Ethiopia is a near ally with its capitate racemes, but the racemes are much smaller, pedicels and flowers are shorter, the leaf basal sheaths are visible and striate, while the colour of the leaves is bronze-brown.

143. **A. dawei** Berger in *Notizblatt Berl. Bot. Gart.* 4: 246 (1906), in Engler's *Pflanzenr.* Liliac.–Aloin. 251 (1908); Reynolds in *Journ. S.A. Bot.* 20: 1173 (1954).
—— *A. beniensis* De Wild. in *Plant. Bequaert.* 1: 25 (1921).
—— *A. pole-evansii* Christian in *Fl. Plants S. Afr.* 20: Plate 782 (1940).

DESCRIPTION based on the species as a whole, from personal observations over a wide area.

Plant succulent, forming small to large shrubs, sometimes several metres across. *Stem* 6—8cm. diam., 1—2m. long, erect or divergent, sublaxly foliate in upper half, the apical 30cm. subdensely foliate, old dried leaves persistent below.

Leaves about 16—20, rosulate at apex of stems, basally sheathing and laxer downwards, 40—60cm. long, 6—9cm. broad at base, gradually tapering to the apex, youngest leaves suberectly spreading, older leaves spreading to recurved; *upper surface* flat low down, canaliculate upwards, olive-green to deep-green, sometimes reddish tinged, usually without spots; *lower surface* convex, similar in colour to upper surface and mostly without dull white spots; *margins* sinuate-dentate, armed with deltoid, pungent, reddish-brown teeth averaging 3—4mm. long (sometimes 5mm.), 10—15mm. distant, the interspaces usually rounded. *Sap* dries yellow.

Inflorescence an erect branched panicle 60—90cm. high.

Peduncle brown, plano-convex and 20—25mm. broad at base, slenderer and terete upwards, 5—8-branched from about the middle, the lowest branch subtended at base by a broadly ovate-cuspidate bract 12—15mm. broad, 6mm. long, thin, scarious, with several nerves.

Racemes subdensely flowered, mostly broadly cylindric-conical, the terminal averaging 10—15cm. long, 8cm. diam., the lateral usually a little shorter, the youngest buds denser, suberect, grey-green tipped, older buds spreading, open flowers slightly laxer, subpendulous.

Bracts ovate-acute, thin, scarious, averaging 4mm. long, 3—5mm. broad at base, 3-nerved.

Pedicels averaging 14mm., the colour of the perianth.

Perianth dull scarlet to bright reddish-scarlet, paler at mouth, often minutely white-spotted throughout, cylindric-trigonous, averaging 33—35mm. long, obtusely tapering at base to the articulation, cylindric and 8mm. diam. across the ovary, thence trigonous and slightly narrowed on underside only, the mouth open; *outer segments* free for 12mm., paler at the edges, 3-nerved, the apices straight, subacute; *outer segments* free but dorsally adnate to the outer for two-thirds their length, broader than the outer, with 3 congested nerves forming a scarlet keel, the apices brownish-tipped, broader, more obtuse and more spreading than the outer.

Filaments lemon, filiform-flattened, the 3 inner narrower and lengthening before the 3 outer with their *anthers* in turn exserted 3—5mm.; *style* yellow; *stigma* at length exserted 4—6mm.; *ovary* yellowish-green, 6mm. long, 3·5mm. diam. (Plate 84, Figs. 373–375).

UGANDA. Buganda, Mengo, near Lake Victoria, Old Entebbe, alt. 3,850 ft., fl. 3 Aug. 1954, Reynolds 7510 (PRE, K, EA); near Entebbe Airport, 3 Aug. 1954, Reynolds 7511, Lectotype (PRE) syntypes (K, EA).

KENYA. Hills 6 miles NW of Kisumu, coll. Pole Evans et Erens, 7 Aug. 1938, cult. D.O.B., Pretoria, fl. 23 March 1940, Pole Evans et Erens 1650—as type of *A. pole-evansii* (PRE); 5 miles NW of Kisumu on Yala road, 3,850 ft., 8 Aug. 1954, Reynolds 7513 (K, PRE, EA); 8 miles NW of Kisumu, 8 Aug. 1954, Reynolds 7515 (PRE, K, EA); Kisumu, Sept. 1964, Tweedie 2458 (EA).

CONGO (LEO). Coll. F. L. Hendrickx near Nyanza, Ruanda, cult. INEAC Station Mulungu, fl. 18 June 1954, Reynolds 7263 (PRE, K, BR). *Kivu Prov.:* Nord Kivu Dist., Semliki River Valley, cult. Kalindabwiki Village, 4 miles SE of Beni, alt. 4,300 ft., fl. 28 June 1954, Reynolds 7274 (PRE, K, BR); Between Beni and Kasindi, 11 Aug. 1914, J. Bequaert 5255 (BR) as *A. beniensis* De Wild. *Oriental Prov.*, Kibali-Ituri Dist., near Marabu, 10 miles east of Irumu, 3,100 ft., fl. 2 July 1954, Reynolds 7279 (PRE, K, BR).

FIG. 373.   FIG. 374.

A. dawei Berger.

FIG. 373. Plants from the Semliki Valley, cultivated at native village Kalindabwiki, 4 miles SE of Beni, Kivu Province, Congo (Leo). Height 6 feet.

FIG. 374. Plants from near Nyanza, Ruanda, cultivated at INEAC station Mulungu, near Bukavu, Congo.

FIG. 375.

A. dawei Berger. Flowers 1/1 from a plant near Old Entebbe, Uganda.

PLATE 84

ALOE DAWEI   Berger.

Plants 6 miles NW of Kisumu, Kenya. Height 6 feet.   Near Entebbe Airport, Uganda—Young plant.

Type locality: Berger states: "Widely distributed for 100 miles around Entebbe at 1250m.—1660m., flowering in the rainless time from January to March and June to September." He states that Mr. Dawe (at that time Curator of the Botanical Gardens at Entebbe) sent Herbarium specimens, living plants and seeds to him in 1905. Berger cites no type material, there is none at Berlin, and none has been traced elsewhere. A lectotype has therefore been proposed, i.e. Reynolds 7511. Since no type material or figures were available the author specially visited Entebbe in 1952 and 1954 for the express purpose of studying *A. dawei* at its type locality, and to describe it more fully, and illustrate it.

DISTRIBUTION

UGANDA, Buganda, Mengo, near Entebbe, near the Airport, at Old Entebbe, Hippo Bay, all near Lake Victoria at about 3,850 ft.; hills near Jinja; Ankole, south bank of the Kazinga Channel, opposite the Mweya Safari Lodge, Queen Elizabeth National Park.

KENYA: Plentiful along the foot of the Nandi Escarpment, 2—5 miles NE of Kisumu on road to Kakamega; abundant for 8 miles NW of Kisumu along the road to Yala. Flowers July–August.

RUANDA: Near Nyanza, about 28 miles N of Astrida; between Kigali–Kakitumba, near Gabiro.

CONGO (LEO): *South Kivu Dist.*, about 4 miles N of Uvira, near Kavimvira and Lake Tanganyika, alt. 2,650 ft.; Kabe, near Lake Kivu. *Kivu-North Dist.*, Kashero Village, on volcanic rocks near edge of Lake Kivu, 4 miles W of Goma, 4,780 ft.; in the Semliki Valley, SE of Beni, also in the Parc National Albert on the Congo–Uganda border. *Eastern Province: Kibali-Ituri Dist.*, in the Ituri forest between Beni and Irumu; on Mbeye Hill, 6 miles N of Irumu; near Marabu, 10 miles E of Irumu, at about 3,000 ft.

When growing in small groups, stems average 1m. and are erect. When in large thickets, stems reach 2m. and more, especially when supported by bushes. Leaves of young shoots may be copiously white-spotted, the spots usually disappearing with age. Flowers vary little in colour, but the perianth which is thick and somewhat fleshy varies from copiously and very minutely white-spotted to not at all spotted, both forms being found in the same area. Length of perianth varies from 30mm. in weak forms to 40mm. in robust forms, about 33—35mm. being the average.

A. dawei and *A. nyeriensis* appear to be closely related, but the latter is a larger taller plant, with slenderer stems which become thicker from base upwards, with larger leaves, a green peduncle, and slightly less fleshy, longer flowers.

NATIVE NAMES

KENYA: "*Tangaratwet*" in the Nandi tongue of the Nilo-Hamitic Nandi tribe, near Kisumu. Frequently seen planted in rows demarcating fields, especially near Kisumu.

UGANDA: "*Kakarutanga*" in the Lutoro tongue of the Batoro tribe of Toro, Western Province.

CONGO (LEO): "*Kokorutanga*" in the Kinyoro tongue of the Banyoro, also in the Kihema tongue of the Bahema who are descended from the Banyoro of Uganda. Near Irumu, *A. dawei* was seen around the flagpole in a chief's village.

144. **A. gossweileri** Reynolds in *Journ. S.A. Bot.* 28: 205 (1962).

DESCRIPTION: A shrub forming thickets, with stems averaging 1—1·5m. long, 3—4cm. diam., branched from base (not higher), ascending or divergent, the apical 10—20cm. subdensely foliate.

Leaves about 16, rosulate at apex of stem, averaging 30cm. long, 5cm. broad at base and gradually attenuate, spreading to slightly recurved; *upper surface* canaliculate, green, mostly without spots or markings; *lower surface* green, rounded; *margins* armed with deltoid teeth up to 3—4mm. long, 15mm. apart.

Inflorescence a divaricately 6—8-branched pyramidal panicle averaging 40—50cm. tall.

Peduncle basally flattened and 10—12mm. broad, divaricately branched well below the middle, the branches spreading to almost horizontal.

Racemes 10—15cm. long, 5—6cm. broad, the terminal the longest, the flowers subsecund, buds grey-green tipped, open flowers scarlet.

Bracts ovate-acute, 3mm. long, 2mm. broad, thin, subscarious, 3—5-nerved.

Pedicels 10mm. long.

Perianth scarlet, paler at mouth, 30mm. long, basally slightly rounded, 6mm. diam. across the ovary, very slightly narrowed above the ovary, thence very slightly enlarging to the throat, the mouth trigonal; *outer segments* free for

10—12mm., obscurely 3-nerved, paler at margins, the apices subacute, slightly spreading; *inner segments* broader than the outer, with 3 crowded nerves forming a scarlet keel, the apices brownish, more obtuse and more spreading.

Filaments pale lemon, the 3 inner narrower and lengthening before the 3 outer, with their *anthers* in turn exserted 1—2mm.; *stigma* at length exserted 2—3mm.; *ovary* very pale brown, 4mm. long, 2·5mm. diam. (Figs. 376–378).

ANGOLA. *Cuanza Sul Dist.,* Seles, 7 miles SE of Vila Nova de Seles, c. 11° 28′ S, 14° 24′ E, on rocks at 3,400 ft. alt., fl. 15 July 1961 at Mbabane, Swaziland, Reynolds 9760 holotype (PRE); Fl. again 7 July 1964, Reynolds 9760A (K, LISC); Vila Nova de Seles, alt. 1,100m., March 1930, Gossweiler 13313 (LUA). A note on this sheet reads, "Stem erect, undivided, up to 2m. high. Corolla copper-red, lasting only two days. The photo no. 73 of the *Carta Fitogeografica de Angola* represents this species in its rocky, more exposed situation at Nova Seles. Flowers in March." A note in Gossweiler's hand on a sheet of Gossweiler 13313 at LISC reads: "These inflorescences were collected by me in March 1941 from plants cultivated in garden in Luanda."

FIG. 376.   FIG. 377.

A. gossweileri Reynolds.

FIG. 376. Plants with dry dehisced capsules, at the type locality, 7 miles SE of Vila Nova de Seles, Cuanza Sul, Benguela Dist., Angola, approx. 11° 28′ S., 14° 24′ E. On rocks at 3,400 ft.

FIG. 377. Flowering branch × 1/10 approx., cult. Mbabane, Swaziland – Collected at type locality.

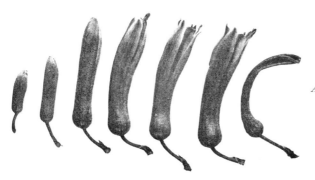

FIG. 378.

A. gossweileri Reynolds. Flowers natural size.

This distinctive species was named after the late Mr. John Gossweiler who collected very extensively throughout Angola, and who discovered it in 1930. Gossweiler's *Carta Fitogeografica de Angola* (1939) is an outstanding contribution to the botany of Angola. Photo 73, at p. 204, depicts a group of shrubby Aloes, without flowers, with the legend "Aloe (angolensis?)" but it is not that species.

In the wild state, plants form thickets sometimes several yards across; stems average 1—1·5m. in length, and are branched at ground level, not higher up. An outstanding character is the divaricately branched pyramidal inflorescence with almost horizontal racemes with subsecund flowers.

A. gossweileri grows in numbers on several rocky hills near Vila Nova de Seles, and also near Amboiva about 35 miles to the east. Further south, plants were found near Bocoio about 50 miles E of Lobito, c. 12° 30′ S, 14° 08′ E, alt. c. 2,800 ft.

A. gossweileri appears to be nearest allied to *A. palmiformis* Bak. near Sá da Bandeira in Huila District, but it differs chiefly in having a more branched inflorescence with oblique racemes and subsecund flowers. In *A. palmiformis* the inflorescence is only 1—2-branched, the racemes being erect and twice as long.

145. **A. catengiana** Reynolds in *Kirkia* 1: 160, Feb. (1961).

DESCRIPTION. *Plant* shrubby, forming thickets 1—2m. and more across. *Stems* slender, simple or branched low down, averaging 1·5—2m. long (sometimes 3m. and more when supported in bushes), ascending, divergent or sprawling, the apical 30cm. sublaxly foliate, the sheathing leaf bases lineate and 15—20mm. apart.

Leaves 16—20, narrowly lanceolate-attenuate, averaging 30cm. long, 3·5cm. broad, spreading to deflexed near base; *upper surface* pale yellowish grey-green (near Light Cress Green RCS XXXI), flat low down, slightly canaliculate upwards, with numerous very pale green lenticular spots in lower half, fewer and more scattered upwards; *lower surface*

FIG. 379.

A. catengiana Reynolds. Plants collected at Catengue, 60 miles SE of Benguela, Angola, flowering in the author's garden. Height 5 feet.

convex, similar in colour, with numerous very pale-green lenticular spots throughout, more numerous and crowded low down, more scattered upwards; *margins* with firm, pale, deltoid, reddish brown-tipped teeth about 3mm. long, 8—10mm. apart.

Inflorescence slender, a branched panicle 40cm. tall, erectly or sub-erectly produced.

Peduncle green, plano-convex and 8mm. broad at base, divaricately about 6-branched from the middle or lower, the lowest branch subtended at base by a narrowly deltoid, scarious, many-nerved bract about 25mm. long, 7mm. broad.

Racemes cylindric-acuminate, rather laxly flowered, the terminal the longest, 16cm. long, 4cm. diam., the lateral shorter, oblique, with the flowers subsecund.

Pedicels 10mm. long.

Bracts ovate-acute, thin, scarious, many-nerved, 5mm. long, 3mm. broad.

Perianth dull scarlet, cylindric, slightly decurved, 28mm. long, 7mm. diam. across the ovary, very slightly narrowed above the ovary, thence slightly enlarging to the throat; *outer segments* free for 10mm., paler at the edges, obscurely 3-nerved, the apices subacute and slightly spreading; *inner segments* broader than the outer, the apices more obtuse and slightly more spreading.

Filaments pale-lemon, the 3 inner narrower and lengthening before the 3 outer with their *anthers* in turn exserted 1—2mm.; *stigma* at length exserted 2mm.; *ovary* green, 6mm. long, 3mm. diam. (Figs. 379, 380).

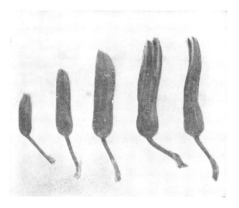

Fig. 380.

A. catengiana Reynolds. Flowers natural size.

ANGOLA. *Benguela Dist.*, at Catengue, 60 miles SE of Benguela, c. 13° S, 13° 45′ E, alt. c. 1,700 ft., cult. Bryanston, Johannesburg, fl. 17 July 1960, Reynolds 9307, holotype (PRE), isotype (K).

This distinctive species was found by the late Dr. N. R. Smuts and the author just east of Catengue Railway Station, which is about 60 miles SE of Benguela, in hot, arid bush country, in association with *Adansonia digitata*, *Adenium boehmianum*, *Aloe littoralis*, *Euphorbia spp.*, etc., at 1,700 ft. alt.

A. catengiana forms dense thickets of more or less tangled stems in patches 3m. and more across. Stems are slender, and leaves are of a peculiar pale yellowish grey-green colour and are usually copiously spotted on both surfaces. The inflorescence is slender and divaricately branched. Racemes vary from the terminal erect with flowers evenly distributed around the axis, to oblique when flowers are somewhat secund.

The late Dr. Gossweiler collected specimens at Catengue in July, 1940, and queried the species as belonging to *A. palmiformis* Bak. Plants of *A. palmiformis* that the author has seen near the type locality, on a spur of the Serra da Chela, 8 miles SW of Sá da Bandeira, in Huila District, at 6,400 ft. are quite distinct and differ in having much more robust stems, larger green leaves with much larger teeth, a more stout, taller, less-branched inflorescence, and longer pedicels and flowers.

NATIVE NAME: *Okandolle* in the local Umbundu tongue of Catengue – *fide* Gossweiler in *Nomes Indiginas de Plantas de Angola* 491 (1953).

146. **A. kedongensis** Reynolds in *Journ. S.A. Bot.* 19: 4 (1953).

DESCRIPTION: *Plants* succulent, fruticose, forming shrubs varying from 2m. high to dense thickets 3—4m. high and sometimes several metres across. *Stems* slender, spindly, about 4cm. thick, up to 4m. tall, mostly branched from the base, sometimes with few to many shoots produced at random, the terminal 30—60cm. of main stems sublaxly foliate, with the internodes 2—3cm. distant, the sheaths obscurely striate; the apical portion of stems usually with old dried leaves persistent for about 1m., nude downwards.

Leaves dull grey-green to dull yellowish-green, basally sheathing, 3·5cm. broad at base, 30cm. long, gradually narrowing from base to apex, varying from spreading to recurved; *upper surface* canaliculate, *lower surface* rounded; *both surfaces* unspotted except sometimes in young shoots, the spots disappearing with age; *margins* armed with pale, deltoid teeth with reddish-brown apices, the teeth sometimes forward-uncinate and averaging 2—3mm. long, 10mm. distant.

Inflorescence 50cm. tall, 2—4-branched from about the middle, the branches mostly arcuate-ascending.

Peduncle brown with a slight bloom, basally plano-convex and 12—15mm. diam., terete upward, the lowest branch subtended at base by an ovate-cuspidate, thin, scarious, 5-nerved bract, 6mm. long, 12mm. broad at base.

Racemes broadly cylindric-acuminate, the terminal 10—12cm. long, about 8cm. diam., laterals a little smaller.

Bracts ovate-acute, 5mm. long, 5mm. broad at base, thin, scarious, about 3-nerved.

Pedicels 20—25mm. long, the colour of the perianth.

Perianth scarlet, cylindric, slightly trigonous, averaging 35mm. long, shortly stipitate, obtusely tapering into the pedicel, 7mm. diam. over the ovary, thence slightly curved and very slightly constricted on the underside only, the mouth wide open; *outer segments* free for 14mm., paler at their margins, 5-nerved, the apices subacute, spreading; *inner segments* themselves free but dorsally adnate to the outer for 30mm., broader than the outer and with more obtuse, more spreading brownish apices.

Filaments pale-yellow, filiform-flattened, the 3 inner narrower and lengthening in advance of the 3 outer with their *anthers* in turn exserted 2—3mm.; *style* lemon, filiform, with *stigma* at length exserted 4mm.; *ovary* green, 7mm. long, 3mm. diam., finely grooved; *capsule* 22m. long, 9mm. diam., broadly 3-angled. (Plate 85, Figs. 381, 382).

Fig. 381.

A. kedongensis Reynolds. Plants forming dense thickets 10 ft. high, in the Rift Valley, near Lake Naivasha, 6 miles S of Naivasha, Kenya, alt. 6,200 ft.

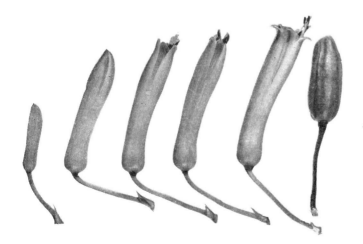

Fig. 382.

A. kedongensis Reynolds. Flowers 1/1 from bud to fruit stage.

PLATE 85

ALOE KEDONGENSIS   Reynolds.

Gilgil Escarpment, 3 miles NW of Gilgil, on Nairobi-Nakuru road,
Kenya; Alt. 6,500 ft. Height 8 feet.

KENYA. Rift Valley near Lake Naivasha, 2 miles S of Lake Hotel, 6 miles S of Naivasha, c. 0° 48′ S, 36° 25′ E, alt. 6,100 ft. fl. 19 April 1952, Reynolds 6546, holotype (PRE), isotype (K, EA); Gilgil Escarpment, 3 miles NW of Gilgil, 19 April 1952, Reynolds 6552 (K, PRE, EA); Gilgil, A. G. McLoughlin 938, Christian 1240, without date, (SRGH); near top of Kedong Escarpment, 24 miles NW of Nairobi, 19 April 1952, Reynolds 6544 (PRE, K); Rift Valley Escarpment near Kijabe, 17 Jan. 1960, Polhill 173 (EA), excellent material; Mt. Margaret, June 1940, Bally 10893 (EA); Narok Dist., roadside near Siyibei Mission, thickets, 6,500 ft., 22 May 1961, Glover, Gwynne and Samuel 1512 (PRE, EA); Siyibei Gorge, Narok Road, March 1940, Bally 11422 (EA).

TANZANIA (TANGANYIKA). West slopes of Kilimanjaro, in rocky river gorge of Ngare Nairobi North River, 5,500 ft., 25 June 1946, P. J. Greenway 7843 (K, BM, EA); same loc. and date, Greenway 7844 (K, BM, PRE, EA); same loc., which is 11 miles N of Sanya Juu, 45 miles NW of Moshi, 6 July 1958, Reynolds 8793 (PRE, K).

A. kedongensis is named after that part of the Kenya portion of the Great Rift which appears to be the specific centre. It occurs in dense bush from near the top to near the foot of the Kedong Escarpment, 24—28 miles NW of Nairobi, also on Mt. Longonot nearby, where Mr. P. R. O. Bally has collected it. At the type locality, which is 2 miles S of the Lake Hotel (6 miles S of Naivasha), near the south-eastern shore of Lake Naivasha, *A. kedongensis* occurs in flatter country in dense masses, sometimes forming untidy impenetrable thickets up to 10 ft. high and several yards across. On dry slopes of volcanic rock near the southern extremity of Lake Naivasha, it is also found in large numbers growing socially with masses of *A. secundiflora* Engler. Although both species were seen in flower (April) no trace of hybrids was found.

A. kedongensis also grows in large numbers on rocky slopes of the Gilgil Escarpment, overlooking Lake Elmenteita, 2—3 miles NW of Gilgil, and was also observed 10 miles S of Nakuru. During the last war Major A. G. McLoughlin sent plants from the Gilgil Escarpment, with photographs to the Division of Botany, Pretoria.

Characters which distinguish *A. kedongensis* from its nearest allies, include slender spindly stems up to 4m. long, and narrow leaves up to 30cm. long, but not exceeding 3·5cm., broad at base, the leaves being unspotted and having small marginal teeth only 2—3mm. long.

A. rabaiensis Rendle, which grows near Mombasa to near Nairobi, differs in having thicker stems, much larger, greyer leaves, and smaller, almost capitate racemes, and could never be confused.

A. nyeriensis Christian, which occurs near Nanyuki and southwards along the Nyeri road has much larger leaves, and much thicker stems which are slenderer near base becoming thicker upwards.

A. dawei Berger, from near Kisumu in Kenya and near Entebbe in Uganda, is a totally different species with thicker stems about 1m. or a little more long, and much larger, different leaves, and having thick fleshy perianths.

Kedong is the Swahili word for the species of *Dracaena* which grows abundantly in the Rift Valley at the foot of the Kedong Escarpment, about 27 miles NW of Nairobi.

147. A. ngobitensis Reynolds in *Journ. S.A. Bot.* 19: 6 (1953).

DESCRIPTION: *Plants* succulent, fruticose, forming shrubs about 2m. high and broad. *Stems* 2m. tall, 4—5cm. diam., mostly branched from base, the terminal portion sublaxly foliate for 30—50cm., the old dried leaves persistent, with the lower half of stems nude.

Leaves 5cm. broad at base, gradually attenuate and 35cm. long, basally sheathing, with the internodes 2—3cm. distant, the sheathing portion obscurely lineate; *upper surface* flat to slightly canaliculate; *lower surface* rounded; *both surfaces* grey-green, without lines or spots except sometimes in young shoots, the spots disappearing with age; *margins* armed with teeth the colour of the leaf at base, paler upwards and pale brown at apex, averaging 3—4mm. long, 8—12mm. distant, the interspaces rounded.

Inflorescence 80cm. high, rather compactly 3—5-branched from about the middle.

Peduncle flattened at base, terete upwards, with the branches slender.

Racemes cylindric-acuminate, the terminal 15cm. long, 7cm. diam., subdensely flowered.

Bracts ovate-acute, 5mm. long, 4mm. broad at base, thin, scarious, about 5-nerved.

Pedicels the lowest of terminal racemes 20mm. long.

Perianth bright sheeny orange-scarlet, greenish tipped, 36mm. long, cylindric, slightly trigonous, basally obtusely tapering into the pedicel, 7mm. diam. over the ovary, thence slightly constricted on the underside, enlarging slightly to the mouth; *outer segments* free for 15mm., paler at the edges, with the apices subacute, slightly spreading; *inner segments* themselves free but dorsally adnate to the outer for two-thirds their length, broader than the outer, and with more obtuse, more spreading apices.

Filaments pale-lemon, filiform-flattened, the 3 inner narrower and lengthening in advance of the 3 outer, with their *anthers* in turn exserted 3—4mm.; *style* pale yellow, filiform, with *stigma* at length exserted 5mm.; *ovary* pale olive-green, 5mm. long, 3mm. diam., finely 6-grooved. (Plate 86, Figs. 383, 384).

KENYA. Bushy slopes near Ngobit Bridge, 31 miles NW of Nyeri on direct road to Mutara and Thomson's Falls, approx. 0° 5′ S, 36° 50′ E, 22 April 1952, Reynolds 6579 holotype (PRE), isotype (K, SRGH, EA); same loc. and date, Bally 11555 (G, EA); 18 miles E of Thomson's Falls, 22 April 1952, Reynolds 6559 (PRE, K); Suguroi River, 28 miles E of Thomson's Falls, 22 April 1952, Reynolds 6582 (K, PRE).

PLATE 86

ALOE NGOBITENSIS   Reynolds.

Near Ngobit Bridge, 31 miles NW of Nyeri, Kenya. Height 6 feet.

FIG. 383.

A. ngobitensis Reynolds. On bushy slopes near Ngobit Bridge 31 miles NW of Nyeri, on direct road to Mutara Police Post, Kenya.

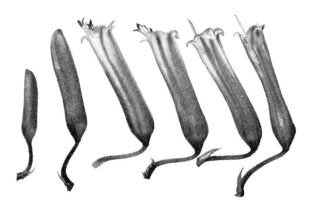

FIG. 384.

A. ngobitensis Reynolds. Flowers natural size from bud to post-anthesis stages.

A. ngobitensis was named after the locality which appeared to be its specific centre, namely, the valley of the Ngobit River, near Ngobit Bridge, 31 miles NW of Nyeri, on the direct road from Nyeri to Mutara Police Post and Thomson's Falls, Kenya Colony. For a mile or more each side of Ngobit Bridge, large numbers of plants were found on bushy slopes in stony ground, forming shrubs about 6 ft. high and broad, and mostly branched from the base with the main stems slightly divergent.

The most striking feature of *A. ngobitensis*, and one which immediately distinguishes it from other shrubby Aloes in Kenya and elsewhere in Africa, is the remarkable colour of the flowers which is a striking and most attractive bright sheeny orange-scarlet, the perianth being usually minutely white-spotted. It is also distinguished by having rather slender peduncles and branches, and subdensely flowered somewhat narrow racemes about 15cm. long. Stems branch at ground level, very slightly increasing in thickness upwards, which is also a character of *A. nyeriensis* found further east near Manyuki and for some miles along the road southwards towards Nyeri, but the latter is a larger plant with thicker stems, larger leaves, and different racemes with dull scarlet flowers, and could hardly be confused.

Near Ngobit Bridge numbers of *A. ngobitensis* were seen growing socially with large numbers of *A. secundiflora*. Both were flowering in April, but no crosses were noticed.

At the Suguroi River, 14 miles northwest of Ngobit Bridge (which locality is 32 miles W of Nanyuki and 28 miles E of Thomson's Falls), *A. ngobitensis* was found among similar Aloe shrubs having slightly shorter denser racemes of dull scarlet flowers. Whether the latter are colour forms of *A. ngobitensis*, or more probably forms of *A. nyeriensis* extending westwards from Nanyuki, requires further investigation.

At a point 18 miles E of Thomson's Falls, an occasional plant of *A. ngobitensis* with its bright sheeny orange-scarlet flowers stood out vividly among numbers of Aloe shrubs with dull scarlet flowers.

148. **A. nyeriensis** Christian in *Fl. Plants Afr.* 29: Plate 1126 (1952).

DESCRIPTION. A shrub branching from base and forming dense groups; *stems* averaging 2m. tall, erect or divergent, gradually thicker from base upwards, about 5—6cm. diam., the apical 30—50cm. sublaxly foliate, old dried leaf remains persistent.

Leaves about 20, rosulate, basally amplexicaul, the sheath bases 2—4 cm. apart, the youngest erectly spreading, the older spreading to decurved, narrowly lanceolate-attenuate 50—60cm. long, about 7cm. broad at base; *upper surface* green, sometimes spotted in young plants, the spots disappearing with age, somewhat concave; *lower surface* convex; *margins* armed with deltoid, pungent teeth, 3mm. long, 10mm. apart.

Inflorescence a branched panicle, arising in the axils of uppermost leaves, 60cm. high, 5—8-branched, the branches arcuate-ascending, with the lowest sometimes with 1—2 branchlets.

Racemes cylindric-conical, subdensely flowered, the terminal usually the longest and 15cm. long, the lateral a little shorter, the buds greenish-tipped.

Bracts ovate-acute, 5—7mm. long, 3—4mm. broad at base, thin, scarious, 3—5-nerved.

Pedicels 15—20mm. long, nutant at apex.

Perianth cylindric, slightly trigonous, somewhat glossy coral-red to scarlet, averaging 40cm. long, basally obtuse and shortly stipitate, 8—9mm. diam. across the ovary, thence very slightly constricted on underside only and enlarging again to the throat, the mouth wide open; *outer segments* free for 15mm., 3-nerved, the apices subacute, spreading; *inner segments* themselves free but dorsally adnate to the outer for 25mm., the apical portion with 3 crowded nerves forming a keel, the apices more obtuse, more spreading.

Anthers the 3 inner and 3 outer in turn exserted 2—3mm.; *stigma* at length exserted 5mm.; *ovary* green, 6mm. long, 3mm. diam. (Plate 87, Fig. 385).

KENYA. Nyeri, fl. 8 July 1938, Pole Evans et Erens 1198 (SRGH); 24 miles N of Nyeri, coll. I. B. Pole Evans and J. Erens in 1938, cult. D.Ó.B., Pretoria, fl. June 1951, I. B. Pole Evans et J. Erens 1198, in Herb. Christian 984, in Nat. Herb. No. 28486 holotype (PRE), isotype (SRGH); 5 miles S of Nanyuki, 6,000 ft., 22 April 1952, Reynolds 6575 (K; SRGH, PRE); half-mile N of Nanyuki, 6,300 ft., 22 April 1952, Reynolds 6573 (K, PRE); Naro Moru (between Nyeri and Nanyuki), 19 Nov. 1958, Verdcourt 2312 (EA, PRE).

The type locality is 6 miles S of Nanyuki, 24 miles N of Nyeri and 116 miles N of Nairobi. *A. nyeriensis* grows in abundance from this point northwards to Nanyuki, Naro Moru, and to near the top of Ngare Ndare Escarpment, 24 miles NE of Nanyuki.

When describing *A. nyeriensis* the late Mr. Christian pointed out that plants form thickets, and stems are erect, divergent, or fall over and re-root where they touch the ground.

Leaves of young plants are sometimes white-spotted but the spots usually disappear with age, except that occasionally the basal part of lower leaf surface may have a few crowded white spots.

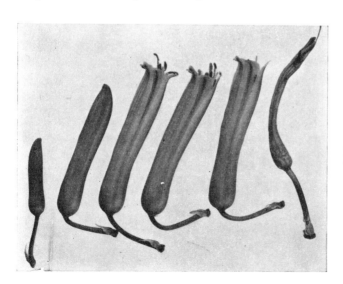

FIG. 385.

A. nyeriensis Christian. Flowers 1/1 from a plant near Nanyuki, Kenya. Alt. 6,000 ft.

PLATE 87

ALOE NYERIENSIS Christian.

At type locality, 24 miles N of Nyeri, Kenya. Height 8 ft.

A. nyeriensis is very closely related to *A. dawei* in which connection Mr. Christian wrote: "The nearest affinity to *A. nyeriensis* is *A. pole-evansii* (now in synonymy under *A. dawei*) but there are some unvarying differences. In the latter the peduncle and branches are always dark red-brown, whereas they remain green in *A. nyeriensis*, which is also a taller plant". Mr. Christian based his observations on plants cultivated in his gardens at Ewanrigg. It seems that *A. nyeriensis* may also have slenderer taller stems, which become thicker from base upwards. Flowers are longer, being 40mm. against 33—35mm. long in *A. dawei*.

Plants vary in different localities, and it might well be found eventually that *A. dawei* and *A. nyeriensis* are forms of one variable species, differing chiefly in quantitative not qualitative characters.

149. **A. arborescens** Mill. *Gard. Dict.* ed. 8 No. 3 (1768) etc., etc. *Note:* For pre-Linnean citations, the lengthy synonymy, numerous figures, colour plate, hybrids, etc., see *Aloes of S. Afr.* 407–414 (1950).

DESCRIPTION based on plants in Rhodesia and Malawi.

Plants large arborescent, many-branched shrubs, 2—3m. high and as broad. *Stem* up to 30cm. diam. at base, many-branched and rebranched from base or higher, old dried leaf remains usually persistent, rosettes of leaves up to 60—70cm. diam.

Leaves multifarious, densely rosulate, erectly spreading to spreading and somewhat falcately decurved, rather fleshy, averaging 40—60cm. long, 5—7cm. broad at base, gradually narrowing to an acute apex; *upper surface* usually flat, unicoloured dull-green to grey-green; *lower surface* convex, dull green, without spots or markings; *margins* armed with firm, pale teeth, 3—5mm. long, about 10—15mm. apart, the teeth usually forward-uncinate, smaller and more crowded near base, larger and more distant upwards.

Inflorescence usually simple, sometimes with a short branch, about 60cm. high, sometimes 2—4 simultaneously from a rosette.

Peduncle arcuate-ascending with the raceme erect, clothed with several many-nerved sterile-bracts that are broadly ovate, fleshy, about 20mm. long, 15mm. broad at base.

Racemes varying from conical (broader and shorter) to cylindric-acuminate (narrower and longer), 20—30cm. long, 10—12cm. diam., densely flowered, the apical buds crowded and forming a somewhat acuminate apex, open flowers subpendulous, laxer.

Bracts ovate-acute, 15—20mm. long, 10—12mm. broad, thin, subscarious, many-nerved, clasping the pedicel.

Pedicels the lowest reaching 35—40mm. long.

Perianth scarlet, averaging 40mm. long, cylindric-trigonous, 7mm. diam. across the ovary, thence exceedingly slightly narrowed above the ovary and enlarging to the throat; *outer segments* free to base, obscurely nerved, the apices subacute, slightly spreading; *inner segments* broader than the outer, pale, with 3 crowded nerves forming a keel the colour of the perianth turning greenish near apex, the apices more obtuse, more spreading than the outer.

Filaments filiform-flattened, the 3 inner narrower and lengthening before the 3 outer with their *anthers* in turn exserted up to 5mm.; *stigma* at length exserted 5mm.; *ovary* green, 9—10mm. long, 3mm. diam. (Figs. 386–388).

RHODESIA. *Melsetter Dist.:* Mt. Pene, 7,000 ft., Oct. 1908 (capsules dehisced), Swynnerton 6046! (BM); Summit of Mt. Pene, 6,000 ft., 6 May 1958, N. C. Chase 6886 (SRGH, K, PRE); Melsetter, June 1935, Eyles 8434 (K, SRGH). *Victoria Dist.:* Coll. Chumberi, Glenlivet near Fort Victoria, cult. Greendale, fl. 22 May 1958, L. C. Leach 301 (SRGH). *Inyanga Dist.:* Inyangwe Fort, 2 miles E of Rhodes Hotel, 6,500 ft., 18 July 1956, Reynolds 8207 (K, PRE); 10 miles N of Troutbeck, 6,000 ft., May 1957, L. C. Leach 426 (SRGH); 10 miles E of London Service Station, 2 June 1958, L. C. Leach 546 (SRGH).

MOÇAMBIQUE. Inhaca Island, Ponta Rasa, 10 July 1957, L. A. Grandvaux Barbosa 7650! (K, LM); Inhaca Island, 23 miles E of L. Marques, Ponte Punduini head, in forest shrubs to 8ft., 8—26 July 1957, A. O. D. Mogg 29679/27295 (K).

MALAWI. *Southern Prov.:* Mlanje Mountain, SW ridge, 2400m., 28 June 1946, L. J. Brass 16525 (SRGH). *Central Prov.:* Mwera Hill, 48 miles NE of Lilongwe, alt. 5,200 ft., scapes very dry on 22 July 1952, Reynolds 6698 (PRE, K).

NATIVE NAMES: In Malawi the Chinyanja name for Aloe in general is *Chintembwe*, and in Chitumbuka it is *Chiwiriwiri*.

DISTRIBUTION

RHODESIA: Along the eastern mountains in the Melsetter, Umtali and Inyanga Districts. *Melsetter:* Bridal Veil Falls, farms Marangi and Mutsarara, 21 miles S of Melsetter at 5,400 ft.; Mt. Pene, 6—7,000 ft., high peaks of the central area of the Chimanimanis, Musapa Mountain, 10 miles N of Melsetter. *Inyanga:* Hills near Dannakay Hotel, 9 miles SW of Rhodes Hotel, 6,400 ft.; Inyanga Downs, hilltop 16 miles NE of Inyanga Village. (*Note:* At this locality crosses with *A. inyangensis* occur among both parents which grow socially in profusion.) Abundant at Inyangwe Fort, 2 miles E of Rhodes Hotel; near Worlds View, 4 miles W of Troutbeck at 7,200 ft.; and north slopes of Black Mountain, 5 miles N of Troutbeck. Mr. Ted Bullock of Bulawayo has found *A. arborescens* on top of Mberingwa (Mt. Belingwe) at 4,750—5,200 ft., which is the furthest west known.

Fig. 386.   Fig. 387.

A. arborescens Mill.

Fig. 386. Plants at Inyangwe Fort, 2 miles E of Rhodes Hotel, Inyanga Downs, Rhodesia, alt. 6,500 ft., with flowers almost over. Height 9 feet.

Fig. 387. Plants with dry scapes, 48 miles NE of Lilongwe, Kota Kota Dist., Central Prov., Malawi. Height 10 ft.

Fig. 388.

A. arborescens Mill. Buds and flowers with separate bract natural size.

MOÇAMBIQUE: High up on east slopes of the Chimanimanis at 6,500 ft.; summit of Gorongosa Mountain at 5,900 ft.; on Inhaca Island, east of L. Marques.

MALAWI: *Southern Prov.* Along the top of Mt. Mlanje. *Central Prov.:* along the top of Dedza Mountain at 7,000 ft.; on Mwera Hill, 48 miles NE of Lilongwe, at 5,200 ft., and on Chenje Hill nearby, both in Kota Kota District. This is the furthest north known.

REPUBLIC OF SOUTH AFRICA. *A. arborescens* is essentially a South African species where it grows in considerable numbers over a wide area from the Rivier Zonder Einde Mountains near Genadendal in the Western Province of the Cape, through the Eastern Province, Transkei, Natal, Zululand, Swaziland, Eastern and Northern Transvaal (Soutpansberg), to the eastern mountains of Rhodesia, and to Malawi.

TYPE LOCALITY: South Africa, without precise locality. Caspar Commelin, who was the first to illustrate a young plant in his *Horti Medici Amstelaedamensis* 2: p. 27, Fig. 14 (1701) stated: "This *Aloe* is produced from seeds which I received in 1698 from Africa, and sowed." Miller, who described *A. arborescens* in his *Dict.* Ed. 8, no. 3 (1768) makes no mention of any locality.

A. arborescens grows readily from cuttings, and eventually forms many-branched shrubs 6—9 ft. high and broad. It is a very handsome plant in full bloom, and is probably the best known and most widely cultivated of all the shrubby *Aloes*.

MEDICINAL USES

Accounts have stated that the leaf of *A. vera* (now in synonymy under *A. barbadensis* Mill.) is of great use in the treatment of X-ray burns, and that it had been used in China for centuries in the treatment of ordinary burns. A leading Johannesburg dermatologist, when informed that *A. vera* leaves were not available locally in South Africa, used the leaves of *A. arborescens* in the treatment of X-ray burns. Subsequently in a personal communication to the present author, he stated: "I have now treated three cases of Radiodermatitis (X-ray burns) with the leaf of *Aloe arborescens*. This was used since the *Aloe vera* was unobtainable. My cases were given the split leaf, i.e. with the juicy pulp exposed as a dressing on the raw area. The first two patients were given it continuously, while the third had a dressing at night only. All healed well, and far more promptly than one could expect from any other form of local treatment. I conclude from these few cases that this is a valuable method of treatment of X-ray burns."

NATURAL HYBRID

A cross of *A. arborescens* with *A. cameronii* Hemsl. has been collected by Mr. L. C. Leach in the Inyanga District, about 10 miles SE of London Garage.

Another cross, with *A. inyangensis*, has also been collected in the Inyanga District, about 16 miles NE of Inyanga Village. This attractive hybrid has been grown at Ewanrigg for many years.

GROUP 20

TALL TREES, DICHOTOMOUSLY BRANCHED AND REBRANCHED

Leaves densely rosulate, deeply channelled and recurved. *Inflorescence* 50—60cm. high, 3—4-branched. *Racemes* cylindric, subdensely to densely flowered. *Pedicels* short. *Bracts* small to large. *Perianth* 25—40mm. long; *outer segments* free almost to base (tube about 5mm.).

Three species fall naturally into this group, *A. sabaea* from the Western Yemeni Escarpment, *A. eminens* from Somalia North, and *A. bainesii* from South Africa, Swaziland, and the southern parts of Moçambique.

KEY TO THE SPECIES

1. *Plants* to 9m. *Leaves* 60—100cm. long. *Racemes* 15—30cm. *Bracts* ovate-acute, 15mm. long. *Perianth* rosy or flesh-coloured, 25—33mm. long .. .. 150 *A. sabaea*

2. *Plants* to 15m. *Leaves* 45cm. long. *Racemes* 16cm. long. *Bracts* narrowly deltoid, 6mm. long, 3mm. broad. *Perianth* bright glossy-red, 40mm. long .. .. 151 *A. eminens*

3. *Plants* to 18m. *Leaves* to 80cm. × 8cm. *Racemes* very densely flowered, 20—30cm. *Bracts* almost hair-like and coiled backwards. *Perianth* rose-pink, 35mm. long. Genitals exserted 15mm... .. .. — *A. bainesii*

For *A. bainesii* synonymy, full description, colour plate and figures, see *Aloes of South Africa* 498 (1950).

150. **A. sabaea** Schweinf. in *Bull. Herb. Boiss.* 2: App. 2, 74 (1894); Engler in *Notizblatt K. Bot. Gart.* 1: 4 (1895); Berger in Engler's *Pflanzenr.* Liliac.-Aloin 320 (1908); Blatter in *Fl. Arab. Rec.⁴Bot. Surv. Ind.* 8: 6, 463 (1936); 0. Schwartz in *Fl. Trop. Arab.* 351 (1939).

DESCRIPTION by Schweinfurth and Berger.

Plant a tall tree, with stem dichotomously branched, up to 9m. tall.

Leaves densely rosulate, ensiform, gradually attenuate, recurved, obliquely falcate, 60—100cm. long, 5—12cm. broad, 15mm. thick; *upper surface* pale green, broadly canaliculate; *lower surface* convex; *margins* serrate-dentate, with crowded slightly incurved, pale, triangular teeth, obsolete towards apex.

Inflorescence about 50cm. high, 3—4-branched.

Racemes subdensely flowered, elongate, 15—30cm. long.

Bracts triangular-ovate, acute, scariose, white, erectly spreading, 15mm. long, 3—5-nerved.

Pedicels 12—15mm. long, slender, erectly spreading.

Perianth 25—33mm. long, companulate-cylindric; *outer segments* connate at base into a tube scarcely 6mm. long, rosy or flesh-coloured, paler at apex, with 5 reddish nerves; *inner segments* broader and more obtuse, with a reddish keel.

Filaments pale, with *anthers* distinctly exserted; *stigma* exserted; *capsule* 22—24mm. long, 16mm. diam. (Figs. 389-391).

YEMEN. Wadi Madfar near Hodjela, 700—800m., fruiting 30 Jan. 1889, Schweinfurth 941! (K); Agara near Hodjela, 600m., Schweinfurth 1010 (K); above Ussil (Uossil), 1400m., 14 Feb. 1889, Schweinfurth 1344! (K).

FIG. 389.   FIG. 390.

A. sabaea Schweinfurth. Herb. sheets at Kew – much reduced.

FIG. 389. Schweinfurth 1344, Uossil, Yemen, 1400m., 14 Feb. 1889. A second label reads "Agara bei Hodjela, 600m. 1 Feb 1889 Schweinfurth 1010."

FIG. 390. Wadi Hadfar bei Hodjela, 700m., 30 Jan. 1889, Schweinfurth 941.

Photographs: By Courtesy The Director Royal Botanic Gardens, Kew.

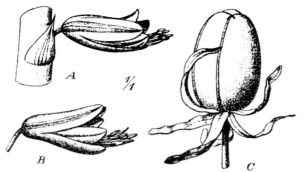

Fig. 391.

A. sabaea Schweinfurth. Reproduction 1/1 of Berger's figures in Engler's *Pflantzennreich* Liliac–Aloin. p. 321. (1908).

Fig. 138. *Aloe sabaea* Schweinfurth. *A* Perigonium. *B* Idem paullum postea. *C* Capsula. (Icon. orig.)

A. sabaea was described from plants found by Schweinfurth on the foothills of the Western Yemeni Escarpment. It has not been reported outside of the Yemen. The author has not succeeded in tracing any illustrations of plants in their natural surroundings, while the only available descriptions are not as full as they might be.

Fig. 392.   Fig. 393.

A. eminens Reynolds et Bally.

Fig. 392. Plants 14 miles N of Erigavo, (below the tunnel), on road down to Mait, Somalia North, Alt. 5,100 ft. Height 40 feet.

Fig. 393. Plants in the Surud, 11 miles NW of Erigavo, in a sheltered ravine on west side of Tabah Pass, alt. 6,ooo ft. Height 40—50 feet.

From published descriptions it seems that *A. eminens* from Somalia North differs from *A. sabaea* in having shorter leaves, more crowded teeth, shorter racemes, shorter, narrower bracts, shorter pedicels, and 40mm. glossy-red perianths.

The South African species *A. bainesii* is distinguished by having densely flowered racemes 20—30cm. long, bracts linear and coiled backwards, and pink perianths with anthers exserted 15mm. and more.

151. A. eminens Reynolds et Bally in *Journ. S.A. Bot.* 24: 187 (1950).

DESCRIPTION: A tree 10—15m. high. *Stem* up to 1·5m. diam. at ground level, more slender upwards, irregularly branched, the branches slender.

Leaves 16—20, rosulate at apices of branches, basally sheathing-imbricate, the imbricate portion with 5mm. broad white border, about 5cm. broad at base, 40—45cm. long, gradually narrowing to an obtuse apex, the leaves recurved with their apices pointing downwards; *upper surface* unicoloured dull-green, rather deeply canaliculate and U-shaped in cross section; *lower surface* rounded; *margins* with narrow white cartilaginous edge armed with blunt, cartilaginous (not pungent) white teeth that are longer (2—3mm.) low down and 3—5mm. apart, becoming smaller to obsolescent upwards except for a few short crowded teeth in the apical 4—5cm.

Inflorescence branched, averaging 50—60cm. high.

Peduncle basally plano-convex and 15mm. broad, 3—5-branched from below the middle.

Racemes subdensely flowered, broadly cylindric-acuminate, averaging 16cm. long, 8—9cm. diam., the apex a tuft of dried bracts, the youngest buds sub-erect, older buds spreading, open flowers nutant.

Bracts narrowly deltoid, 6mm. long, 3mm. broad, pale brown, thin, scarious, 1-nerved, the nerve raised and prominent.

Pedicels averaging 10mm. long.

Perianth red, somewhat glossy, rather thick and fleshy, cylindric-trigonous, averaging 40mm. long, basally obtuse to rounded, 12mm. diam. across the ovary, thence trigonous and slightly narrowing to the mouth; *outer segments* free for about 32mm. (tube 8mm.), the apices subacute and spreading; *inner segments* broader than the outer, obtusely keeled, with thin margins, the apices more obtuse and more recurved to revolute.

Filaments yellow, the 3 inner narrower and lengthening before the 3 outer with their *anthers* in turn exserted 3—4mm.; *stigma* at length exserted 5mm. (Figs. 392–396).

FIG. 394.   FIG. 395.
A. eminens Reynolds et Bally.

FIG. 394. Portion of a flowering branch × 1/10 approx.

FIG. 395. Raceme × 1/4 approx.

SOMALIA NORTH (formerly Somaliland Prot.). *Erigavo Dist.:* In a ravine of the Surud, W side of Tabah Pass, 11 miles NW of Erigavo, c. 10° 46′ N, 47° 14′ E, 6,000 ft. alt., 9 Sept. 1957, Reynolds 8435 holotype (PRE), isotype (K, EA); 18 miles N of Erigavo on road to Mait, 5,500 ft., 3 Nov. 1954, Bally 10300 (K, G, EA).

A. eminens occurs in numbers in sheltered well-wooded ravines of the Surud, 11 miles N of Erigavo at 6,000 ft., and repeatedly for the next 7 miles down the spectacular escarpment road (which leads to Mait Ruins on the coast) down to 4,500 ft. It was not seen in drier bush country at lower altitudes. Mr. Bally has also found it along the Al Madu range much further east.

A. eminens is a tree 30—40 ft. and more in height, and is irregularly branched and of somewhat straggly untidy growth. Sometimes a few slender, very elongated branches stand out above the others. The leaves of young plants may be larger, but in mature specimens they are only 45cm. long and 5cm. broad, with a cartilaginous marginal edge armed with firm (not pungent) blunt white teeth that are 2—3mm. long, 3—5mm. apart, becoming obsolescent towards the apex. Racemes are sub-densely flowered and average 16cm. long, while bracts are narrowly deltoid, only 6mm. long and 1-nerved. Pedicels average 10mm. long, and the perianths are 40mm. long, rather thick and fleshy, and glossy red. At a quick glance *A. eminens* recalls *A. bainesii* Th. Dyer in South Africa, but the latter is a quite different species with much larger leaves, densely flowered racemes 20—30cm. long, bracts linear and coiled backwards, shorter perianths with anthers exserted 15mm. and more.

A. sabaea Schweinfurth from the Yemen is a closer ally. The author has not seen plants, and this species is known to him only from Schweinfurth's and Berger's descriptions, and from the material at Kew of Schweinfurth 941 from the Yemen in Arabia. *A. sabaea* differs from *A. eminens* in having much larger leaves, more widely spaced teeth, longer racemes, much longer broader 5. nerved bracts, pedicels up to twice as long, shorter perianths with segments free almost to bas ("tubo brevissime").

He had hoped to study *A. sabaea* in the Yemen, but hostilities along the Aden–Yemeni border made that impossible.

A. eminens flowers mostly from November to January, and is called *Daar der* – the tall Aloe – by the Somalis.

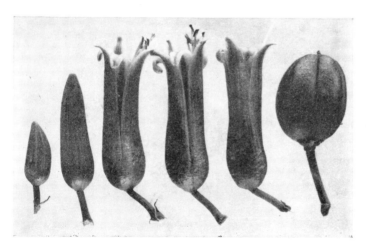

FIG. 396.
A. eminens Reynolds et Bally. Flowers from bud to fruit stages 1/1.

50°E

COMORO ISLANDS

MAYOTTE

DIÉGO-SUAREZ

AMBANJA

MADAGASCAR
MALAGASY REPUBLIC

AUTHOR'S JOURNEYS
IN SEARCH OF ALOE

ANTSOHIHY

15°S

15°S

0   100   200
KMS.

MAJUNGA

MAROVOAY

MOZAMBIQUE
CHANNEL

MAEVATANANA

ANKAZOBE

ANGAVOKELY

TAMATAVE

MIARMARIVO

TANANARIVE

MANDOTO

20°

ANTSIRABE

AMBOSITRA

INDIAN
OCEAN

20°

AMBATOFINANDRAHANA

FIANARANTSOA

AMBALAVAO

ZAZAFOTSY

RANOHIRA

IHOSY

IVOHIBE

TULÉAR

TONGOBORY

BETROKA

BENENITRA

BETIOKY

MANANTENINA

TRANOROA

RANOMAFANA

AMPANIHY

ANTANIMORA

FT. DAUPHIN

25°S

BELOHA

AMBOVOMBE

25°S

TSIHOMBE

CAP STE. MARIE

Eunice Murdoch del.
Mbabane 1965

50°E

PART 2

THE ALOES OF MADAGASCAR

INTRODUCTION

Etienne de Flacourt, an early Governor of Madagascar, published his *Histoire de la Grande Ile de Madagascar* in Paris in 1658 – with a second edition in 1661 – but no Aloe was included among his descriptions of the plants of the Ile.

Bojer, in *Hort. Maurit.* 345 (1837) listed two species of Aloe from Madagascar that were cultivated in the Royal Gardens, Pamplemousses, Mauritius. One was *A. leptocaulon* Bojer, recorded as growing on the hills along the Onilahy River which flows into the Bay of Saint Augustin. The other was *A. sahundra* Bojer from the sandy beaches which bound the south-west of the Bay of Saint Augustin.

Both of Bojer's epithets are *nomina nuda*, and cannot be upheld. They are referred to under *A. antandroi* (R. Decary) H. Perr., and *A. divaricata* Berger.

The first validly described species of Aloe from Madagascar were *A. deltoideodonta* Bak., *A. capitata* Bak. and *A. macroclada* Bak. in *Journ. Linn. Soc.* 20: 271–273 (1883). Baker's *A. oligophylla* proved to be a Lomatophyllum, and so has *A. lomatophylloides* Balf. f. from Rodriguez Island.

Four years later, Baker described another species, *A. haworthioides*, in *Journ. Linn. Soc.* 22: 529 (1887), while in 1891, Scott Elliot described *A. bakeri* in the same *Journal* 29: 60 (1891).

In 1900, R. Decorse, in *Notes, Reconn. Explor.* 623 (1900), discussed the medicinal uses of two species of Aloe and he referred to them only by the single native names of "*Vaotsohy*" (*Vaotsoy*) and "*Vaombe*". Notwithstanding a description and figures, these single native names have no status, and cannot be upheld.

Poisson recognised this, and in *Recherch. Fl. Merid. Madag.* 96 (1912) he validly described *A. vaotsohy* Decorse et Poisson and *A. vaombe* Decorse et Poisson – Decorse's name now being coupled with Poisson's at Poisson's request.

In 1905, however, Berger had described *A. divaricata* in *Bot. Jahrb.* 36: 64 (1905) which antedated Poisson's description of the species *A. vaotsohy*.

Three years later, Berger described three new species in *Pflanzanreich* Liliac.-Aloin (1908) namely *A. parvula* and *A. laeta* from Madagascar, and *A. mayottensis* from Mayotte Island in the Comoros.

The next contribution was made by R. Decary in *Bull. Econ. Madag.* 18 (1): 19–25 (1921) wherein he described *A. vaotsanda* and *A. suzannae,* also two varieties, as well as *Gasteria antandroi* which is now *A. antandroi* (R. Decary) H. Perrier.

The greatest credit is due to M. H. Perrier de la Bâthie for bringing order out of chaos. After lengthy and extensive travels throughout Madagascar he monographed the Malgache Aloes in *Mem. Soc. Linn. Norm.* 1 (1): 17–49 (1926). In this noteworthy publication, Perrier described thirteen new species and twelve new varieties, and added two more new species (*A. viguieri* and *A. isaloensis*) in *Bull. Econ. Madag.* 10: 20 (1927).

The last species described by Perrier de la Bâthie was *A. humbertii* in *Bull. Mus. Hist. Nat. Paris* 2 (3): 692 (1941). This brought his contribution up to sixteen new species and twelve new varieties.

Perrier revised the Aloes and brought them up to date in his monograph in *Fl. Madag.* Liliac. 77–142 (1938) – an outstanding achievement.

P. Danguy described *A. helenae* in *Bull. Mus. Hist. Nat. Paris.* 2 (1) : 433 (1929), while in the same publication Professor A. Guillaumin described *A. albiflora* (1940), *A. decaryi* (1941), *A. boiteaui* (1942), *A. versicolor* (1950) and *A. madecassa* H. Perr. var. *lutea* Guillaum. (1955) – from plants that flowered in Paris. Of these, *A. albiflora* and *A. versicolor* are upheld as good species.

During 1955, the present author travelled extensively almost throughout Madagascar, studying the Aloes and photographing them in the wild state. As a result of these studies, four new species and two new varieties were described in the *Journal of South African Botany* 22: 23–29, 131–132 (1956), and three more new species were described in the same *Journal* 23: 68–71 (1957).

This brought the total number of good species to thirty-eight, with several varieties, that were included in *The Aloes of Madagascar, Revision,* published in 1958.

Subsequently, five new species (*A. descoingsii, A. calcairophila, A. rauhii, A. fievetii, A. cryptoflora*) were described by the present author, while Professor W. Rauh contributed *A. buchlohii* and *A. schomeri*. These, with *A. boiteaui* Guillaumin, bring the total Madagascar species to forty-six that are included in this work.

The largest numbers of Aloe species are found along the moister central north-south mountain ranges, and in the arid south and south-west of the Island. They comprise a group of very diverse forms ranging from the small *A. haworthioides* and *A. parvula* to large tall-stemmed species such as *A. vaombe* and *A. suzannae*, the latter being probably the most primitive of the Malgache Aloes.

Compared with species found on the African mainland, any attempt to suggest trends of evolution would be mere guesswork, but some comparisons and observations might be of value.

Firstly, there are no known "Grass-Aloes" such as *A. myriacantha* (Haw.) R. & S. in Madagascar. There are also no plants even remotely resembling such species as *A. nuttii* Bak., and *A. inyangensis* Christian in the Leptoaloe Group. There are also no species in Madagascar with oblique or horizontally disposed racemes with unilateral flowers such as occur in *A. secundiflora* Engler (Tanzania, Kenya) and *A. mawii* Christian in Malawi and Moçambique.

In *A. haworthioides* Bak. and *A. parvula* Berger (Madagascar) the leaves and small rosettes are related to those of *A. humilis* (L) Mill. in the Cape Province of South Africa, but the flowers are in all ways different. Again, in the Malgache species *A. viguieri* H. Perr. and *A. imalotensis* Reynolds, leaves and rosettes are sometimes almost indistinguishable from the "Coral Aloe" of the Cape, *A. striata* Haw., but the inflorescences and flowers are very different.

Species with densely multiflowered cylindric racemes with short sessile or subsessile flowers are represented by *A. conifera* H. Perr., *A. betsileensis* H. Perr. and *A. macroclada* Bak. in Madagascar, and by *A. sessiliflora* Pole Evans, *A. aculeata* Pole Evans and *A. petricola* Pole Evans in the Transvaal.

Against this, the strikingly handsome species *A. capitata* Bak. has no counterpart on the mainland of Africa, or elsewhere, and is the only species of Aloe known in which the uppermost pedicels are much longer than the lowest, with the flowers opening from the apex downwards. There is no known species of Aloe with this character in Africa, although I have seen two species of Kniphofia in Ethiopia with the uppermost flowers opening first.

Again, *A. bulbillifera* H. Perr. and the var. *paulianae* Reynolds are unique in producing bulbils on the branches of the inflorescence, or on the main peduncle.

A. suzannae R. Decary from the far south of the Island is the only species known with a simple inflorescence 3m. long. The flowers appear to close by day and open at night — which suggests nocturnal pollination.

A most noteworthy fact is the absence of the "Maculates" (*Saponariae*) from Madagascar. This group is characterized by having lanceolate, or lanceolate-attenuate spotted leaves and branched inflorescences bearing flowers which are much inflated at base and constricted above the ovary. This extensive group occurs almost throughout Africa, and is represented by *A. saponaria* (Ait.) Haw. in the Cape and Natal, *A. zebrina* Bak. in Angola and Rhodesia, *A. greatheadii* Schonl. in Rhodesia, *A. lateritia* Engler in Tanzania and Kenya, and *A. macrocarpa* Tod. in Ethiopia, Eritrea and Nigeria. The fact that not one representative of this very large group has been found in Madagascar, suggests that the *Saponariae* evolved on the African mainland *after* the severance of Madagascar took place.

As in Africa, so in Madagascar, some species occur in very restricted areas while others are widely distributed and are variable in their various geographical stations.

I believe there are still a few species of Aloe in Madagascar awaiting discovery and description.

KEY TO THE GROUPS

GROUP 1. SMALL TO VERY SMALL PLANTS

This Group includes the smallest Malgache Aloe plants known. They do not comprise a homogeneous group. Species with widely divergent characters are included only on account of their small size to facilitate identification.

Type species: *A. haworthioides* Bak.
Malgache species: 13   ..   ..   Page 394

GROUP 2. PLANTS WITH LEAVES DISTICHOUS

Plants with little or no stem; *inflorescence* simple or 1-branched; *raceme* subcapitate, densely flowered; *pedicels* very short or negligible; *perianth* white or scarlet, 25—55mm. long, *outer segments* free.

One species: *A. compressa* H. Perr., with 2 varieties.
Note: A very small species with distichous leaves (*A. calcairophila*) is included under Group 1 .. .. Page 424

GROUP 3. PLANTS ACAULOUS. LEAVES ROSULATE, GREEN, UP TO 50CM. LONG, 5CM. BROAD. INFLORESCENCE SIMPLE OR FEW-BRANCHED. RACEMES SHORTLY CYLINDRIC, OUTER SEGMENTS FREE.

Malgache species: 2, *A. schomeri* Rauh, *A. buchlohii* Rauh.
The species in this group are characterized mostly by having narrow leaves about 10 times longer than broad .. .. Page 429

GROUP 4. LEAVES OVATE-ACUTE OR LANCEOLATE, OBSCURELY OR PROMINENTLY LINEATE.

With slight or prominent cartilaginous marginal border, the border white, yellowish or pinkish with teeth the same colour; *Inflorescence* simple or branched; teeth spaced or contiguous.

Type species: *A. deltoideodonta* Bak.
Malgache species: 6 .. .. Page 431

GROUP 5. PLANTS WITH LARGE ROSETTES, ACAULOUS OR CAULESCENT, LEAVES ASCENDING OR RECURVED, TO 70CM. LONG, 6—10CM. BROAD; INFLORESCENCE BRANCHED (except in *A. decorsei*).

Racemes short and densely flowered to long and laxly flowered. One species with perianths minutely puberlulent.

Type species: *A. bulbillifera* H. Perr.
Malgache species: 5 .. .. Page 450

GROUP 6. PLANTS WITH DENSELY FLOWERED GLOBOSE OR CORYMBOSE CAPITATE RACEMES; THE LOWEST PEDICELS ALWAYS MUCH SHORTER THAN THE UPPERMOST.

Perianth campanulate or cylindric-trigonous, the apical flowers opening first – except in *A. trachyticola*.

Type species: *A. capitata* Bak.
Malgache species: 2 .. .. Page 461

GROUP 7. RACEMES DENSELY MULTIFLOWERED, CYLINDRIC, SHORT OR LONG; PERIANTH SESSILE TO LONG PEDICELLATE.

Plants acaulous or tall-stemmed; *inflorescence* simple or branched.

Type species: *A. macroclada* Bak.
Malgache species: 5 .. .. Page 476

GROUP 8. PLANTS OF SHRUBBY GROWTH, FROM SMALL LOW UNDER-SHRUBS TO TALL-STEMMED SHRUBS.

Leaves small to large; *inflorescence* simple or branched; *raceme* subcapitate and more densely flowered to cylindric-acuminate and laxly flowered.

Type species: *A. acutissima* H. Perr.
Malgache species: 8 .. .. Page 486

GROUP 9. PLANTS DEVELOPING A THICK, ERECT, SIMPLE STEM 2—3M. OR MORE HIGH; LEAVES DENSELY ROSULATE AT APEX OF STEM.

Leaves large, ascending or deeply canaliculate and much recurved; *inflorescence* simple or multi-branched.

Type species: *A. vaombe* Decorse et Poisson   . .   . .   Page 508
Malgache species: 5

GROUP 1

VERY SMALL TO SMALL PLANTS

Included in this group are the smallest Aloe plants found in Madagascar. They are not a homogeneous group, but contain species with widely divergent characters and not closely allied. They are included here for convenience, and to facilitate identification. One species with leaves distichous, the others rosulate.

KEY TO THE SPECIES

1. PLANTS WITH DISTICHOUS LEAVES

Plants acaulous. *Leaves* 5—6cm. long. *Inflorescence* simple, 20—25mm. long. *Raceme* laxly flowered, 4cm. long. *Perianth* white, cylindric-trigonous, 10mm. long   . .   . .   157 *A. calcairophila*

2. PLANTS ACAULOUS, WITH ROSULATE LEAVES

Acaulous, suckering freely and forming dense groups. *Inflorescence* simple.
  A. *Rosettes* 4—5cm. diam., *leaves* 24—30, densely rosulate, 4—6cm. long, 6—8mm. broad at base; *inflorescence* simple (sometimes 1-branched), 25—35cm. high; *raceme* 4—6cm. long:
    (1) *Raceme* 12mm. diam.; *pedicels* 0—1mm.; *perianth* white or pale pink, 6—8mm. long, *outer segments* free, *anthers* exserted 5mm.   . .   . .   152 *A. haworthioides*
    (2) Whole spike including axis, bracts, pedicels and flowers bright orange-red   . .   . .   152A var. *aurantiaca*
  B. Slightly larger plants with *leaves* only 9—12mm. broad, *racemes* 12—16cm. long, laxly about 35-flowered, *perianth* cylindric-campanulate, *outer segments* free for 7—8mm., *anthers* exserted 0—1mm.
    (1) *Leaves* minutely verrucose, 10—13cm. long, 9—10mm. broad; *inflorescence* 60cm., simple or 1-branched; *raceme* 12—16cm.; *pedicels* 12mm.; *perianth* bright coral-red, 13mm. long. .   154 *A. bellatula*
    (2) *Leaves* 30cm. long, 10—15mm. broad; *inflorescence* 30—40cm.; *pedicels* 15mm.; *perianth* 16mm.   . .   . .   155 *A. perrieri*
  C. *Leaves* 15cm. long, 15mm. broad, *spirally twisted to rosulate:*
    (1) *Inflorescence* 35cm.; *raceme* 9cm., laxly flowered; *pedicels* 8mm.; *perianth* white, broadly campanulate, 10mm. long, 14mm. across the mouth, *segments* free; *anthers* exserted 8mm. . .   . .   156 *A. albiflora*
  D. *Leaves only* 30mm. *long,* 15mm. *broad:*
    (1) *Inflorescence* 12cm. long. *Pedicels* 5mm. *Perianth* scarlet-red, 7—8mm. long   . .   . .   158 *A. descoingsii*
  E. *Leaves* 8—11cm. *long,* 15mm. *broad:*
    (1) *Leaves* smooth both sides, copiously H-spotted. *Inflorescence* 30cm. *Raceme* 7cm. long. *Pedicels* 10mm. *Perianth* 25mm.; *outer segments* free to base   . .   . .   159 *A. rauhii*

(2) *Leaves* muricate-verrucose, shortly tuberculate-spinulescent, unspotted. *Inflorescence* 60cm. *Raceme* to 20cm. long. *Pedicels* 15mm. *Perianth* deep-rose, 28mm.; *outer segments* free 10mm.   153   *A. parvula*

(3) *Leaves* 15cm. long, 20mm. broad; *inflorescence* 30—40cm. *Raceme* sub-capitate. *Pedicels* 18mm. *Perianth* cylindric, coral-red 25mm., *segments* free   163   *A. versicolor*

3. PLANTS DEVELOPING A STEM, LEAVES ROSULATE

Leaves basally sheathing:

   A. Stems prolongate, 10—20cm. long. Plants forming large dense groups; outer segments free.
     (1) *Leaves* about 12, 7cm. long, 8mm. broad, *inflorescence* 20—30cm., *raceme* sub-capitate, 3—4cm. long, laxly 8—12-flowered; *pedicels* 10—12mm., *perianth* cylindric-trigonous, 23mm. long..   160   *A. bakeri*

   B. *Stem 5cm. or more, with a few shoots from base:*
     (1) *Leaves* about 6—7, 15cm. long, 6mm. broad at base, 10mm. at the middle, very fleshy; *inflorescence* 30—40cm.; *raceme* sub-capitate; *pedicels* 30mm.; *perianth* rose-pink, cylindric, 30mm. long   161   *A. parallelifolia*

   C. *Doubtfully included here:*
     Stem length? *Leaves* 20cm. × 14mm. *Inflorescence* simple 10—15cm. high. *Raceme* 5cm. long sublaxly flowered. *Pedicels* 10mm. *Perianth* bright-scarlet, 25mm. long, segments free 18mm.   ..   162   *A. boiteaui*

Note: *A. parallelifolia* is included here for convenience – it does not fit well into any group.

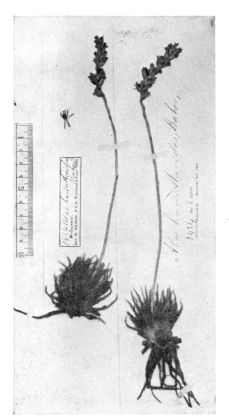

Fig. 397.

A. haworthioides Bak. Portion of sheet of Baron 3424, holotype (K).
Photo: Royal Botanic Gardens, Kew.

152. **A. haworthioides** Baker in *Journ. Linn. Soc.* 22: 529 (1887); Berger in Engler *Pflanzenr.* Liliac.–Aloin. 163, fig. 54 (1908); H. Perrier in *Mém. Soc. Linn. Norm.* 1 (1): 49, Plate 8 (1926), in *Fl. Madag.* Liliac. 111, Fig. XII (1938); Reynolds in *Aloes Madag. Revis.* 11 (1958);—*non* Francois in *Mém. Acad. Malg.* fasc. 24: 50, Plate XX (1937).

DESCRIPTION: *Plant* small, solitary or suckering and forming dense groups. *Roots* fusiform. *Rosettes* compact, about 4—5cm. diam.
    Leaves about 30, densely rosulate, narrowly lanceolate-deltoid, 3—4cm. long, terminating in a short pellucid point; *upper surface* flat to slightly concave, dark grey-green, covered with white pustules sometimes tipped with a short white hair; *lower surface* convex, similar to upper surface; *margins* ciliate with crowded, narrowly deltoid, cartilaginous, soft to firm white teeth 1—2mm. long.
    Inflorescence simple, 20—30cm. high.
    Peduncle slender, with 8—15 sterile bracts.
    Raceme subdensely 20—30-flowered, cylindric, slightly acuminate, 4—6cm. long, 12mm. diam., buds suberect and almost hidden by their bracts, open flowers suberect, almost sessile.
    Bracts suborbiculate, obtuse, shortly mucronate, 5mm. long, 3—5-nerved.
    Pedicels none or negligible.
    Perianth white to pale pink, cylindric, slightly campanulate, 6—8mm. long; *outer segments* linear-oblong free to base, 1—3-nerved, the apices obtuse, slightly spreading; *inner segments* free, 1—3-nerved.
    Filaments dilated, remarkably thick and fleshy, the 3 inner narrower and lengthening before the three outer with their *anthers* in turn exserted 5mm. (Figs. 397–398).

CENTRAL MADAGASCAR. Without precise locality, Baron 3424 (K). *Central Region:* Fianarantsoa Prov., South Betsileo, exposed gneissic rocks, Mont Belambana, 1200m., fl. May, Perrier 2177; Andringitra massif, 1800m., fl. March, Perrier 13691. *West Betsileo:* Quartzite mountain W of Itremo, 1600m. (Monts Ambatomenaloha).

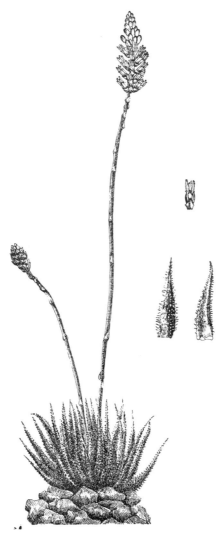

FIG. 398.

A. haworthioides Bak. Sketch by native artist Alfred Razafinjohany, of a plant collected by Prof. Humbert on the Itremo, flowering in Tsimbazaza Gardens. – Half natural size.

152A. var. **aurantiaca** H. Perrier in *Mém. Soc. Linn. Norm.* 1 (1): 49 (1926), in *Fl. Madag.* Liliac. 111 (1938); Reynolds in *Aloes Madag. Revis.* 14 (1958).

Differs from the typical form in having the whole spike, including the axis, bracts and perianths of a beautiful bright orange-red, with the stamens yellow. (Figs. 399–402).

FIANARANTSOA PROV. *South Betsileo*, Mont Iaody, to the N of the Andringitra massif, 2000m., fl. March, Perrier 14582; 30km. NW of Fianarantsoa, cult. Pretoria, Sept. 1963, Prof. W. Rauh 10328 (PRE). Professor W. Rauh (Heidelberg University, W. Germany), found numbers of plants on granite 30km. NW of Fianarantsoa.

The locality where the Rev. R. Baron collected the type is not known. Mont Belambana, where Perrier found the species, lies to the NE of Zazafotsy, and E of the main road to the N of Ambalavao. Mont Ambatomenaloha is SW of Itremo Village which is SW of Ambatofinandrahana on the road from Ambositra and Ivato to Morondava on the west coast.

Mont Iaody (2000m.) type locality of the var. *aurantiaca* is one of the northern peaks of the Andringitra range, and can be approached from Mahasoa Village (1400m.), 50km. S of Ambalavao.

A. haworthioides is a most distinctive and unique little species, with negligible pedicels. It is nearest allied in small rosettes and leaves only to *A. parvula* Berger (*non* Perrier), but in the latter the flowers are cylindric-ventricose, 24mm. long, with 10—13mm. pedicels. Plants occur singly, or in groups, while racemes vary from almost capitate, to the more frequent cylindric-acuminate.

FIG. 399.

A. haworthioides Bak. var. *aurantiaca* H. Perr. Plants natural size, 30km. NW of Fianarantsoa, near a small village Andomaranomaitso ("green water").
Photo: Prof. Dr. W. Rauh.

153. **A. parvula** Berger in Engler *Pflanzenr.* Liliac.—Aloin. 172 (1908); Reynolds in *Journ. S.A. Bot.* 22: 129, Plates XVII, XVIII (1956), in *Fl. Pl. Afr.* 31: Pl. 1234 (1956), in *Aloes Madag. Revis.* 14 (1958); *non* H. Perrier in *Mém. Soc. Linn. Norm.* 1 (1): 27 (1926), et *Fl. Madag.* Liliac. 90 (1938)—*A. sempervivoides* H. Perr. in *Mém. Soc. Linn. Norm.* (*l.c.*) 28 (1926), et *Fl. Madag.* 90 (1938).

DESCRIPTION: *Plant* small, with cylindric roots, acaulous, solitary or sometimes forming small groups.
Leaves about 24, densely rosulate, compactly suberectly spreading, about 10cm. long, 12mm. broad at base, gradually narrowing to an acute apex, rather thick and fleshy; *upper surface* flat, pale bluish-grey, not spotted, muricate throughout with rough processes ·5—1mm. long; *lower surface* convex, similar to upper surface; *margins* armed with soft to firm (not pungent) narrowly deltoid white cartilaginous teeth 1—2mm. long low down, 1—2mm. distant, the interspaces rounded and the colour of the leaf.

398　*Aloe parvula*

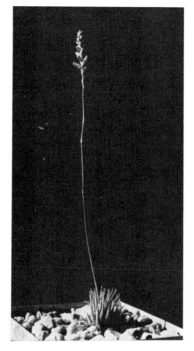 

Fig. 400.　　　　　　　Fig. 401.

A. haworthioides Bak. var. *aurantiaca* H. Perr.

Fig. 400. Plant × 1/4 flowering at Mbabane.

Fig. 401. Raceme 1/1 from plant flowering at Mbabane.

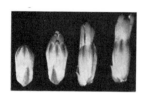

Fig. 402.

A. haworthioides Bak. var. *aurantiaca* H. Perr. Flowers 1/1 from a plant flowering at Heidelberg University.
Photo: Prof. Dr. W. Rauh.

Inflorescence simple, sometimes 2, about 35cm. high.

Peduncle basally flattened and 3mm. broad, terete and slightly narrower upwards, clothed with a few sterile-bracts, the lowest deltoid-acuminate, 12mm. long, 3mm. broad, about 7-nerved, smaller and more ovate-acute upwards.

Raceme up to 10cm. and more long, 5cm. diam., laxly about 12—15-flowered, the apex a small tuft of dried bracts, youngest buds spreading and greenish-grey tipped, open flowers pendulous.

Bracts lowest ovate-deltoid, subscarious, 3—5-nerved, clasping the pedicel, about half as long as the pedicel.

Pedicels lowest 12—15mm. long, obliquely spreading, recurved near apex.

Perianth light coral-red 26mm. long, cylindric-ventricose, distinctly trigonous and somewhat flat-sided, obtusely tapering at base into the pedicel, shortly stipitate, enlarging to the middle, thence narrowing to the mouth; *outer segments* free for 7mm. (tube 17mm.), white at the margins, obscurely 5-nerved, the nerves greenish at apex, the apices acute, straight, scarcely spreading; *inner segments* themselves free but dorsally adnate to the outer for 17mm., broader than the outer, and with broad, white marginal border, the apices more obtuse than the outer.

Filaments pale rose, filiform-flattened, the 3 inner narrower and lengthening before the 3 outer with their *anthers* in turn not or scarcely exserted; *style* filiform, with *stigma* at length scarcely exserted; *ovary* olive-green, 3mm. long, 1·5mm. diam., truncate at apex. (Plate 88, Figs. 403–406).

Fianarantsoa Prov. W. Betsileo, Ambatomenaloha, Grandidier s.n. (P); Mt. Analamamy to the W of Itremo, 2000m., "the locality which Grandidier called Ambatomenaloha", in large numbers, fl. Feb., Perrier 12493 (P); mountains W of Itremo, coll. Prof. J. Millot, cult. Johannesburg, fl. 24 Nov. 1951, Reynolds 6017 (PRE), fl. 12 Dec. 1963, Reynolds 10016 (PRE).

PLATE 88

ALOE PARVULA   Berger.

Plant collected by Prof. J. Millot on the Itremo, West Betsileo,
Fianarantsoa Province, Madagascar, flowering in Johannesburg. Height
30cm.

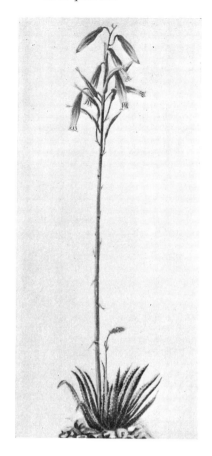

Fig. 403.

A. parvula Berger. Sketch by native artist Alfred Razafinjohany of a plant collected by Professor J. Millot on the Itremo, flowering in Tsimbazaza – × 1/3.

Fig. 404.

A. parvula Berger. Raceme 1/1 from a plant that flowered in Johannesburg.

Fig. 405.

A. parvula Berger. Flowers 1/1 – from a different plant.

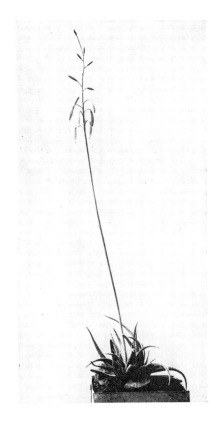

Fig. 406.

A. parvula Berger. Plant collected by Mr. Gerard Fievet, on the Alarobia – Ambovombe road, 20km. S of the Ivato – Ambatofinandrahana main road, Fianaratsoa Province – a form with longer laxer racemes than usual. Flowering at Mbabane, Swaziland. Height 50cm.

The Analamamy (Ambatomenaloha) mountains in West Betsileo lie SW of Itremo Village which is 40km. W of Ambatofinandrahana on the road from Ambositra and Ivato to Morondava on the west coast. Perrier found this species in large numbers at about 2000m.

The specimen collected by Bernier on rocks at Cap Manambato in the north of the Island (Bernier 2nd coll. n. 118), is without leaves and needs further investigation.

A. parvula is somewhat near *A. haworthioides* Baker in leaf characters and rosettes, but the latter has much smaller rosettes, suberect flowers only 8mm. long with negligible pedicels. *A. parvula* is perhaps nearest allied to the South African species *A. humilis* (L) Mill., var. *echinata* (Willd.) Bak., but the latter has much longer bracts, longer pedicels and longer flowers. – See *Aloes S. Afr.* 177–8 (1950). A plant of *A. parvula* from W of Itremo, collected by Professor Millot in 1949, and grown in Johannesburg for five years has produced a few suckers and flowers in October–November.

154. **A. bellatula** Reynolds in *Journ. S.A. Bot.* 22: 132 (1956), in *Aloes Madag. Revis.* 14 (1958); Verdoorn in *Fl. Pl. Afr.* 36: Pl. 1402 (1963).

DESCRIPTION: *Plant* small, with cylindric roots, acaulous, suckering and forming dense tufts.

Leaves about 16, densely rosulate, linear-attenuate, compactly ascending, slightly incurved-spreading, 10—13cm. long, 9—10mm. broad at base, 3mm. thick, gradually tapering to an acute apex; *upper surface* slightly canaliculate; *lower surface* convex; *both surfaces* minutely verrucose, rough with minute papillae-like points, dark green, copiously spotted throughout, the spots pale green, sublenticular, averaging 1mm. long, ·5mm. broad; *margins* armed with soft, cartilaginous, deltoid teeth 1mm. long, 1mm. apart low down, smaller to obsolescent upwards.

Inflorescence up to 60cm. high, simple or with 1 branch from about the middle, 2—3 consecutively.

Peduncle flattened and 3mm. broad at base, slightly slenderer upwards, clothed with about 5 sterile-bracts which are narrowly ovate-acuminate, thin, white, subscarious, prominently 1-nerved, the lowest 10mm. long, 3mm. broad, smaller upwards.

Racemes cylindric-acuminate, 12—16cm. long, 4cm. diam., about 35-flowered, laxer below, slightly denser upwards, youngest buds suberect, older buds horizontally disposed, open flowers nutant.

Bracts deltoid-acuminate, thin, white, prominently 1-nerved, the lowest 4—6mm. long, 2mm. broad, smaller upwards.

Pedicels lowest 12mm. long, nutant at apex, becoming erect in the fruit, the colour of the perianth.

Perianth light coral-red, cylindric-campanulate, 13mm. long, basally obconic and shortly stipitate, 6mm. diam. at the middle, the mouth wide open; *outer segments* free for 7mm., obscurely 3-nerved, the apices subacute, slightly spreading; *inner segments* free but dorsally adnate to the outer to the middle, pale rose-pink with pale coral-red keel, the apices slightly more spreading than the outer.

Filaments pale-rose, the 3 inner narrower and lengthening before the 3 outer with their *anthers* in turn scarcely exserted; *stigma* at length scarcely exserted; *ovary* pale orange, 2·5mm. long, 1·5mm. diam., obtuse at apex. (Plate 89. Figs. 407–409).

FIANARANTSOA PROV. *W. Betsileo*, W of Itremo Village, c. 20° 39′ S, 46° 36′ E, c. 1500m., leg. Prof. J. Millot, cult. Johannesburg, fl. 29 Jan. 1956, Reynolds 6591, holotype (PRE), second inflorescence 8 Feb. 1956, isotype (TAN), third inflorescence 19 Feb. 1956, isotype (P).

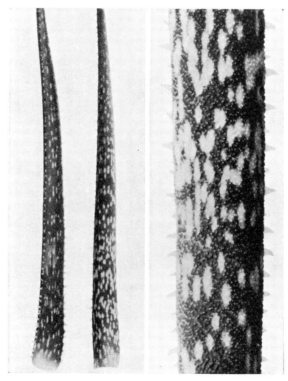

FIG. 407.   FIG. 408.
A. bellatula Reynolds.
FIG. 407. Portion of leaves 1/1. *Left:* Upper surface.
Right: Lower surface.

FIG. 408. Portion of leaf lower surface × 4 showing
minute papillae-like points.

ALOE BELLATULA   Reynolds.

Plants collected by Prof. J. Millot on the Itremo, Fianarantsoa Prov.,
Madagascar, flowering in Johannesburg. Height 55cm.

Fig. 409.

A. bellatula Reynolds. Flowers 1/1 from bud to
post-anthesis stages.

A. bellatula was collected in 1949 by Professor J. Millot on mountain slopes W of Itremo Village, between the village and the top of the road over the Itremo range. Itremo Village lies SW of Ambatofinandrahana on the road from Ambositra and Ivato westwards to Morondava on the west coast.

Plants cultivated in Johannesburg produce 3 consecutive inflorescences in January and February.

A. bellatula is characterized by having verrucose linear-attenuate leaves up to 13cm. long, 10mm. broad at base, and a very slender simple or 1-branched inflorescence which is five times taller than the leaves.

Fig. 410.

A. perrieri Reynolds. Reproduction of Perrier de la Bâthie's Fig. XIII, 4, in *Flore de Madagascar* Liliacees 95 (1938) – *A.parvula* H. Perr. (*non* Berger) ¼ natural size.

A. perrieri Reynolds is a close affinity in flowers, but differs in having leaves up to 30cm. long, and a simple inflorescence that is less than twice the length of the leaves.

In leaf characters *A. bellatula* is near *A. albiflora* Guillaumin, but the latter has broadly-campanulate snow-white flowers 10mm. long.

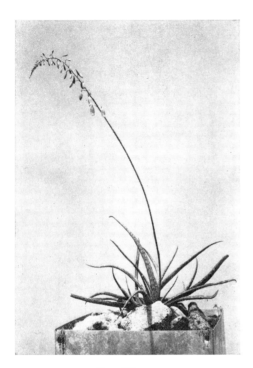 

FIG. 411.   FIG. 412.

A. perrieri Reynolds.

FIG. 411. Young plant flowering at Mbabane, Swaziland. Height 50cm.

FIG. 412. Lower half of raceme natural size.

155. **A perrieri** Reynolds in *Journ. S.A. Bot.* 22: 131, Plates 19, 20 (1956), in *Aloes Madag. Revis.* 19 (1958).

—— *A. parvula* Perrier (*non* Berger) in *Mém. Soc. Linn. Norm.* 1 (1): 27 (1926), et *Fl. Madag. Liliac.* 90 (1938) *pro parte.*

DESCRIPTION (based partly on Perrier's description of *A. parvula* Perrier *non* Berger, partly on Perrier n. 10995 from Mont Amboloandro, and partly on a plant flowering at Mbabane).

Plant succulent, with fusiform roots, acaulous, suckering at base and forming dense tufts.

Leaves about 10, rosulate, linear-attenuate, rather compactly suberect, up to 30cm. long, 15—20mm. broad at base, gradually narrowing to the apex; *upper surface* slightly canaliculate; *lower surface* convex; both surfaces rough to the touch, studded with minute asperities, maculate, the spots very pale green; *margins* armed with small, narrowly deltoid, firm, cartilaginous white teeth about 1mm. long, 1—2mm. distant.

Inflorescence simple, slender, 40—50cm. high.

Peduncle 4mm. broad at base, clothed with a few sterile bracts.

Raceme cylindric-acuminate, 15—20cm. long, rather laxly about 20—30-flowered.

Bracts ovate-acute, scarious, 3-nerved, 3—4mm. long, 2mm. broad at base.

Pedicels 15mm. long, the colour of the perianth, nutant at apex.

Perianth deep rose, almost white at mouth, cylindric-campanulate, 16mm. long, basally tapering into the pedicel articulation and shortly stipitate, gradually enlarging to a wide-open mouth; *outer segments* free to the middle, 3-nerved.

Anthers and *stigma* not, or very shortly exserted; *ovary* pale-olive, 3mm. long, 1·5mm. diam. (Figs. 410–412).

FIANARANTSOA PROV.: *S. Betsileo*, Mont Amboloandro, 1000m., March 1912, Perrier 10995! holotype (P); M. Decary 5701! without locality (P) appears to belong here. (This may be the specimen cited by Perrier from Mont Ivohibory, W of Ivohibe, cult. Tananarive.) Perrier 11021! from the southern end of the Isalo range near Benenitra is neither *A. perrieri* nor *A. bellatula*, and may be an undescribed species. Plant ex Mont Amboloandro, cult. Mbabane, fl. 15 Feb. 1965, Reynolds 10023 (PRE, K).

This is the species that Perrier considered was *A. parvula* Berger, and he described it under that name in *Mém. Soc. Linn. Norm.* (*l.c.*) and *Fl. Madag.* (*l.c.*). Recent investigations, however, revealed that *A. sempervivoides* H. Perr. was in fact the true *A. parvula* Berger. It was therefore necessary to reduce *A. sempervivoides* H. Perr. to synonymy under *A. parvula* Berger, and to re-name Perrier's species from Mont Amboloandro. This species was re-named *A. perrieri* in commemoration of M. Perrier de la Bâthie who contributed such a considerable amount to the knowledge of the Aloes of Madagascar.

A. perrieri is characterized by having leaves 25—30cm. long, 15—20mm. broad, and a 40—50cm. tall simple inflorescence, which is less than twice the length of the leaves. The nearest affinity is *A. bellatula* Reynolds which is a smaller plant with leaves only 10—13cm. long, 9—10mm. broad, and with an inflorescence up to 50cm. high which is nearly 5 times as long as the leaves. On Mont Amboloandro, which is near Zazafotsy, South Betsileo, Perrier found plants flowering in March 1912.

156. **A. albiflora** Guillaumin in *Bull. Mus. Hist. Nat. Paris* ser. 2: XII, 353 (1940; Reynolds in *Aloes Madag. Revis.* 23 (1958).

—— *Guillauminia albiflora* (Guillaumin) Bertrand in *Cactus Français* 49:41 (1956).

DESCRIPTION: *Plant* small, with cylindric (not fusiform) roots, acaulous, suckering and forming small groups of compact rosettes.

Leaves about 10, spirally twisted to rosulate, linear-attenuate, narrowly arcuate-ascending, slightly curved inwards towards apex, 15mm. broad at base, gradually narrowing to a point, 15cm. long; *upper surface* grey-green, flat low down, canaliculate upwards, minutely muricate and marked throughout with numerous very small crowded dull-white spots; lower surface rounded, similar to upper surface in colour and markings; *margins* with narrow dull-white cartilaginous edge ciliate-dentate with very crowded dull-white, soft to firm (not pungent) teeth ·5—1mm. long low down, smaller to obsolescent upwards.

Inflorescence simple, 2—3 consecutively, 30—36cm. tall.

Peduncle erect, very slender (1·5—2mm. diam.), with about 5 sterile-bracts, the lowest narrowly deltoid-acuminate, 10mm. long, 3mm. broad at base, very thin, white, 3—5-nerved, smaller upwards.

Raceme 9cm. long, laxly about 18-flowered, the buds denser, grey-brown striped in upper half, gradually laxer downwards with the lowest flowers nutant and 15mm. apart.

FIG. 413.

A. albiflora Guillaumin. Plant flowering at Mbabane. Height 25cm.

Bracts ovate-long acuminate, 5—6mm. long, 2mm. broad at base, thin, pale, obscurely 3—5-nerved, the nerves pink.

Pedicels the lowest spreading, 8mm. long, ·5mm. thick, shorter and suberect upwards.

Perianth white, broadly campanulate, 10mm. long, 14mm. across the mouth, tapering to a point at base; *outer segments* free almost to base, 3-nerved in upper third, the nerves grey-brown, white below, the apices subacute and recurved to revolute; *inner segments* free, broader than the outer, 3-nerved in upper third only, the apices more obtuse than the outer and slightly less recurved.

Filaments filiform, white, the 3 inner narrower and prominently lengthening before the 3 outer; *anthers* orange, the 3 inner and 3 outer in turn exserted 8mm.; *style* white, with stigma at length exserted 9mm.; *ovary* 2mm. long, 1·5mm. diam., almost truncate. (Figs. 413, 414).

Note: *Guillauminia albiflora* cannot be upheld as a genus distinct from Aloe.

TULÉAR PROV. *Fort Dauphin Div.,* est de Tsivory, Boiteau f. 227! 1939, type (P); ex Vihabano, Est Tsivory, cult. Johannesburg, fl. 9—27 March 1955, Reynolds 7589 (PRE, K). The type consists of one inflorescence without leaves and was collected by Boiteau in 1939 E of Tsivory which is about 100km. NNE of Antanimora, at c. 24° 04′ S, 46° 05′ E, in the far south.

FIG. 414.

A. albiflora Guillaumin. Raceme and flowers natural size.

A. albiflora is a most distinctive little species with narrow, muricate leaves, and widely campanulate snow-white flowers that are 10mm. long and 14mm. across the mouth. Although the flowers are not closely allied to those of any other known species of Aloe, it seems that *A. bellatula* Reynolds is its nearest affinity in leaf characters only.

A noteworthy character of *A. albiflora* is that the 3 inner filaments lengthen very prominently before the 3 outer, and the anthers are in turn exserted 8mm. which is nearly the length of the perianth.

Under a lens against the light, the whole perianth glistens as if composed of countless minute water globules.

Flowering time is not stated on the stype sheet, but in Johannesburg and Mbabane, plants flower in March.

157. **A. calcairophila** Reynolds in *Journ. S.A. Bot.* 27: 5 (1961).

DESCRIPTION: *Plant* with cylindric roots, small, acaulescent, suckering and forming groups.

Leaves c. 10, distichous, spreading almost horizontally and slightly recurved, 5—6cm. long, 14mm. broad at base, narrowing to an acute point; *upper surface* dull grey-green, without spots or markings, canaliculate; *lower surface* grey-green, rounded; *margins* ciliate with slender pointed, cartilaginous, rather soft white teeth 2—3mm. long, 2—3mm. apart.

Inflorescence simple, 20—25cm. long.

Peduncle very slender, clothed with several white sterile bracts that are narrowly ovate-acute, 6mm. long, 3mm. broad, obscurely 3-nerved, shorter upwards.

Raceme 3—4cm. long, laxly 8—12-flowered.

Bracts ovate-acute, 3mm. long, 2mm. broad, white, thin, scarious, obscurely 3-nerved.

Pedicels 5—6mm. long.

Perianth white, cylindric-trigonous, slightly ventricose, 10mm. long, basally obtuse, 4mm. diam. at the middle, slightly constricted at the throat, the mouth wide open; *outer segments* free for 5mm., with 3 crowded greenish nerves at apex, the apices subacute, spreading to slightly revolute; *inner segments* broader than the outer, dorsally adnate to the outer to the middle, with a greenish keel in upper half, the apices more obtuse, and more spreading than the outer.

Filaments white, the 3 inner narrower and lengthening before the 3 outer with their *anthers* in turn not exserted; *stigma* not exserted; *ovary* green, about 1·5mm. long, 1·5mm. diam. (Figs. 415–419).

MADAGASCAR. FIANARANTSOA PROV.: On limestone hill, 2km. S of Ambatofinandrahana, alt. c. 1400m., fl. 27 Jan. 1957, Descoings 2114, holotype (TAN), isotype (K); cult. Johannesburg, fl. 28 May 1960, Descoings et Reynolds 8305 (PRE).

This is the second species of Aloe discovered by Monsieur B. Descoings, when he was botanist at the Institut de Recherche Scientifique de Madagascar, Tsimbasasa, Tananarive.

M. Descoings found plants on a south slope of a small dusty white hill of limestone, about 2km. S of Ambatofinandrahana (which is W of Ambositra) on the road to Fenoarivo, at an altitude of about 1400m., in the Province of Fianarantsoa, at c. 20° 34′ S, 46° 48′ E.

Professor W. Rauh of Heidelberg University, W. Germany, has also found plants in a similar limestone habitat, but 3km. NW of Ambatofinandrahana.

FIG. 415.

A. calcairophila Reynolds. Plants natural size growing in limestone rubble 3km. NW of Ambatofinandrahana, Madagascar.

Photo: Prof. W. Rauh.

FIG. 416.

A. calcairophila Reynolds.   Plant × 2/5, from 2km. S of Ambatofinandrahana, Fianarantsoa Prov., Madagascar, flowering in Johannesburg.

FIG. 417.

A. calcairophila Reynolds. Leaf cluster 1/1 of a plant from 2km. S of Ambato-finandrahana.

A. calcairophila is a charming little species with white flowers that are only 10mm. long. The roots are cylindric, not fusiform. Plants sucker from base, and also at the axils of the lowest leaves, forming small dense groups. Leaves are distichous, the margins being ciliate with somewhat soft cartilaginous, narrow, long-pointed, white teeth. Plants flower in April–May in cultivation, and in January–February in the wild state.

A. calcairophila is nearest allied to *A. descoingsii* Reynolds, but the latter has shorter, rosulate, spotted leaves, and shorter red flowers that are broader at base and narrower at the mouth.

FIG. 418.

A. calcairophila, Reynolds. Raceme and flowers natural size.

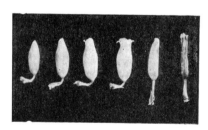

FIG. 419.

A. calcairophila Reynolds. Flowers natural size.

158. **A. descoingsii** Reynolds in *Journ. S.A. Bot.* 24: 103 (1958).

DESCRIPTION: *Plant* succulent, suckering freely and forming dense groups. *Stem* none or very short.

Leaves about 8—10, densely rosulate, ovate-attenuate, up to 30mm. long, 15mm. broad at base, spreading to recurved; *upper surface* flat low down, canaliculate upwards, rough to the touch, dull green with numerous dull white tubercular excrescences throughout giving a white-spotted effect; *lower surface* rounded, similar to upper surface in colour and tubercular excrescences; *margins* somewhat involute, armed with firm white, cartilaginous, deltoid teeth that are 1mm. long, 1—1·5mm. apart low down, smaller upwards, obsolescent near apex.

Inflorescence simple, 12—15cm. tall.

Peduncle 1·5mm. thick near base, 1mm. below the raceme, brown with a slight bloom, clothed with up to 10 sterile-bracts that are amplexicaul, narrowly deltoid, about 6mm. long, 2mm. broad at base.

Raceme capitate, about 10-flowered, the pedicellate portion 12mm. long, 25mm. diam., youngest buds obliquely spreading to horizontally disposed, open flowers nutant.

Bracts ovate-acute, 2mm. long, 1mm. broad, thin, scarious, white, 1-nerved.

Pedicels slender, 5mm. long, 1mm. thick.

Perianth scarlet, paler to slightly orange at mouth, cylindric, 7—8mm. long, basally flat and shortly stipitate, 4mm. diam. across the ovary, narrowing to 3mm. at the mouth; *outer segments* free for 2mm., 3-nerved, the apices subacute, slightly spreading; *inner segments* broader than the outer, with more obtuse, more spreading apices.

Filaments filiform, the 3 inner narrower and lengthening before the 3 outer with their *anthers* not exserted; *stigma* not exserted; *ovary* green, 1·5mm. long, 1mm. diam. (Plate 90, Figs. 420, 421).

TULÉAR PROV. Top of limestone cliff near Anjamala Village, about 46 km. NE of Tuléar, 350m. alt., c. 44° E, 23° 11′ S, cult. Tananarive, fl. 15 June 1957, Descoings 2440! holotype (TAN), isotype (PRE); cult. Johannesburg et Pretoria, fl. Aug. 1957, Descoings et Reynolds 8304 (PRE).

A. descoingsii was discovered in 1956 by Mr. B. Descoings (then Botanist at the Institut de Recherche Scientifique de Madagascar, Tsimbazaza, Tananarive), about 1km. beyond Anjamala Village, which village is about 45km. NE of Tuléar on the south-eastern side of the Fiherenana River.

FIG. 420.

A. descoingsii Reynolds. Plants in natural habitat, on top of a limestone cliff near Anjamala Village, 46km. NE of Tuléar, Madagascar, × ⅛ approx.

Photo: Prof. W. Rauh.

FIG. 421.

A. descoingsii Reynolds. Raceme and flowers natural size.

PLATE 90

ALOE DESCOINGSII   Reynolds.

Plants from top of limestone cliff 46km. NE of Tuléar, Madagascar,
flowering in Johannnesburg, Height 12cm.

Mr. Descoings found large numbers of plants on the top of a limestone cliff in scanty soil facing south. This locality is c. 44° E, 23° 11′ S, at c. 350m. alt. Professor W. Rauh has also found plants at this locality.

A. descoingsii is a most distinctive little species with rosettes of leaves only 5—6cm. across, a very slender, simple inflorescence 12—15cm. high and red flowers only 8—10mm. long in a capitate raceme.

In habit of growth, rosettes, and leaf characters, *A. descoingsii* bears a very striking resemblance to *A. jucunda* Reynolds on Gaan Libah, western end of the Golis Range, between Hargeisa and Sheikh, in Somalia North, but the latter has a thicker peduncle, a taller inflorescence 20—30cm. high, and lax racemes of rose-pink cylindric flowers 24mm. long.

FIG. 422.   FIG. 423.
A. rauhii Reynolds.
FIG. 422. Plant × ½, originally collected by Prof. W. Rauh, 10km. SE of Ampanihy, Tuléar Prov., Southern Madagascar.   FIG. 423. Raceme and flowers 1/1.
Photos: Prof. W. Rauh.

159. **A. rauhii** Reynolds in *Journ. S.A. Bot.* 29: 151 (1963).

DESCRIPTION: *Plant* succulent, acaulescent, or with very short stem, forming dense groups, with rosettes averaging 10cm. across.

Leaves up to 20, densely rosulate, lanceolate-deltoid, 7—10cm. long, 15—20mm. broad at base, gradually narrowing to an acute apex, the younger leaves suberectly spreading, the older spreading; *upper surface* canaliculate, grey-green, sometimes with brownish tinge, with numerous narrowly H-shaped spots scattered irregularly throughout; *lower surface* rounded, otherwise as the upper; *margins* with white cartilaginous edge armed with very small white cartilaginous deltoid teeth about ·5mm. long, 1—2mm. apart.

Inflorescence simple, or rarely with a short branch low down, 30cm. tall.

Peduncle basally plano-convex and 4mm. broad, terete upwards, brownish-maroon with a whitish waxlike bloom, with a few sterile bracts that are white, scarious, semi-amplexicaul, 6mm. long, 3mm. broad, 3—5-nerved.

Raceme cylindric, slightly acuminate, laxly 12—18-flowered, about 7cm. long, 4cm. diam., open flowers nutant to pendulous.

Bracts ovate-acute, long-pointed, 4—5mm. long, 2mm. broad, white, scarious, 3—5-nerved.

Pedicels slender, 10mm. long, the colour of the perianth.

Perianth rose-scarlet, paler at mouth, 25mm. long, shortly stipitate at base, 5mm. diam. across the ovary, very slightly constricted above the ovary, thence very slightly enlarging trigonously to an open mouth; *outer segments* free to base, obscurely 3-nerved; *inner segments* free, broader than the outer, with a scarlet keel throughout, the apices more obtuse and slightly more spreading than the outer.

Filaments lemon-yellow, filiform-flattened, the 3 inner narrower and lengthening before the 3 outer with their *anthers* in turn exserted 0—1mm.; *style* lemon-yellow with *stigma* at length exserted 1mm.; *ovary* pale olive, 4·4mm. long, 2mm. diam.; *fruit* 10—15mm. long, 7mm. diam. at middle. (Figs. 422, 423)

TULÉAR PROV. 10km. SE of Ampanihy on sandstone rocks in dense bush, fl. 3 Oct. 1961, W. Rauh 7594 holotype (K), isotype (HEID); plant coll. Rauh, cult. Mbabane, Swaziland, fl. 15 Sept. 1963, Rauh et Reynolds 10114 (PRE).

This very distinctive and charming little species was named after Professor Dr. W. Rauh (Heidelberg University, W. Germany), who discovered it in October 1961 on sandstone rocks, in dense bush about 10km. SE of Ampanihy, near the Tuléar–Ambovombe main road in the dry southwestern region of Madagascar. Professor Rauh found plants growing in groups with rosettes averaging 10cm. across, and with inflorescences that were mostly simple although an occasional inflorescence was found with a short branch arising from below the middle.

A. rauhii is a very distinctive species, nearest allied to *A. parvula* Berger in size, inflorescence and general habit of growth, but the latter is a slightly larger plant and differs in having unspotted leaves both surfaces of which are muricate to shortly tuberculate-subspinulescent. In *A. rauhii* leaf surfaces are smooth with numerous narrowly H-shaped spots scattered irregularly throughout.

160. **A. bakeri** Scott Elliot in *Journ. Linn. Soc.* 29: 60 (1891); Berger in Engler *Pflanzenr.* Liliac.–Aloin. 254 (1908); H. Perrier in *Mém. Soc. Linn. Norm.* 1 (1): 26 (1926), et *Fl. Madag.* Liliac. 85 (1938); Reynolds in *Aloes Madag. Revis.* 25 (1958); Verdoorn in *Fl. Plants Afr.* 36: Plate 1401 (1963).

DESCRIPTION: *Plant* small, proliferous, branching at base and with off-shoots forming small to large densely packed groups of 50—100 and more individuals. *Stem* prolongate, 10—20cm. long, 5—7mm. diam., with the apical 5—8cm. subdensely to sublaxly foliate, with the internodes 5—10mm. distant.

Leaves about 12, basally sheathing, averaging 8mm. broad at base, gradually narrowing to a pointed apex and 7cm. long, spreading to recurved; *upper surface* flat to slightly canaliculate, green with reddish tinge, without spots or sometimes with a few dull pale greenish spots throughout; *lower surface* rounded, dull green, varying from unspotted to copiously spotted throughout, the spots more elongated and more obscure than upper surface; *margins* armed with firm (not pungent) cartilaginous deltoid white teeth that are 1mm. long, 1—2mm. apart, usually larger and more crowded low down, smaller to obsolescent towards apex.

Inflorescence simple, averaging 25—30cm. tall.

Peduncle slender, plano-convex and 3mm. broad at base, terete upwards, reddish-brown, with 3—4 sterile-bracts in upper half, the bracts ovate-acuminate, 3—4mm. long, 2·5mm. broad, thin, pale, scarious, with 3 crowded nerves.

Raceme subcapitate, 3—4cm. long, laxly 8—12-flowered, the buds suberectly spreading, open flowers nutant.

Bracts ovate-acuminate, thin, scarious, white, 3mm. long, 1·5mm. broad, 3-nerved.

Pedicels 10—12mm. long, the colour of the peduncle.

Perianth cylindric-trigonous, slightly curved, averaging 23mm. long, apricot-scarlet in lower third, shading through orange to yellowish at the mouth and greenish tipped, shortly stipitate at base, very slightly constricted above the ovary, slightly decurved, thence enlarging and very slightly ventricose; *outer segments* free to base but slightly cohering in lower half, the nerves green at apex, apices subacute and slightly spreading; *inner segments* free, thinner at the edges, keeled throughout, the apices more obtuse and more spreading than the outer.

Filaments pale lemon, the 3 inner narrower and lengthening before the 3 outer with their *anthers* in turn exserted 0—1mm.; *style* lemon-yellow, with *stigma* at length exserted 0—1mm.; *ovary* orange-green, 4mm. long, 2mm. diam., apex truncate. (Plate 91. Figs. 424-426)

TULÉAR PROV. Fort Dauphin Div.: Dry ground, Fort Dauphin, June–July (no year stated), Scott Elliot 2957, holotype (K). No mention is made of "sand dunes" on the type sheet. Perrier cites Decary 8926, 9856, 10272, 10324, 10325 (P). On a rocky whaleback low hill, 8 km. west of Fort Dauphin on road to Vinanibe, c. 25°04′S., 46°54′., c. 40 m, fl. 1 July 1955, Reynolds 7806 (TAN, P, K, PRE).

PLATE 91

ALOE BAKERI   Scott Elliot.

Plants flowering on a low rocky hill near Fort Dauphin, Madagascar.
Height 25cm.

FIG. 424.

A. bakeri Scott Elliot. Dense group on rocky hill near Fort Dauphin, S. Madagascar.

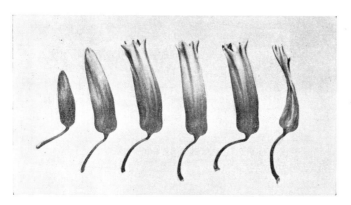

FIG. 425.

A. bakeri Scott Elliot. Flowers natural size.

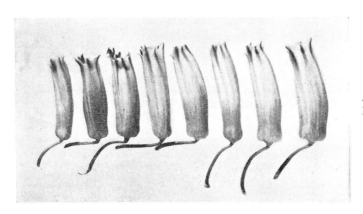

FIG. 426.

A. bakeri Scott Elliot. Various flowers 1/1, gathered at random, showing variation.

I found this most charming little species mostly along the top of a low semi-denuded whale-back hill 8km. W of Fort Dauphin in considerable numbers, and in small to large dense groups of 60–100 plants and more. Plants were found only in rock-crevices, and in shallow pockets of soil – never in loose sand as the previously published misleading term "sand-dunes" implied. Stems vary in length. In exposed places crowded stems average 10—15cm. in length with the apical 5—8cm. foliate, while in deep crevices and in low undergrowth they may reach 30cm. with the apical 20cm. laxly foliate. The average is 10—15cm. long with the apical 5cm. subdensely to sub-laxly foliate. Leaves vary from entirely without spots on both surfaces, to sparingly or copiously spotted on both sides.

The flowers are one of the most beautiful in the genus, the lower third of the perianth being apricot suffused scarlet, shading through orange to yellow at the mouth, with the segment apices green-tipped. The outer segments are visibly free to the middle, thence slightly cohere to base and can be easily freed with the fingers. They are not concrescent or connate into a tube, hence are now described as free to base.

A. bakeri does not seem to be closely allied to any other species, although in habit of growth, and prolongate stems with the apical 5—10cm. sublaxly foliate, it may be allied to *A. millotii* Reynolds from Cap Ste. Marie. In racemes, pedicels and flowers, but not leaves, *A. bakeri* appears to be allied to *A. versicolor* Guillaumin which I found in flower 17km. SW of Manantenina in the Manampaniky Valley, 131km. by road NNE from Fort Dauphin. The latter, however, is acaulous, and has much larger leaves and rosettes, and differently shaped flowers.

161. **A. parallelifolia** H. Perr. in *Mém. Soc. Linn. Norm.* 1 (1): 31, Plate 4 (1926) et *Fl. Madag.* Liliac. 92, Fig. XIII, 4, (1938); Reynolds in *Aloes Madag. Revis.* 29 (1958).

DESCRIPTION: *Plant* with fibrous roots. *Stem* very slender, erect, about 4cm. long, with a few shoots from base forming compact groups. *Leaves* 4—7, basally sheathing, laxly rosulate, rather divaricately arcuate-ascending with upper third slightly twisted, very fleshy, linear, 15cm. long, 6mm. broad at base, 10mm. broad at the middle and 7mm. thick, the apex rounded and armed with 4—5 1mm. long pale-brown teeth; *upper surface* slightly convex, dull olive-green without spots or markings; *lower surface* much rounded, similar in colour to upper surface; *margins* more or less parallel, obtuse to rounded, irregularly dentate with pale-brown pointed teeth up to 2mm. long, 4—8mm. and more apart.
Inflorescence simple, erect, 30—40cm. long.
Peduncle basally plano-convex and 6mm. broad, terete upwards and 4mm. diam., with 5—10 sterile-bracts, the lowest ovate-acuminate, 9mm. broad at base, 14mm. long, subscarious, 5-nerved, smaller upwards.
Raceme varying from longer and laxer to subcapitate, and 12—18-flowered, the apex a tuft of dried bracts, buds sub-erect, open flowers nutant.
Bracts lanceolate-acute, clasping the pedicel, rather thick and fleshy at base, 10mm. long, 4mm. broad at base, 5-nerved.
Pedicels slender, spreading, 30mm. long, the colour of base of perianth.
Perianth rose-pink to rose-red with segment apices almost white, cylindric, very slightly narrowly campanulate, 30mm. long, basally obtuse, 5mm. diam. across the ovary, enlarging to 8mm. at the throat with the mouth wide open; *outer segments* themselves free but tightly cohering to the inner segments in lower half, rose-red in lower half, greenish-white upwards, the margins thin, with white border, apices acute, spreading; *inner segments* free but dorsally cohering to the outer to the middle, broader than the outer, with thin white edges and a prominent keel throughout, the apices more obtuse and more spreading than the outer.
Filaments lemon, filiform-flattened, the 3 inner narrower and lengthening before the 3 outer with their *anthers* in turn exserted 0—1mm.; *stigma* at length exserted 1—2mm.; *ovary* pale yellowish-green, 4mm. long, 2mm. diam., apex truncate or obtuse. (Plate 92, Figs. 427, 428).

TANANARIVE PROV. Quartzite detritus on the Laniharina–Tsitondraina range near the confluence of the Manandona and Mania Rivers, 1800—2000m., flowering in Oct.—Nov., Perrier 13981 (P. holotype, K).

Perrier states that this species has only been found on quartzites of the Laniharina—Tsitondraina range where it grows in large numbers, and on Mont Ibity the adjoining mountain to the north, at 2300m. These mountains lie to the west of the Antsirabe—Ambositra main road.

Perrier's Plate 4 is a photograph of a plant flowering in Tananarive, and depicts a laxly-flowered raceme which is about 8cm. long. A plant that flowered in Johannesburg produced a more densely flowered capitate raceme, the pedicellate portion being only 2cm. long with the ovary acuminate into the style. The type is described with ovary truncate at apex.

A. parallelifolia is a most distinctive species. The fleshy leaves are sometimes almost cylindric at the middle, and marginal teeth vary considerably in the distance between them. The outer segments are best described as free to the middle although they cohere tightly in lower half, but can be freed with the fingers without tearing.

It seems that racemes vary from more densely flowered and capitate, to fewer flowered, longer and much laxer.

In leaf characters and flowers, *A. parallelifolia* shows some affinity with *A. versicolor* Guillaumin but it does not seem to be closely allied to any Malagasy species.

PLATE 92

ALOE PARALLELIFOLIA   H. Perr.

A form with raceme shorter than usual, flowering in Johannnesburg.
Height 30cm.

FIG. 427.

A. parallelifolia H. Perr. Reproduced from *Mem. Soc. Linn Norm.*, plate 4 (1926). –Perrier's original figure.

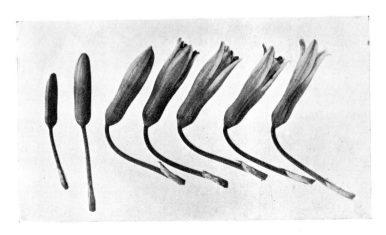

FIG. 428.

A. parallelifolia H. Perr. Flowers natural size, from a plant that flowered in Johannesburg.

162. **A. boiteaui** Guillaumin in *Bull. Mus. Hist. Nat. Paris* 2 (14): 349 (1942).

DESCRIPTION based partly on Prof. Guillaumin, but mostly on cultivated plants.

Plants acaulescent, or with short stem?

Leaves about 10, rosulate, erectly spreading, recurved at apex, 15—20cm. long, 14mm. broad, with margins almost parallel but narrowing slightly to an obtuse apex; *upper surface* flat; *lower surface* convex; both surfaces olive-green without lines or markings; *margins* with narrow, continuous, cartilaginous, pinkish edge, armed with pinkish teeth that are very small and crowded near base, longer and more distant upwards, ·5—1mm. long, 2mm. apart in upper third, obsolescent near apex.

Inflorescence simple, 10—15cm. high, scarcely longer than the leaves.

Raceme rather laxly about 14-flowered, 5cm. long.

Pedicels the lowest up to 10mm. long, the reddish colour of the perianth.

Bracts lowest deltoid-acute, thin, whitish, 5mm. long, 3mm. broad, 5-nerved.

FIG. 429.

A. boiteaui Guillaumin. Plant approx. × ½ flowering at Heidelberg University, W. Germany.
Photo: Prof. W. Rauh.

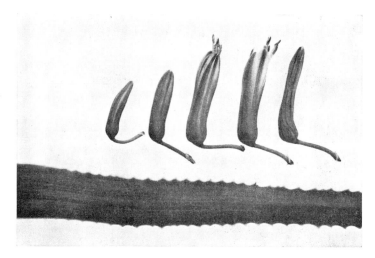

FIG. 430.

A. boiteaui Guillaumin. Flowers and portion of leaf, both 1/1, **as** received in liquid from Prof. W. Rauh.

Perianth bright scarlet-red, cylindric-trigonous, 25mm. long, slightly narrowed on underside only above the ovary, thence trigonously enlarging to the throat; *outer segments* free for 18mm. (tube 7mm.), with 3 greenish nerves near apex, the apices acute, straight; *inner segments* broader than the outer, with a median scarlet-red keel in lower two-thirds, turning green upwards.

Filaments very pale-lemon, with the 3 inner and 3 outer *anthers* in turn exserted 1—2mm.; *stigma* at length exserted 2—3mm.; *ovary* lemon, 5mm. long, 2mm. diam. (Figs. 429, 430).

MADAGASCAR. Fort Dauphin (Boiteau, f. 227 (1939), flowers in June (P). No precise locality given.

Professor Guillaumin kindly sent me a leaf and an inflorescence from the type plant when it flowered in Paris in November 1956 – originally received from Boiteau in 1939. The leaf, 19cm. long, 15mm. broad, gradually tapered to an acute apex which conflicts with the description *"apicem versus fere haud attenuata"*. The 9cm. long, simple inflorescence bore a 4cm. long raceme with 15 flowers.

Humbert 13738! (quoted by Guillaumin as 13–7–1938) is placed by Guillaumin under *A. boiteaui*, but this material very cosely resembles the type of *Lomatophyllum citreum* Guillaumin, which is Boiteau s.n.! (f. 227–1939). The type of *A. boiteaui* is also Boiteau s.n. – f. 227, 1939. Professor Humbert (*in litt.*) states that his 13738 resembles the type specimen of *Lomatophyllum citreum* very closely and may well be that species, as well as his 13190 from the same area.

A. boiteaui is a peculiar little species with ascending leaves, and a simple inflorescence scarcely longer than the leaves. A plant grown at Mbabane has put out several shoots from base, but has not flowered in 3 years.

163. **A. versicolor** Guillaumin in *Bull. Mus. Hist. Nat. Paris*. ser. 2, 21: 723 (1950); Reynolds in *Aloes Madag. Revis.* 29 (1958).

DESCRIPTION: *Plant* acaulous or with very short stem, suckering and forming small to large dense groups of compact rosettes.

Leaves averaging 15, ascending, almost linear, densely rosulate, 15cm. long, 20mm. broad at base, gradually tapering to the apex which is acutely rounded and armed with 3—5 small white cartilaginous teeth about 1mm. long; *upper surface* flat to slightly canaliculate, dull bluish-green with a bloom, without spots or markings; *lower surface* rounded, similar to upper surface; *margins* with narrow white cartilaginous edge armed with firm (not pungent) deltoid cartilaginous white teeth about 1·5—2mm. long, 5—6mm. apart. *Sap* dries deep brown.

Inflorescence always simple, erect, rigid, 30—40cm. tall.

Peduncle basally plano-convex and 8—9mm. broad, terete upwards, brown with a bloom, with 6—9 sterile-bracts in upper half, the lowest averaging 15mm. long, 8mm. broad, many-nerved, smaller upwards.

Racemes cylindric, subcapitate, the pedicellate portion averaging 5cm. long, sublaxly flowered, youngest buds spreading horizontally or slightly downwards, open flowers subpendulous.

Bracts ovate-acute, dirty white, 7mm. long, 4mm. broad, subscarious, paler at the margins, 5-nerved.

Pedicels 15—20mm. long (18mm. the average), spreading almost horizontally, nutant at apex, the colour of the base of the perianth.

Perianth cylindric, straight, averaging 25mm. long, coral-red to pale scarlet at base, paler upwards, yellowish at the tips, basally slightly rounded to obtusely tapering into the pedicel and sometimes shortly stipitate, 7mm. diam. across the ovary, the mouth open; *outer segments* free almost to base, with pale margins, prominently 3-nerved throughout, the apices subacute, slightly spreading; *inner segments* free, with broad pale border, prominently keeled, the apices more obtuse and slightly more spreading than the outer.

Filaments very pale lemon, the 3 inner narrower and lengthening before the 3 outer with their *anthers* in turn exserted 2—3mm.; *style* lemon; *stigma* at length exserted 4mm.; *ovary* pale olive, trigonal, 6mm. long, 3mm. diam., the apex obtuse. (Plate 93, Figs. 431, 432).

TULÉAR PROV. Fort Dauphin Div.: Lower Manampaniky, about 100km. N of Fort Dauphin, about 50m. alt., silicious rocks in full sunlight, in flower and fruit 18—23 March 1947, Humbert f.150, 1947 = 20617! type (P).

On rocks in scanty soil, in valley of the Manampaniky River, 17km. SW of Manantenina, c. 24° 18′ S, 47° 10′ E, alt. 50m., 2 July 1955, Reynolds 7812 (TAN, P, K, PRE); 32 km. SW of Manantenina, 70m. alt., leaf only, Reynolds 7815 (TAN, P, K, PRE).

A. versicolor was discovered by Professor Humbert in the Manampaniky Valley in March 1947. Professor Humbert states (*in litt.*) that the type (Humbert 20617) was taken from a plant that flowered in the greenhouse in Paris in December 1949, and that this plant was raised from seeds that he had collected in 1947. The type consists of a peduncle only without flowers, and with no leaf.

On 2 July 1955 Mr. Descoings and I found large numbers of plants in flower in the Manampaniky Valley 17km. SW of Manantenina, a distance of 131km. by road from Fort Dauphin. Continuing along the Ranomafana road numbers were found in the same valley 32km. and 40km. SW of Manantenina at 70—80m. alt., but plants were only in young bud. These plants were larger than those

PLATE 93

ALOE VERSICOLOR   Guillaumin.

Plants in the Manampanihy Valley, 17km. SW of Manantenina, N of
Fort Dauphin, Madagascar. Height 35cm.

nearer the sea, leaves reaching 26cm. in length and 3·5cm. broad. Professor W. Rauh has found plants much further south, between Fort Dauphin and Ranomafana.

Racemes vary from shorter and more densely flowered to longer and laxer – 5cm. being the average.

A striking character of the racemes is that the uppermost pedicels are almost horizontal with their buds disposed horizontally to slightly downwards. The buds are laxer, with the open flowers more densely grouped and almost pendulous.

The inflorescence is erect, rigid, and not flexuous as described.

In raceme characters, the spreading pedicels and young buds disposed horizontally or slightly downwards, *A. versicolor* is allied to *A. bakeri* Scott Elliot. The latter, however, is a considerably smaller plant with slender, prolongate stems and very different leaves.

Fig. 431.

A. versicolor Guillaumin. A weak form in the Manampanihy Valley, 17km. SW of Manantenina, about 130km. N. of Fort Dauphin, Madagascar. Height about 30cm.

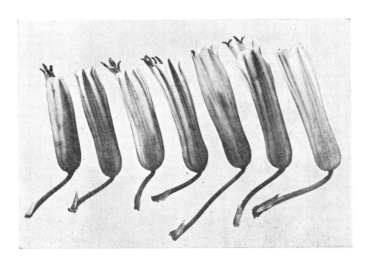

Fig. 432.

A. versicolor Guillaumin. Flowers 1/1 gathered at random, showing variation.

GROUP 2

PLANTS SMALL WITH LITTLE OR NO STEM; LEAVES DISTICHOUS; INFLORESCENCE SIMPLE OR RARELY 1-BRANCHED; RACEME CAPITATE OR SUBCAPITATE, DENSELY FLOWERED; PEDICELS VERY SHORT; PERIANTH WHITE OR SCARLET, 25—55MM. LONG; OUTER SEGMENTS FREE; ANTHERS SCARCELY EXSERTED.

One Species: *A. compressa* H. Perrier.

One very small species with distichous leaves (*A. calcairophila* Reynolds) is included in Group 1.

(1) Perianth white 25—33mm. long; bracts large, 20mm.; plant robust with smooth leaf surfaces, marginal teeth spaced (on quartzites) 164 *A. compressa*

(2) Perianth red, 22mm. long, small plants with almost confluent marginal teeth (on schists) .. .. 164B var. *schistophila*

(3) Perianth white, 55mm. long; with verrucose leaf surfaces and spaced marginal teeth (on quartzites) .. .. 164A var. *rugosquamosa*

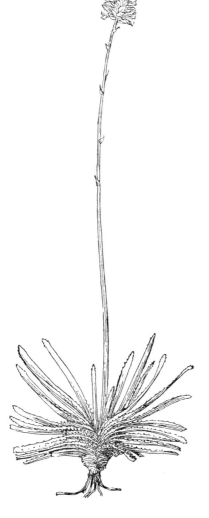

FIG. 433.

A. compressa H. Perr. Reproduction of Perrier's Fig. XII, 6, in *Fl. Madag.* 91 (1938) − × 1/5 natural size.

164. **A. compressa** H. Perrier in *Mém. Soc. Linn. Norm.* (*l.c.*) 33 (1926), et *Fl. Madag.* 97, Fig. XII, 6–7 (1938); Reynolds in *Aloes Madag. Revis.* 35 (1958).

DESCRIPTION: *Plant* solitary, without suckers, acaulous or sub-acaulescent.
Leaves 15—20, distichous, smooth, glaucous, 12—15 cm. long, 5cm. broad, suberect to spreading, 5—6mm. thick, gradually narrowing to a rounded apex; *marginal teeth* flattened, green or with red apices, 2mm. long, 4—5mm. apart, almost confluent near base, wider apart upwards.
Inflorescence simple, rarely 1-branched, 60—70cm. high.
Peduncle very long with 15—20 sterile-bracts that are white, scarious, broadly triangular-acute, 4—5-nerved.
Raceme dense, almost oval, (7—8 × 6cm.), with 40—60 white flowers.
Bracts white, scarious, large (20—24 × 10—17mm.), 5—6-nerved, the lower prolonged into a long acute point, the upper with gradually shorter points, more obtuse and even emarginate at the top.
Pedicels very short (1—2mm.).
Perianth 25—33mm. straight, sub-trigonous, with free segments, the outer ones connivent into a tube in their lower half and recurved and rolled backwards above; the inner connivent right up to the top in a sub-arcuate tube with the tips broadened and strongly imbricate. *Stamens* subequal. *Ovary* subobtuse. – H. Perrier. (Figs. 433, 434).

TANANARIVE PROV. On quartzite rocks, between 1000m. and 1500m., left bank of the Mania River, flowers March–May, Perrier 12556! type (P); Laniharina–Tsitondraina range, right bank of the Mania, Perrier 12556*bis*!, specimens differing from the type in having narrower bracts, more numerous and closer marginal teeth and perianths striped with red; other mountains on right bank of the Mania, Perrier 15872! (P); also observed at Anjanabonoina, basin of the Andratsay, specimens differing from the type in having longer leaves with conical not flattened marginal teeth.

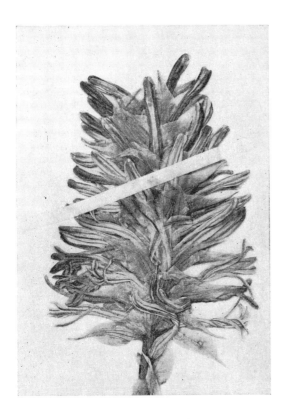

FIG. 434.

A. compressa H. Perr. Raceme 1/1 of Perrier 12556, type (P).

164A var. **rugo-squamosa** H. Perr. in *Mém. Soc. Linn. Norm.* (*l.c.*) 34, et *Fl. Madag.* (*l.c.*) 98; Reynolds in *Aloes Madag. Revis.* 37 (1958).

Differs from the type in being more robust, in having longer leaves up to 23cm., narrower and 3—3·5cm. broad, greyish, with leaf upper surface covered with tiny obsolete obtuse protuberances which make it rough, smaller closer marginal teeth, stouter often-branched inflorescence, much larger bracts, about as long as the perianth (15mm. broad), and much longer perianths (55mm.). – H. Perrier. (Fig. 435).

TANANARIVE PROV. Quartzites of Monts Ivohibe and Iarambo, at about 1350m. in the Andratsay–Mahajilo basin, central region, March 1914, Perrier 10993! (P).

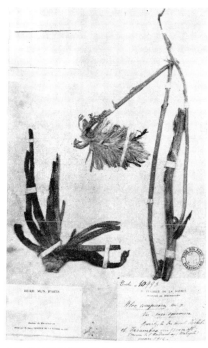

FIG. 435.

A. compressa H. Perr. var. *rugosquamosa* H. Perr. Photograph (considerably reduced) of the holotype, Perrier 10993 (P).

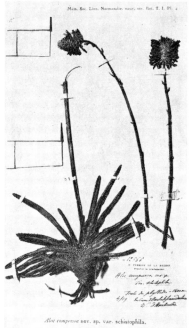

FIG. 436.

A. compressa H. Perr. var. *schistophila* H. Perr. Reproduced from *Mem. Soc. Linn. Norm.* Pl. 4 (1926). Perrier 12566 (P).

164B. var. **schistophila** H. Perr. in *Mém. Soc. Linn. Norm.* (*l.c.*) 34, et *Fl. Madag.* (*l.c.*) 99; Reynolds in *Aloes Madag. Revis.* 37 (1958).

Differs from the type by its smaller size, more compressed leaf cluster, more numerous leaves that are smaller (12cm. × 20—25mm.), marginal teeth, almost confluent; raceme shorter (4cm.) and sometimes as broad (4cm.) as long; the smaller perianth (22mm.) which is reddish, by the ovary, which is straight at the top and almost attenuate. The capsules are subcylindrical (20 × 8mm.), and its seeds (5 × 2·5mm.) are shortly winged. – H. Perrier. (Figs. 436–440).

FIANARANTSOA PROV. West Betsileo, on schistose rocks to the N of Ambatofinandranhana, about 1400m., June 1912, Perrier 11005 (P), April 1919, Perrier 12566! (P).

Fig. 437.

A. compressa H. Perr. ? var. *schistophila* H. Perr. Possibly a weak form. Height 30cm., collected by Mr. G. Fievet on the Alarobia – Ambovombe road, 24km. S of the Ivato – Ambatofi-nandrahana road, Fianarantsoa Prov., Madagascar.

Fig. 438.

A. compressa H. Perr. ? var. *schistophila* H. Perr. Raceme 1/1 – Note remarkably revolute outer segments.

Perrier records that the var. *schistophila* only propagates by seed, is very constant in any given locality, and has as many geographical races as there are known localities. It is a remarkable example of adaptation to the very friable schistose rocks of the mountains of West Betsileo. Perrier also states that the various races of *A. compressa* grow in crevices of fissile strata, schists and quartzites, and that it is hardly possible not to notice a close relation between the compact shape of the plants and the fissibility of the rocks.

A plant (collected by Professor W. Rauh, on the Itremo, W of Ambatofinandrahana) has flowered in the author's gardens at Mbabane, Swaziland. It has produced no suckers, and has:

Leaves 12, distichous, 18cm. long, 20mm. broad, both surfaces deep green, smooth, without spots or markings; *marginal teeth* 1—2mm. long, 5—10mm. apart.

Inflorescence 80cm. tall, with one short branch from the middle. *Raceme* sub-capitate, 5cm. long. *Bracts* 15mm. long, 10mm. broad when pressed flat. *Pedicels* negligible.

Perianth cylindric, pale rose-pink, 24mm. long, very slightly curved; *outer segments* free to base, with 3 deep-rose nerves, the upper half of outer segments remarkably recurved and revolute with their apices pointing backwards. *Anthers* and *style* scarcely exserted.

The var. *schistophila* has a slender inflorescence no less than 80cm. high from a small distichous leaf cluster. The outer segments are astonishingly recurved to revolute for half their length, with their apices pointing backwards, and completely exposing the upper 10mm. of the inner segments. This character is unique in the genus *Aloe*.

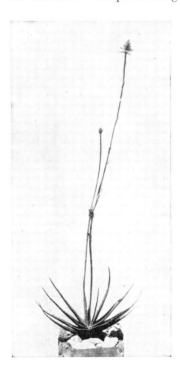

Fig. 439.

A. compressa H. Perrier var. *schistophila* H. Perr. Plant collected by Prof. W. Rauh, on the Itremo, flowering at Mbabane, Swaziland. Height 80cm. A remarkably tall inflorescence from a very small plant; leaves only 18cm. long.

Fig. 440.

A. compressa H. Perr. var. *schistophila* H. Perr. Flowers 1/1 from bud to post-anthesis stage.

GROUP 3

PLANTS ACAULOUS. LEAVES ROSULATE, GREEN, UP TO 50CM. LONG, 3–5CM. BROAD. INFLORESCENCE SIMPLE OR ONLY 1—2-BRANCHED. RACEMES SHORTLY CYLINDRIC, SUBDENSELY FLOWERED. OUTER SEGMENTS FREE.

1. Leaves up to 30cm. long, 3·5cm. broad. Pedicels 14mm. long. Perianth yellow, 21mm. long, slightly campanulate. Anthers exserted 9mm.   .. ..   165 *A. schomeri*
2. Leaves 40—50cm. long, 3cm. broad. Pedicels 15—20mm. Perianth yellow, 25—28mm. long, cylindric-trigonous. Anthers exserted 4mm.   166 *A. buchlohii*

The species in this group are characterized by being acaulous, and by having long, comparatively narrow attenuate leaves averaging about ten times longer than broad.
The inflorescence is simple or only 1—2-branched, and up to 60cm. tall.

165. **A. schomeri** Rauh in *Kakteen und andere Sukkulenten*, 17 Jahrgang, Heft 2, Februar 1966. S. 22—24.

DESCRIPTION: *Plant* acaulescent or with very short stem, growing singly or in groups, with rosettes of leaves up to 30cm. across.

Leaves about 30, densely rosulate, 20—30cm. long, 3—5cm. broad at base, gradually narrowing to the apex, the youngest suberect, the oldest spreading; *upper surface* dark green, slightly channelled; *lower surface* dark-green, convex; *margins* with pale almost white cartilaginous edge armed with deltoid teeth of the same colour, 2mm. broad and 5—8mm. apart.

Inflorescence mostly simple, sometimes 1- or 2-branched. *Peduncle* basally flattened and somewhat triangular, ebracteate to the middle, thence with a few sterile-bracts upwards that are 12mm. long, many-nerved, slightly keeled and with hyaline edge.

Raceme subcapitate or shortly cylindric, 6—10cm. long, 7cm. diam., densely 60—70-flowered.

Bracts about 9mm. long, 5mm. broad at base, with 7 dark-green nerves, the margins white.

Pedicels 12mm. long, 1·5mm. thick, yellowish, suberect.

Perianth yellow, cylindric, slightly campanulate, 21mm. long; *outer segments* free almost to base, the apices rounded and slightly recurved, 4mm. broad, with white edges, and with 3 pale-greenish nerves; *inner segments* a little narrower than the outer, with a median nerve.

Filaments very pale yellow, with their anthers exserted 5—8mm.; *ovary* bright greenish-yellow, 5mm. long. (Figs. 441–444).

FIG. 441.

A. schomeri Rauh. Between Fort Dauphin and Ranomafana, South-Eastern Madagascar.
Photo: Prof. W. Rauh, University of Heidelberg.

S.-E. MADAGASCAR. Fort Dauphin Div., on gneissic rocks between Fort Dauphin and Ranomafana, cult. Heidelberg Bot. Gdn., fl. 27 Oct. 1959, Rauh M.1382, holotype (HEID), isotype (PRE).

A. schomeri is nearest allied to *A. buchlohii* Rauh which it closely resembles in general habit of growth, rosettes, leaves, and racemes of yellow flowers, but it differs in having shorter leaves (30cm. against 40—60cm.), shorter pedicels (12mm. against 15—20mm.), and a perianth which is shorter (21mm.) and more campanulate.

The anthers of *A. schomeri* are also very much more exserted (9mm.) than in *A. buchlohii* (3—4mm.).

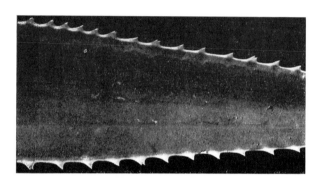

FIG. 442.

A. schomeri Rauh. Portion of leaf 1/1.
Photo: Prof. W. Rauh.

FIG. 443.   FIG. 444.

A. schomeri Rauh.

FIG. 443. Raceme × 9/10.   FIG. 444. Flowers × 9/10.

Photos: Prof. W. Rauh.

Fig. 445.

A. buchlohii Rauh. On rocks 20km. NE of Fort Dauphin on road to Manantenina, in the far SE corner of
Madagascar.
Photo: Professor W. Rauh.

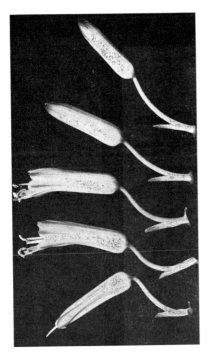

Fig. 446.   Fig. 447.

A. buchlohii Rauh.
Fig. 446. Flowers 1/1 from bud to post-   Fig. 447. Raceme approx. 2/3rds
pollination stages.   natural size.
Photos: Professor W. Rauh.

166. **A. buchlohii** Rauh in *Kakteen und anderer Sukkultenen*, 17 Jahrgang, Heft 1, January 1966, S. 2—4.

DESCRIPTION: *Plant* succulent, acaulescent, solitary or with offshoots from base forming groups, the rosettes about 30cm. across.

Leaves 10—20, densely rosulate, 40—50cm. long, 3cm. broad at base, suberect, very narrowly lanceolate-attenuate, the apex a small spine; *upper surface* unicoloured green, sometimes with reddish tinge, with a few spots near base, flat low down, very slightly canaliculate upwards; *lower surface* convex, otherwise as the upper; *margins* armed with pungent deltoid teeth that are reddish-brown-tipped springing from an almost white base, smaller and more crowded low down, about 3mm. long at the middle of the leaf, 8mm. apart.

Inflorescence to 60cm. high, simple, or in cultivation to 3-branched from about the middle, the branches slender and only 4mm. thick.

Peduncle basally flattened and 10mm. broad, the upper third with a few sterile-bracts the lowest of which fleshy, 15mm. long, 12mm. broad, long-pointed, many-nerved.

Raceme the terminal the longest, sub-capitate, averaging 10cm. long, 7cm. diam., subdensely flowered, the apex a tuft of dried bracts.

Bracts small, ovate-long-pointed, 7mm. long, 2·5mm. broad, thin, scarious, dirty-white, 3-nerved.

Pedicels pale green, 15—20mm. long.

Perianth cylindric-trigonous, 25mm. long, pale yellow, or pale rose at base, yellowish upwards, basally obconic, shortly stipitate, 7mm. diam. across the ovary, the mouth open; *outer segments* free, obscurely 3-nerved, the apices subacute, slightly spreading; *inner segments* a little longer than the outer, pale yellowish with a thick green median nerve.

Filaments unequal, pale yellowish, with their *anthers* in turn exserted about 4mm.; *stigma* at length exserted 5mm.; *ovary* lemon, 6mm. long, 2·5mm. diam. (Figs. 445–447).

MADAGASCAR. Fort Dauphin Div., on bare gneissic rocks 20km. S of Manantenina, 100m. alt., 12 June 1960, Rauh M.1381 (1959) holotype (HEID). Also occurs 20km. NE of Fort Dauphin on road to Manantenina.

When first collected, the leaves suggested that plants might belong to *Lomatophyllum* but when plants subsequently flowered at Heidelburg University, the fruits proved to be dehiscing capsules and not berries, hence belonged to Aloe.

A. buchlohii (named after Dr. Gunther Buchloh of Hohenheim near Stuttgart) is nearest allied to *A. schomeri* Rauh (which also occurs in the Fort Dauphin District) but the latter is a smaller plant with shorter leaves, small marginal teeth, larger bracts, shorter pedicels and shorter (21mm.) more campanulate yellow flowers. The anthers of *A. schomeri* flowers are also much more exserted (9mm.) than in *A. buchlohii* (4mm.).

GROUP 4

LEAVES OVATE-ACUTE OR LANCEOLATE, OBSCURELY OR PROMINENTLY LINEATE, WITH SLIGHT OR PROMINENT CARTILAGINOUS MARGINAL BORDER, THE BORDER WHITE, YELLOWISH, PINK OR REDDISH-PINK, WITH SMALL TEETH OF THE SAME COLOUR. ANTHERS NOT OR VERY SHORTLY EXSERTED.

A. LEAVES WITH VERY NARROW PALE OR WHITE CARTILAGINOUS

MARGINAL BORDER, OBSCURELY LINEATE:

    1. Leaves 10—11cm. long, 2·5—3cm. broad, marginal teeth straw-coloured, 1·5—2mm. long, 3—5mm. apart; bracts small; pedicels 10—12mm., perianth 25—30mm.:

        (*a*) Inflorescence 1—2-branched, 40—60cm.; racemes narrowly cylindric-acuminate, 15—20cm. long; perianth basally obconic..   167 *A. deltoideodonta*

        (*b*) Inflorescence simple, 30cm. high, raceme conical, 6—10cm. long .. ..   167B var. *brevifolia*

    2. Leaves larger, 15—20cm. long, 5—6cm. broad, marginal teeth 1—2mm. long, 5—8mm. apart; inflorescence 1—2-branched, 35—50cm. high; raceme 10—15cm. long; bracts large, snow-white, brittle, 15mm. long, 7mm. broad, usually longer than the 12—15mm. pedicels; perianth 25—30mm., basally obtuse .. .. ..   167A var. *candicans*

B. LEAVES WITH CONSPICUOUS CARTILAGINOUS MARGINAL BORDER 1—1·5mm. BROAD:

    1. *Leaf margins ciliate with narrow long-deltoid soft teeth, 2mm. long with their bases contiguous:*

        (*a*) Leaves 20cm. long, 7—8cm. broad, covered with minute rugosities, rosettes 25—30cm. diam.; inflorescence simple or 1-branched, 40—60cm. high; pedicels 20—25mm.; racemes subcapitate; perianth cylindric-ventricose, 15mm. long .. .. 168 *A. laeta*

(b) Leaves smaller, 8cm. long, 2cm. broad, rounded at apex, rosettes not over 12cm. diam. .. .. 168A var. *maniaensis*

2. *Leaf margins with obtuse marginal teeth 1mm. long, 1—4mm. apart:*

(i) Inflorescence simple, 45cm. long, raceme cylindric, 20—25cm. long, laxly-flowered:

(a) Leaves 30—40cm. long, 8—9cm. broad, light green, lineate, the cartilaginous border and teeth white; bracts very small; pedicels 11mm. long; perianth 22mm. long, outer segments free for 11mm. .. .. 169 *A. viguieri*

(ii) Inflorescence 2—4-branched, 50—80cm. high, racemes more densely flowered:

(a) Leaves 25—30cm. long, 7cm. broad, conspicuously lineate, the cartilaginous border and teeth pale yellow; racemes cylindric-acuminate, 20—25cm. long; pedicels 14mm., perianth 26mm. long, basally obconic .. .. 170 *A. ibitiensis*

(b) Leaves 30cm. long, 12—15cm. broad, the border and teeth reddish-pink; racemes 15cm. long, 7cm. diam.; pedicels 15—18mm. long, perianth 30—34mm. long, basally obtuse; outer segments almost free .. .. 171 *A. imalotensis*

C. LEAVES WITH SLIGHTLY HORNY SINUATE-DENTATE MARGINS AND LARGER MORE SPACED MARGINAL TEETH:

1. Leaves 25cm. long, 8cm. broad, marginal teeth deltoid, sub-pungent, 2mm. long, 5—8mm. apart; inflorescence 6—10-branched, 1m. high; racemes narrowly cylindric-acuminate, 20cm. long, perianth 25mm., basally obconic. Sap white, like a milky froth (the only species with this character) .. .. 172 *A. madecassa*

167. **A. deltoideodonta** Baker in *Journ. Linn. Soc.* 20: 271 (1883); Durand et Schinz in *Consp. Fl. Afr.* 305 (1893); Berger in Engler *Pflanzenr.* Liliac.-Aloin. 186 (1908); H. Perrier in *Mém. Soc. Linn. Norm.* 1 (1): 24 (1926), et *Fl. Madag.* Liliac. 85 (1938); Reynolds in *Journ. S.A. Bot.* 23: 66 (1957), in *Aloes Madag. Revis.* 39 (1958).

—— *Non* Francois in *Mém. Acad. Malg.* fasc. 24, plate 18 (1937).

—— *A. Rossi* Todaro in *Hort. Bot. Panorm.* 58, t. 40 (1894) – *fide* Berger (*l.c.*).

DESCRIPTION: Based on Baker's account, and Baron's material.

Plant acaulous or with short stem, probably suckering and forming groups.

Leaves 12—16, densely rosulate, erectly spreading, lanceolate-deltoid, 10—13cm. long, 2·5—3cm. broad, probably without spots; *margins* with continuous cartilaginous narrow straw-coloured border armed with teeth of the same colour that are deltoid, 2mm. long, 3—5mm. apart.

Inflorescence simple or 1—2-branched, 40—60cm. tall, the peduncle slender, basally flattened and about 12mm. broad, terete upwards.

Raceme rather narrowly cylindric-acuminate and narrowing almost to a point, 15—20cm. long, subdensely flowered, the youngest buds suberect, denser and almost hidden by their bracts, gradually laxer downwards.

Bracts lanceolate-deltoid, white, shorter than the pedicels, about 10mm. long, 5-nerved.

Pedicels the lowest 10—12mm. long.

Perianth probably scarlet and cylindric, about 25mm. long (dry), obtusely tapering at base into the pedicel; *outer segments* free for about 10mm.

Filaments exserted 0—1mm. (Fig. 448).

CENTRAL MADAGASCAR. Rev. R. Baron 946! holotype (K), 752!, 5181! (K, BM).

Baron 752 (received in Kew in October 1881) and Baron 946 (type) – received Oct. 1882 – are both on one sheet labelled "Central Madagascar". Baron 5181 was received in Sept. 1887, and is labelled "Chiefly from north-west Madagascar". No date of flowering is stated, and precise locality of origin is unknown.

Little is known in botanical literature about the Rev. R. Baron who collected about 11,800 specimens in Madagascar between the years 1880 and 1896. Baron lived in Fianarantsoa and collected many plants on the southern part of the ridge of high ground running south through central Madagascar in the country known as Betsileo. The type might have been collected somewhere in this area.

Baron 5181 is a whole flowering plant, and has a slender 10cm.-long stem of a kind that suggests it is a sucker taken from a group, and that plants are proliferous. It is not known whether Baron's material is from a juvenile or adult plant.

Fig. 448.

A. deltoideodonta Bak. Photograph of Baron 946 holotype (K) on right, Baron 752 on left. *Photo by courtesy The Chief, Botanical Research Institute, Pretoria.*

A. rossi Todaro in *Hort. Bot. Panorm.* 2: 58, *tab.* 40 (1894) is placed by Berger (*l.c.*) in synonymy under *A. deltoideodonta* Bak. but this does not appear to be correct. Todaro states that his plant came from Madagascar and that the seeds were mixed with those of *A. percrassa* Tod. *Tab.* 40 depicts a raceme that is too densely flowered for *A. deltoideodonta*, while the leaf which is 20cm. long, and 9cm. broad, has a very prominent dentate keel dorsally throughout. That is a character neither of *A. deltoideodonta* nor of *A. percrassa* which I have seen in large numbers in northern Ethiopia and on the Kohaito Plateau in Eritrea. No species with such leaves is known to me in Madagascar. *A. rossi* it seems, might well be a hybrid.

A. deltoideodonta is known to me only from Baker's description and Baron's material. The species is characterized by being a small plant, probably proliferous, with leaves 10—13cm. long and 3cm. broad, with a simple or 1—2-branched inflorescence 40—60cm. tall, and with narrowly cylindric-acuminate subdensely-flowered racemes up to 20cm. long, the flowers being about 25mm. long.

Perrier does not appear to have collected typical *A. deltoideodonta* and he cites no material of his own collecting. He described four varieties of *A. deltoideodonta* and of these, only the varieties *candicans* and *brevifolia* are now upheld. The other two differ in too many characters to be varieties of *A. deltoideodonta* – see *A. imalotensis* Reynolds and *A. intermedia* (H. Perr.) Reynolds.

167A. var. **candicans** H. Perr. in *Mém. Soc. Linn. Norm.* (*l.c.*) 25, et *Fl. Madag.* (*l.c.*) 86; Reynolds in *Journ. S.A. Bot.* 23: 66 (1957), in *Aloes Madag. Revis.* 43 (1958).

Differs from the type in having much larger leaves, shorter, more conical racemes, longer and broader snow-white bracts that are usually longer than the pedicels.

DESCRIPTION: Based on observations in South Betsileo, and on plants flowering in Johannesburg.

Plants acaulous or with short stems, usually forming dense groups 1m. and more across.

Leaves 12—16, rosulate, compactly ascending, lanceolate-attenuate, averaging 15—20cm. long, 5—6cm. broad; *upper surface* flat to slightly canaliculate, grey-green with reddish tinge, obscurely lineate, the nerves 1—2mm. apart; *lower surface* rounded, similar to upper surface; *margins* with slight cartilaginous edge armed with pale teeth, 1—2mm. long, 5—8mm. apart.

Inflorescence simple or 1—2-branched, 35—50cm. high.

Peduncle flattened and 10—14mm. broad at base, when simple clothed with a few sterile-bracts that are ovate-acute, 15mm. long, 7mm. broad, thin, scarious, brittle, very white, many-nerved.

Raceme cylindric-conical, 10—20cm. long, 6cm. diam., the apex a tuft of dry white bracts, apical buds denser and almost hidden by their white bracts, laxer downwards, open flowers nutant to subpendulous.

Bracts usually longer than the pedicels, ovate-acute, thin, scarious, brittle, very white, 7—9-nerved, usually deflexed near base, about 15mm. long, 7—8mm. broad.

Pedicels 12—16mm. long.

Perianth pale scarlet, 25—30mm. long, cylindric, slightly curved-clavate, basally obtuse, 6mm. diam. across the ovary, slightly constricted above the ovary, thence slightly decurved and enlarging to the throat, the mouth open; *outer segments* free for two-thirds their length, thinner and paler at the margins, obscurely 5-nerved, with subacute spreading apices; *inner segments* broader than the outer, with prominent scarlet keel, the apices more obtuse and more spreading than the outer.

Filaments pale-rose, the 3 inner narrower and lengthening before the three outer with their *anthers* in turn exserted 1—2mm.; *stigma* at length exserted 2—3mm.; *ovary* dark olive-green, 6mm. long, 2·5mm. diam., obtuse at apex. (Figs. 449—451).

FIANARANTSOA PROV. Betsileo: Ikalamavony (NW of Fianarantsoa), 800m. alt., form with broad leaves, Perrier 13121! (P); form with leaves averaging 30cm. long, 5cm. broad, Perrier 13121!*bis* (P); Mont Amboloandro near Zazafotsy, alt. 800m., rocky places with xerophytes, leaves 16—18cm. long, 5—7cm. broad, Perrier 11026! (P); ex Ivohipolaka, cult. Johannesburg, 9 March 1952, Reynolds 6208 (PRE).

FIG. 449.

A. deltoideodonta Bak. var. *candicans* H. Perr. Plant ex Ivohipolaka, Madagascar; flowering in Johannesburg. Height 45cm.

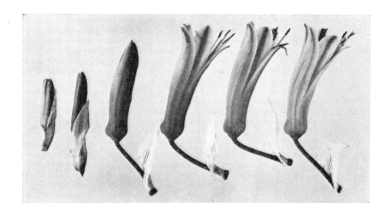

FIG. 450.
A. deltoideodonta Bak. var. *caudicans* H. Perr. Flowers natural size.

FIG. 451.

A. *deltoideodonta* Bak. var. *candicans* H. Perr. In large numbers on semi-denuded rocks.
56km. SW of Ambalavao, S. Betsileo, Madagascar.

DISTRIBUTION: Occurs in considerable numbers on semi-denuded rocky slopes and pavements repeatedly between km. 22 and km. 52 NE of Zazafotsy on the road to Ambalavao at 660—720m.; at foot of the southern end of the Andringitra, 24km. N of Ivohibe, 660m. alt.; north end of the Andringitra near Mahasoa; Ikalamavony; Ivohipolaka.

167B var. **brevifolia** H. Perrier in *Mém. Soc. Linn. Norm.* (*l.c.*) 24, et *Fl. Madag.* (*l.c.*) 86; Reynolds in *Journ. S. A. Bot.* 23: 68 (1957), in *Aloes Madag. Revis.* 45 (1958).

TULÉAR PROV. Betioky District: denuded sandstones near Benenitra (Onilahy Valley), c. 100m. alt., July 1919, Perrier 12740! type (P.).

Perrier states that his var. *brevifolia* has "leaves at least 50mm. broad," but his type (Perrier 12740) comprises two very small plants with *leaves* up to 10cm. long, but only 2·5cm. broad, with *marginal teeth* 1·5—2mm. long and 2—5mm. apart. The *inflorescence* is simple and 30cm. tall, with *raceme* cylindric, 6—10cm. long, sublaxly flowered. *Bracts* are thin, white, 10mm. long, 4mm. broad. *Pedicels* about 12mm. long. *Perianth* 22mm. long (dry) – possibly 25mm. or more when alive. (Fig. 452).

FIG. 452.

A. deltoideodonta Bak. var. *brevifolia* H. Perr.
Photograph of Perrier 12740 holotype (P).
*Photo by courtesy The Chief, Botanical Reserach
Institute. Pretoria.*

This material in rosettes, leaves and marginal teeth, bears a striking resemblance to Baron 5181 – *A. deltoideodonta* Bak. – but in the latter the inflorescence is 60cm. tall with racemes 18cm. long. Perrier also has a note, "In the same locality (i.e. Benenitra) I have found a different form (Perrier 13496) with still broader leaves, 7cm. and more, with the surface covered with scattered small white spots and with bracts that are shorter than half the length of the pedicels."

Perrier 13496! has a leaf 25cm. long, 10cm. broad, which closely resembles that of *A. imalotensis*, but the inflorescence characters, raceme 15—18cm. long and narrowing to an acute apex are nearer the typical form of *A. deltoideodonta*. Perrier 13496 is hardly a form of the var. *brevifolia*, and may represent an undescribed species.

The var. *brevifolia*, it seems, closely resembles typical *A. deltoideodonta* in rosettes, leaves and marginal teeth, but differs in having a lower inflorescence (30cm. against 60cm.) and shorter, denser racemes (6—10cm. long against 18cm. long).

168. A. laeta Berger in Engler *Pflanzenr.* Liliac.–Aloin. 256 (1908); H. Perrier in *Mém. Soc. Linn. Norm.* 1 (1): 28 (1926), et *Fl. Madag.* Liliac. 94 (1938); Reynolds in *Aloes Madag. Revis.* 47 (1958).

DESCRIPTION: *Plant* rather small, with cylindric roots, acaulous or sometimes with short stem up to 5cm. long, 3·5cm. diam., solitary.

Leaves about 24, densely rosulate and forming a compact rosette about 30cm. across, lanceolate-attenuate, up to 20cm. long, 7—8cm. broad near base; *upper surface* flat low down, slightly canaliculate upwards, bluish-grey, somewhat obscurely lineate; *lower surface* flat to very slightly rounded, without spots or markings; *both surfaces* covered with minute waxy pustules or rugosities and rough to the touch; *margins* with conspicuous narrow pink cartilaginous edge ciliate with teeth the same colour, the teeth narrowly deltoid, confluent at base, 2mm. long, firm (not horny or pungent), more crowded low down, slightly wider apart near apex.

Inflorescence usually simple, sometimes 2—3-branched from about the middle, 40—60cm. high.

Peduncle biconvex and 12mm. broad at base, terete upwards, reddish-brown, with a few sterile bracts; when branched the branch subtended at base by an ovate-acute, thin, scarious, many-nerved bract 13mm. long, 10mm. broad at base.

Raceme capitate or subcapitate, the pedicellate portion 5—7cm. long, 6cm. diam., rather densely flowered.

Bracts small, deltoid-acute, 5mm. long, 2·5mm. broad at base, thin, scarious, 3—5-nerved.

Pedicels 20—25mm., longer in fruit, the youngest horizontally disposed or slightly up-curved, the lowest obliquely spreading with apex nutant.

Perianth crimson-red, cylindric-ventricose, averaging 15mm. long, basally tapering into the pedicel and shortly stipitate, enlarging to 7mm. diam. at the middle, thence narrowing a little to an open mouth; *outer segments* free almost to base, long-oval with subacute slightly spreading apices, 3—5-nerved; *inner segments* free to base, a little narrower than the outer, with 3 crowded nerves forming a keel throughout, the apices more obtuse and more spreading than the outer.

Filaments lemon-yellow, the 3 inner narrower and lengthening before the 3 outer with their *anthers* in turn not or scarcely exserted; *style* pale yellow, with *stigma* scarcely exserted; *ovary* brown, 3mm. long, 2mm. diam., finely 6-grooved, the grooves pale orange; the apex truncate. (Figs. 453–456).

TANANARIVE PROV. Ambohiponana, at the base of the east side of Mont Ibity, May 1889, Catat 1115 (P); north and west flanks of Mont Ibity between 1600m. and 2200m., Perrier 13777, 13978 (P); coll. Mt. Ibity, cult. Mbabne, fl. 4 July 196+, Reynolds 11655 (PRE).

FIG. 453.

A. laeta Berger. Plant collected on Mount Ibity, Madagascar, at 1,650m. alt. flowering in Johannesburg. Height 45cm.

Fig. 454.

A. laeta Berger. Plants from Mount Ibity, flowering at Mbabane, Swaziland – with inflorescence branched. Height 45cm.

Fig. 455.

A. laeta Berger. Portion of leaf showing ciliate-dentate margin, natural size.

Fig. 456.

A. laeta Berger. Flowers 1/1 from bud to post-pollination stages.

168A. var. **maniaensis** H. Perrier in *Mém. Soc. Linn. Norm.* (*l.c.*) 30, et *Fl. Madag.* (*l.c.*) 96; Reynolds (*l.c.*) 50.

Differs from the type by its smaller leaves (8 × 2cm.) rounded at the top, in rosettes not more than 12cm. in diameter, and by the straighter perianth which is always infundibuliform and stipitate. – Perrier.

FIANARANTSOA PROV. Mountain quartzites between the Mania and Ivato Rivers at about 1400m., Perrier 11003 (P).

Catat's locality Ambohiponana (Ambolohiponana) is a Malgache village at the foot of Mont Ibity, just west of the Manandona River and a few kilometres west of Manandona Village which village is 24km. S of Antsirabe on the road to Ambositra.

Mr. B. Descoings and I found no plants of this species near the village, or near the foot of Mont Ibity.

A. laeta was not found until we had climbed up to 1700m. At that altitude, and higher, numbers were found on rocks in well drained positions, with *A. trachyticola* nearby. *A. ibitiensis* H. Perr. was found a little lower down.

Numbers were also found along the summit of the north-western end of Mont Ibity 27km. from Antsirabe and 16km. SW of Vinaninkarena Village on a track across the Sahalambo River to Firavahana Village, at a point 3km. S of the highest point of the road at about 1650m. (c. 20° 0′3 S, 47° 00′ E).

A. laeta is a most distinctive species with capitate racemes of cylindric-ventricose flowers that are only 15mm. long. In cultivation, the inflorescence is sometimes 3—4-branched. In floral characters (not leaves) *A. laeta* is nearest allied to *A. bellatula* Reynolds and *A. perrieri* Reynolds. In leaf characters (not flowers) *A. ibitiensis* H. Perr. is a near ally but the latter differs in having larger, greener leaves that are conspicuously lineate, and margins that are also cartilaginous but the teeth are more obtuse and shorter, and 5—8mm. apart.

In *A. laeta* the margins are ciliate-dentate with firm cartilaginous teeth that are 2mm. long and confluent at base.

Berger described the species as having a stem of 1m. from Catat's notes "Hampe de 1m.", but this is clearly wrong. Perrier found no caulescent Aloes on Mont Ibity and states that his 13777 matches Catat's specimen. All Aloes known on Mont Ibity are stemless – or almost so.

Berger also made no mention of the rugosities on leaf surfaces that make them rough to the touch, and this is a conspicuous character.

Flowering time on Mont Ibity appears to be May. A plant collected on Mont Ibity and grown in Johannesburg and Mbabane, flowered in May.

169. **A. viguieri** H. Perr. in *Bull. Acad. Madag.* nov. ser. 10: 20 (1927), et *Fl. Madag.* Liliac. 96, Fig. XIII, 2—3 (1938); Reynolds in *Aloes Madag. Revis.* 52 (1958).

DESCRIPTION: *Plants* acaulous and growing singly, or forming compact groups of 4—6 rosettes per plant with slender stems averaging 20—30cm. long, up to 1m. long when hanging down cliff faces, the old dried leaf remains persistent.

Leaves 12—16, densely rosulate, lanceolate-attenuate, averaging 30—40cm. long, 8—9cm. broad at base, about 10mm. thick; *upper surface* flat to very slightly convex, light-green, lineate, without spots; *lower surface* deeper green, convex, slightly less lineate; *margins* with narrow white cartilaginous border about 1mm. broad, armed with small, firm, white cartilaginous teeth ·5—1mm. long, 1—2mm. apart, smaller and more crowded low down, larger at the middle and smaller to obsolescent towards apex.

Inflorescence simple, slender, averaging 45cm. long.

Peduncle plano-convex and 7mm. broad at base, terete upwards, brown with a bloom, with a few small sterile bracts, the lowest 4mm. long, 2·5mm. broad.

Raceme 20—25cm. long, cylindric, laxly about 22-flowered, youngest buds grey-green tipped, spreading, open flowers pendulous.

Bracts very small, ovate-acute, 1·5mm. long, thin, dry, white, 3-nerved.

Pedicels 11mm. long, the colour of the perianth, almost horizontally spreading.

Perianth reddish-scarlet, cylindric, slightly clavate, 22mm. long, shortly stipitate at base, 4mm. diam. across the ovary, thence trigonously enlarging to the throat; *outer segments* free to the middle (11mm.) with tube 11mm., paler at the edges, 3-nerved, the apices subacute; *inner segments* free but dorsally adnate to the outer for half their length, with scarlet keel in upper half, broader than the outer and with more obtuse apices.

Filaments almost white, filiform-flattened, the 3 inner narrower and lengthening before the 3 outer with their *anthers* in turn exserted 0—1mm.; *style* pale lemon, with *stigma* at length exserted 1—2mm.; *ovary* orange, 5mm. long, 2mm. diam., apex slightly obtuse (Plate 94, Figs. 457—459).

TULÉAR PROV. Limestone cliff bounding the Fiherenana River, very abundant, Perrier 17592 (P holotype, K). On limestone slopes overlooking the Onilahy River, 23km. SE of Tuléar, c. 23° 27′ S, 43° 52′ E, c. 60m. alt., 9 July 1955, Reynolds 7858 (TAN, PRE).

A. viguieri appears to be localised on Eocene limestone cliffs bounding the Bara Plateau. It is particularly abundant on cliffs on the south side of the Fiherenana River for 30km. ENE of Tuléar at from 60m. to 356m. alt.

ALOE VIGUIERI H. Perr.
Growing on limestone, 23km. SE of Tuléar, Madagascar. Height 50cm.

Along the road eastwards from Tuléar to Tongobory, *A. viguieri* was found at km. 23, (alt. 60m.) and seen repeatedly to km. 80 (22km. W of Tongobory) where it grows in considerable numbers on limestone cliff faces on the north side of the Onilahy River at 120m. alt.

The inflorescence is simple, rarely 1-branched, with very laxly flowered racemes.

In rosettes and leaf margins with 1mm.-broad, white, cartilaginous border armed with small cartilaginous teeth only 1mm. long, *A. viguieri* is closely allied to *A. ibitiensis* but the latter has a taller branched inflorescence with longer pedicels and flowers. The South African species *A. striata* Haw. is also closely allied in leaf characters but has no marginal teeth.

In flatter places *A. viguieri* usually has little or no stem, but when hanging downwards on sheer cliff faces stems may reach 1m. in length with the old dried leaf remains persistent.

FIG. 457

A. viguieri H. Perr. Limestone cliff bounding the Fiherenana River, 20km. NE of Tuléar, Madagascar – Habitat of *A. viguieri* H. Perr.

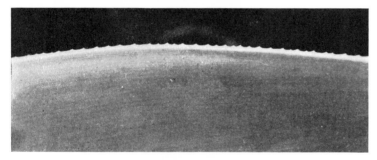

FIG. 458.

A. viguieri H. Perr. Portion of leaf 1/1 showing marginal border and very small teeth.

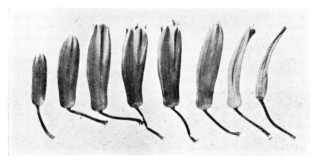

FIG. 459.

A. viguieri H. Perr. Flowers 1/1 from bud to post-anthesis stages.

170. **A. ibitiensis** H. Perrier in *Mém Soc. Linn. Norm.* 1 (1): 30 (1926); in *Bull. Acad. Malg.* nov. ser. 10: 19 (1927), et in *Fl. Madag.* Liliac. 97 (1938); Reynolds in *Aloes Madag. Revis.* 54 (1958).

DESCRIPTION: *Plant* with fibrous roots, acaulous, usually growing singly.

Leaves 12—16, densely rosulate, lanceolate-acute, averaging 25—30cm. long, 7cm. broad, ascending and slightly recurved towards apex; *upper surface* almost flat, yellowish- to olive-green, prominently lineate-striate; *lower surface* slightly convex, similar to upper surface; *margins* with pale-yellowish cartilaginous 1mm.-broad border with firm teeth that are 1—2mm. long, 3—5mm. apart.

Inflorescence slender, about 80cm. tall, 2—4-branched.

Peduncle basally plano-convex and 13mm. broad, terete upwards, branched from about the middle with 2—4 slender branches.

Racemes cylindric-acuminate, the terminal averaging 25cm. long, 5cm. diam., sublaxly-flowered, the buds suberect and denser, open flowers subpendulous and laxer.

Bracts ovate-acute, 4—7mm. long, 2—3mm. broad at base, dirty white, thin, scarious, about 5-nerved.

Pedicels lowest averaging 14mm. long, the colour of the perianth.

Perianth scarlet, cylindric-trigonous, averaging 26mm. long, basally tapering into the pedicel, cylindric and 4—5mm. diam. across the ovary, thence slightly enlarging upwards; *outer segments* free for about 9mm., 3—5-nerved, the apices sub-acute and slightly spreading; *inner segments* broader than the outer and with more obtuse, more spreading apices.

Filaments almost white, filiform-flattened, the 3 inner narrower and lengthening before the 3 outer with their *anthers* in turn exserted up to 1mm.; *style* pale lemon; *stigma* eventually exserted 1—2mm.; *ovary* orange-brown, 4mm. long, 1·5mm. diam., finely 6-grooved. (Figs. 460–462.)

TANANARIVE PROV.: Betsileo, moist rocky places, western slopes of the upper Mania, about 1600m., Perrier 13175 (P), quartzite outcrops of Mont Ibity, about 2000m., Perrier 13980 (P).

FIG. 460.

A. ibitiensis H. Perr. Plants from Mount Ibity, flowering in Johannesburg. Height 75cm.

Perrier also records the species at Anjanabonoina, in the lower basin of the Andratsay, at about 1200m., on quartzites.

Mr. Descoings and I found this species on north-eastern rocky slopes of Mont Ibity on a path above Ambolohiponana Village (W of the Manandona River) at about 1450m., c. 20° 05′ S, 47° 01′ E. Plants grow on sheer rock faces, or on overhanging rocky ledges in very well drained positions, and occur singly or in small groups. Flowering time appears to be April–May. In Johannesburg plants flower in March.

Leaves vary in colour from yellowish- to olive-green and are conspicuously lineate-striate. Perrier states that the marginal teeth are robust and non-cartilaginous, but on Mont Ibity I found that the teeth were obtuse, cartilaginous, and firm but not pungent.

F/ɢ. 461.

A. ibitiensis H. Perr. Portion of leaf 1/1, showing lineation and marginal teeth.

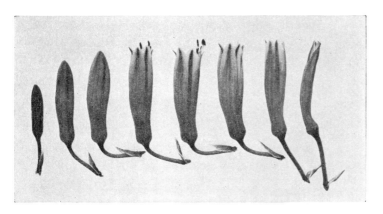

Fɪɢ. 462.

A. ibitiensis H. Perr. Flowers 1/1 from bud to post-pollination stage.

171. **A. imalotensis** Reynolds in *Journ. S.A. Bot.* 23: 68 (1957).

—— *A. deltoideodonta* Bak. var. *contigua* H. Perr. in *Mém. Soc. Linn. Norm. (l.c.)* 25, et *Fl. Madag. (l.c.)* 86.

—— *A. contingua* (H. Perr.) Reynolds in *Aloes Madag. Revis.* 57 (1958).

DESCRIPTION: Based on flowering plants near Ranohira and Benenitra.

Plants growing singly or in small groups, acaulescent or with short procumbent stem up to 10—20cm. long, 3cm. diam.

Leaves 20—24, densely rosulate, compactly arcuate-ascending, broadly ovate-acute, up to 30 cm. long, 12—15cm. broad, very fleshy; both *surfaces* dull bluish-green with reddish tinge, flat to slightly convex, obscurely lineate, without spots or markings; *margins* with 1mm.-broad pink to reddish cartilaginous border armed with deltoid or obtuse pink teeth 1—1·5mm. long, and varying from 1—4mm. apart to sometimes contiguous. *Sap* dries yellow.

Inflorescence a 2—4-branched erect or suberect panicle 50—65cm. high, 2—3 simultaneously.

Peduncle basally plano-convex and 20mm. broad, terete upwards, 2—4-branched from about the middle, the lowest branch subtended at base by a broadly ovate-acute bract which is thin, scarious, white, many-nerved.

Racemes subdensely flowered, cylindric, slightly acuminate, 10—20cm. long (15cm. the average), 7cm. diam., erect, buds suberect and grey-green tipped, older buds spreading, open flowers pendulous.

Bracts ovate-acute, thin, scarious, white, 7—10mm. long, 3—4mm. broad, 5-nerved, usually less than half the length of the pedicel.

Pedicels the lowest 15—18mm. long.

Perianth cylindric, slightly curved, coral-red, 30—34mm. long, basally obtuse, 6mm. diam. across the ovary, very slightly constricted above the ovary thence slightly decurved and slightly enlarging towards the throat; *outer segments* free almost to base, obscurely 3—5-nerved, the apices subacute and slightly spreading; *inner segments* broader than the outer, with broad white border, keeled throughout, the apices more obtuse and more spreading than the outer.

Filaments pale lemon, the 3 inner narrower and lengthening before the 3 outer with their *anthers* in turn exserted 1—2mm.

Style lemon, with *stigma* at length exserted 2mm.; *ovary* pale green, 6mm. long, 2·5mm. diam., the apex truncate. (Plate 95, Figs. 463–464).

FIANARANTSOA PROV. Ihosy Dist.: On Triassic shales of the Imaloto Valley near Ranohira, 600m. alt., July 1910, Perrier 11022! type (P); 14km. SW of Ranohira, c. 22° 37′ S, 45° 21′ E, c. 600m. alt., 12 July 1955, Reynolds 7897 (TAN, P, K, PRE).

FIG. 463.

A. imalotensis Reynolds. Plants 21km. W of Benenitra, Tuléar Prov., Madagascar. Alt. 270m. Height 65cm.

PLATE 95

ALOE IMALOTENSIS   Reynolds.

On sandstone, Isalo Range, 14km. SW of Ranohira, Fianarantsoa
Prov., Madagascar. Height 65cm.

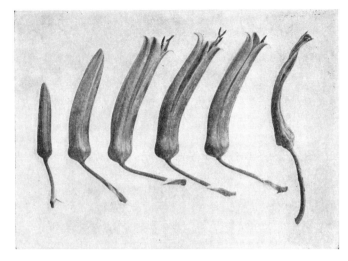

FIG. 464.

A. imalotensis Reynolds. Flowers 1/1 from a plant 14km. SW of Ranohira, Fianarantsoa Prov., Madagascar.

TULÉAR PROV. Denuded sandstones, about 600m. alt., Mont Ambohibe, Manombo du Sud, May 1910, Perrier 11019! (P); 21km. W of Benenitra, c. 23° 26′ S, 44° 54′ E, c. 270m. alt., 10 July 1955, Reynolds 7864 (TAN, P, K, PRE).

Plants of *A. imalotensis* occur in the largest numbers in the valley of the Imaloto River from near Ranohira in the north (600m.) to the Onilahy Valley near Benenitra (270m.) in the south.

In leaf characters *A. imalotensis* is closely allied to *A. viguieri* H. Perr. near Tuléar, but in *A. viguieri* the inflorescence is simple, with very lax racemes and flowers only 22mm. long.

In the Isalo range near Ranohira, rosettes of leaves with pink edge bear a striking resemblance to those of the South African species *A. striata* Haw., but the latter has no marginal teeth.

Large numbers of *A. imalotensis* occur 14km. and 18km. ENE of Ranohira (770m. alt.). In this area plants were found with leaves with short obtuse marginal teeth that varied from contiguous to 1—4mm. apart, hence Perrier's *forma latifolia* and *forma longifolia* are regarded as forms of this species.

172. **A. madecassa** H. Perrier in *Mém. Soc. Linn. Norm.* (*l.c.*) 23, Plate 3 (1926), et *Fl. Madag.* (*l.c.*) 87 (1938); Reynolds in *Aloes Madag. Revis.* 59 (1958) – *non* Francois in *Mem. Acad. Malg.* fasc. 24, Plate 18 (1937).

(*Note:* Francois's figure in *Mém. Acad. Malg.* (*l.c.*) is clearly not of *A. madecassa* which has very different leaves and grows singly. The racemes are too densely flowered and too broad, while the pedicels are too long for *A. acutissima.* It is probably the South African species *A. arborescens* Mill., grown in the Gardens.)

DESCRIPTION: *Plant* acaulous or with negligible stem, solitary, without suckers.

Leaves about 20, densely rosulate, lanceolate-acute, about 25cm. long, 7—9cm. broad, ascending, somewhat incurved and forming a compact rosette, the apices slightly spreading; *upper surface* green, obscurely lineate, without spots or markings; *lower surface* convex, similar to upper surface; *margins* sinuate-dentate with narrow pink cartilaginous edge armed with paler pink teeth that are deltoid, pungent, 2mm. long. 5—8mm. apart. *Sap* dries white, resembling a milky froth.

Inflorescence a branched panicle 1m. or more high.

Peduncle brown with a bloom, basally flattened and 20mm. broad, with 6—10 branches from about the middle, the lowest branch subtended at base by a thin, scarious, many-nerved bract about 15mm. long, 25mm. broad at base.

Racemes narrowly cylindric-acuminate, narrowing almost to a point, the terminal about 20cm. long, 5—6cm. diam., the lateral a little shorter.

Bracts narrowly lanceolate, clasping the pedicel, about 9mm. long, 3mm. broad, thin, white, 5-nerved.

Pedicels lowest 14mm. long, the colour of the perianth.

Perianth scarlet, about 25mm. long, cylindric, slightly clavate, obtusely tapering at base into the pedicel and shortly stipitate, about 5mm. diam. across the ovary, enlarging to near the throat, the mouth open; *outer segments* free to the middle (tube 13mm.), obscurely 3-nerved, the apices subacute, slightly spreading; *inner segments* scarlet-keeled, the apices more obtuse than the outer.

Filaments filiform-flattened, the 3 inner narrower and lengthening before the 3 outer with their *anthers* in turn exserted 1mm.; *stigma* at length exserted 1—2mm.; *ovary* brown, 4mm. long, 2mm. diam., apex truncate. (Figs. 465–468).

Cultivated in Perrier's garden in Tananarive, the roots having come from the mountains of Imerina, Central Region, Perrier 13062! type (P).

Imerina is now the Province of Tananarive, and no precise locality of origin is stated.

A plant from Iharanandriana, near Behenje, 36km. S of Tananarive, has flowered in Johannesburg and fits Perrier's description.

A striking and unusual character of *A. madecassa*, is that the leaf sap is white and resembles a milky froth. This character appears to be unique in Aloe.

A. madecassa, with leaf margins with narrow cartilaginous edge armed with 2mm. teeth, narrowly cylindric-acuminate racemes 15—20cm. long, 9mm. bracts, 14mm. pedicels, 25mm. perianths with outer segments free to the middle, suggests a very close affinity with *A. deltoideo-donta* Bak., but the latter is a much smaller plant with smaller leaves, a lower, less branched inflorescence, and is possibly proliferous.

172A. var. **lutea** Guillaumin in *Bull. Mus. Nat. Hist.* 27: 86 (Jan. 1955).

Differs from the type in having rose-coloured teeth, bracts scarcely coloured, 2cm. pedicels, buds orange-yellow at base, green at apex, perianth lemon with green nerves. – A. Guillaumin.

MADAGASCAR: Perrier de la Bâthie, f.221 (1928).

No locality of origin is stated and no flowering time. Professor J. Millot, who investigated this matter in Paris, found that this plant had been received in the Paris Garden from Perrier de la Bâthie on 27 July 1928, and was entered in the Acquisitions Register under f.221 (1928). The plant flowered for the first time in 1954, when the short description was drawn up, and herbarium material made.

If this plant had grown in Paris for 26 years before flowering under conditions very different from its sunny natural habitat in Madagascar, it would almost certainly have modified considerably, and the variety, it seems, is of doubtful value.

FIG. 465.

A. madecassa H. Perr. Reproduction of Perrier's figure in *Mém. Soc. Linn. Norm.* pl. 3 (1926).

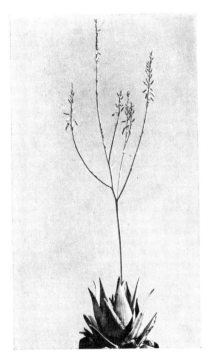

FIG. 466.

A. madecassa H. Perr. Plant collected at Iharanandriana, near Behenje, 36km. S of Tananarive, flowering in Johannesburg. Height 1m.

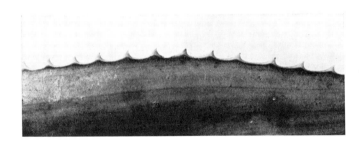

FIG. 467.

A. madecassa H. Perr. Portion of leaf margin 1/1.

FIG. 468.

A. madecassa H. Perr. Flowers natural size.

GROUP 5

PLANTS LARGE, SOLITARY, ACAULOUS OR SHORTLY CAULESCENT, WITH LARGE ROSETTES OF ASCENDING OR RECURVED LEAVES, UP TO 70CM. LONG, 6—10CM. BROAD; INFLORESCENCE BRANCHED (EXCEPT IN *A. decorsei*).

A. PLANT ACAULOUS, LEAVES ASCENDING, PERIANTH YELLOW, STRAIGHT, CAMPANULATE, 20—22MM. LONG:

(1) *Inflorescence simple*, 80—120*cm. high:*
Leaves 60—70cm. long, 5—6cm. broad; pedicels rigid, appressed to the axis, 30—40mm. long; raceme at first densely conical and 5—6cm. long, lengthening to 20cm. with lowest flowers widely spaced; segments free almost to base .. ..   173 *A. decorsei*
(2) *Inflorescence 2—5-branched, over 1m.:*
Leaves rough to the touch, 40—50cm. long; 6—7cm. broad, with horny margins; raceme short, subcorymbose, 7—12cm. long, pedicels 20—22mm.; outer segments free to the middle (tube 11mm.) .. ..   174 *A. andringitrensis*

B. STEM 1—2M., ONLY 5CM. DIAM., ALWAYS SIMPLE, RARELY STRAIGHT, perianth 28—30mm. long:

(1) Leaves canaliculate, spreading to reflexed, 45—50cm. long, 7—8cm. broad; inflorescence 3-branched, 50—60cm.; raceme short, oblong, 6—8cm. long; pedicels 20—22mm.; outer segments free ..   175 *A. silicicola*
Note: I have not seen plants of *A. decorsei* and *A. silicicola.*

C. PLANTS PRODUCING BULBILS ON THE PEDUNCLE OR BRANCHES OF THE INFLORESCENCE:

(1) Plants acaulescent; leaves up to 60cm. long, 8—10cm. broad; inflorescence branched, 2m. or more; pedicels 8—10mm.; perianth about 25mm.:
(*a*) Bulbils produced on the branches and not on the main peduncle; inflorescence divaricately about 30-branched from below the middle, the lowest branch itself a panicle about 1m. long .. ..   176 *A. bulbillifera*
(*b*) Bulbils produced on the main peduncle and not on the branches; inflorescence compactly 10—12-branched in upper quarter only, the lowest branch 25—30cm. long .. ..   176A *A. bulbillifera*
                       var. *paulianae*
The only species producing bulbils.

D. PERIANTH WITH OVOID OR SUBGLOBOSE BASAL SWELLING, CONSTRICTED ABOVE THE OVARY; PERIANTHS AND PEDICELS MINUTELY PUBERULENT:

(1) Plants acaulous or with short stem; leaves 50—60cm. long, canaliculate, recurved; inflorescence branched; perianth 26—30mm. long, outer segments free .. ..   177 *A. suarezensis*
The only Malgache species with perianth puberulent.

173. **A. decorsei** H. Perrier (errore *decorsii*) in *Mém. Soc. Linn. Norm. (l.c.)* 43, et *Fl. Madag. (l.c.)* 100, Fig. XIV, 5; Reynolds in *Aloes Madag. Revis.* 65 (1958).

DESCRIPTION: *Plant* acaulescent, without suckers, with fibrous roots, and with rosettes of 12—15 ascending leaves that are slightly falcate.

Leaves green, 60—70cm. long, 5—6cm. broad, narrowing from the base to the slightly acute tip; *prickles* small (1—1·5mm.).

Inflorescence simple, 80—120cm. high, rigid; peduncle 4—10 times longer than the spike, with 7—8 sterile loosely amplexicaul bracts that are shortly-acute and about 10-nerved; *spike* at first short (5—6cm.), finally much longer (18—30cm.), the rachis thickening in proportion as the spike elongates; the lower and median flowers very distant, the upper condensed into a head before they open; *bracts* reddish-scarious, broadly oblanceolate (15 × 6mm.), shortly acute, 6—7-nerved, about one-third the length of the pedicel; *pedicels* 3—4cm., straight, thickened in fruit.

Perianth yellow, 20—22mm. long, the tip of the segments green and margined with white, the *segments* free nearly to base where they are united for 2mm. only, the outer 5-nerved, the inner 1-nerved. *Stamens* subequal and similar, included; *ovary* truncate at apex; *capsule* oblong (25 × 7—8mm.), subtrigonous; *seeds* irregularly trigonous (6 × 2—3mm.), scarcely winged. – H. Perrier. (Fig. 469).

FIANARANTSOA PROV. South Betsileo: Rocks, gneiss, Massif Andringitra between 1600 and 2200m. alt., Sept. 1911, Perrier 11002! (P).

FIG. 469.

A. decorsei H. Perr. Reproduction of Perrier's Fig. XIV, 5, in *Fl. Madag.* 101 (1938)
Inflorescence × 1/2.

Perrier states that this species is localised on southern slopes of the Andringitra Range between 1600—2200m. alt., where he found plants in large numbers. He did not find it at any other locality.

The precise locality of origin is not recorded, and "southern slopes of the Andringitra" is vague and covers a wide area.

I have not seen plants either wild or cultivated, but from the description and type material, *A. decorsei* is characterized by being stemless, solitary, with rosulate leaves up to 70cm. long, 6cm. broad, inflorescence simple, about 1m. high, with racemes at first somewhat densely conical and 5—6cm. long, lengthening to 20cm. and more with the lowest flowers far apart, pedicels almost twice as long as the 20—22mm. yellow flowers, and perianth segments free almost to base.

A. decorsei is allied to *A. andringitrensis* H. Perr. in having 20—22mm. yellow flowers, but the latter has a branched inflorescence, pedicels as long as the perianth, and outer segments free only for half their length.

174. **A. andringitrensis** H. Perrier in *Mém. Soc. Linn. Norm.* (*l.c.*) 41, Plate 7, et *Fl. Madag.* (*l.c.*) 104, Fig. XIV, 3–4; Reynolds in *Aloes Madag. Revis.* 65 (1958).

DESCRIPTION: Based on plants collected by Dr. R. Paulian near Pic Boby, Andringitra Range (type locality), and which have flowered repeatedly at Johannesburg and Mbabane.

Plants solitary, acaulescent, roots fusiform.

Leaves about 16—20, rosulate, ascending, rather compact, up to 50cm. long, 7cm. broad at base and gradually attenuate; *upper surface* flat to slightly canaliculate, grey-green, without spots or markings, very slightly asperulous; *lower surface* convex, otherwise as the upper surface; *margins* armed with small pinkish teeth that are 1mm. long, 5—10mm. apart. (Phyllotaxis 2/6 – H. Perrier).

Inflorescence a branched panicle 80—90cm. high, 3—4 produced consecutively.

Peduncle stout, brown with a bloom, basally plano-convex and 4cm. broad, 6—8-branched from about the middle, the whole inflorescence rather compact.

Racemes sub-capitate, conic at first, 6—10cm. long, densely flowered, buds at first orange-red, open flowers yellowish.

Bracts ovate-acute, clasping the pedicel, thin, brown, 8mm. long, 3mm. broad, 5—7-nerved.

Pedicels spreading-nutant, the lowest 25mm. long.

Perianth dull orange to yellowish, narrowly cylindric-campanulate, 22mm. long, slightly shorter than their pedicels, basally obtuse, 4mm. diam. across the ovary, enlarging upwards, the mouth wide open and 9mm. across; *outer segments* free almost to base (tube 5mm.) paler at margins, 3-nerved, apices subacute; *inner segments* free but dorsally adnate to the outer for 5mm., with 3 crowded nerves forming an orange to green keel, the apices more obtuse, more spreading.

Filaments lemon, filiform-flattened, the 3 inner narrower and lengthening before the 3 outer with their *anthers* in turn not exserted; *stigma* at length exserted 1mm.; *ovary* green, 5mm. long, 2mm. diam. (Figs. 470–473).

Fig. 470.

Northern end of the Andringitra Range, as viewed from Mahasoa, 50km. S of Ambalavao, Madagascar. – Habitat of *A. andringitrensis* H. Perr. at alt. 1,800—2,600m.

Fig. 471.

A. andringitrensis H. Perr. Plant originally collected by Dr. R. Paulian on the Andringitra Range near Pic Boby (type locality), alt. 2,400m., flowering in the author's gardens in Mbabane, Swaziland. Height 1m.

FIG. 472.   FIG. 473.

A. andringitrensis H. Perr. Raceme and flowers natural size.

FIANARANTSOA PROV. South Betsileo: Centre, but especially on the Andringitra Massif, gravelly places between 2000m. and 2600m., very common on the eastern escarpment, Perrier 14609! (P, K); abundant towards the western end of the Andringitra Range, between 1800m. and the summit, Perrier 13637! type (P). Plant ex type locality, cult. Johannesburg, fl. 24 April 1959, Reynolds 8353 (K, PRE).

Perrier states that *A. andringitrensis* is allied to *A. silicicola* H. Perr., but differs in having distinctly thicker leaves with minute papillae which make them rough to the touch, much larger bracts thickened at the base, and in the shape of the perianth. Perrier describes the pedicels as being 20—22mm. long and lengthening in fruit, but in the type, pedicels of lowest open flowers are 30mm. long.

A. decorsei is another ally, but this species differs in having a simple inflorescence, elongated racemes with the lowest open flowers widely spaced, and pedicels almost twice as long as the perianth.

175. **A. silicicola** H. Perrier in *Mém. Soc. Linn. Norm.* (*l.c.*) 42, et *Fl. Madag.* (*l.c.*) 105; Reynolds in *Aloes Madag. Revis.* 69 (1958).

DESCRIPTION: Perrier's description, supplemented by his notes on the type sheet.

Plant with stem up to 2m. long but quite slender, at most 5cm. diam., rarely straight, always simple.

Leaves densely rosulate, green, thin, canaliculate, recurved or spreading, 45—50cm. long, 7—8cm. broad at base, 3—4mm. thick, narrowed from the base to the tip into a long point, shortly acute at the apex; *marginal teeth* green, more crowded and subconfluent low down, 1—1·5mm. long, wider spaced upwards but never more than 7mm. apart.

Inflorescence 3—4-branched, 50—60cm. high. Common peduncle very compressed at the base, as long as the branches; secondary peduncles elongated, with 6—8 sterile-bracts.

Racemes short, floriferous axis 6—8cm. long, not very dense, with 20—25 ascending flowers with pedicels of equal length; flowers yellow tinged with red.

Bracts scarious, lanceolate-acute, 5—6mm. long, 1—2mm. broad, 3-nerved at the base, about one-fifth the length of the pedicel.

Pedicels equal, 20—22mm. long, thickened at the top, yellow- or orange-coloured.

Perianth reddish-orange, straight, 28—30mm. long, tubular-subtrigonous at base, contracted at the middle, dilated in the upper third; *segments* free, all narrower at the base than the apex, the inner longer and wider (7mm.) in the upper third. *Stamens* and *style* all included; *anthers* oblong, orange-coloured, 4mm. long, 2·25mm. wide; *ovary* obtuse (Fig. 474).

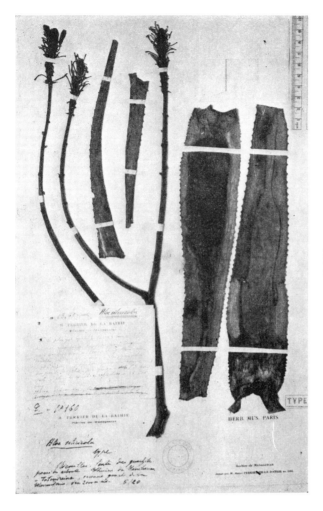

Fig. 474.

A. silicicola H. Perr. Photograph of Perrier 13160, holotype (P). *Photo by courtesy The Chief, Botanical Research Institute, Pretoria.*

TANANARIVE PROV. On quartzites of the Laniharina–Tsitondraina range, left bank of the Manandona River, about 2000m. alt., Perrier 13160! type (P).

Perrier states that this species is abundant at the type locality and has not been found elsewhere.

I have not seen living plants either wild or in cultivation. The species is known to me only from the type material, Perrier's copious notes on the sheet, and his description.

The stem is described as being 2m. long, but only 5cm. diam. at most, always simple and rarely straight. Whether erect, decumbent, or supported by bushes is not stated. A 2m. stem only 5cm. diam. is almost certainly too slender to support the weight of a rosette of leaves 50cm. long and 8cm. broad, which suggests that the stem is either procumbent or supported.

Perrier gives *A. andringitrensis* as a near ally. This species differs in being acaulous, and in having thick leaves with minute papillae on the surfaces, larger bracts thickened at base, and a differently shaped yellow perianth 20—22mm. long, with outer segments free to the middle.

A. silicicola is distinguished by having a very slender 2m. long stem only 5cm. thick, recurved canaliculate thin leaves 45—50cm. long, smaller bracts, and longer, 28—30mm. perianths with outer segments free to base.

176. **A. bulbillifera** H. Perrier in *Mém. Soc. Linn. Norm.* 1 (1): 22 (1926), in *Bull. Acad. Malgache,* nouv. sér. 10: 19 (1927), in *Fl. Madag.* Liliac. 88 (1938); François in *Mém. Acad. Malgache* 24: 31 (1937); Reynolds in *Journ. S.A. Bot.* 22: 26, Plate VII, fig. 1 (1956), in *Aloes Madag. Revis.* 71 (1958).

DESCRIPTION: *Plants* usually solitary and acaulous; sometimes developing a stem and with shoots from base when growing in shady places.

Leaves 24—30, densely rosulate, suberectly spreading, 40—60cm. long, 8—10cm. broad at base, gradually narrowing to an acute apex; *upper surface* green without spots or markings, flat low down, canaliculate upwards; *lower surface* rounded, similar in colour to upper surface; *margins* sinuate-dentate, armed with deltoid teeth that are firm to sub-pungent, larger and 15mm. long near base, gradually smaller upwards, 10—12mm. apart. *Sap* dries deep orange to purple.

Inflorescence a many-branched panicle 2—2·5m. high, sometimes 2—3 simultaneously, usually curved over sideways.

Peduncle brown with a bloom, basally plano-convex and 4cm. broad, terete upwards, divaricately branched below the middle with up to 30 slender branches, the lowest branches themselves a panicle 1m. long with up to 12 slender branches, with leaf buds or bulbils developing in the axils of bracts on the branches below the racemes and not on the main peduncles.

Racemes cylindric-acuminate, averaging 20—25cm. long, laxly flowered, the terminal the highest, laterals a little shorter, the buds spreading, open flowers subpendulous.

Bracts deltoid, clasping the pedicel, 3mm. long, 2mm. broad, thin, scarious, 5-nerved.

Pedicels 8—10mm. long, very slender (1mm. diam.), the pedicels of young buds about as long as those of open flowers.

Perianth scarlet, 25mm. long, subcylindric, basally flat, 5mm. diam. across the ovary, thence slightly decurved and slightly narrowing on the underside only, enlarging a little to the throat; *outer segments* visibly free for 12mm. thence tightly cohering to base but not concrescent or connate into a tube; *inner segments* free, broader than the outer, with thin pale edges and with 3 crowded nerves forming a keel, the apices more obtuse than the outer and slightly spreading.

Filaments white or very pale lemon, the 3 inner narrower and lengthening before the 3 outer with their *anthers* in turn exserted 1—2mm.; *stigma* at length exserted 2–3mm.; *ovary* pale olive-brown, 4mm. long, 2mm. diam., the apex truncate. (Figs. 475–476).

MAJUNGA PROV. Upper Bemarivo: Analamaitso Forest, basin of the Bemarivo du Boina, 800m. alt., Perrier 11017 (P). Sambirano: On the edge of the Andranomalaza on the southern escarpment of the Manongarivo massif Perrier 17391 (P, R); to the north of the Manongarivo massif above the valley of the Sambirano, 600m. alt., Perrier 11013 (P); cult. Tzimbazaza, 9 June 1955, Reynolds 7657 (PRE, K).

Perrier states that his type was gathered in his garden at Morovoay from rootstocks originally collected in the forest of Analamaitso, in Upper Bemarivo, and that this species is characteristic of the mountains of the north-west region from 300—800m. alt.

Fig. 475.

A. bulbillifera H. Perr. Plant flowering in the Tsimbazaza Gardens, Tananarive, Madagascar – the sprawling inflorescence held up by Mme. Tolliez for clearer detail. Develops bulbils on the branches only – not on the peduncle.

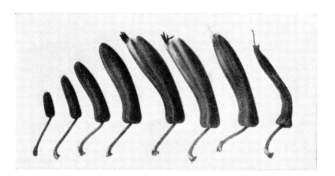

Fig. 476.

A. bulbillifera H. Perr. Flowers 1/1 from bud
to post-pollination stages.

A. bulbillifera is a most distinctive and unique species, separated from all other species by producing leaf buds or bulbils on the branches of the inflorescence in the axils of bracts below the racemes and above the main peduncle, not below the first branch. These bulbils are very small when plants are in flower, and develop to their full size only after anthesis.

The peduncle is too slender to support the weight of a many-branched inflorescence 2—2·5m. long, and curves over sideways, or sprawls almost on the ground. When the peduncle dries out the bulbils drop off and take root 1—2m. away from the parent plant.

176A. var. **paulianae** Reynolds in *Journ. S.A. Bot.* 22: 26, Plates 7, 8 (1956), in *Aloes Madag. Revis.* 74 (1958).

DESCRIPTION: *Plants* acaulescent or with stem up to 20cm. *Leaves* about 20, densely rosulate, ensiform or lanceolate-attenuate, up to 60cm. long, 9cm. broad at base, slightly canaliculate, green without markings; *marginal teeth* dull white, 3mm. long, 12mm. apart.

Inflorescence a branched panicle up to 2m. high, 2—3 simultaneously from a rosette.
Peduncle compactly branched in upper quarter, with 8—12 arcuate-ascending branches, the 2—3 lowest branches with 1—2 branchlets, and producing bulbils on the main peduncle and not on the branches.
Racemes cylindric-acuminate, the terminal 25—30cm. long, branch racemes 15—20cm. long.
Bracts ovate-acute, 4mm. long, 3mm. broad at base.
Pedicels slender, reddish-brown, 8—10mm. long.
Perianth scarlet, paler at mouth, 25—27mm. long, basally flat, 7mm. diam. across the ovary; *outer segments* free to base but tightly cohering in lower half.
Anthers exserted 2mm.; *stigma* at length exserted 3—4mm.; *ovary* pale olive, 5mm. long, 2mm. diam., obtuse at apex. (Plate 96, Figs. 477–478).

MAJUNGA PROV. Ex 85 km. SW of Antsohihy, coll. Madame L. Paulian, cult. Tsimbazaza, fl. 9 June 1955, Reynolds 7656, holotype (TAN), isotype (P, K, PRE); 85 km. SW of Antsohihy, 270m. alt. c. 15° 03′ S, 47° 44′ E, 20 July 1955, bulbils only, Reynolds 7904 (TAN, P, K, PRE).

This distinctive variety was named after Madame L. Paulian (wife of Dr. R. Paulian, Deputy Director of the Institut Scientifique de Madagascar) who first collected plants about 85km. SW of Antsohihy. Plants were cultivated in the Gardens at Tsimbazaza, Tananarive, where I saw them flowering in June 1955, together with flowering plants of the typical form.

Subsequently, on 20 July 1955, while travelling to Diego Saurez, I found large numbers of the var. *paulianae* on rocky slopes of a ridge above forest, at a point 24km. S of the Analalava road junction and 85km. SW of Antsohihy. Capsules had dehisced and were then very dry, but the bulbils were well developed on the peduncle below the branches.

In the typical form of *A. bulbillifera* the inflorescence is taller (over 2m.) considerably more branched and re-branched from below the middle, the branches are considerably longer (up to 1m.), the peduncle is more slender, and unable to support the weight of the inflorescence, is curved sideways. Bulbils form only on the slender branches below the racemes and not on the main peduncle.

In the var. *paulianae*, the peduncle is thicker, rigid, erect or suberect, and is compactly 10—12-branched only in the upper quarter, the branches being considerably shorter (30cm.). Bulbils form only on the main peduncle from near the middle upwards to the first branch, and not on the branches. These bulbils commence developing after anthesis. After the capsules dehisce and become very dry, the bulbils comprise sessile rosettes of 4—6 leaves which are up to 5cm. long, 15mm. broad at base, with dentate margins. When the peduncle dries completely and eventually lies almost along the ground, the bulbils fall and take root.

There is little difference between the two in leaf characters, bracts, pedicels and flowers.

PLATE 96

ALOE BULBILLIFERA   H. Perr. var. PAULIANAE Reynolds.

Flowering in the Gardens at Tsimbazaza, Tananarive, Madagascar.
Height 2m.—Bulbils form on the main peduncle, not on the branches.

FIG. 477.

A. bulbillifera H. Perr. var. *paulianae* Reynolds. Plants on rocks, 85km. SW of Antsohihy, Majunga Prov., Madagascar showing well developed bulbils on the main peduncle.

FIG. 478.

A. bulbillifera H. Perr. var. *paulianae* Reynolds. Flowers natural size, from the Plate 96 plant.

177. **A. suarezensis** H. Perrier in *Mém. Soc. Linn. Norm.* (*l.c.*) 21, et *Fl. Madag.* (*l.c.*) 87; Reynolds in *Aloes Madag. Revis.* 76 (1958).

DESCRIPTION: *Plants* solitary, acaulous or with 20—30cm. erect stem, occasionally up to 80cm. in deeper soil in sheltered positions, the old dried leaf remains persistent.

Leaves 20—24, densely rosulate, lanceolate-attenuate, up to 50—60cm. long, 9—10cm. broad at base, spreading to recurved, sometimes falcately twisted, the apex rounded and with 2—3 short teeth; *upper surface* dull green with reddish tinge, of uniform colour without spots or markings, concave low down, deeply canaliculate upwards; *lower surface* rounded, similar to upper surface; *margins* armed with dirty-white to pale pinkish teeth that are cartilaginous, sub-pungent, deltoid, about 2mm. long, 10mm. apart; *sap* dries pale yellow.

Inflorescence a 4—12 branched panicle 60—80cm high.

Peduncle plano-convex and 12—18mm. broad at base, branched below the middle with 4—12 brownish-red branches, the lowest sometimes with 1—2 short branchlets, the branches spreading-ascending.

Racemes rather densely flowered, the terminal the highest and longest and averaging 10—15cm. long, 6cm. diam., lengthening to 20—25cm. when fruits develop, branch-racemes a little shorter, the apex a tuft of dried bracts, youngest buds suberectly spreading, open flowers nutant to subpendulous.

Bracts dirty-white, turning white in the fruit, ovate-attenuate, subscarious, 10—12mm. long, 4—6mm. broad, 5-nerved.

Pedicels 10—12mm. long, the colour of the base of the perianth and minutely puberulent.

Perianth dull to bright scarlet, paler at mouth, averaging 28mm. long, minutely puberulent, slightly obtuse at base and very shortly stipitate, with a round-oval basal swelling 7mm. diam. across the ovary, constricted to 5·5mm. above the ovary, thence slightly decurved and slightly enlarging to the throat; *outer segments* free to base but cohering around the ovary, with pale markings in upper half, obscurely 3-nerved, the apices subacute and slightly spreading; *inner segments* free, with thin edges, scarlet-keeled, the apices more obtuse and more spreading than the outer.

Filaments filiform-flattened, the 3 inner narrower and lengthening before the 3 outer with their *anthers* in turn exserted 2—3mm.; *style* lemon; *stigma* at length exserted 3mm.; *ovary* dark-green to olive-green, round-oval in outline, 5mm. long, 3mm. diam., at the middle, the apex rounded; *capsule* 16mm. long, 12mm. diam. (Plate 97, Figs. 479—481).

MAJUNGA PROV. Diégo Suarez Division: On the limestones of the Montagne des Français near Diégo Suarez, very abundant, Perrier 16221, type (P). On limestone, north end of the Montagne des Français, 8km. E of Diégo Suarez, c. 12° 15′ S, 49° 22′ E, c. 40m. alt., 23 July 1955, Reynolds 7911 (TAN, PRE, K).

FIG. 479.

A. suarezensis H. Perr. On limestone, Montagne-des-Français a few Km. E. of Diégo-Suarez, North Madagascar.

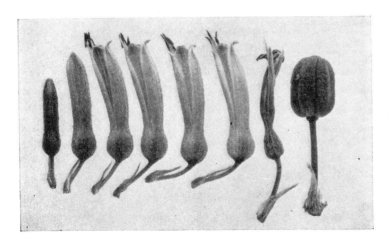

FIG. 480.

A. suarezensis H. Perr. Flowers 1/1 from bud to fruit stages.

PLATE 97

ALOE SUAREZENSIS H. Perr.

On limestone, Montagne des Français, E of Diégo-Suarez, Northern
Madagascar. Height 70cm.

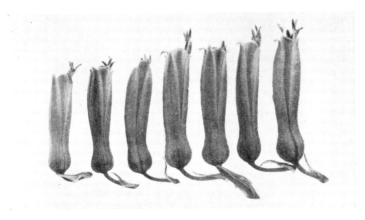

Fig. 481.

E. suarezensis H. Perr. Flowers 1/1
gathered at random showing variation.

A. suarezensis is a very distinctive species, found only on limestone on the Montagne des Français and neighbouring hills near Diégo Suarez in the extreme north of Madagascar. It grows in very scanty soil, on limestone in well-drained positions. The stem is usually short, but sometimes reaches 50—90cm. in length in protected positions in deeper soil.

It is the only species known in Madagascar in which the pedicels and perianth are minutely puberulent. This suggests a remote affinity with *A. trichosantha* Berger in Eritrea and Ethiopia, but the latter is in all ways a very different species.

A. suarezensis is also characterized by having perianths with a round-oval or subglobose basal swelling that is constricted above the ovary – sometimes almost as in some African species of *Saponariae*.

This character and the puberulence distinguish *A. suarezensis* from all other known species in Madagascar (and in Africa).

GROUP 6

PLANTS WITH GLOBOSE OR CORYMBOSE, DENSELY FLOWERED, CAPITATE RACEMES, THE LOWEST PEDICELS USUALLY MUCH SHORTER THAN THE UPPERMOST.

A. PERIANTH CYLINDRIC-TRIGONOUS, SLIGHTLY CURVED (NOT CAMPANULATE); INFLORESCENCE SIMPLE, THE LOWEST FLOWERS OPENING FIRST:

Leaves 10—15cm. long, 3—4cm. broad; lowest pedicels 3—5mm., the uppermost 15—20mm., perianth up to 35mm. long .. .. ..   178 *A. trachyticola*

B. PERIANTH CYLINDRIC-CLAVATE, INFLORESCENCE 1-BRANCHED, ONLY 50CM. HIGH:

Perianth 28mm. long, outer segments free only to the middle, genitals scarcely exserted .. ..   179 *A. fievetii*

C. PERIANTH DISTINCTLY CAMPANULATE, INFLORESCENCE BRANCHED, THE UPPERMOST FLOWERS OPENING FIRST, THE LOWEST LAST:

1. *Stem none or short:*
   Leaves up to 50cm. long, 6cm. broad, inflorescence 90cm., 3—4-branched, lowest pedicels 10mm., lengthening upwards to 30mm., perianth 25mm.   .. ..   180 *A. capitata*

   Leaves grey-green, 50—60cm. long, 3—4cm. broad, pedicels 8—40mm., perianth at most 20mm. .. ..   180A. var. *silvicola*

   Leaves glaucous, 40—45cm. long, 4—5cm. broad, inflorescence 3-branched, 80cm., pedicels 5—35mm., perianth 35mm. .. ..   180B var. *gneissicola*.

Leaves bluish-grey, 30—40cm. long, 9—12cm. broad, inflorescence
3—5-branched, lowest pedicels 15—20mm., the uppermost 40—
50mm., perianth 27mm...   .. ..   180c. var. *quartziticola*

2. *Stem 2—3m. erect:*
Leaves 60cm. long, 6—6·5cm. broad, inflorescence 6-branched,
lowest pedicels exceedingly short   .. ..   180d. var. *cipolinicola*

178. **A. trachyticola** (H. Perr.) Reynolds in *Journ. S.A. Bot.* 23: 72, Plates 26, 27 (1957), in *Aloes Madag. Revis.* 81 (1958).

—— *A. capitata* Bak. var. *trachyticola* H. Perr. in *Mém. Soc. Linn. Norm.* 1 (1): 38 (1926), et *Fl. Madag.* Liliac. 103 (1938).

DESCRIPTION: *Plants* solitary, mostly acaulous, but sometimes developing a procumbent stem.

Leaves 6—10 when young and distichous, up to 14 when spirally twisted to subrosulate, 10—15cm. long, 3—4 cm. broad, the apex obtusely rounded and shortly-dentate; *upper surface* bluish-grey with reddish tinge, glabrous, flat to slightly concave; *lower surface* convex, similar to upper surface; *margins* armed with reddish-brown teeth that are deltoid, pungent, 1—1·5mm. long, 3—5mm. apart.

Inflorescence simple, 65—90cm. high.

Peduncle brown with a bloom, with a few sterile-bracts in upper half, the lowest ovate-cuspidate, 10mm. long, 18mm. broad, 5—7-nerved, smaller upwards.

FIG. 482.

A. trachyticola (H. Perr.) Reynolds. Plant on a NE spur of Mont Ibity, Tananarive Province, Madagascar, c. 20° 05′ S., 47° 01′E., 1,600m. alt. Height 75cm.

Raceme densely capitate, the pedicellate part 2—3cm. long, 7—8cm. diam., the apex a tuft of dried bracts, the lowest flowers opening first, the uppermost last, the apical buds nutant, the lowest open flowers pointing downwards and closely grouped around the axis.

Bracts ovate-acute, thin, 10mm. long, 6mm. broad at the middle, 5—7-nerved.

Pedicels the lowest 3—5mm. long, gradually lengthening upwards, with the uppermost 15—20mm. long.

Perianth red, rather thick and fleshy, up to 35mm. long, cylindric-trigonous, slightly curved, very slightly rounded at base, 8mm. diam. across the ovary, thence very slightly enlarging to the throat; *outer segments* free almost to base, obscurely 3-nerved, the apices subacute; *inner segments* broader than the outer, with 3 crowded nerves forming a prominent red keel, the apices more obtuse than the outer.

Filaments yellowish, the 3 inner narrower and lengthening before the 3 outer with their *anthers* in turn exserted 1—2mm.; *stigma* at length exserted 2—3mm.; *ovary* olive-brown, 7mm. long, 3·5mm. diam., tapering into the style. (Figs. 482–484).

TANANARIVE PROV. On trachytes, on the top of Famoizankova, N of Antsirabe, about 2200m. alt., March 1912, Perrier 11000! type (P); on a north-eastern spur of Mont Ibity, 1600m. alt., c. 20° 05′ S, 47° 01′ E, 17 June 1955, Reynolds 7688 (TĂN), 7690 (PRE).

FIANARANTSOA PROV. On quartzites, mountains between the Ivato and Mania Rivers, about 1400m. alt., Perrier 11009 (P) – with slightly broader and shorter leaves and larger marginal teeth.

FIG. 483.

A. trachyticola (H. Perr.) Reynolds. apical half of leaf 1/1.

FIG. 484.

A. trachyticola H. Perr. Pedicels of uppermost buds considerably longer than those of lowest open flowers.

On 17 June 1955, Mr. Descoings and I found many plants of *A. trachyticola* high up on north-eastern slopes of Mont Ibity, near the top of a spur known locally as Kobouï. This locality is W of the Manandona River, about 5km. above Ambolohiponana Village, at about 1500m. alt., and c. 20° 05′ S, 47° 01′ E.

In *Mém. Soc. Linn. Norm. (l.c.)* 38, Perrier had described *A. capitata* Bak. var. *trachyticola* from mountains between the Ivato and Mania Rivers in the northern part of Fianarantsoa Prov. (Perrier 11009), and from the top of Famoizankova, north of Antsirabe, at about 2200m. alt., in the southern part of Tananarive Prov. (Perrier 11100). Mont Ibity lies between these two localities.

I have not seen Perrier 11009, but I have examined Perrier 11100 from the top of Famoizankova and found that that specimen and the Mont Ibity plants were unquestionably one and the same species. But they differed in too many essential characters to constitute a variety of *A. capitata*, and they well merited specific rank.

Leaves are distichous in young plants, becoming spirally twisted to rosulate with age; they are much shorter and narrower and are not of the kind associated with *A. capitata* and varieties.

The inflorescence is simple – not branched.

The raceme is somewhat similar to *A. capitata* with the lowest pedicels much shorter than the uppermost ones, but is smaller, and the lowest flowers open first, the apical ones last, whereas in *A. capitata* the apical flowers open first.

In *A. trachyticola* the perianth is thick, fleshy, cylindric-trigonous, curved, and up to 35mm. long with the anthers scarcely exserted, and is in all ways very different from the campanulate flowers with long-exserted (10mm.) anthers of *A. capitata* and varieties.

179. A. fievetii Reynolds in *Journ. S.A. Bot.* 31: 279 (1965).

DESCRIPTION: *Plants* acaulescent or with short stem, mostly solitary.

Leaves 12—16, densely rosulate, spreading, narrowly lanceolate-attenuate, averaging 35cm. long, 5—6cm. broad at base; *upper surface* unicoloured-green with slight reddish tinge, flat low down, concave to canaliculate upwards; *lower surface* convex, green with slight reddish tinge in upper half; *margins* with a reddish-pink edge armed with deltoid teeth of the same colour, that are 2—3mm. long, 7—10mm. apart low down, smaller and more distant upwards, the leaf apex slightly twisted to the left, shortly rounded and with 3—4 very small teeth.

Inflorescence simple or 1-branched, up to 50cm. tall.

Peduncle basally plano-convex and 16mm. broad.

Raceme corymbose-capitate, densely many-flowered, about 9cm. across, the pedicellate portion 4cm. long, the buds dull scarlet suberect, open flowers orange-yellow, nutant to subpendulous.

Bracts ovate-acute, brownish-red with membranous edge, 5mm. long, 5mm. broad at base, 3-nerved.

Pedicels 30mm. long, the youngest suberect and straighter, the lowest more oblique and nutant at apex.

Perianth orange, cylindric slightly clavate, 27—30mm. long, basally obtusely obconic, cylindric and 5—6mm. diam. across the ovary, thence enlarging trigonously to a wide open mouth; *outer segments* free to the middle (14mm.) with 3 greenish nerves; *inner segments* themselves free but dorsally adnate to the outer to the middle, broader than the outer and with a prominent greenish median nerve, the apices more obtuse.

Filaments very pale-yellow, the 3 inner narrower and lengthening before the 3 outer with their *anthers* in turn exserted 0—1mm.; *stigma* at length exserted 1mm.; *ovary* green, 6mm. long, 2·5mm. diam. (Figs. 485–487).

MADAGASCAR. Fianarantsoa Prov., on granite rocks 30km. NW of Fianarantsoa, coll. Mr. Gerard Fievet, cult. Mbabane, Swaziland, fl. 1 June 1965, Reynolds 11620 (Rauh 10332) holotype (PRE), isotype (K, P, TAN).

This species was named after Mr. Gerard Fievet who discovered plants on granite rocks 30km. NW of Fianarantsoa near the village Andomaranomaitso (meaning "green water") at an elevation of 1200m., with plants of *A. haworthioides* Bak. and the showy *A. capitata* Bak. var. *quartziticola* H. Perr. growing nearby.

FIG. 485.

A. fievetii Reynolds.   Plant 30km. NW of Fianarantsoa, Madagascar. Height 50cm.

Photo: Prof. W. Rauh.

FIG. 486.

A. fievetii Reynolds. Plant from 30km. NW of Fianarantsoa, Madagascar, flowering at Mbabane, Swaziland. Height 55cm.

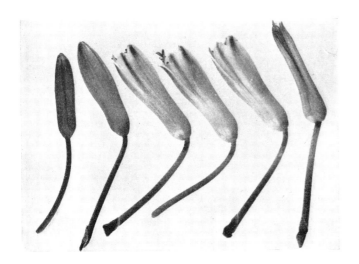

FIG. 487.

A. fievetii Reynolds. Buds and flowers 1/1.

It seems that *A. fievetii* is nearest allied to the typical form of *A. capitata* Bak. from which it differs in being a smaller plant with comparatively narrower channelled leaves, and in having a much lower (50cm.) inflorescence which is mostly only 1-branched; the perianth is nearer slightly clavate than campanulate, while the outer segments are free only to the middle – not to base as in *A. capitata*. Anthers and stigma are exceedingly shortly exserted. The flowers of *A. fievetii* open from the bottom of racemes upwards – not from the apex downwards as occurs in *A. capitata*.

180. **A. capitata** Baker in *Journ. Linn. Soc.* 20: 272 (1883); Durand et Schinz *Conspect. Fl. Afr.* 5: 305 (1893); Berger in Engler *Pflanzenr.* Liliac.-Aloin. 254, Figs. 95, 96 (1908); Perrier de la Bâthie in *Mém. Soc. Linn. Norm.* 1 (1): 36, Plate 5 (1926), in *Fl. Madag.* Liliac. 102, Fig. XIX, 1, 2 (1938); Francois in *Mém. Acad. Malg.* 24: Plate XII (1937); Reynolds in *Aloes Madag. Revis.* 84 (1958).

—— *A. cernua* Todaro in *Hort. Bot. Panorm.* 2: 49, *t.* 36 (1890).

Description: *Plants* acaulous in exposed positions, or developing a stem up to 60cm. in shady places, usually solitary.
Leaves 20—30, densely rosulate, ascending, about 50cm. long, 6cm. broad at base, thick and rigid, gradually narrowing to the apex which is slightly twisted, obtusely rounded and shortly dentate; *upper surface* flat to slightly canaliculate, green, with reddish tinge; *lower surface* rounded, green, without spots or markings; *margins* with brownish-red horny edge armed with reddish, deltoid, pungent teeth averaging 2mm. long, irregularly 8—12mm. distant. *Sap* dries yellow.
Inflorescence erect, about 80cm. high, 3—4-branched from about the middle.
Racemes densely capitate, corymbose (or sometimes with a short slender prolongation of the axis carrying a few flowers), the pedicellate portion 3—4cm. long, 9—10cm. diam., about 8cm. from the uppermost pedicels to the lowest buds, the uppermost flowers spreading horizontally to slightly downwards, the lowest buds pointing downwards and closely grouped around the axis.
Bracts ovate-acute, 6mm. long, 4mm. broad, white, thin, scarious, 5-nerved.
Pedicels the lowest pointing downwards and 10mm. long, gradually longer upwards with the uppermost pedicels curved horizontally and 25—30mm. long.
Perianth orange-yellow, narrowly campanulate, 25mm. long, basally obtuse, 6mm. diam. across the ovary, 10mm. across the mouth; *outer segments* free to base but cohering (not connate) in lower half; *inner segments* broader than the outer, with 3 crowded nerves forming a keel, the apices more obtuse and slightly more spreading than the outer.
Filaments the 3 inner narrower and lengthening before the 3 outer with their *anthers* in turn exserted 8—10mm.; *stigma* at length exserted 10mm.; *ovary* 7mm. long, 3mm. diam., obtusely tapering into the style. (Plate 98, Fig. 488).

Tananarive Prov. At Andringitra, Rev. R. Baron 897 (type), 1353 (K); ex Mont Andringitra to the N of Tananarive, cult. Tananarive, Perrier 19239*bis* (P); Angavokely, E of Tananarive, c. 1800m. alt., Perrier 19239 (P); ex Angavokely, cult. Tananarive, 10 June 1955, Reynolds 7666 (TAN, PRE).

Perrier records that *A. capitata* is common on granite and gneissic mountains of Imerina, Tananarive Prov.

I found considerable numbers at the top of Angavokely, about 45km. E of Tananarive, at 1550—1600m. alt. Plants were growing on rocks, and sometimes in crevices and shallow pockets of soil on very steep slopes.

Baron's locality, Andringitra, lies to the north of Tananarive, and must not be confused with the majestic Andringitra range in the south in Fianarantsoa Prov.

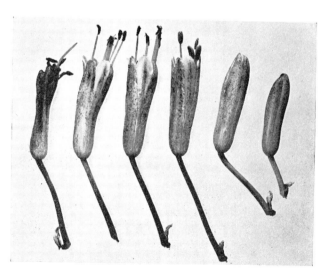

Fig. 488.

A. capitata Bak. Flowers 1/1 from the plant depicted on Plate 98

ALOE CAPITATA Bak.

Plant from Angavokely, E of Tananarive, flowering in the Tsimbazaza
Gardens, Tananarive, Madagascar. Height 80cm.

A. capitata is a species of startling beauty, characterized by having large, densely capitate, corymbose to almost globose racemes of bright orange-yellow flowers which open from the top downwards. This character is not known to me in any other species of Aloe, although I have seen it in two species of Kniphofia in the mountains of Southern Ethiopia. Another unique character is that the uppermost pedicels are arched horizontally, 25—30mm. long, and gradually become shorter downwards with the lowest pedicels only 10mm. long and pointing downwards. The youngest buds also point downwards and are closely pressed around the axis.

180A. var. **silvicola** H. Perr. in *Mém. Soc. Linn. Norm.* (*l.c.*) 39, et *Fl. Madag.* (*l.c.*) 104; Reynolds in *Aloes Madag. Revis.* 86 (1958).

Epiphytic plant in forests, differing from all the other forms of the species by its long narrow *leaves* (50—60cm. × only 3—4cm.), the *marginal* teeth very small, almost nil and sometimes totally absent; lower *pedicels* 8mm., the upper ones reaching 40mm.; *perianth* small, at most 20mm. long; *bracts* about as broad as long (7 × 6mm.), rounded at the top; *stem* short, lying on tree trunks or on rocks. – H. Perrier.

FIG. 489.

A. capitata Bak. var. *gneissicola* H. Perr.   Plant collected 3km. S of Mahatsinjo, 199km. N of Tananarive, Majunga Province, Madagascar – flowering in Johannesburg. Height 80cm.

M ajunga Prov. Forests, on tree trunks or on very shaded rocks at 1000—1200m. alt., on the Manongarivo Massif, Perrier 11012 (P). This form was also observed on Ambre Mountain in the north of the Island. – H. Perrier.

The Manongarivo Massif lies to the east of the main road between Maromandia and Ambanja. I have not seen living plants or Perrier's material.

180B. var. **gneissicola** H. Perr. in *Mém. Soc. Linn. Norm.* (*l.c.*) 37, et *Fl. Madag.* (*l.c.*) 102; Reynolds in *Aloes Madag. Revis.* 86 (1958).

Differs from the typical form in having fewer leaves that are glaucous and only 3·5—4cm. broad at base, fewer-flowered racemes, longer (6—10mm.) brittle bracts, shorter lowest pedicels (5mm. against 10mm.), the uppermost pedicels 35mm. long but not longer than the perianth, and longer flowers (35mm. against 25mm.). (Figs. 489, 490).

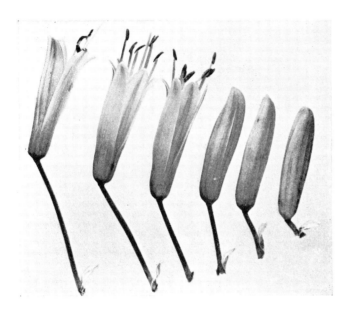

Fig. 490.

A. capitata Bak. var. *gneissicola* H. Perr. Flowers natural size.

M ajunga Prov.: Gneissic rocks of Andriba Peak at the limit of the western area, 600m. alt., Perrier 662 (P); Mahatsinjo, on the Tampoketsa of Ankazobe, c. 1000m. alt. (marginal teeth yellowish, leaves very glaucous), Perrier 13490 (P); Tampoketsa, on the Mahajamba in the neighbourhood of Tsaratanana (with bracts 12mm. and some perianths shorter than their pedicels), Perrier 13500 (P); also on the Bemarivo, left affluent of the Sofia. Ex 3km. S of Mahatsinjo, cult. Johannesburg, fl. 9 June 1956, Reynolds 7893 (PRE).

I found this variety in numbers on the Tampoketsa, on rocks in scanty soil, 65km. N of Ankazobe (38km. S of Mahatsinjo), c. 17° 53′ S, 47° 05 E.,′ 1440m. alt., also on rocks 3km. S of Mahatsinjo (at km. 199 from Tananarive) at 1080m. alt. When plants collected near Mahatsinjo subsequently flowered in Johannesburg, the following description was completed:

D escription: *Plants* mostly solitary. *Stem* 0—20cm. with old dried leaf remains persistent.

Leaves about 20, densely rosulate, compactly ascending, 40—45cm. long, only 3·5—4cm. broad at base, broadening to 5cm. about 10cm. from base, thence narrowing to the apex which is rounded and armed with 3—5 very short teeth; *upper surface* flat low down, slightly concave upwards; *lower surface* rounded; *both surfaces* grey-green to glaucous with reddish tinge, without spots or markings; *margins* armed with reddish-brown, deltoid, pungent teeth that are smaller and more crowded low down; 3mm. long and 8—10mm. distant at the middle, smaller to obsolescent towards apex.

Inflorescence 3-branched from the middle, 80cm. high.

Racemes densely capitate, 12cm. diam., the pedicellate portion 4cm. long, the uppermost flowers opening first, the lowest last.

Bracts ovate-acute, thin, white, brittle, 10mm. long, 5mm. broad, 5-nerved.

Pedicels the uppermost arched-spreading, and up to 35mm. long, gradually shorter downwards with the lowest 5mm. long, deflexed and lying against the axis.

Perianth yellow, narrowly campanulate, 35mm. long, basally obtuse and shortly stipitate, 5mm. diam. across the ovary, thence enlarging to an open mouth 15mm. across; *outer segments* free to base, thinner and whiter at the edges, apices subacute, slightly spreading; *inner segments* broader than the outer, lemon, with 3 crowded nerves forming a broad keel, the apices more obtuse and more spreading than the outer.

Filaments lemon, the 3 inner narrower and lengthening before the 3 outer with their *anthers* in turn exserted 8mm.; *stigma* at length exserted 10mm.; *ovary* green, 6mm. long, 3mm. diam., apex obtuse.

180c. var. **quartziticola** H. Perr. in *Mém. Soc. Linn. Norm. (l.c.)* 38, Plates 5, 6, et *Fl. Madag. (l.c.)* 103; Reynolds in *Aloes Madag. Revis.* 89 (1958).

Differs from the typical form in having shorter, broader, more fleshy leaves (30—40cm. × 9—12cm.), that are glaucous to bluish-grey, larger, wider-spaced marginal teeth (3—4mm. long, 10—20mm. apart), larger racemes with more flowers, narrowly deltoid longer bracts (7—10mm. × 3—4mm.), lowest pedicels longer (15—20mm. against 10mm), longer uppermost pedicels (40—50mm. against 30mm.). Flowers are about the same length (26mm.). (Plate 99, Figs. 491—494).

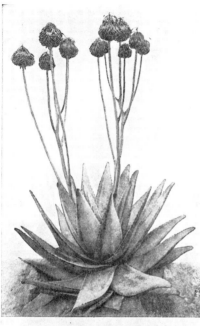

FIG. 491.

A. capitata Bak. var. *quartziticola* H. Perr. Reproduction of Perrier's Plate 5 in *Mém. Soc. Linn. Norm.* (1926).

FIANARANTSOA PROV. Quartzites of West Betsileo: In the neighbourhood of Ikalamavony in the Matsiatra basin, about 1000m. alt., Perrier 11001 type (P); mountains of the upper basin of the Mania, about 1000m. alt., Perrier 11001*bis* (P); on quartzite in valley near Itremo village road fork, 1200m. alt., c. 20° 39′ S, 46° 37′ E, about 40km. W of Ambato-finandrahana, 19 June 1955, Reynolds 7704 (TAN, PRE, K); 2km. S of Zazafotsy, 2,300 ft., fl. 13 July 1955, Reynolds 7882 (TAN, K, PRE).

DISTRIBUTION: East of Antsirabe on road to Vontovorona at 1560m. alt.; near Betafo, W of Antsirabe; 45km. W of Ivato (1350m. alt.); 14—30km. E of Ambafofinandrahana from 1200—1400m. alt.; plentiful along the top of the Itremo at 1560m. alt. Perrier records a form on the basalts of the Analamaitso (north of Tananarive) at 900m. alt.

DESCRIPTION: Based on many flowering plants observed E and W of Ambatofinandrahana.

Plants always solitary. *Stem* none or very short.

Leaves 24—30, densely rosulate, thick and fleshy, averaging 30cm. long, 9—10cm. broad (sometimes reaching 40 × 11cm. in robust specimens), ascending; *upper surface* glaucous to bluish-grey with reddish tinge, flat to slightly concave; *lower surface* slightly rounded, similar in colour to upper surface, without spots or markings; *margins* with reddish or reddish-brown horny edge armed with broadly deltoid, pungent, reddish-brown teeth that are 3—4mm. long, 10—20mm. apart, mostly smaller and more crowded low down, larger and more distant upwards, the leaf apex rounded and with a few small teeth; *sap* dries yellow.

Inflorescence a branched panicle up to 1m. high.

Peduncle brown with a bloom, plano-convex and 4cm. broad at base, terete and more slender upwards, 3—5-branched from about the middle, the lowest branch subtended at base by a many-nerved thin scarious, ovate-acute bract 20mm. long, 10mm. broad.

Racemes capitate, densely multi-flowered, 10—12cm. diam., 9—10cm. from apex to lowest buds, the pedicellate portion 3—5cm. long, the apex a small tuft of dried bracts, apical flowers spreading slightly downwards and opening first, lowest buds pressed against the axis, pointing downwards, and opening last.

Bracts deltoid, thin, subscarious, 6—10mm. long, 3—5mm. broad.

Pedicels the uppermost reddish, curved-spreading slightly downwards, 40—50mm. long, the lowest green, 15—20mm. long.

PLATE 99

ALOE CAPITATA Bak. var. QUARTZITICOLA H. Perr.

Near Itremo Village, 45km. W of Ambatofinandrahana, Fianarantsoa
Prov., Madagascar. Height 1m.

Fig. 492.   Fig. 493.

A. capitata Bak. var. *quartziticola* H. Perr.

Fig. 492. On rocky slopes 45km. W of Ivato; height 90cm.   *Photo G. W. Reynolds.*

Fig. 493. Near Ambatofinandrahana, Fianarantsoa Prov. Height 90cm.   *Photo: Prof. W. Rauh.*

Perianth orange-yellow, cylindric-campanulate, averaging 26mm. long, obtusely tapering at base into the pedicel, 5mm. diam. across the ovary, enlarging to 10—12mm. across the mouth; *outer segments* free to base but cohering (not connate) in lower third, with pale thin edges, faintly 3-nerved, apices subacute; *inner segments* free, broader than the outer, with 3 crowded nerves forming a keel, the apices more obtuse and more spreading than the outer.

Filaments lemon below, yellow upwards, the 3 inner narrower and lengthening before the 3 outer with their *anthers* in turn exserted 9—10mm.; *style* pale yellow, with *stigma* at length exserted 10mm.; *ovary* green, 6mm. long, 3mm. diam., apex obtuse.

NATURAL HYBRID

A. capitata Bak. var. *quartziticola* H. Perr. × *A. macroclada* Bak. This cross was observed among both parents 60km. W of Ivato, which is 14km. E of Ambatofinandrahana, at 1470m. alt.

A plant in the gardens at Tsimbazaza, labelled "*A. pseudomacroclada* no. 55, Pl. 50, Perrier 19004" without locality, is obviously this cross.

Characters nearer *A. macroclada* include shape and size of leaves and rosette, densely-flowered elongated cylindric-acuminate racemes, comparatively short pedicels, fleshy perianths with much recurved segment apices.

Inflorescence 3—4-branched is a character of *A. capitata* var. *quartziticola*.

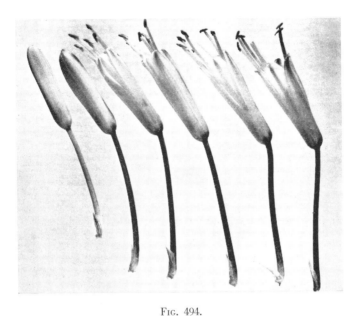

180D. var. **cipolinicola** H. Perr. in *Mém. Soc. Linn. Norm.* (*l.c.*) 39, et *Fl. Madag.* (*l.c.*) 104; Reynolds in *Aloes Madag. Revis.* 92 (1958).

Differs from the typical form, and from the other varieties in having a stem 2—3m. high, and with the lowest pedicels almost nil. (Figs. 495—498).

TANANARIVE PROV. Basin of the Sahatany, an affluent on the right bank of the Manandona, to the S of Antsirabe, about 1300m. alt., specimen with very small crowded red marginal teeth, Perrier 13225 (P); SW of Betafo, about 1400m. alt., specimen with more obtuse leaves, and wider spaced (at least 6mm.), pinkish marginal teeth, Perrier 13172 (P).

FIANARANTSOA PROV. Ambatofangehana, to the W of Ambositra, about 1400m. alt., identical with n. 13225, Perrier 11004 (P). Perrier states that the var. *cipolinicola* occurs exclusively on marble formations.

Mr. Descoings and I found large numbers of plants 37km. W of Ambatofinandrahana, near the Itremo Village roadfork, c. 20° 39′ S, 46° 37′ E., at about 1250—1400m. alt., and on other hills near-by. Plants also occur 14km. E of Ambatofinandrahana.

Plants were in very young bud only when seen, and only the following was noted:

DESCRIPTION: *Plants* with simple, erect stem 2—3m. high, 20cm. diam., old dried leaf remains persistent.

Leaves 60—100 in a dense rosette, up to 60cm. long, 5—6·5cm. broad at base, the apices acute and with 2—3 small teeth; *upper surface* glossy green, with or without reddish tinge, unicoloured, mostly flat and not canaliculate; *lower surface* rounded, glossy green, *margins* mostly with reddish horny edge armed with deltoid, pungent, reddish teeth averaging 3—4mm. long, 10mm. apart at the middle, smaller and more crowded low down, larger and more distant upwards.

Inflorescence a branched panicle about 1m. high.

Peduncle robust, 4—5cm. broad near base and 2·5cm. thick, about 6-branched (sometimes 10-branched) from the middle.

Perrier gives the following: *Inflorescence* always branched; head with a fusiform rachis (5 × 2cm.). Lower *pedicels* nearly nil, shorter than the bracts. *Bracts* obtuse, oval, 6 × 4mm.

Perrier states that sometimes the lowest flowers open first, but he does not give the length of the uppermost pedicels, or of the perianth.

Fig. 495.

A. capitata Bak. var. *cipolinicola* H. Perr. Plants 37km. W of Ambatofinandrahana, Fianarantsoa Prov., Height 2—3m.

Fig. 496.

A. capitata Bak. var. *cipolinicola* H. Perr. A few km. W of Ambatofinandrahana, Fianarantsoa Prov., Madagascar. Height 2m.
Photo: Prof. W. Rauh.

Fig. 497.

A. capitata Bak. var. *cipolinicola* H. Perr. Raceme
× 7/10 approx. Grown by Mr. David Hardy, Pretoria
North.

Photo: Botanical   Research   Institute,   Pretoria.

Fig. 498.

A. capitata Bak. var. *cipolinicola* H. Perr.
Flowers natural size.

GROUP 7

PLANTS ACAULOUS OR TALL-STEMMED, LEAVES ROSULATE, RACEMES DENSELY MULTI-FLOWERED, SHORT- OR LONG-CYLINDRIC, PERIANTHS SESSILE OR WITH SHORT TO LONG PEDICELS.

A. PERIANTHS QUITE SESSILE, plants acaulous or with negligible stem, genitals shortly exserted:

(1) Leaves up to 30cm. × 6cm., inflorescence 50—80cm., 2—3-branched, racemes 8cm., subdense, perianth 20mm., outer segments free to the middle   .. ..   181 *A. humbertii*

(2) Leaves bluish-grey, up to 15cm. × 4·5cm., inflorescence 50cm., simple or 1-branched, raceme 10—15cm. long, buds hidden by densely imbricate bracts, perianth 14mm., outer segments free..   182 *A. conifera*

(3) Leaves deep-green, 20—25cm. long, 6·5cm. broad, margins with continuous brownish-red edge: perianth yellow, 10mm. long, outer segments free.. .. ..   183 *A. cryptoflora*

(4) Leaves 30—40cm. × 7—9cm., inflorescence 60—80cm., 2—4-branched, raceme 30—35cm., buds visible, perianth 15mm., outer segments free.. .. ..   184 *A. betsileensis*

B. PERIANTHS WITH 4—5MM. PEDICELS, plants acaulous:

(1) Leaves 75cm. × 13cm., inflorescence 1·75m., simple or 1-branched, raceme 60—75cm., buds visible, perianth 20—25mm., outer segments free, genitals exserted 8—10mm.   .. ..   185 *A. macroclada*

C. PERIANTHS WITH 28—30MM. PEDICELS:

(1) Stem 3—4m., leaves 1m. × 8—9cm., inflorescence 3m. simple, raceme 2m., perianth 33mm., outer segments free to the middle (tube 16mm.), genitals exserted 10mm. .. ..   197 *A. suzannae*

Note: A. suzannae is included here only because of its long, densely multi-flowered cylindric raceme; in all other characters it has no near affinities. It is the largest of all the Malgache Aloes, and is described under Group 9.

181. **A. humbertii** H. Perrier in *Bull. Mus. Paris*, 2e ser., 3, 692 (1931), in *Fl. Madag.* Liliac. 109 (1938); Reynolds in *Aloes Madag. Revis.* 95 (1958).

DESCRIPTION: *Plant* without suckers, acaulous or with short stem, and with a rosette of 7—12 obliquely ascending leaves.

Leaves 25—30cm. long, 5—6cm. broad, narrowed from the base to the apex (which is rounded and dentate), *margins* horny, with yellow teeth 3—6mm. apart.

Inflorescence 35—40cm. (up to 80cm.), simple or sometimes with 1—2 branches.

Raceme short (8cm.), rigid, quite lax (rather densely flowered in the type), the flowers yellow-tinged with red.

Sterile-bracts 5—7-nerved. *Floral-bracts* lanceolate, 11mm. long, 5mm. broad, shortly cuspidate, 5-nerved.

Perianth (red) sessile, straight, about 2cm. long, the segments united into a compound tube in lower half (free for 10mm.), the outer 5-nerved, the inner 1-nerved.

Stamens scarcely exserted; *anthers* sagittate, 4·5mm. long.

Ovary obtuse; *style* with 6 grooves separated by narrow almost winged angles, slightly attenuate at apex. – H. Perrier (*l.c.*), with the data in parenthesis added from an examination of the type material.

TULÉAR PROV. Fort Dauphin Division: Andohahelo Massif, on crests and silicious rocks of the summit between 1800m. and the summit (1,979m.), flowers red, sessile, 21–22 Oct. 1928, Humbert 6211! type (P); Jan. 1934, Humbert 13635! (P).

I have not seen living plants. The species is known to me only from the description and the type material. I was unable to reach the Andohahelo Massif which lies to the east of Behara in the far south of the Island, in an area where there are no roads.

In the type, Humbert 6211!, the apex of the leaf is rounded and shortly dentate, while the raceme is 8cm. long. Perrier described the inflorescence as being 35—40cm. high, but a sketch on the label depicts an acaulous plant with a 3-branched inflorescence, with "5—8 dcm." written at the side.

A. humbertii is characterized by being an acaulous plant with a rosette of 7—12 leaves that are about 25cm. long, 5—6cm. broad, inflorescence simple or 2—3-branched and up to 80cm. high, racemes rather densely flowered and 8cm. long, perianth red, sessile and 20mm. long, with outer segments connate into a tube in lower half, i.e., free for 10mm.

182. **A. conifera** H. Perrier in *Mém. Soc. Linn. Norm.* 1 (1): 47, Plate 8 (1926), et *Fl. Madag.* Liliac. 109, Fig. XIV 6–7 (1938); Reynolds in *Aloes Madag. Revis.* 96 (1958).

DESCRIPTION: *Plants* solitary, acaulous or with short stem up to 10cm. long.

Leaves 20—24, densely rosulate, narrowly lanceolate-attenuate, spreading and somewhat incurved, averaging 16cm. long, 4—4·5cm. broad at base, 18—20mm. thick, the apex rounded and armed with a few very short teeth; *upper surface* flat to slightly concave, bluish-grey with reddish tinge, of uniform colour, without spots or markings; *lower surface* convex, similar to upper surface; *margins* armed with broadly deltoid, pungent, reddish teeth that are 2—3mm. long, 5—10mm. apart, isolated or sometimes joined by a reddish line, smaller and closer low down, larger and more distant upwards.

Inflorescence 1—2 simultaneously, averaging 50cm. in height, usually simple, rarely with 1—2 branches.

Peduncle plano-convex and 12mm. broad at base, terete upwards, brown with a bloom, with several many-nerved sterile-bracts, the lowest amplexicaul, fleshy, reddish-brown, ovate-acute, 15mm. long, 12—20mm. broad, smaller and more crowded upwards.

Raceme cylindric, averaging 10—15cm. long (rarely 20cm.), 3·5cm. diam., very densely multi-flowered, young racemes at first conical with densely imbricate bracts somewhat resembling a narrow pine-cone, the open flowers almost entirely hidden by their large bracts.

Bracts broadly obovate-cuspidate, averaging 12mm. long and broad, many-nerved.

Pedicels none.

Perianth sessile, trigonous, slightly campanulate-clavate, averaging 14mm. long, 4mm. diam. across the ovary, lemon in lower half where covered by bracts, yellow near the mouth where exposed to the sun, the mouth open; *outer segments* free, narrowly spathulate, obscurely 3—5-nerved at apex, the apices subacute; *inner segments* free, broader in upper half, 1-nerved, the apices more obtuse and more spreading than the outer.

Filaments lemon, filiform-flattened, the 3 inner narrower and lengthening before the 3 outer, with their *anthers* in turn exserted 2 mm.; *style* yellow; *stigma* at length exserted 3mm.; *ovary* green, 3mm. long, 2mm. diam., at base, tapering into the style. (Plate 100, Figs. 499–501).

FIANARANTSOA PROV. West Betsileo: Denuded granite rocks, Mont Ravotay to the S of Ambatofinandrahana, c. 1300m., Perrier 13123, type (P). On a semi-denuded granite hill 9km. SW of Ivato, c. 20° 38′ S, 47° 07′ E, alt. 1450—1500m., 18 June 1955, Reynolds 7692 (TAN, P, PRE, K).

I could not reach Mont Ravotay, but Mr. Descoings and I found considerable numbers of *A. conifera* on a semi-denuded granite whale-back hill known locally as Ambohitsileobodo, about 9km. SW of Ivato on the road to Ambatofinandrahana, and also in large numbers on flat rocky slopes, 5km. further west.

FIG. 499.

Ambohitsileabodo Hill, 9km. SW of Ivato on road to Ambatofinandrahana, Fianarantsoa
Prov., Madagascar – Habitat of *A. conifera* H. Perr.

Fig. 500.

A. conifera H. Perr. Growing on Ambohitsileabodo Hill, 9km. SW of Ivato, on road to Ambatofinandrahana.

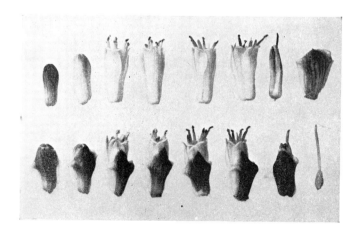

Fig. 501.

A. conifera H. Perr. Flowers natural size. *Upper row:* Sessile perianths with bracts removed. *Lower row:* Flowers with bracts.

PLATE 100

ALOE CONIFERA   H. Perr.

Plant 9km. SW of Ivato on road to Ambatofinandrahana, Fianarantsoa
Prov. Madagascar. Height 60cm.

Plants grew in shallow pockets of soil, or at the soil margin of bare rocks. In young plants, the lower surface of leaves is frequently tuberculate-spinulescent, but this disappears with age. The floral bracts are broader than the perianth and almost as long. When fully open, only the mouth of the flowers is visible together with the exserted genitals. Flowers open first along the sunny side of racemes and have a copious supply of nectar to above the ovary.

183. **A. cryptoflora** Reynolds in *Journ. S.A. Bot.* 31: 281 (1965).

DESCRIPTION: *Plant* succulent, solitary, acaulous or with a short stem.

Leaves 15—20, densely rosulate with slight spiral twist, lanceolate-attenuate, spreading, 20—25cm. long, 6·5cm. broad; *upper surface* deep-green with slight reddish tinge, rather flat, without spots or markings; *lower surface* convex, otherwise as the upper surface; *margins* with continuous brownish-red edge armed with teeth of the same colour that are deltoid, 2—3mm. long, 5—10mm. apart.

Inflorescence usually 1-branched, 40cm. high, sometimes 60cm. in the wild state.

Peduncle reddish-brown, basally plano-convex and 15mm. broad, with one short branch from about the middle, with a few sterile-bracts above the base of the branch that are broadly ovate-cuspidate, thick and fleshy, the lowest about 12—15mm. long and broad, 7—9-nerved.

Racemes cylindric, very slightly conic, the terminal 14cm. long, 3cm. diam., the lateral only half as long, very densely many-flowered, all buds at first hidden by densely imbricate bracts.

Bracts broadly ovate-orbicular-cuspidate, rounded and somewhat cupped, thick, fleshy, pale-green, 11mm. long, 12mm. broad when pressed flat, 7—9-nerved, the nerves greenish.

Pedicels none.

Perianth cylindric-campanulate, slightly trigonous, 10mm. long, 3·5mm. diam. across the ovary, greenish-yellow low down, orange-yellow at the mouth; *outer segments* free to base, obscurely 3—5-nerved; *inner segments* broader than the outer, with one median nerve.

Filaments lemon, the 3 inner narrower and lengthening before the 3 outer with their *anthers* in turn exserted 2—3mm.; *stigma* at length exserted 3mm.; *ovary* pale-green, 4mm. long, 2mm. diam. (Figs. 502, 503).

MADAGASCAR. Fianarantsoa Prov., on granite 25km. NW of Fianarantsoa, coll. G. Fievet, cult. Mbabane, Swaziland, fl. 10 June 1965, Reynolds (11619 holotype (PRE), isotype (K).

This remarkable species was discovered by Mr. Gerard Fievet of Fianarantsoa. Plants were sent by him to Mbabane, Swaziland, where some of them flowered in June 1965.

FIG. 502.

A. cryptoflora Reynolds. Plant from 25km. NW of Fianarantsoa, Madagascar, flowering at Mbabane, Swaziland. Height 50 cm.

Fig. 503.

A. cryptoflora Reynolds. *Upper:* Flowers with bracts 1/1. *Lower:* Buds and flowers 1/1, without bracts; a bract 1/1 on right.

A. cryptoflora was so named because, when in full bloom, the flowers are hidden by their large, fleshy, somewhat rounded, as if cupped, bracts, only the mouth of the flower and the exserted orange stamens being visible.

In shape and size of the deep green leaves, *A. cryptoflora* is nearest allied to *A. fievetii* but is nothing like it in floral characters. With its 10mm.-long sessile flowers and densely flowered cylindric racemes (but not in leaves), *A. cryptoflora* is closely allied to *A. conifera* H. Perr., but the latter has a more compact rosette of bluish-grey leaves.

The bracts of *A. cryptoflora* are remarkably thick, fleshy, orbicular-cuspidate, and are somewhat cupped around the flower which it touches with the base, apex and margins of the bract. There is a distinct space between the middle of the bract and the perianth.

As is usual with racemes of this kind, the flowers open first up the sunny side of the raceme.

184. **A. betsileensis** H. Perrier in *Mém. Soc. Linn. Norm.* 1 (1): 48 (1926), et *Fl. Madag.* Liliac. 110 (1938); Reynolds in *Aloes Madag. Revis.* 99 (1958).

DESCRIPTION: *Plant* acaulous, solitary.

Leaves 20—30 in average specimens (50 in very large plants), densely rosulate, spreading-ascending, 30—40cm. long, 7—9cm. broad at base, narrowing to the apex which is slightly twisted, obtusely rounded and shortly toothed; *upper surface* dull green with reddish tinge, without spots or markings, flat to slightly canaliculate; *lower surface* convex, similar to upper surface; *margins* with reddish edge armed with deltoid, pungent, reddish teeth 2—3mm. long and 8—12mm. apart; *sap* dries yellow.

Inflorescence simple and 60cm. high in young plants, 3—4-branched and 70—80cm. high in old specimens, sometimes 5-branched and over 1m. high in very large plants.

Peduncle robust, brown with a bloom, plano-convex and 3—4cm. broad at base, more slender upwards, with 1—4 branches from about the middle, clothed below the racemes with several fleshy sterile-bracts that are 10—12mm. long and broad low down, smaller upwards.

Racemes cylindric, the terminal 30—35cm. long, 4—5cm. diam., the lateral a little shorter, very densely multi-flowered, the flowers arranged in 13 spirally twisted rows, the flowers orange and opening first on the sunny side, all buds visible and not hidden by bracts.

Bracts ovate-obtuse, fleshy, reddish, 8—10mm. long, 6—8mm. broad, about 7-nerved.

Pedicels none.

Perianth cylindric slightly campanulate, yellow with orange tips, averaging 15mm. long, 7mm. diam. across the ovary, 9mm. across the mouth, with a copious supply of clear nectar to above the ovary; *outer segments* free, long-oval, 3—5-nerved, the apices subacute, straight; *inner segments* free, broader than the outer, with 3 crowded nerves forming a slight keel, the apices obtusely rounded.

Filaments lemon below, the exserted portion orange, filiform-flattened, the 3 inner narrower and lengthening before the 3 outer with their *anthers* in turn exserted 3—4mm.; *stigma* at length exserted 4—5mm.; *ovary* pale green, 6mm. long, 3mm. diam., obtusely rounded at apex. (Figs. 504—506).

TULÉAR PROV. S. Betsileo: Rocks and dry plains between the Ionaivo and Ihosy Rivers, 800m.—1400m. alt., Perrier 13676 (P). Rocky grasslands, 100km. S of Ihosy (40km. N of Betroka), c. 22° 55′ S, 46° 09′ E, 990m. alt., 27 June 1955, Reynolds 7782 (TAN, PRE, K).

I was unable to visit Perrier's type locality between the Ionaivo and Ihosy Rivers, but found this species at km. 83, 87, 100 and 102 S of Ihosy on the road to Betroka at an average of 990 m. alt.

The leaves of *A. betsileensis* are distinguished from those of *A. macroclada* by their apices being obtusely rounded and shortly dentate. The inflorescence is shorter and often 2—4-branched. The racemes of *A. betsileensis* are also shorter, while the perianths are quite sessile, a little shorter, and most densely arranged in 13 spirally twisted rows. The flowers open first along the sunny side of racemes, and are more orange-coloured, those on the shady side being paler to yellow.

At a quick glance, young plants of *A. betsileensis* bear a slight resemblance to those of *A. conifera*, but all buds are clearly visible and are not hidden by densely imbricate bracts.

FIG. 504.

A. betsileensis H. Perr. Plant on rocks, 38km. N of Betroka, 102km. S of Ihosy, Fianrantsoa Province. Alt. 1,020m. Height 70cm.

FIG. 505.

A. betsileensis H. Perr.. Plant collected 102km. S of Ihosy, flowering at Mbabane, Swaziland. Height 1m.

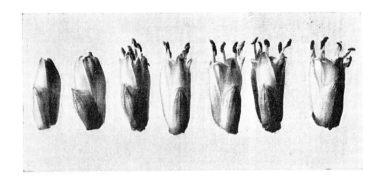

FIG. 506.

A. betsileensis H. Perr. Sessile flowers 1/1.

185. A. macroclada Baker in *Journ. Linn. Soc.* 20: 273 (1883); Durand et Schinz *Conspect. Fl. Afr.* 5: 309 (1893); Berger in Engler *Pflanzenr.* Liliac.–Aloin. 298 (1908); H. Perrier in *Mém. Soc. Linn. Norm.* 1 (1): 46, Plate 7 (1926), et *Fl. Madag.* Liliac. 108 (1938); Reynolds in *Aloes Madag. Revis.* 101 (1958).

DESCRIPTION: *Plant* large, always acaulous, solitary.

Leaves about 36, densely rosulate, arcuate-ascending, broadly ensiform-attenuate, averaging 75cm. long, 15cm. broad at base, 1—2cm. thick, narrowing to an acute apex; *upper surface* unicoloured green without spots or markings, slightly concave at base, slightly canaliculate upwards; *lower surface* convex, similar to upper surface; *margins* sinuate-dentate, with a more or less horny edge armed with pungent, deltoid teeth that are paler low down, orange-brown upwards, 3mm. long, about 10mm. apart.

Inflorescence usually simple, sometimes with one short branch, averaging 1·75m. tall, sometimes reaching as much as 2·40m. in old specimens.

Peduncle plano-convex and 6cm. broad at base, 3cm. thick near the raceme, brown with a bloom, with numerous sterile-bracts the lowest being 20mm. long, 35mm. broad, thin, scarious, many-nerved, smaller upwards.

Raceme very densely flowered, cylindric, averaging 60—75cm. long, 7cm. diam., sometimes reaching 1m. in old specimens, the flowers horizontally disposed and opening first on the sunny side.

Bracts broadly ovate-acute and shortly cuspidate, 10mm. long, 7mm. broad, reflexed at base, thin, subscarious, 5-nerved.

Pedicels 4—5mm. long, 3mm. thick.

Perianth campanulate, pale scarlet, greenish inside the mouth, 20—25mm. long, 6mm. diam. at base, 20mm. across the mouth; *outer segments* free to base, with thin margins, 5-nerved throughout, the apices at first spreading, then revolute; *inner segments* free, broader than the outer, with broad (3mm.) thin border and a 2mm. broad keel throughout, the apices spreading to revolute and more obtuse than the outer.

Filaments lemon, flattened, the 3 inner narrower and lengthening before the 3 outer, with their *anthers* in turn exserted 8—10mm., the *anthers* orange, 8mm. long, 2mm. broad; *style* pale yellow; *stigma* at length exserted 10mm.; *ovary* green, trigonous, 14mm. long, 4mm. diam. at base, slightly narrowing to the apex which obtusely tapers into the style. (Plate 101, Figs. 507—509).

TANANARIVE PROV. Top of Angavo, Baron 1178, 1656 (K), received in Jan. 1882 and Oct. 1882 respectively. Chiefly from north-west Madagascar: Baron 5922 (K, BM), received Sept. 1887. Antsirabe, N. Betsileo, on dry mountain slopes, Aug. 1880, Hildebrandt 3603 (P, BM); near Tananarive, June 1926, H. Perrier 17649! (K); Iandratsay Valley, 30km. W of Antsirabe, c. 19° 49′ S, 46° 49′ E, 1170m., 14 June 1955, Reynolds 7673 (TAN, P, K, PRE).

SOUTH BETSILEO: Andringintra Massif, 1200m., Perrier 11006 (P).

Perrier has a note that Baron 1178 (which I have not seen) seems to him to be a mixture of *A. macroclada* Bak. and *A. betsileensis* H. Perr. Against this, Baron's 1178 was collected on Angavo, east of Tananarive, where *A. betsileensis* has never been known to occur. *A. betsileensis* occurs considerably further south, i.e. on the Horombe Plateau, south and west of Ihosy.

In Baker's original description *A. macroclada* is described as having a "caudex 3 or 4 feet long", but as Perrier has pointed out, this is incorrect. *A. macroclada* is always acaulous. Baker also states: "Allied to *A. vera* and *A. sahundra*". The species hitherto known as *A. vera* L. (and which must now be known as *A. barbadensis* Mill.) is in all ways different.

A. sahundra Bojer (*nomen nudum*) in *Hort. Maurit.* 345 (1837), from sandy shores of the south-west of St. Augustin Bay (south of Tuléar), is stated to be a shrub forming thickets. This suggests *A. divaricata* Berger which is a shrub, rather than *A. vaombe* Decorse et Poisson, both of which occur near St. Augustin Bay.

DISTRIBUTION: *A. macroclada* appears to be the most widely distributed species in Madagascar, from near Mont Tsaratanana in the north to the Fort Dauphin district in the south. It can be seen repeatedly for 200km. along the road from Tananarive northwards to Ankazobe and Mahatsinjo, mostly between 1200m. to 1500m. East of Tananarive it occurs on slopes of Angavo and Anga-

PLATE 101

ALOE MACROCLADA   Bak.

In the Iandratsay Valley, 30km. W of Antsirabe, Madagascar. Height
2·50m.—With the author.

FIG. 507.

A. macroclada Bak.
Raceme $\times$ $\frac{1}{6}$. Flowers open first along the sunny side.

FIG. 508.

A. macroclada Bak. Flowers 1/1 from
bud to post-pollination stages.

vokely. South of Tananarive, it is found near Antsirabe, eastwards to Mont Vontovorana, west-wards to Betafo and is abundant in the Iandratsay Valley for 50km. to Soavina and further west, at about 1100—1200m.

Along the road westwards from Ivato to Ambatofinandrahana, *A. macroclada* grows socially with *A. capitata* var. *quartziticola* and crosses were seen. It occurs near Fianarantsoa, is abundant near Ambalavao, and on northern foothills of the Andringitra range; also west and north of Ivohibe at about 700m. alt., at the southern end of the Andringitra.

A. macroclada is essentially a species inhabiting grasslands subject to burning, and appears to be nearest allied to *A. betsileensis* H. Perr., but the latter (which grows on the Horombe Plateau 80—100km. S of Ihosy) differs in having rounded, dentate leaf apices, a lower 2—4-branched inflorescence, shorter racemes (30—35cm. long) and sessile yellow-orange flowers averaging 15mm. long.

Fig. 509.

A. macroclada Bak. In the Iandratsay Valley, 9km. W of Betafo, 30 km. W of Antsirabe, Madagascar. 1,170m. alt. Height 1·60m.

GROUP 8

PLANTS OF SHRUBBY GROWTH; SMALL LOW UNDERSHRUBS TO TALL-STEMMED SHRUBS, 2—3M. AND MORE HIGH; PERIANTHS WITH ANTHERS NOT OR VERY SHORTLY EXSERTED.

A. PEDICELS 6—8MM. LONG. Perianth slightly rounded at base (not obconic), slighty constricted above the ovary:

    1. RACEMES CAPITATE OR SUBCAPITATE; PERIANTH 22MM. LONG:
        (*a*) Stems 20—25cm. long, 7—9mm. diam., leaves 8—10mm. long, 7—9mm. broad; inflorescence simple, 12—15cm.; raceme 6—8-flowered; outer segments free .. ..   186 *A. millotii*
        (*b*) Stems up to 1m. long, mostly subscandent, 7—9mm. diam.; leaves 10—15cm. long, 6—10mm. broad; inflorescence 16cm., simple or 1-branched; outer segments free 15mm. (tube 6—7mm.)   187 *A. antandroi*

2. Racemes Cylindric-Acuminate, 10—20cm. Long, Laxly 20—30-Flowered:

(*a*) Stems 30cm. long, 8—10 cm. diam.; leaves up to 20cm. long, 12mm. broad; inflorescence 3—5-branched, 30—50cm. high; perianth 22mm., outer segments free 11mm. (tube 11mm.)   ..   188 *A. isaloensis*

(*b*) Stems 3—4m. and more high; leaves up to 65cm. long, 7cm. broad; marginal teeth 5—6mm. long; inflorescence a many-branched pyramidal panicle 1m. high; perianth scarlet, 28mm., outer segments free   ..   ..   192 *A. divaricata*

(*c*) Perianth pale pink   ..   ..   192a var. *rosea*

3. Racemes Cylindric-Acuminate, 15—20cm. Long, Subdensely Flowered:

(*a*) Stem short. Leaves obliquely spreading-recurved, 30cm. long, 4·5cm. broad; inflorescence 1—1·2m. high, 2—3-branched; perianth cylindric-clavate, 25mm. long, basally obconic, outer segments free   ..   ..   190 *A. itremensis*

B. PEDICELS 15mm. LONG. Perianth obconic at base, 28—30mm. long; racemes cylindric-acuminate, 10—15cm. long; outer segments free for one-third their length (tube about 19mm.):

1. *Larger plants:*
(*a*) Stems more erect, 60cm.—1m., leaves long-pointed, spreading to recurved, 30cm. long, 3—4cm. broad; inflorescence 2—3-branched, 40—50cm. high   ..   ..   189 *A. acutissima*

(*b*) Stems more procumbent, up to 1cm. long, rosettes more compact, leaves ascending-spreading, 25—30cm. long, 5—6cm. broad; marginal teeth 3—4mm.; buds hidden by imbricate bracts   ..   ..   191 *A. intermedia*

2. *Smaller plants:*
Stems 6—9mm. diam., leaves 15—20mm. broad; pedicels 10mm.; perianth 20mm.   ..   ..   189a *A. acutissima* var. *antanimorensis*

C. PERIANTH THICK, FLESHY, CYLINDRIC, STRAIGHT, 28mm. LONG, BASALLY OBTUSE:

1. Stems 50cm. with shoots at random; leaves 40—50cm. long, 6—7cm. broad; inflorescence 1m., 3—4-branched; racemes cylindric-acuminate 20—25cm. long, subdensely flowered; pedicels 6—7mm.; outer segments free to the middle   ..   ..   193 *A. mayottensis*

Note: *A. itremensis* seems nearest allied to *A. acutissima* and is included here although it is not a shrub.

A. mayottensis appears to be of shrubby growth, and is provisionally included here, but further investigation is necessary.

186. A. millotii Reynolds in *Journ. S.A. Bot.* 22: 23 (1956), in *Aloes Madag. Revis.* 107 (1958).

Description: *Plant* a small low undershrub, much branched at base.

Stems decumbent, divergent or ascending, averaging 20—25cm. long in exposed position, 7—9mm. diam. near base, slightly thicker upwards, 10—20-branched from base or higher, the apical 5—7cm. sublaxly to subdensely foliate with the internodes 5—10mm. apart.

Leaves 8—10, spreading to recurved, distichous in young shoots becoming spirally twisted to rosulate with age, basally sheathing, 8—10cm. long, 7—9mm. broad at base, gradually tapering to the apex which is obtusely rounded and armed with about 5 rather soft white cartilaginous teeth about ·5—1mm. long; *upper surface* canaliculate, dull grey-green with reddish tinge when in full sun, greener in partial shade, with or without a few small dull-white spots low down; *lower surface* convex, usually greener than upper surface and with many scattered dull-white spots throughout, the spots about 2mm. long, 1—1·5mm. broad at the middle and sometimes minutely subspinulescent; *margins* armed with small, white, cartilaginous, deltoid, isolated teeth up to 1mm. long, 5—10mm. apart, the inter-spaces straight and the colour of the leaf, sometimes obsolescent near apex.

Inflorescence always simple, averaging 12—15cm. long.

Peduncle plano-convex and 3—5mm. broad at base, terete upwards, about 3mm. diam. below the raceme, with about 5 sterile-bracts in upper half, the lowest ovate-acuminate, thin, scarious, white, about 8mm. long, 5mm. broad at base, many-nerved, smaller upwards.

Raceme laxly 6—8-flowered, 4—5cm. diam., the pedicellate portion 3—5cm. long, the scarlet buds grey-green tipped, spreading, open flowers nutant to subpendulous.

Bracts ovate-acute, the lowest 7mm. long, 4mm. broad at base, reflexed, thin, scarious, 3—5-nerved.

Pedicels spreading, averaging 6—8mm. long.

Perianth scarlet, paler at mouth, averaging 22mm. long, basally flat to very slightly rounded, 7mm. diam. across the ovary, constricted to 6mm. above the ovary, thence slightly decurved and enlarging to the throat, the mouth wide open; *outer segments* free to base but cohering in lower half, obscurely 3-nerved, the nerves green at apex, the apices subacute, slightly spreading; *inner segments* free, thin and white at the edges, with a scarlet keel turning green at apex, the apices more obtuse and more spreading than the outer.

Filaments almost white, filiform-flattened, the 3 inner narrower and lengthening before the 3 outer with their *anthers* in turn exserted 1mm.; *style* pale lemon, with *stigma* at length exserted 1—2mm.; *ovary* pale orange-yellow, 5mm. long. 2mm. diam., truncate at apex. *Capsule* round-oval, 15mm. long, 12mm. diam. (Plate 102, Figs. 510–512).

TULÉAR PROV. Fort Dauphin Division: Cap Ste. Marie, xerophytic bush and limestone plateau, alt. 100—150m., 22 Feb. 1947, Humbert 20342! (P, PRE); on limestone at Cap Ste. Marie, c. 23° 35′ S, 49° 05′ E, 100m. alt., 5 July 1955, Reynolds 7840, holotype (TAN), isotype (P, K, PRE); ex Cap. Ste. Marie, cult. Johannesburg, fl. 22 Jan. 1960, J. Lavranos s.n. (PRE).

In July 1955, Mr. B. Descoings and the author visited Cap Ste. Marie and found considerable numbers of plants growing on Eocene limestone for about 5km. northwards from the Cap, many being then in flower.

A. millotii, a very distinctive species with a rather sprawling habit of growth, was found only on limestone, in exposed positions or in partial shade, under intensely arid conditions. Plants form very small low undershrubs which are much-branched at base, the outer stems being mostly decumbent with the centre ones divergent to erect, and averaging 20—25cm. long, with the apical 5cm. subdensely foliate. When partly supported by twiggy bush, stems may reach 50cm. in length, with 16—20 leaves laxly grouped along the apical 20cm. of stems.

FIG. 510.

A. millotii Reynolds. Flowering stem × ⅓ – at Cap Ste. Marie, the southernmost point of Madagascar.

ALOE MILLOTII Reynolds.

On limestone at Cap Ste. Marie, the southernmost point of Madagascar.
Height 20cm.

Leaves are at first distichous in young stems, but become spirally twisted to rosulate, with age. Racemes are few-flowered, and only 2—4 simple inflorescences were noticed in a much-branched plant.

In inflorescence characters, especially in pedicels and shape and size of flowers, *A. millotii* and *A. antandroi* (R. Decary) H. Perr. are very closely allied, but the latter (which is found on the road to Tsihombe and elsewhere) is a much larger plant with erect, rigid, slender stems 50cm.—1m. long, and very different leaves.

FIG. 511.

A. millotii Reynolds. Flowers 1/1 from bud to fruit stages.

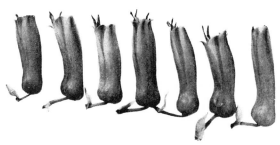

FIG. 512.

A. millotii Reynolds. Flowers 1/1 gathered at random showing variation.

187. **A. antandroi** (R. Decary) H. Perrier (*errore antandroy*) in *Mém. Soc. Linn. Norm.* 1 (1): 19 (1926), et *Fl. Madag.* Liliac. 84 (1938); Reynolds in *Aloes Madag. Revis.* 111 (1958).

—— *Gasteria antandroi* R. Decary in *Bull. Econ. Madag.* 18 (1): 27 (1921) cum fig.
——? *A. leptocaulon* Bojer, *nomen nudum* in *Hort. Maurit.* 347 (1837).

DESCRIPTION: *Plant* of slender, shrubby growth, with woody rootstock, with several stems branched at base or higher, usually ascending through dry twiggy bush and partly supported.
Stems 60cm.—1m. long, 5—7mm. diam., the terminal 10—15cm. laxly foliate.
Leaves about 12—20, basally sheathing, the sheaths green-striate and 10mm. apart, 10—15cm. long, 6—10mm. broad, gradually narrowing to an acute apex which is obtusely rounded and armed with about 3 very small, soft, cartilaginous, white teeth about ·5—1mm. long, the youngest leaves erectly spreading, older leaves spreading to recurved; *upper surface* canaliculate, grey-green, with or without a few scattered small white spots; *lower surface* convex, grey-green, with numerous dull white spots throughout; *margins* armed with small white to very pale-brown, deltoid teeth that are ·5—1mm. long, 2—5mm. apart in young leaves, 7—10mm. apart in old leaves.
Inflorescence simple or 1-branched, 2—3 to a stem, averaging 16cm. long and arising laterally from the axil of upper leaves.
Peduncle plano-convex and 3mm. broad at base, terete and 2mm. diam. below the raceme, with about 5 sterile-bracts, the lowest ovate-acute, 5mm. long, 2mm. broad, thin, scarious, dirty white, 5—7-nerved.
Raceme subcapitate, 5cm. diam., the pedicellate portion averaging 3cm. long, laxly about 10-flowered, the buds grey-green tipped and spreading, open flowers nutant to subpendulous.
Bracts ovate-acute, dirty-white, 4mm. long, 3mm. broad at base, scarious, 3—5-nerved.
Pedicels reddish, spreading, averaging 8mm. long.
Perianth scarlet-red, averaging 22mm. long, basally flat, 6mm. diam. across the ovary, very slightly constricted above the ovary, thence slightly decurved and enlarging towards the throat; *outer segments* free for 15mm. (definite tube of 6—7mm.), green-nerved near apex, the apices subacute and very slightly spreading; *inner segments* free but dorsally adnate to the outer for 6mm., thin and white at the edges, scarlet-keeled, the keel turning green at apex, the apices more obtuse than the outer.
Filaments pale lemon, flliform-flattened, the 3 inner narrower and lengthening before the 3 outer with their *anthers* in turn exserted 1mm.; *stigma* at length exserted 1—2mm.; *ovary* 5mm. long, 2mm. diam., obtuse at apex; *capsule* 18mm. long, 12mm. diam. (Plate 103, Fig. 513).

MADAGASCAR without precise locality, native name *Tsikyvahombaho*, 12 Sept. 1918, R. Decary s.n.! (as *Gasteria antandroi*) type (P).

TULÉAR PROV. Fort Dauphin Division: Eocene calcareous rocks, very dry, Mahafaly plateau, in neighbourhood of Cap. Ste. Marie, June 1910, Perrier de la Bâthie, n. 11018! (P); limestone rubble in dry bush, 10km. W of Tsihombe on Beloha road, c. 25° 18′ S, 45° 24′ E, 165m. alt., 6 July 1955, Reynolds 7849 (TAN, P, K, PRE). Near La Table, 15km. SE of Tuléar, 9 July 1955, Reynolds 7857 (TAN, P, K, PRE).

PLATE 103

ALOE ANTANDROI   (R. Decary) H. Perr.

On limestone rubble 10km. W of Tsihombe, Fort Dauphin Div.,
Madagascar. Height 1m.

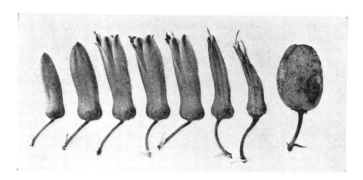

FIG. 513.

A. antandroi (R. Decary) H. Perr. Flowers 1/1 from bud to fruit stages – from the plant depicted on Plate 103.

Perrier cites the following material which I have not seen: La Table near Tuléar, Poisson 171, 217; valley of the Onilahy, Humbert 2633; Behara, Decary 4419; Tsihombe, Decary 9886; Ambovombe, Decary 2790, 3415, 8915, 9097, 9107; Vohitsiombe, Decary 8979, all in Paris.

Decary states that "Tsikyvahombaho" is the Antandroy name for this species, and that it means "resembling a small Aloe". Decary also gives the localities Cap Ste. Marie, Reankily and Ankaboa.

A. antandroi occurs in the intensely hot and dry parts of the south and south-west, from Tsihombe and near Cap Ste. Marie, north-westwards along the Mahafaly plateau to the Onilahy Valley and near Tuléar. It forms very slender-stemmed shrubs and is usually found among dry twiggy bushes with the stems rising through bush and partly supported. In clearings in between bushes, stems are erect and more rigid.

In general habit of growth, woody rootstocks, slender stems, and shape and size of leaves, *A. antandroi* bears a strong resemblance to the South African species *A. tenuior* Haw., but the latter differs in having much longer cylindric racemes, and much shorter, tubulose yellow flowers only 12—14mm. long.

Near La Table, I found some plants with leaves only 5mm. broad at base, growing socially with *A. viguieri*.

In racemes and flowers *A. antandroi* is very closely allied to *A. millotii* at Cap Ste. Marie, but the latter is a low undershrub with considerably shorter, sprawling stems and very different leaves.

Decary originally regarded this species as belonging to Gasteria, but in no characters does it even remotely resemble any South African species of Gasteria.

Bojer in *Hort. Maurit.* 345 (1837) gives the following account of his *Aloe leptocaulon* (*nomen nudum*):

West coast of Madagascar. Grows among the bushes which cover the tops of the mountains along the mouth of the River Onilahi which flows into the bay of Saint-Augustin. Cultivated in the Royal Garden, Pampl. Perrenial. Fls. Sept., Oct. The stem of this plant is very long, thin, and with a tendency to climb.

As Perrier has already pointed out, this can hardly be referred to any other species but *A. antandroi*.

The Royal Gardens, Pamplemousses, where *A. antandroi* was cultivated, were originally laid out by M. Poivre in 1769, and are situated 10km. NE of Port Louis, in the north-western part of Mauritius.

188. A. isaloensis H. Perrier in *Bull. Acad. Malg.* nouv. ser. 10: 20 (1927), et *Fl. Madag.* Liliac. 93 (1938); Reynolds in *Aloes Madag. Revis.* 114 (1958); Verdoorn in *Fl. Pl. Afr.* 36: Plate 1419 (1963).

DESCRIPTION: *Plants* forming small shrubs 30—50cm. high, branching from base and with 6—12 stems that are erect, divergent or procumbent and averaging 20—30cm. in length, 8—10mm. diam. (old specimens sometimes reaching 40—50cm. long and 12mm. diam.), the apical 6—10cm. sublaxly foliate.

Leaves 10—14, basally sheathing, the sheaths 5mm. apart and obscurely striate, sublaxly disposed and averaging 13—20cm. long, 10—13mm. broad at base, 4—6mm. thick, linear-attenuate, arcuate-ascending and forming a rather compact cluster; *upper surface* grey-green, flat to slightly channelled, without spots or markings; *lower surface* rounded, similar to upper surface; *margins* armed with firm to subpungent greenish to pale-brown, cartilaginous teeth that are 1—1·5mm. long, 5—10mm. apart, usually larger low down, smaller upwards; *sap* yellow-orange, very abundant.

Inflorescence varying from simple and 30cm. high in young plants to 3—5-branched and 50cm. high in old specimens.

Peduncle slender, brown with a bloom, plano-convex and 5mm. broad at base, about 4mm. diam. upwards, up to 3—5-branched from about the middle.

Racemes cylindric, slightly acuminate, 10—14cm. long, 4—5cm. diam., rather laxly 20—30-flowered, the youngest buds greenish tipped, spreading, open flowers nutant.

Bracts very small, deltoid, 3mm. long, 1·5mm. broad, thin, scarious, dirty-white, 3-nerved.

Pedicels suberectly spreading to oblique, averaging 6—7mm. long.

Perianth reddish-scarlet, 22mm. long, shortly stipitate at base, 6mm. diam. across the ovary, constricted to 5mm. above the ovary, thence slightly decurved and slightly enlarging trigononously to the throat; *outer segments* free to the middle (tube 11mm.), obscurely nerved, the apices greenish, subacute, slightly spreading; *inner segments* free but dorsally adnate to the outer to the middle, with white edges and more obtuse more spreading apices.

Filaments pale lemon, the 3 inner narrower and lengthening before the 3 outer with their *anthers* in turn exserted 0—·5mm.; *style* lemon, with *stigma* st length exserted 1mm.; *ovary* pale green, 4—5mm. long, 2mm. diam., the apex slightly rounded. (Figs. 514–517).

FIANARANTSOA PROV. Ihosy Dist., on secondary sandstones in Tapia (*Uapaca sp.*) bush, Isalo range, about 1200m. alt., Perrier 17232 (holotype P, K); Isalo Range, Ranohira, 30 July 1928, C. F. Swingle et Humbert 78464 (BM); on sandstone slopes of the Isalo Range, 13km. SW of Ranohira, c. 22° 37′ S, 45° 21′ E, c. 600m. alt., locally abundant, 12 July 1957, Reynolds 7875 (TAN, P, K, PRE); near Ranohira, 900m., 22 Dec., 1959 H. J. Schlieben 8246 (PRE).

Perrier states that *A. isaloensis* is limited to the Isalo range where it is quite abundant.

A. isaloensis is closely allied to *A. millotii* and to *A. antandroi* in shape and size of perianth, which is slightly constricted above the ovary – not in leaves.

A. divaricata is also an ally in shape of perianth, but the flowers are larger, and the inflorescence is a many-branched and re-branched panicle, with very considerably larger leaves, and stems 2—3m. and more high.

FIG. 514.

A. isaloensis H. Perr. Plants on sandstone, Isalo Range, 13km. SW of Ranohira, Fianarantsoa Prov., Madagascar. 600m. alt.

FIG. 515.

A. isaloensis H. Perr. Flowering stem × 1/4, from a plant on the Isalo.

FIG. 516.

A. isaloensis H. Perr. Plant collected on the Isalo, Madagascar, flowering at Mbabane, Swaziland.   Height 40cm.

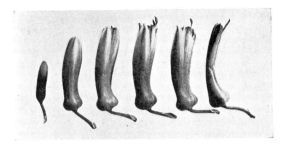

Fig. 517.

A. isaloensis H. Perr. Flowers natural size.

189. A. acutissima H. Perrier in *Mém. Soc. Linn. Norm.* 1 (1): 17, Plate 3 (1926), et *Fl. Madag.* Liliac. 83 (1938); Francois in *Mem. Acad. Malg.* 24: Plate 19 (1927); Reynolds in *Aloes Madag. Revis.* 117 (1958).

DESCRIPTION: *Plant* a shrub 1m. and more across, with several stems that are erect, divergent or procumbent, branched at base or higher, up to 1m. long, 20—30mm. diam. the apical 20—30cm. foliate, with old dried leaf remains persistent for 30cm. below the leaves.

Leaves about 20, subdensely rosulate, the lowest basally sheathing, the sheaths green-striate and 5—10mm. apart, spreading to recurved, narrowly lanceolate long-attenuate, averaging 30cm. long, 4cm. broad at base, 1cm. thick, gradually tapering to a long slender point; *upper surface* grey-green with reddish tinge, without spots or markings, flat to slightly canaliculate; *lower surface* rounded, similar to upper surface; *margins* sinuate-dentate armed with deltoid pungent, pale-brown teeth averaging 3mm. long, 10mm. apart, smaller and more crowded low down, larger upwards, sometimes obsolescent near apex, the apex a very small single or bifid prickle.

Inflorescence averaging 2—3-branched, and 50cm. high.

Peduncle plano-convex and 10mm. broad at base, 2—4-branched from the middle, the lowest branch subtended at base by a thin, scarious, many-nerved, deltoid bract about 20mm. long, 12mm. broad.

Racemes cylindric-acuminate, the terminal 10—15cm. long, 5—6cm. diam., laterals a little shorter, the apical buds suberect and denser, open flowers nutant and laxer.

Bracts narrowly deltoid, clasping the pedicel, 10—15mm. long, thin, scarious, 5-nerved.

Pedicels averaging 15mm. long, the colour of the perianth.

Perianth reddish-scarlet, averaging 30mm. long, basally obconic or tapering into the pedicel articulation, 5·5mm. diam. across the ovary, slightly constricted above the ovary, thence slightly decurved and trigonously enlarging to the throat with the mouth trigonal and wide open; *outer segments* connate into a tube for 20mm. (free for about 10mm.),

Fig. 518.

A. acutissima H. Perr. Reproduction of Perrier's original figure in *Mém. Soc. Linn. Norm.,* 1 (1): 17, Plate 3 (1926).

obscurely 3-nerved, the apices subacute, slightly spreading; *inner segments* free but dorsally adnate to the outer to the middle, broader than the outer, with thin pale edges, scarlet-keeled, the apices more obtuse and more spreading than the outer.

Filaments very pale rose, the 3 inner narrower and lengthening before the 3 outer with their *anthers* in turn exserted 1mm.; *stigma* at length exserted 1—2mm.; *ovary* pale olive, 5mm. long, 2mm. diam. (Figs. 518–522).

Fianarantsoa Prov. Bekinoly, near Zazafotsy, a smaller form, Perrier 1107 (P); mountains of Betsileo, cult. Tananarive, Perrier 13334! (P); South Betsileo, granite rocks near Ambalavao, 1200m. alt., Perrier 1258! (P); Mont Amboloandro, 900m. alt., Perrier 11025 (P); on denuded granite slopes 36km. S of Fianarantsoa (26km. N of Ambalavao), 1080m. alt., 21 June 1955, Reynolds 7720 (TAN, PRE, K); near Sendrisoa Village, 25km. S of Ambalavao, 1020m. alt., 22 June 1955, Reynolds 7723 (TAN, PRE, K); in large numbers on rocky slopes 16km. SW of Ambalavao, c. 21° 42′ S, 46° 48′ E, c. 900m. alt., 23 June 1955, Reynolds 7736 (TAN, K, PRE).

Tuléar Prov. On calcareous rocks near Manombo du Sud, Perrier 11024 (P); on rocks in large numbers, 47km. N of Beloha (13km. S of Tranoroa), c. 24° 49′ S, 45° 06′ E, c. 240m. alt., 6 July 1955, Reynolds 7851 (TAN, P, K, PRE).

Fig. 519.

A. acutissima H. Perr. Plants on rocks 16km. SW of Ambalavao, Fianarantsoa Prov., Madagascar.

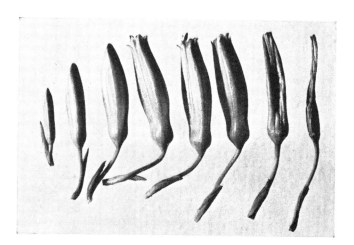

Fig. 520.

A. acutissima H. Perr. Flowers 1/1 from a plant 16km. SW of Ambalavao.

A. acutissima grows mostly on rocks in scanty soil, and is variable in length and diameter of stems, length and width of leaves, and length of perianth. It is nearest allied to *A. intermedia* with the perianth obconic at base and having a definite tube of about 20mm. (segments free for only 10mm.), but the latter differs in having broader leaves with larger marginal teeth, and racemes with the apical buds hidden by imbricate bracts.

A. acutissima is abundant in the neighbourhood of Ambalavao. It occurs on rocks 9km., 12km. and 26km. N of Ambalavao (1080m. alt.) on the road to Fianarantsoa; also near Sendrisoa Village, 25km. S of Ambalavao (1020m. alt.), and near Mahasoa Village, 25km. further south. Large numbers occur (with Euphorbia and Pachypodium) on rocky slopes 16km. SW of Ambalavao; seen at km. 19, 39 and 43 on the road to Zazafotsy where it was also seen, also near Ihosy. Plants 13km. S of Tranoroa (47km. N of Beloha) are weaker forms.

It seems that at higher altitudes plants are of more robust growth, and that at lower altitudes with lower rainfall, plants are smaller.

Fig. 521.

A. acutissima H. Perr. A form 47km. N of Beloha, 13km. S of Tranoroa, Tuléar Province, Madagascar. 240m. alt. Height 1·60m.

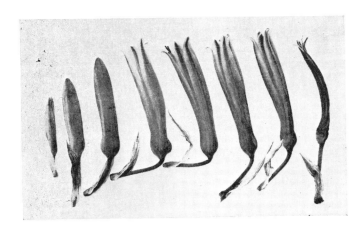

Fig. 522.

A. acutissina H. Perr. Flowers 1/1 from a plant 13km. S of Tranoroa, Tuléar Province.

189A. var. **antanimorensis** Reynolds in *Journ. S.A. Bot.* 22: 27 (1956), in *Aloes Madag. Revis.* 121 (1958).

Differs from the typical form in having much shorter stems that are only 6—9mm. diam. (against 20—30mm.), leaves shorter and only 15—20mm. broad at base, pedicels 10mm. (against 15mm.), shorter racemes (8—10cm.), shorter flowers (20mm.), and with the inflorescence mostly simple and as long as the stem plus leaves combined. (Figs. 523, 524).

Tuléar Prov. On flat rocks 8km. NW of Antanimora, c. 24° 44' S, 45° 36' E, c. 300m. alt., 28 June 1955, Reynolds 7792 holotype (TAN), isotype (P, K, PRE).

Large numbers of plants occur on flat rock surfaces among thorn bushes and tall-stemmed Pachypodiums, 8km. NW of Antanimora, at km. 313 on the main road from the north to Ambovombe and Fort Dauphin. Plants are of low shrubby growth and form dense patches 1—2m. and more across.

Description: *Stems* 30—50cm. long, 6—9mm. diam., mostly erect, branched at base, the apical 10—15cm. sublaxly about 10-foliate.

Fig. 523.

A. acutissima H. Perr. var. *antanimorensis* Reynolds. On flat rocks 8km. SW of Antanimore, on road to Ambovombe and Fort Dauphin, Southern Madagascar.

Fig. 524.

A. acutissima H. Perr. var. *antanimorensis* Reynolds. Flowers 1/1 from bud to fruit.

Leaves about 10, basally sheathing, the sheaths striate and 10mm. apart, narrowly lanceolate-attenuate, spreading, 15—20cm. long, 18—20mm. broad at base; *upper surface* dull grey-green, unicoloured, flat to slightly canaliculate; *lower surface* rounded, similar to upper surface; *margins* armed with deltoid, firm, pale-brownish teeth 2mm. long, 8mm. apart.

Inflorescence simple, or sometimes with a short branch, 40—50cm. long.

Racemes cylindric-conical, 8—10cm. long, subdensely flowered, the youngest buds suberect and partly hidden by their bracts.

Bracts narrowly deltoid, up to 12mm. long, 3mm. broad at base, thin, scarious, 7-nerved.

Pedicels 10mm. long.

Perianth reddish-scarlet, 25mm. long, obtusely tapering at base into the pedicel, 5mm. diam. across the ovary, slightly constricted above the ovary, thence slightly decurved and enlarging a little to the throat; *outer segments* free for 12mm. (tube 13mm.); *inner segments* broader than the outer, keeled in upper half, the apices more spreading than the outer.

Anthers in turn exserted 1mm.; *stigma* at length exserted 1—2mm.; *ovary* olive-brown, 4mm. long, 2mm. diam., apex truncate.

190. **A. itremensis** Reynolds in *Journ. S.A. Bot.* 22: 29, Plate X (1956), in *Aloes Madag. Revis.* 123 (1958).

DESCRIPTION: *Plant* succulent, solitary, not forming groups. *Stem* none, or up to 20cm. long, 3cm. diam.

Leaves 12—16, rosulate, arcuate-ascending, spreading to recurved in upper quarter, up to 30cm. long, 4·5cm. broad at base, gradually tapering to an acute apex; *upper surface* flat low down, slightly canaliculate upwards, dull green with reddish tinge, without spots or markings; *lower surface* convex, similar to upper surface; *margins* armed with broadly compressed-deltoid, brownish teeth that are paler at apex, 1—1·5mm. long, 5—8mm. distant, larger near base, smaller upwards, obsolescent towards apex.

Inflorescence a slender 2—3-branched panicle, 1—1·20m. high.

Peduncle plano-convex and 14mm. broad at base, terete upwards, brown with a bloom, compactly 2—3-branched from the middle or higher.

Racemes cylindric-acuminate, the terminal 15—20cm. long, the lateral a little shorter, the buds suberect, older buds spreading, open flowers subpendulous, all unicoloured reddish-scarlet.

Bracts narrowly deltoid, 6mm. long, 2mm. broad at base, reflexed at the middle, thin, subscarious, with 3 crowded nerves sometimes appearing as 1-nerved.

FIG. 525.

A. itremensis Reynolds. On top of the Itremo, 54km. W of Ambatofinandrahana, Fianarantsoa Prov., Madagascar, approx. 20° 37′ S., 46° 34′ E. Height 1·20m.

Pedicels reddish-brown, slender, 8—9mm. long.

Perianth reddish-scarlet, narrowly cylindric-clavate, averaging 25mm. long, basally obconic, 5mm. diam. across the ovary, thence enlarging a little to the throat and slightly constricted at the open mouth; *outer segments* free to base, with pale thin edges, obscurely 5-nerved throughout, the apices subacute and slightly spreading; *inner segments* free, slightly narrower than the outer, with broad white border, prominently scarlet-keeled, the apices more obtuse than the outer.

Filaments filiform-flattened, the 3 inner narrower and lengthening before the 3 outer with their *anthers* in turn exserted 1mm.; *stigma* at length exserted 1mm.; *ovary* pale olive, 4·5mm. long, 2mm. diam. obtusely tapering into the style, faintly 6-striped longitudinally. (Figs. 525–527).

Fianarantsoa Prov. On the Itremo, 54km. W of Ambatofinandrahana, c. 20° 37′ S, 46° 34′ E, 1700m. alt., 20 June 1955, Reynolds 7706 holotype (TAN), isotype (P, K, PRE); Coll. Prof. W. Rauh, 25km. E of Ambatofinandrahana, cult. Mbabane, fl. 28 June 1964, Rauh 10755 et Reynolds 10561 (PRE).

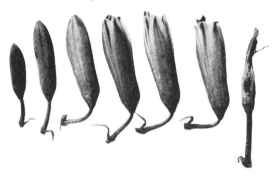

Fig. 527.

A. itremensis Reynolds.

Fig. 526. Plant collected by Prof. W. Rauh on the Itremo, flowering at Mbabane, Swaziland. Height 1m.

Fig. 527. Flowers 1/1 from a plant on the Itremo.

Fig. 526.

A. itremensis was found on the western side of the plateau along the top of the Itremo range, at a point on the roadside 54km. W of Ambatofinandrahana, and 94km. W of Ivato on the road to Amborampotsy and Morondava on the west coast, at an elevation of 1700m. Plants were noticed only on steep sandstone slopes and outcrops, usually in exposed positions, but sometimes in partial shade.

A. itremensis occurs as solitary plants with little or no stem. It is characterised by its very small marginal teeth, slender, tall inflorescence which is compactly 2—3-branched from the middle or higher, and by its very narrow, short (6mm.), deltoid bracts. The perianth averages 25mm. long and tapers at base to the pedicel articulation. The ovary is faintly 6-striped longitudinally.

191. **A. intermedia** (H. Perr.) Reynolds in *Journ. S.A. Bot.* 23: 70, pl. 25 (1957), in *Aloes Madag. Revis.* 126 (1958).

—— *A. deltoideodonta* Bak. var. *intermedia* H. Perr. in *Mém. Soc. Linn. Norm.* (*l.c.*) 24, et *Fl. Madag.* (*l.c.*) 86.

Description: *Plants* of shrubby growth, with erect, divergent, or procumbent creeping and rooting stems up to 1m. long and 3cm. diam., the apical 20cm. or more subdensely foliate, with old dried leaf remains persistent.

Leaves about 20—26, rosulate, basally sheathing, lanceolate-attenuate, up to 25—30cm. long in old specimens, 5—6cm. broad; *upper surface* dull green with reddish tinge, without spots or markings, flat to slightly canaliculate; *lower surface* slightly rounded, dull green; *margins* armed with reddish-brown, deltoid teeth that are paler at the tips, 3—4mm. long, 10mm. apart in upper half, smaller and closer lower down.

Inflorescence branched, about 60cm. tall.

Peduncle basally plano-convex and 10mm. broad, terete upwards, 2—3-branched from the middle or lower.

Racemes cylindric-acuminate, 10—15cm. long, the apical buds denser suberect and hidden by their imbricate bracts, slightly laxer downwards with the open flowers nutant to subpendulous.

Bracts clasping the pedicel, lanceolate-acute, thin, subscarious, 12mm. long, 3—5-nerved.

Pedicels 15mm. long, the colour of the perianth, 20mm. in the fruit.

Perianth reddish-scarlet, averaging 28mm. long, obconic at base, 5mm. diam. across the ovary, constricted to 4mm. above the ovary, thence slightly decurved and enlarging to the throat; *segments* free for 11mm., obscurely 3-nerved, the apices subacute and slightly spreading; *inner segments* free but dorsally adnate to the outer to beyond the middle, broader than the outer and with more obtuse more spreading apices.

Filaments filiform-flattened, the 3 inner narrower and lengthening before the 3 outer with their *anthers* in turn exserted 0—1mm.; *stigma* at length exserted 1mm.; *ovary* olive-green, 4·5mm. long, 2mm. diam., truncate at apex. (Plate 104. Figs. 528, 529).

TULÉAR PROV. Between Itrongay and Benenitra, W of Betroka (Onilahy Basin), c. 600m. alt., Perrier 12690! holotype (P).

FIANARANTSOA PROV. South Betsileo, Ihosy Dist., on flat rocks, 52km. NE of Zazafotsy, c. 21° 57′ S, 46° 26′ E, c. 960m. alt., 23 June 1955, Reynolds 7741 (TAN, K, PRE); same locality, 12 July 1955, Reynolds 7885 (TAN, K, PRE).

FIG. 528.

A. intermedia (H. Perr.) Reynolds. Plants (not flowering) on flat rocks 1km. S of Zazafotsy, on road to Ihosy, Madagascar. Alt. 690m.

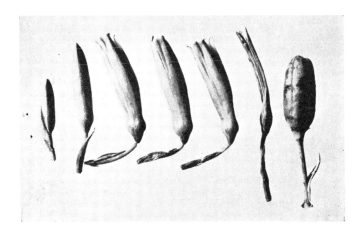

FIG. 529.

A. intermedia (H. Perr.) Reynolds. Flowers 1/1 from bud to fruit stages.

PLATE 104

ALOE INTERMEDIA   (H. Perr.) Reynolds.
On rocks, 52km. NE of Zazafotsy, Fianarantsoa Prov., Madagascar.
Height 80cm.

I could not reach Perrier's locality between Itrongay and Benenitra, but I found this species in considerable numbers about midway between Ambalavao and Zazafotsy in south Betsileo, on flat rocks 52km. NE of Zazafotsy. Large numbers occur on rocks 1—4km. N of Zazafotsy, also between Zazafotsy and Ihosy, and east and south of Ihosy. A smaller form was found on the edge of the Horombe plateau at 1000m. alt., about 40km. S of Ihosy.

A. intermedia is a plant of low shrubby growth, with erect divergent or creeping and rooting procumbent stems up to 1m. long in old specimens. It is nearest allied to *A. acutissima* H. Perr. in shrubby growth, racemes and shape of flowers, but the latter is of taller, more erect growth, with more spreading comparatively narrower and longer leaves, smaller marginal teeth, and other differences.

192. **A. divaricata** Berger in Engler *Bot. Jahrb.* 36: 64 (1905), in Engler *Pflanzenr.* Liliac.–Aloin. 266 (1908); H. Perrier in *Mém. Soc. Linn. Norm.* 1 (1): 20 (1926), et *Fl. Madag.* Liliac. 82 (1938); Reynolds in *Aloes Madag. Revis.* 128 (1958).

—— *A. vaotsohy* Decorse et Poisson in *Recherch. Fl. Merid. Madag.* 96 (1912); R. Decary in *Bull. Écon. Madag.* 18 (1): 25 (1921).
—— *A. vahontsohy* H. Perrier, *nomen nudum*, in *Fl. Madag.* (*l.c.*) 82.
—— "*vaotsohy*" et "*vaotsoy*" Decorse in *Notes, Reconn. Explor.* 623 (1900) cum fig. – without status.
—— *Aloe Sahundra* Bojer (*nomen nudum*) in *Hort. Maurit.* 345 (1837).

Note: In 1900 Dr. J. Decorse (*l.c.*) discussed the medicinal uses of two species of Aloe and referred to one of them only by the single native names of *vaotsohy* and *vaotsoy*. Nowhere did Decorse use the term *Aloe vaotsohy*. Notwithstanding a description and figure, these single native names have no status whatever, and cannot be upheld.

Poisson (*l.c.*) recognised this, and in 1912 validly described *A. vaotsohy* Decorse et Poisson (Decorse's name now being coupled with Poisson's at Poisson's request), but in 1905, however, Berger had validly described the same species as *A. divaricata*. Hence, *A. divaricata* Berger is the earliest correct name, and must be upheld.

DESCRIPTION: *Plants* of tall, shrubby growth with stems 2—3m. and more high, usually branched low down, or with shoots from base or higher and forming shrubs much taller than broad.
Leaves 30 or more, subdensely grouped along the apical 50cm.—1m. of stems, the uppermost denser and rosulate, laxer downwards, basally sheathing, the sheaths 2—3cm. apart and not imbricate, the old dried leaf remains persistent; ensiform, up to 65cm. long, 7cm. broad at base, gradually narrowing to an obtuse apex; *upper surface* dull grey-green with reddish tinge, flat low down, canaliculate upwards; *lower surface* rounded, similar to upper surface in colour; *margins* armed with pungent, deltoid, reddish-brown teeth that are 5—6mm. long, 15—20mm. apart in upper half of leaf, closer and smaller downwards; *sap* dries yellow, abundant.
Inflorescence a many-branched pyramidal panicle about 1m. high, sometimes 2—3 simultaneously.
Peduncle plano-convex and 20—25mm. broad at base, divaricately branched very low down, the lowest branches themselves sometimes 8—10-branched and producing a total of 60—80 racemes per inflorescence.
Racemes cylindric-acuminate, 15—20cm. long, laxly about 30-flowered.
Bracts small, deltoid, 4mm. long, 2mm. broad, subscarious, 3-nerved.
Pedicels averaging 6mm. long.
Perianth reddish-scarlet, averaging 28mm. long, slightly rounded at base, 7mm. diam. across the ovary, constricted to 6mm. above the ovary, thence slightly decurved and enlarging trigonously to the throat, the mouth wide open; *outer segments* free to base but cohering (not connate) in lower third, obscurely 3-nerved, the apices subacute, slightly spreading; *inner segments* free, broader than the outer, keeled throughout, the apices more obtuse and more spreading than the outer.
Filaments filiform-flattened, the 3 inner much narrower and lengthening before the 3 outer, with their *anthers* in turn exserted 2mm.; *style* at length exserted 3—4mm.; *ovary* pale-green, 7mm. long, 3mm. diam. (Plate 105, Figs. 530-532).

WEST COAST. Beravina (Beravi), in beach thickets, July 1879, Hildebrandt n. 3047 type (P), syntypes (BM, K).

MAJUNGA PROVINCE. Ankirihitra (Boina) and near Majunga, Perrier 11016 (P).

FIANARANTSOA PROV. Mountains of South Betsileo at Zazafotsy, 800m. alt., Perrier 11016*bis* (P).

TULÉAR PROV. Near the Onilahy River, Perrier 12750 (P); near Tuléar, Perrier 11023, Humbert 5414 (P); Behara, Decary 2741m 2742 (P); Ambovombe, Decary 3266*bis*, 3360, 3575 (P); neighbourhood of Fort Dauphin, Humbert 5980, Decary 10179 (P); Tongobory, Humbert 2725 (P) – all according to Perrier.
Sandy soil, 18km. W of Ambovombe, 170m. alt., 4 July 1955, Reynolds 7834 (TAN, PRE, K); 10km. W of Bezaha (14km. ENE of Tongobory), 23° 29′ S, 44° 27′ E, 300m. alt., 9 July 1955, Reynolds 7860 (TAN, K, PRE).

PLATE 105

ALOE DIVARICATA   Berger.

In dry bush, 14km. ENE of Tongobory, Tuléar Prov., Madagascar.
Height 3·50m.

FIG. 530.

A. divaricata Berger. A simple-stemmed plant, 18km. W of Ambovombe, Fort Dauphin Dist., Southern Madagascar. Height 2·30m.

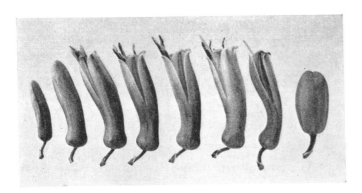

FIG. 531.

A. divaricata Berger. Flowers 1/1 from bud to fruit, from a plant between Antanimore and Ambovombe.

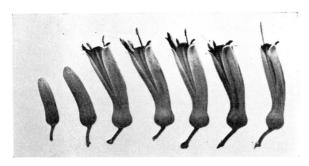

FIG. 532.

A. divaricata Berger. Flowers 1/1 from a plant
15km. NW of Tongobory, Tuléar Prov.

Bojer gives the following account of his *A. Sahundra* (*nomen nudum*) in *Hort. Maurit*. 345 (1837):
"Native of Madagascar. Grows on the sandy shores of the SW part of the Bay of Saint Augustine. This plant is also found in the interior of the Island, particularly in the Province of 'Emirne', where it often forms considerable thickets. Cultivated in the Royal Garden, Pampl. (Vernacular name in Madagascar, *Sahoundra*). Shrub. Flowers in April."
Two species found today near St. Augustine Bay south of Tuléar are *A. divaricata* and *A. vaombe* and neither is found in Imerina (Tananarive). Bojer's reference to thickets, and the plant being a shrub points to *A. divaricata* being the species cultivated in the Royal Garden, Pamplemousses, 10km. NE of Port Louis, Mauritius. These gardens were first laid out by M. Poivre in 1769.
A. divaricata is widely distributed in the western, south-western, and southern parts of the Island, and is found mostly in arid bush country in sandy soils. In dense bush stems are sometimes simple and reach 5—6m. in height. Usually plants form shrubs that are taller than broad, with stems averaging 2—3m. in height, the main stem usually being taller than the others.
Perrier states that *A. divaricata* is the richest in juice of all the Madagascar Aloes, and that it had been used for medicinal purposes for a long time. Since 1630 the product had been handled by the agents of the East India Company, the juice fetching a higher price than that of the Socotra Aloes.

192A. var. **rosea** (R. Decary) Reynolds.

—— *A. vaotsohy* Decorse et Poisson var. *rosea* R. Decary in *Bull. Écon. Madag.* 18 (1): 25 (1921); Reynolds in *Aloes Madag. Revis.* 133 (1958).
Same habit and aspect as the type, but flowers a very light pink, No. 71. Flowers in October. Forms a small population mixed with *A. vaombe*, 3 hours N of Ambovombe on the road to Antanimora. – R. Decary (*l.c.*). No type is stated; doubtful whether this can be upheld.
Ambovombe is in the far south of the Island. I did not succeed in finding the var. *rosea* between Ambovombe and Antanimora.

193. **A. mayottensis** Berger in Engler *Pflanzenr.* Liliac.–Aloin. 246 (1908); Reynolds in *Aloes Madag. Revis.* 133 (1958). (*Note:* Not included by Perrier in *Mém. Soc. Linn. Norm.* (*l.c.*) and *Fl. Madag.* (*l.c.*)).

DESCRIPTION: Based on plants found on Mayotte Island, near Mamoutzou, by native collector Andria Robinson.
Plants of shrubby growth, with shoots from base and along the stem at random. *Stems* 50cm. and more, 3—4cm. diam.
Leaves about 20, erectly spreading, the lower recurved, 40—50cm. long, 6—7cm. broad at base, gradually narrowing to an acute apex; *upper surface* green, without spots or markings, flat low down, canaliculate upwards; *lower surface* rounded, similar to upper surface; *margins* armed with pale yellow to pale brown teeth that are deltoid, subpungent, 3mm. long, 10—15mm. apart.
Inflorescence a branched panicle about 1m. high.
Peduncle slender, 7—8mm. thick, with 3—4 branches from about the middle.
Racemes subdensely flowered, cylindric-acuminate, the terminal 20cm. long, 6cm. diam. the lateral a little shorter, youngest buds suberect and denser, open flowers laxer, nutant to subpendulous.
Bracts lowest of terminal racemes ovate-acute, thin, scarious, 6mm. long, 4mm. broad, 5—7-nerved.
Pedicels about 6mm. long.
Perianth cylindric-trigonous, rather fleshy, straight, 28mm. long, basally obtuse to slightly obconic, shortly stipitate, 8mm. diam. across the ovary, slightly compressed laterally upwards; *outer segments* free to the middle (tube 14mm.), thinner and paler at the edges, 5—7-nerved, the apices subacute and slightly spreading; *inner segments* broader than the outer, with broad white border and with 3 crowded nerves forming a keel in upper half, the apices more obtuse and more spreading than the outer.
Filaments filiform-flattened, the 3 inner narrower and lengthening before the 3 outer with their *anthers* in turn exserted 2—3mm. *Stigma* at length exserted 3—4mm.; *ovary* green, 7mm. long, 3mm. diam., obtuse at apex. (Figs. 533–535).

COMOROS. Mayotte Island, on slopes of Chongui, hill above Dappani, Boivin n. 3071, Exped. 1847–52, type (P); near Mamoutzou, coll. Andria Robinson Feb. 1956, Reynolds 8019 (TAN).

Berger described *A. mayottensis* from Boivin's dried specimen collected during his Expedition of 1847–52, the habit of growth and stem not being stated. Boivin's Chongui might well be the present Chingoni on the west shore of Mayotte Island.

In February 1956, native collector Andria Robinson found flowering plants "growing in the shade rather like a Lomatophyllum" near Mamoutzou which is on the north-east shore of the same Island. Except that in these plants racemes are longer, and pedicels a little shorter than in the type, they agree in other essential characters and I regard them as belonging to *A. mayottensis*. The perianth of the Mamoutzou specimen is thick, fleshy, cylindric, straight, and 28mm. long.

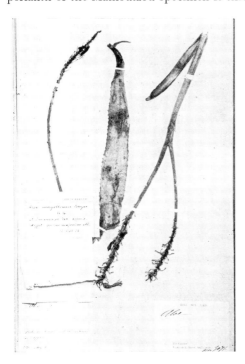

FIG. 533.

A. mayottensis Berger. Boivin 3071, type (P) collected on slopes of Chongui, above Dappani, Mayotte Island, during Boivin's Expedition of 1847-52.

FIG. 534.

FIG. 535.

A. mayottensis Berger.

FIG. 534. Flowers 1/1 from a plant near Mamoutzou, Mayotte Is.

FIG. 535. Flowers 1/1 from a plant flowering in Mr. Hennie Naude's garden. Pretoria North, from a plant originally collected by Prof. J. Millot on Mayotte Island, Grand Comores.

Berger has a note that *A. mayottensis* is allied to *A. lomatophylloides*, but differs chiefly in having larger flowers.

A. lomatophylloides Balf. f. was collected by Dr. I. B. Balfour on 31 May 1877, on Rodriguez Island in the Indian Ocean to the east of Mauritius, and its identity has remained in doubt until recently, when fruits could be studied.

Dr. R. E. Vaughan (Phoenix, Mauritius) has collected plants of "*A. lomatophylloides*" on Rodriguez and grown them for study. He found that the fruits were true berries, remaining on the plant for 2—3 months, then falling off and rotting in the ground, which proved that they belong to the Genus *Lomatophyllum* and not *Aloe*. The name will have to be changed.

A. mayottensis has not been found in Madagascar and does not appear to be closely allied to any species in Madagascar. From the material received from Mayotte it seems that *A. mayottensis* is of shrubby growth. It is therefore provisionally included with the shrubs, but further investigation is necessary.

GROUP 9

PLANTS DEVELOPING SIMPLE ERECT STEMS 2—3M. OR MORE LONG; LEAVES DENSELY ROSULATE.

A. LEAVES DEEPLY CANALICULATE, MUCH RECURVED, 1M. OR MORE LONG:

1. *Inflorescence branched*, racemes 10—15cm.:
   (*a*) Racemes ascending, flowers evenly distributed, pedicels 12mm., perianth curved, 28mm. .. .. 194 *A. vaombe*
   (*b*) Racemes oblique, flowers more or less unilateral, pedicels 4—6mm., perianth slightly ventricose, 22mm. .. .. 195 *A. vaotsanda*
2. *Inflorescence simple*. Racemes very densely multi-flowered:
   (*a*) Racemes ascending, 15cm.; pedicels 2—3cm.; perianth 24—27mm., straight .. .. 196 *A. helenae*

B. LEAVES RATHER FLAT, NOT CANALICULATE, SPREADING, 60CM. LONG:

1. Inflorescence 4—6-branched, racemes densely capitate; the lowest pedicels considerably shorter than the uppermost, perianth campanulate .. .. 180D *A. capitata* var.
   See under *A. capitata* (Group 6).   *cipolinicola*

C. LEAVES ASCENDING, 1M. LONG, INFLORESCENCE SIMPLE, 3M. LONG:

1. Raceme 2m., very densely multi-flowered, pedicels 28—30mm.; perianth 33mm. .. .. 197 *A. suzannae*

194. **A. vaombe** Decorse et Poisson in *Recherch. Fl. Merid. Madag.* 96 (1912); R. Decary in *Bull. Écon. Madag.* 18 (1): 22 (1921); H. Perrier in *Mém. Soc. Linn. Norm.* 1 (1): 16 (1926), et *Fl. Madag.* Liliac. 81 (1938); Reynolds in *Aloes Madag. Revis.* 136 (1958).

—— "*Vaombe*" Decorse in *Notes, Reconn. Explor.* 623 (1900) – name without status.

Note: In 1900 Dr. J. Decorse (*l.c.*) discussed the medicinal uses of two species of Aloe and referred to them only by their native names, one of them being "*Vaombe*". Nowhere did he refer to this species as *Aloe vaombe*. Notwithstanding a description and figure the single native name *Vaombe* has no status. Poisson recognised this, and in 1912 validly published *A. vaombe* Decorse et Poisson, Decorse's name being coupled with Poisson's at Poisson's request, since Decorse had supplied the first description and figure.

DESCRIPTION: *Plants* solitary. *Stem* simple, averaging 2—3m. high, sometimes higher, about 20cm. diam., the old dried leaf remains persistent.

Leaves 30—40, densely rosulate at apex of stem, 80cm.—1m. long, 15—20cm. broad at base when pressed flat, gradually tapering to the apex, about 1cm. thick, youngest leaves suberectly spreading, oldest leaves spreading to much recurved; *upper surface* dull green, without spots or markings, deeply canaliculate and U-shaped in cross-section; *lower surface* rounded, similar in colour to upper surface; *margins* sinuate-dentate, white-edged low down, the edge less prominent upwards, armed with deltoid subpungent teeth that are 5—6mm. long and 15—20mm. apart low down, a little smaller upwards; *sap* abundant, drying deep purple.

Inflorescence a many-branched panicle about 90cm. high, 2—4 simultaneously.

Peduncle 2—4, spreading-ascending, flattened and 35mm. broad at base, about 12-branched very low down, the lowest branches with 4—6 branchlets and producing about 25 racemes per inflorescence, and up to 100 racemes with 4 inflorescences simultaneously.

Racemes ascending, subdensely flowered, cylindric, slightly acuminate, the terminal 15cm. long, 6cm. diam., the laterals slightly shorter, the buds suberectly spreading, open flowers nutant to subpendulous.

Bracts broadly triangular, 8mm. long, 5mm. broad at base, scarious, brownish, many-nerved.

Pedicels averaging 12mm. long.

Perianth bright crimson-red, averaging 28mm. long, cylindric, distinctly curved, basally obtuse, 6—7mm. diam. across the ovary, slightly constricted above the ovary, thence decurved and enlarging towards the throat, the whole perianth with a slightly sulcate or costate appearance; *outer segments* free to the middle (14mm.) with definite basal tube of 14mm., obscurely 3-nerved, the apices sub-acute; *inner segments* free but dorsally adnate to the outer for 14mm., broader than the outer, with pale, thin edges and more obtuse, slightly more spreading apices than the outer.

Filaments pale lemon, filiform-flattened, the 3 inner narrower and lengthening before the 3 outer with their *anthers* in turn exserted 0—1mm.; *style* pale yellow, with *stigma* at length exserted 1mm.; *ovary* green, 6mm. long, 3mm. diam., the apex obtusely rounded. (Plate 106, Figs. 536, 537).

Tuléar Prov. Near Tuléar, fl. July 1910, Perrier 11020! (P); Delta of the Linta, south-west coast, Humbert et Swingle 5418! (P); near Benenitra (Onilahy), Perrier 13497 (P); Ambovombe, Decary 3231, 2911, according to Perrier.

Abundant in bush between Antanimora and Ambovombe, c. 24° 58′ S, 45° 48′ E, c. 270m. alt., 26 June 1955, Reynolds 7793 (TAN, K, PRE).

A. vaombe is widely distributed in the south and south-west of the Island, from the Ambovombe district through the Mahafaly to Tuléar, and inland to near Benenitra and near Sakaraha, between Tuléar and Ranohira.

FIG. 536.

A. vaombe Decorse et Poisson. Plant near Amboasary, Mandrary Valley, on road to Fort Dauphin, Madagascar. alt. 40m. Height 3m.

PLATE 106

ALOE VAOMBE   Decorse et Poisson.

Between Antanimora and Ambovombe, on road to Fort Dauphin,
Southern Madagascar. Height 2·50m.

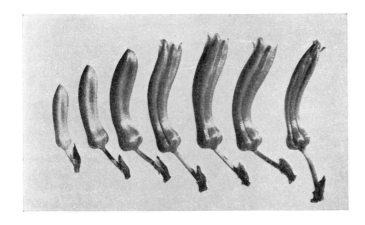

Fig. 537.

A. vaombe Decorse et Poisson. Flowers 1/1 −⁣ from the Colour Plate 106 plant.

It is a most handsome and ornamental species bearing up to 100 racemes from 4 simultaneous inflorescences, and is found mostly in dry bush and thorn country. In June–July the panicles of bright crimson-red flowers stand out conspicuously and embellish an otherwise drab landscape.

A. vaombe is to southern Madagascar what *A. ferox* Mill. is to many parts of the eastern Cape Province in South Africa, but *A. ferox* occurs in considerably larger numbers and sometimes covers whole hillsides, which I have not seen *A. vaombe* do.

194A. var. **poissonii** R. Decary in *Bull. Écon. Madag.* 18 (1): 23 (1912); Reynolds in *Aloes Madag. Revis.* 139 (1958).

Much taller, 4—5m. high, stem much thinner, more slender, rosette of leaves denser, much more deflexed on to the stem, floriferous shoots more abundant, regularly "knee-bent" and spread out in a kind of crown above the leaf-rosette. Grows on gneiss in the neighbourhood of Behara (district Ambovombe). – R. Decary (*l.c.*). No type is stated. I have not seen plants.

195. **A. vaotsanda** R. Decary in *Bull. Écon. Madag.* 18 (1): 23 (1921); H. Perrier in *Mém. Soc. Linn. Norm.* 1 (1): 17 (1926), et in *Fl. Madag.* Liliac. 82 (1938); Reynolds in *Aloes Madag. Revis.* 139 (1958).

DESCRIPTION: *Plant* solitary, developing a stem up to 4m. high, about 15cm. diam., the old dried leaf remains persistent.

Leaves 30—40, densely rosulate at apex of stem, up to 1m. long, about 15cm. broad at base, gradually tapering to the apex, youngest leaves spreading, the oldest recurved to deflexed with the apices pointing downwards or almost touching the stem; *upper surface* green with reddish tinge, deeply canaliculate and U-shaped in cross-section with the edges somewhat involute; *lower surface* rounded, paler green than upper surface; *margins* armed with deltoid-pungent teeth about 5—6mm. long, 15mm. apart. *Sap* yellowish-brown.

Inflorescence a branched panicle, about 50cm. long.

Racemes at first drooping, densely about 50—70-flowered, the buds at first evenly distributed around the axis,when the drooping racemes develop and become more rigid and spreading to oblique, the pedicels turn upwards, the flowers becoming more or less unilateral, buds bright red, open flowers turning orange-yellow.

Bracts triangular, attenuate, papery, white, somewhat wrinkled, 7—8mm. long, 3mm. broad at base, 3-nerved.

Pedicels 4—6mm. long.

Perianth slightly ventricose, about 22mm. long, very slightly inflated around the ovary, slightly constricted above ovary, thence slightly ventricose; *outer segments* connate into a tube for about 8—9mm., free for about 13mm., obscurely nerved, the apices brownish and obtusely spreading.

Filaments filiform-flattened, the 3 inner narrower and lengthening before the 3 outer with their *anthers* in turn exserted 5mm.; *stigma* at length exserted 5mm. (Figs. 538, 539).

TULÉAR PROV. Fort Dauphin Division: Decary s.n. type (P); Vinanibe, near Fort Dauphin, 30 July 1932, R. Decary 10204! (P); near Ambovombe, extreme south, up to 50m. alt., 9 Sept. 1928, Humbert et Swingle 5614! (P).

I have not seen the following, cited by Perrier: Ambovombe, Decary 2990, 3103, 3235; environs of Lac Anony, Decary 9275, 9280; Bekira, Decary 9237.

DISTRIBUTION: Decary (*l.c.*) states: Especially abundant in the south-west of Tsihombe district on calcareous formations, at Tsialangy, Betaimbolo, near Malaimpioky, Antsasavy. In those localities it replaces *A. vaombe* almost completely. It is the only plant in those barren regions producing a stem which is both woody and straight, and is consequently frequently used by the natives for the construction of huts.

I found large numbers of *A. vaotsanda* about 50km. SW of Tsihombe on the track to Cap Ste. Marie in the extreme south of the Island, mostly in dry bush country.

A. vaotsanda resembles *A. vaombe* in general habit of growth, stems and leaves, but differs in having leaves that are more recurved to deflexed with the apices pointing downwards and almost touching the stem. The young leaves are more spreading and the rosette more flat-topped.

The inflorescence is shorter. The racemes are at first drooping with all buds evenly distributed around the axis. With development the racemes become stiffer and oblique, and the pedicels twist upwards with the open flowers becoming somewhat unilateral. The racemes of *A. vaotsanda* are also shorter and more densely flowered than in *A. vaombe* and the pedicels are shorter (4—5mm. against 12mm.). The perianth is slightly ventricose and the anthers are exserted 5mm. (against 0—1mm.).

A. vaotsanda flowers in late August-September, one to two months after *A. vaombe*.

FIG. 538.

A. vaotsanda R. Decary. Plant in young bud, 50km. SW of Tsihombe, on track to Cap Sta. Marie, Southern Madagascar. Height 3m.

Fleur (*gr. nat.*)

FIG. 539.

A. vaotsanda R. Decary. Decary's figure of a flower natural size. – copied from *Bull. Econ. Madag.* 18 (1): 21 (1921).

Aloe Vaotsanda

196. **A. helenae** P. Danguy in *Bull. Mus. Paris* 2 (1): 433 (1929); H. Perrier in *Fl. Madag.* Liliac. 106, Fig. XII, 5 (1938); Reynolds in *Aloes Madag. Revis.* 142 (1958).

DESCRIPTION: *Plants* solitary, with simple *stem* 2—4m. high, 20cm. diam. (thicker near ground level), with old dried leaf remains persistent.

Leaves about 40, densely rosulate at apex of stem, long-ensiform, up to 1·40m. long, 12—15cm. broad at base, gradually narrowing to the apex, youngest leaves erectly spreading, oldest leaves much recurved with their apices almost touching the stem; *upper surface* unicoloured green, deeply canaliculate and U-shaped in cross section; *lower surface* rounded, similar to upper surface in colour, without spots or markings; *margins* armed with pale, pungent, broadly deltoid teeth 2—3mm. long and 15mm. apart at middle of leaf, larger and more crowded low down, obsolescent towards apex.

Inflorescence simple, scapiform, 1—8 (often 4—5) from a rosette, robust, 40—60cm. long.

Scapes erect, compressed, somewhat 2-edged, 20—25cm. long, laxly sterile-bractate, the lowest bracts deltoid, 1—2cm. long and broad, the upper lanceolate.

Racemes cylindric-claviform, densely 300—400-flowered. (15cm. long, 9cm. diam., buds scarlet, open flowers yellowish and opening first up the sunny side.)

Bracts lanceolate, red-tipped, deltoid-acute, 12mm. long, 6mm. broad, rather thick and fleshy, obscurely 5-nerved.

Pedicels sub-erect, 2—3cm. long.

Perianth tubulose-campanulate, straight, 24—27mm. long, greenish at base, reddish at mouth (yellowish, 25mm. long, cylindric in lower half thence widely campanulate, basally obtuse, 4mm. diam. across the ovary); *outer segments* free for 12—15mm., tube 10—13mm., 3—4mm. broad, lanceolate-obtuse, 5-nerved (*inner segments* free but dorsally adnate to the outer to the middle).

FIG. 540.

A. helenae P. Danguy. Reproduction of Perrier's Fig XIII, 5, in *Fl. Madag.* Liliac. 95 (1938) × 1/27 approx.

Fig. 541.

A. helenae P. Danguy. Plant near Vinanibe, 8km. W of Fort Dauphin, Madagascar, with Mr. B. Souchier, Inspector of Forests holding dry spike.

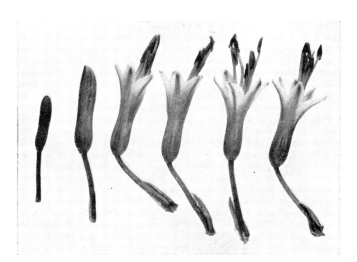

Fig. 542.

A. helenae P. Danguy. Flowers 1/1, from a plant flowering in Johannesburg, collected near Fort Dauphin.

Stamens 30—35mm. long, exserted 6—8mm.
(*Filaments* lemon, filiform-flattened, the 3 inner narrower and lengthening before the 3 outer with their *anthers* in turn exserted 9mm.; *style* at length exserted 10mm.).
Ovary 8mm. long, 3mm. diam. (Figs. 540-542).
Note: Data in parenthesis noted from a plant collected near Fort Dauphin, when it flowered in Johannesburg.

TULÉAR PROV. Fort Dauphin Division: Ambovombe, E of the Mandrare in the littoral zone, 25 Oct. 1924, Decary 3325, type (P); Andrahomana, sands and limestone of littoral zone, flowers yellowish, buds rose, 22 Sept. 1932, Decary 10675! (P); lower basin of the Mandrare River, in dense xerophytic bush, near Behara, 10–13 Sept. 1928, Humbert et Swingle 5654! (P); Rocks, Fort Dauphin, form with small inflorescences, 7 Aug. 1932, R. Decary 10232! (P). Also according to H. Perrier: Littoral zone to the E of the Mandrare in the environs of Ambovombe, Decary 3372, 3375, 3380, 3397; Vinanibe, Decary 9260, 9271, 9273, 9264; Ranopiso, Decary 10717.

I have seen *A. helenae* 8km. W of Fort Dauphin on the track to Vinanibe among bush in sandy soil, but spikes were very dry, and were mostly lying on the ground in July 1955. Perrier does not give the length of the racemes, but from dry spikes it appears that racemes are cylindric, and up to 15cm. long, 10—12cm. diam.

The stem and large, deeply-channelled, much recurved leaves, also Perrier's Fig. XII, 5, in *Fl. Madag.* (*l.c.*) 95, bear a strong superficial resemblance to the South African species *A. thraskii* Bak. which grows along the South Coast of Natal from Durban to Port Shepstone – see Colour Plate 70 in *Aloes of South Africa*, p. 476 (1950).

A. helenae was named after Madame Decary.

FIG. 543.

A. suzannae R. Decary. Plant in dense dry bush 1km. N of Amboasary, near the Mandrary River, W of Fort Dauphin, Southern Madagascar; alt. 40m. Height 7m.–With M. Bernard Descoings.

197. **A. suzannae** R. Decary in *Bull. Écon. Madag.* 18 (1): 26 (1921) *cum fig*; H. Perrier in *Mém. Soc. Linn. Norm.* 1 (1): 44 (1926), at *Fl. Madag.* Liliac. 107 (1938); Reynolds in *Aloes Madag. Revis.* 145 (1958).

DESCRIPTION: *Plant* very large, with stem 3—4m. high, 25—30cm. diam., the stem usually simple, sometimes forked or 2-branched high up, the old dried leaf remains not persistent.

Leaves 60—100, densely grouped along the apical 80—100cm. of the stem, very leathery, basally sheathing-imbricate, ascending, 1m. long, 8—9cm. broad near base, 4·5cm. thick, gradually attenuate with apex obtusely rounded and armed with 5—7 short teeth; *upper surface* dull green without markings, flat low down, canaliculate upwards; *lower surface* rounded, obtusely carinate, similar in colour to upper surface, both surfaces very rough to the touch; *margins* armed with pungent, deltoid, pale-brown teeth that are 2mm. long, 8—10mm. apart at middle of leaf, smaller upwards, becoming obsolescent near apex; teeth of young leaves white; *sap* abundant, drying deep brown-orange.

Inflorescence always simple, about 3m. long.

Peduncle 7cm. diam. low down, terete and 4cm. diam. at the middle, somewhat sulcate, about 1m. long with 2m. raceme above.

Raceme cylindric, very densely multi-flowered, about 2m. long, 17cm. diam., the lowest 50cm. slightly more laxly flowered, very dense upwards.

Bracts narrowly linear-deltoid, green with pale margins, about 15mm. long, 2mm. broad at base.

Pedicels 28—30mm. long, 3mm. thick, suberect in the buds, horizontally spreading in open flowers.

Perianth subcylindric, ivory tinged with pale rose, 33mm. long, 10mm. diam. across the ovary, the mouth wide open; *outer segments* free for half their length (tube 17mm.), leathery, about 9-nerved, the apices decurved to markedly revolute; *inner segments* free, slightly narrower, green-keeled in upper half, with thin white edges, the apices more obtuse than the outer and becoming revolute after the outer.

Filaments lemon, filiform-flattened, the 3 inner narrower and lengthening before the 3 outer with their *anthers* in turn exserted 10mm., the *anthers* 13mm. long, 3mm. broad at the middle; *style* lemon; *stigma* at length exserted 10mm.; *ovary* 8mm. long, 6mm. diam. at the middle, obtusely tapering into the style. (Figs. 543–546).

TULÉAR PROV. Fort Dauphin Division: Dunes and sand, Ambovombe, 21 July 1924, Raymond Decary 2913! (type P), isotype (BM); in dense bush 1km. N of Amboasary, near E bank of the Mandrare River, c. 25° 02′ S, 46° 23′ E, c. 30m. alt., 3 July 1955, Reynolds 7831 (TAN, P, K, PRE).

FIG. 544.

A. suzannae R. Decary. Young plant with 2m. inflorescence near Amboasary, Mandrare Valley, W of Fort Dauphin.

Fig. 545

A. suzannae R. Decary in the middle, *A. vaombe* Decorse et Poisson on the left, with a young plant of *Alluaudia procera* on right. – Near Amboasary.

Fig. 546.

A. suzannae R. Decary. Flowers 1/1 from bud to post-pollination stages. *Note:* Flowers close by day, and open at night.

Perrier cites the following which I have not seen: Dunes at the edge of the sea, between Ambararata and Imanombo, Decary 4562; near Lake Anongy, Decary 2983; Ambovombe, Decary 3153. Also S of Ambara, NE of Faux-Cap, Antaramaitso, S of Malaimpioky – according to Decary.

This remarkable and most distinctive species has no near affinity in the whole genus. The nearest affinity appears to be *A. macroclada* Bak. which has cylindric racemes of shortly pedicellate flowers, but the latter is acaulous, and is in all other characters very different.

A. suzannae was dedicated to Mademoiselle Suzanne Decary, and grows in the extreme south of the Island, mostly in dense bush and in areas of extreme summer heat.

It is the largest of the Malgache Aloes, a stately and unique species, distinguished by having a 3m. simple inflorescence of which the peduncle is 1m. and the densely multi-flowered cylindric raceme is 2m. long. The 3—4m. stem is mostly simple and smooth, the old dried leaf remains not being persistent.

The leaves, which are very rough to the touch, are leathery and very tough in texture, and can only be cut through with difficulty. A saw is necessary for cutting through the peduncle. The pedicels and perianths are also leathery.

Decary and Perrier both state that there are "several inflorescences to a stem", but in the Mandrare Valley near Amboasary, I noticed only one inflorescence from a rosette. It also seems that plants do not flower every year.

An inflorescence gathered at sunset had scarcely any open flowers, but at midnight all flowers were fully open. By nine o'clock next morning almost all flowers had closed again, which suggests that this species is nocturnally pollinated.

PART 3

SPECIES IMPERFECTLY KNOWN, DOUBTFUL, ETC.

(Alphabetically)

(*Note:* All figures are from photographs of type specimens – considerably reduced.)

1. *A. abyssinica* Lam.

Aloe abyssinica Lamarck was described in *Encyclopédie Méthodique* I: 86 (1783) Paris. The description includes (from the French): "Leaves 2½ feet long, 4 ins. broad at base, thick, with red marginal spines, convex on the outside, channelled on the inner face. Peduncle simple, up to 3 feet or more, with yellowish-green flowers disposed on a long, somewhat lax, spike. Flowers deeply cut into 6 parts, stamens protruding a little from the corolla and grouped together against one side." (Fig. 547).

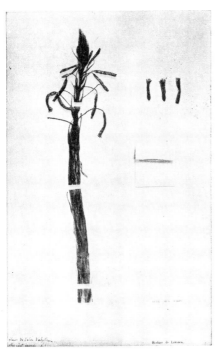

FIG. 547.

A. abyssinica Lam. The type specimen in the Lamarck Herbarium, Natural History Museum, Paris.
Photo: By courtesy of The Director.

Lamarck states: "This plant was brought back from Africa by Bruce and is growing in the King's Garden." (Paris).

The intrepid traveller, James Bruce (b. 1730, d. 1794), landed at Massawa, the Red Sea Port of Eritrea, on 19 Sept. 1769. He travelled southwards through Arkiko, and crossed the Taranta Mountain to Dixan. After crossing the Belesa River – a tributary of the Mareb – he reached Adowa on 5 December. Bruce then went to Axum and continued south-westwards to Gondar. After discovering the source of the Blue Nile, he left Gondar on 26 Sept. 1771 and journeyed westwards to Sennar in the Sudan, then up to Shendi, and reached Cairo on 27 Dec. 1772 – three years and three months after landing at Massawa. Bruce had spent two years between Massawa and Gondar, which is a country very rich in Aloe, and he took fifteen months from Gondar to Cairo. No Aloe has hitherto been recorded from the Sudan part of his journeys.

Where Bruce collected his plant is unknown. It is not impossible that he picked up a cultivated plant in Cairo or Alexandria and took it home.

A photograph is reproduced herein of the specimen named *A. abyssinica* by Lamarck himself in the Lamarck Herbarium, housed in the Natural History Museum, Paris. It will be seen that *A. abyssinica* has unusually large sterile- and floriferous-bracts, apical buds crowded, suberect, and almost hidden by large imbricate bracts, the open flowers being much more laxly disposed.

Professor Millot states that the longest flower is 32mm. (dry), and the longest pedicel on right is 45mm. long. I am assured by Professor Millot that the note in the lower left corner of the sheet is in Lamarck's own handwriting, which eliminates any possibility of the material having been wrongly identified by someone else. The note reads: "Fleurs de l'Aloes d'Abyssinie. Elles sont jaunes. La hampe qui les porte est quelquefois à 3 rameaux."

This authentic material proves conclusively that Salm Dyck was entirely mistaken in his concept of *A. abyssinica*. His figure is of a form of *A. camperi* Schweinf. and differs in all ways from the Lamarck specimen.

Salm Dyck (1842) stated: "The distinguished Bruce in about the year 1777, gave the *seeds* of this plant (which seeds had been collected in Abyssinia) to the Royal Garden in Paris where it has been grown since that time." Against this, Lanarck stated: "This *plant* was *brought back* from Africa by Bruce."

Salm Dyck's figure was the first published of "*A. abyssinica*" and it has misled all subsequent workers up to the present day, including Berger (1908).

Berger's figure of "*A. abyssinica* Lam." depicted a form of *A. elegans* Tod., and not one of Berger's citations and synonyms can now be included under *A. abyssinica* Lam.

A description lacking in several characters, and based on Lamarck's description and on obvious characters of the Lamarck specimen would read as follows:

Aloe abyssinica Lam. in *Encycl. Méthod.* 1: 86 (1783); Reynolds in *Journ. S.A. Bot.* 22: 151 (1956). *Non* Salm Dyck, *non* Roem. et Schult., *non* Kunth, *non* Baker, *non* Schweinfurth, *non* Hooker, *non* Berger.

Habit of growth unknown. *Leaves* in a rather open rosette, 75cm. long, 10cm. broad at base, thick, clear green; *upper surface* channelled; *lower surface* convex; whether unicoloured or spotted not known; *margins* armed with red teeth, size and distance apart unknown; *sap* orange-yellow, resinous, "quickly thickening into a dry reddish matter." *Inflorescence* 1m. or more tall, simple or sometimes 3-branched, with flowers disposed in a long, somewhat lax, spike; *raceme* cylindric-conical, 20cm. long; buds suberect, crowded and partly obscured by large bracts, open flowers laxer, nutant to subpendulous. *Bracts* evidently large and fleshy, narrowly deltoid, about 20mm. long. *Pedicels* up to 45mm. long. *Perianth* yellow, 32mm. or more long, apparently cylindric, "deeply cut into 6 parts" (*outer segments* free to the middle?). *Stamens* shortly exserted and grouped along one side of the perianth.

Until such time as plants agreeing with Lamarck's description and material can be rediscovered, *A. abyssinica* Lam. will remain a *Species non satis cognita*.

* * *

2. *A. agavefolia* Tod. in *Hort. Bot. Panorm.* 1: 85, *t.* 23 (1875). Locality of origin is unknown, but thought to have come from Tropical Africa. The perianth figured bears a striking resemblance to that of *A. buettneri* Berger, but not the rosette of leaves, and the pedicels are much too short. This could well be dropped.

* * *

3. *A. ambigens* Chiovenda in *Plantae Novae vel minus Notae ex Ethiopia* 1: 6 (1928).

SOMALIA MEDIA: Sultanate of Obbia between Attodi and Dolobscio, 26 April 1934, Puccioni et Stefanini n. 447 (499) (FI).

What the Italians called Somalia Media is the country north of Mogadishu. The type locality lies W of Obbia, Dolobscio being at approx. 48° 15′ E, 5′ 20′ N.

Habit of growth and leaves are unknown. Until plants at the type locality can be refound and studied, *A. ambigens* will remain an imperfectly known species.

* * *

4. *A. arabica* Lam. *Encyl.* 1: 91 n. 29 (1783). Lamarck lists this as an imperfectly known species. Berger thinks it might be a form of *A. barbadensis* Mill.

* * *

5. *A. arabica* Salm Dyck *Cat. rais.* 27, 60 (1817). Epithet occupied. Berger thinks it might be a form of *A. microstigma* Salm Dyck.

* * *

6. *A. boehmii* Engler in *Pflanzenwelt Ostafrikas* 141 (1895).

Locality: At the station Gonda, Tanganyika, Böhm 258 (B) April 1882, flowers orange-red, white speckled.

According to travellers' routes shown on the map of Das mittlere Ostafrika in Engler's *Pflanzen-welt Afrikas* I, Veget. Erde I, 1 (1910), Boehm and Reichard travelled south-westwards from Tabora to Lake Tanganyika, the first hundred miles being more or less along the present route from Tabora to Mpanda. Gonda is not shown, but other maps show Igonda about 40 miles SW of Tabora and 5 miles from Igalula. This is Miombo country (Brachystegia-Isoberlinia woodland) at an average of 3,600 ft. The only Aloe found along that road by the present author was *A. secundiflora*.

Berger states *A. boehmii* is allied to *A. lateritia*. The type material suggests it might be an outlying form of *A. lateritia* Engler. (Fig. 548).

FIG. 548.

A. boehmii Engler. The type specimen in Berlin-Dahlem. *Photo: By courtesy The Director, Botanisches Museum, Berlin-Dahlem W. Germany.*

7. *A. boranensis* Cufod, in *Missione Biologica nei paese dei Borana* 4: 316 (1939).

S. ETHIOPIA, Borana, Mega, savanna and bush near Dubuluk coming from Yavello, 2 May 1937 (617).

When the present author searched for *A. boranensis* between Mega and Yavello he found *A. secundiflora* and *A. otallensis* var. *elongata* in many places. Six and eight miles north of the Dubuluk salty wells he found a few flowering plants that fitted the description of *A. boranensis*, but they were clearly hybrids of *A. secundiflora* and *A. otallensis* var. *elongata*.

*   *   *

8. *A. brachystachys* Baker in *Bot. Mag. t.* 7399 (1895), in Th. Dyer *Fl. Trop Afr.* 7: 465 (1898); Berger in Engler's *Pflanzenr.* Liliac.–Aloin. 234 (1908).

Stem long, slender, erect, simple. *Leaves* rosulate, ensiform, 45—60cm. long; in the type specimen the leaf is 6cm. broad at base with marginal teeth 2mm. long, 8—15mm. apart. *Peduncle* simple about as long as the leaves (say up to 60cm. long). *Raceme* dense, simple, oblong, 13cm. long. *Pedicels* ascending 25mm. long, articulated at the tip. *Bracts* orbicular, much shorter than the pedicels – say 12mm. long? *Perianth* cylindric, an inch and a quarter long (say 31mm. long), pale-pink tipped with green; *lobes* shorter than the tube – free for 10mm.? *Stamens* finally shortly exserted. (Fig. 549).

ZANZIBAR. "This new Aloe was sent by Sir John Kirk in 1884 to the Royal Gardens, Kew, from Zanzibar. It flowered for the first time in the Succulent House in January 1894" (K!).

From the *Bot. Mag.* figure here reproduced it will be noticed that the leaves are long, narrow and drooping, while the simple inflorescence is flexuose. These characters can be entirely ignored when a plant has been grown for 10 years under glass. In nature the leaves would doubtless be more ascending and the inflorescence erect.

This is another of Kirk's species sent from Zanzibar which must have originated on the African mainland – but where?

The *Bot. Mag.* figure shows a raceme with large conspicuous bracts, rather resembling those of *A. arborescens*.

FIG. 549.

A. brachystachys Bak. in *Bot. Mag. t.* 7399 (1895). *Photo: By courtesy, The Chief, Botanical Research Institute, Pretoria.*

It has been thought that *A. brachystachys* might be conspecific with *A. volkensii* Engler, but this can hardly be the case because in *A. volkensii* the very small bracts average only 5mm. long and 3mm. broad (against large, orbicular, 13mm. long). The pedicels average 15mm. long (against 25mm.), and the perianth is longer.

Another species to be considered is the shrubby *A. rabaiensis* Rendle, but, apart from other differences, the bracts are very small. It is wiser, at least at present, to regard *A. brachystachys* as being a *Species non satis cognita.*

* * *

9. *A. bussei* Berger in Engler's *Pflanzenr.* Liliac.–Aloin. 273 (1908).

Plant of shrubby growth. Flowers unknown.

TANZANIA (Tanganyika): West Usagara, near Pembamoso, c. 1400m., fruiting 11 Sept. 1900, Busse 294! (K, BM). This material is quite useless. There are no flowers. Berger himself states the species is imperfectly known – then why describe it at all if flowers unknown? There is a Pembemoto in the Western Usagaras on road from Dodoma eastwards to Kilosa, at c. 35° 55′ E, 6° 05′ S. Is this the type locality?

* * *

10. *A. congolensis* De Wild et Th. Dur. in *Ann. Mus. Congo* ser. 2, 1: 1, 61 (1899), *l.c.* ser. 3, 1 (Reliq. Dewèvre) fasc. 2, 240 (1901).

Described as being acaulescent, with *leaves* 32—48cm. long but only 5cm. broad, *margins* with prominent, horny, pungent teeth. *Inflorescence* bifurcate, 90cm. tall. *Racemes* 6—9cm. long. *Pedicels* 20mm. *Bracts* 18mm. long, ovate-linear. *Perianth* cylindric, 35mm. long, 5mm. broad, slightly inflated at base; *outer segments* free for 6mm. *Anthers* and *style* scarcely exserted. (Fig. 550).

CONGO (LEO): In sandy bush near Kimuenza, 13 Dec. 1895, Dewèvre 519 (BR).

Kimuenza is on the Leopoldville–Matadi railway line, 20 miles SW of Leopoldville, half-way to Kasangulu.

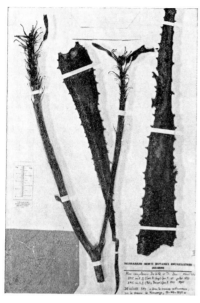

FIG. 550.

The type of *A. congolensis* De Wild. et Th. Dur. (BR). *Photo: By courtesy Prof. W. Robyns, Director, Jardin Botanique de l'Etat, Brussels.*

Is this possibly conspecific with *A. buettneri*? Many plants sent to the author from several localities SW of Leopoldville proved to belong to *A. buettneri*. But there is no mention in the description of *A. congolensis* of an underground bulb-like swelling, and leaves only 5cm. broad is much too narrow for *A. buettneri*.

* * *

11. *A. constricta* Baker in *Journ. Linn. Soc.* 18: 168 (1880), in Th. Dyer *Fl. Trop. Afr.* 7: 464 (1898); etc.

Leaves ensiform, 40cm. long, 5cm. broad; *marginal* teeth 5—6mm. long, 12—15mm. apart. *Inflorescence* height and branching not stated. *Racemes* rather lax, 30cm. long. *Pedicels* 7—10mm. long. *Bracts* small. *Perianth* bright red 35—38mm. long, distinctly constricted above the ovary; *outer segments* shorter than the tube.

MOÇAMBIQUE: On the Zambesi "Nyakwere" near Sena, 8 April 1960, Kirk 34! (K); near Lupata, in fruit June 1859, Kirk 35! (K).

Kirk's figure 243 at Kew is a water-colour showing apical portion of a leaf, with portion of a raceme having 3 fruits, one open flower and 3 buds.

The length of raceme (25–30cm.), and short pedicels, also flowering time, strongly suggest *A. zebrina* Bak. (which comes right across the continent from Loanda, Angola), but flowers 35—38mm. long are much too long for *A. zebrina*.

* * *

12. *A. decaryi* Guillaumin in *Bull. Mus. Hist. Nat. Paris* 2 (12): 318 (1941).

Stem slender, 6—9mm. diam., not at all subscandent. *Leaves* 10—13, 2—2·5cm. apart, erect, slightly recurved towards apex, the sheaths strongly striate; leaf 15—19cm. long, 8—9mm. broad at base, semi-cylindric, dull green; marginal teeth small, white.
Scape simple, as long as the leaves, ancipitous at base, clothed above with 4 scarious sterile bracts.
Raceme 7-flowered, short and rather dense. *Bracts* scarious, white, brown-nerved, broad.
Pedicels about 1cm. long, rose-coloured.
Perianth pale rose, paler at apex and green-brown nerved, 2cm. long, cylindric; *segments* free.
Stamens dilated at base. *Ovary* truncate at apex. – *A. Guillaumin*.

MADAGASCAR: *Ambovombe*. Flowering from August to May, seeds ripening in July–August (in Androy). (Decary s.n. f.346 1931.)

"A very ornamental species near *A. antandroi* from which it differs by its large size, a bushy not lianoid habit, an erect stem. The leaves are longer than in *A. antandroi*, without white markings on the back, the prickles whose pure white colour stands out against the grey-green colour of the leaf. The peduncles are shorter, the bracts longer, at least equal to the pedicels, the perianth pale red with free segments." – A. Guillaumin.

The type material is poor and consists of one leaf 15cm. long, 10mm. broad, and one single inflorescence which is 15cm. long, the 4-flowered raceme being 25mm. long. Length of stem, and whether simple or branched is not stated.

Professor H. Humbert states (*in litt.*), "I doubt whether this specimen is of any value. The type is a piece taken from the plant that flowered in the greenhouse." (In Paris.)

Aloe plants cultivated in a greenhouse are usually of very modified growth form and are often quite different from plants in their natural habitat. "Ambovombe" (in the extreme south of the Island) is very vague, and covers a wide area of varying vegetations.

In this instance, until plants agreeing with the description can be found in the wild state, it seems wiser to regard *A. decaryi* as being a *Species non satis cognita*.

*   *   *

13. *A. defalcata* Chiov. in *Fl. Somal.* 2: 424 (1932).

SOMALIA SOUTH: "Oltregiuba near Uar Scek, Dr. R. Guidotti 1931 no. 64."

The type locality is somewhere along the Juba River N of Margherita. From the present author's observations along the Juba River from Bardera southwards, he found that *A. defalcata* as described is a mixture of species comprising the deeply-channelled, much recurved leaves of *A. microdonta* Chiov. with the small yellow flowers of *A. ruspoliana* Bak.

*   *   *

14. *A. elizae* Berger in Engler's *Bot. Jahrb.* 45: 223 (1911).

Described from the Cameroons at Djutitsas, in burnt-out grass savanna near watercourses, at 1700m., in fruit 13 Dec. 1908, C. Lederman n. 1794 (at B?). Flowers unknown.

*   *   *

15. *A. ellenbeckii* Berger in Engler's *Bot. Jahrb.* 36: 59 (1905), in Engler's *Pflanzenr.* (*l.c.*) 216 (1908).

Berger states: "Habit of growth unknown. Leaves erect? Scape branched it seems. A peculiar species but imperfectly known. Placed in Sect. *Saponariae* on account of the shape of the perianth, leaves slender, minutely dentate, almost as in the Sect. *Macrifoliae*" (i.e. near those of *A. tenuior* or *A. striatula*).

SOUTH SOMALILAND: In bush at Fereschit, 6 July 1901. Dr. Ellenbeck n. 2340 (B).

Fereschit could not be traced, but there is a Hellischid near Bardera. Ellenbeck was in Bardera on 2 July 1901. The present author found nothing in the *Saponariae* group anywhere near Bardera or elsewhere along the Juba River.

*   *   *

16. *A. harmsii* Berger in Engler's *Pflanzenr.* (*l.c.*) 230 (1908).

Cultivated at the Botanical Gardens, Berlin, without collector, date, or type specimen cited.

*   *   *

17. *A. indica* Royle *Ill. Bot. Himal. Mount.* I: 390 (1840).

This is mentioned by Royle as a species with reddish flowers common in dry situations in the North-western Province of India. He did not publish any description or figure of *A. indica* and no herbarium material is known. He merely distinguishes his species with reddish flowers from another Indian species with yellow flowers which he regards as *A. vulgaris* Lam. i.e. *A. barbadensis*. *A. indica* might be a reddish flowered form of *A. barbadensis*, and might have been introduced.

*   *   *

18. *A. kirkii* Baker in *Bot. Mag. t.* 7386 (1894), in *Fl. Trop Afr.* 7: 459 (1898); Berger in Engler's *Pflanzenr.* (*l.c.*) 267 (1908).

DESCRIPTION: *Stem* short. *Leaves* 30—40, densely rosulate, 26—30cm. long, 5—6cm. broad, lanceolate-acuminate, bright green without lines or spots; *marginal teeth* 5mm. long, 10—15mm. apart. *Inflorescence* 60cm. high, 3-branched. *Racemes* rather densely flowered, cylindric-acuminate, the terminal 20—25cm. long. *Pedicels* 8—10mm. long. *Bracts* very small. *Perianth* orange (reddish-yellow), 30mm. long, scarcely constricted above the ovary, slightly enlarging to the throat; *outer segments* shorter than the tube. (Fig. 551).

"Sent from Zanzibar by Sir John Kirk to Kew. It was received from him in 1881, and flowered for the first time in the Succulent House in January 1894."

A. kirkii was evidently collected on the mainland and merely dispatched by Kirk from Zanzibar. Locality of origin is unknown, and it remains an imperfectly known species.

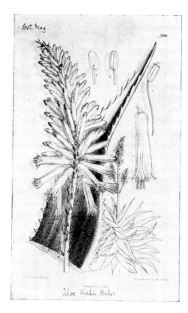

FIG. 551.

A. kirkii Bak. The plate in *Bot. Mag. t.* 7386 (1894). *Photo: By courtesy The Chief, Botanical Research Institute, Pretoria.*

19. *A. lastii* Baker in *Kew Bull.* 135 (1901); Berger in Engler's *Pflanzenr.* Liliac.–Aloin. 233 (1808).

DESCRIPTION based on Baker's description, and the type material at Kew.

Stem simple (always?) slender, a foot and a half long (say 45cm.). *Leaves* densely rosulate, 35cm. long, 7·5cm. broad, face distinctly lineate, unspotted; *margins* sinuate-dentate, teeth 3—4mm. long, 8—10mm. apart. *Inflorescence* described as simple, 50cm. long. *Raceme* 6cm. long, densely flowered, subcapitate, with prominently large bracts. *Pedicels* lowest 20—25mm. long, evidently suberect and partly hidden by large bracts. *Bracts* large, broadly ovate-acute, 15mm. long, 6—7mm. broad, clearly 7—9-nerved (*not at all* "small obtuse" as described). *Perianth* 34mm. long, presumably cylindric-trigonous, "straight, 15 lines (30mm.) long, pale-yellow, greenish at apex, tube very short." (Figs. 552, 553).

"ZANZIBAR. Sent home alive in 1885 by J. T. Last Esq., Zanzibar Government Commissioner, and flowered at Kew in December 1898". – J. G. Baker (K!).

It is most highly unlikely that this species ever grew wild on Zanzibar. In all probability it came from the mainland – but where?

Mr. E. Milne-Redhead has drawn the author's attention to a letter to Sir Joseph Hooker from Zanzibar dated 19 December 1884, in which Sir John Kirk states: "Let me introduce Mr. Last of Mamboio to whom we have been indebted for many new things. Mr. Last has with him some nice plants which he intends giving you" – this probably included the Aloe. Mr. Milne-Redhead considers that Mamboio is almost certainly Mamboya, a village and mission station in the Kilosa District of Tanzania (Tanganyika), at approx. 6° 15′ S, 37° 08′ E, 1210m. alt.

A. lastii flowered at Kew 13 years after having been received, hence it was not a young plant. Leaf face distinctly lineate is a very unusual character for an East African species. *A. lastii* appears to be nearest related to *A. boscowanii* Christian from near Moa, on the Tanga coast. This species has yellow flowers, but is of shrubby growth, and differs in having longer racemes, shorter pedicels, smaller bracts, shorter flowers and less exserted genitals.

Until *A. lastii* can be refound, and studied in the wild state, it is wiser to regard it as an imperfectly known species.

* * *

20. *A. leptocaulon* Bojer in *Hort. Maurit.* 345 (1837). *Nomen nudum.* See notes under *A. antandroi* (R. Decary) H. Perr. – Madagascar.

* * *

21. *A. leucantha* Berger in Engler's *Bot. Jahrb.* 36: 65 (1905), in *Pflanzenr. l.c.* 270 (1908).

DESCRIPTION: *Stem* 1m. high. *Leaves* lanceolate, size not stated. *Inflorescence* paniculate, height?, divaricately about 5-branched; branches 10—12cm. long. *Racemes* laxly flowered, the terminal 10cm. long, the lateral 7cm. long.

Pedicels 8—10mm. long, at length 15mm. long. *Bracts* minute, 1mm. long. *Perianth* cylindric, white, 17mm. long; *outer segments* shorter than the tube.

S. ETHIOPIA. Borana (Galla Hochland) Tarro Gumbi, 22 April 1901, Dr. Ellenbeck 2103 (B).

FIG. 552.   FIG. 553.

A. lastii Bak.

FIG. 552. Photo (considerably reduced) of the type specimen at Kew.   FIG. 553. Raceme of the type 1/1.
Photos: By courtesy The Director, Royal Botanic Gardens, Kew.

Type locality is somewhere along the western bank of the Ganale Doria River N of Dolo in S. Ethiopia. This species has never been collected again, and remains imperfectly known.

* * *

22. *A. maculata* Forskal in *Fl. Aeg. Arab.* 73 (1775), from Lohaja (Lohayya) in the Yemen.

Flowers stated to be yellow, leaves a foot long, inflorescence six feet high. No other information given. Berger thinks it should be referred to a variety of *A. vera* L., the correct name now being *A. barbadensis* Mill. Description very incomplete; total absence of herbarium material; *A. maculata* Forsk. remains an imperfectly known species.

* * *

23. *A. menyharthii* Baker in *Fl. Trop. Afr.* 7: 459 (1898).

MOÇAMBIQUE: Zambesi Valley, at Nhaondue and Boroma, Menyharth 1248 (K). (Fig. 554).

Most of Menyharth's plants were collected near Boroma, a mission station on the Zambesi about 17 miles N of Tete. On the opposite (east) bank, a little higher up is Inhondue which is almost certainly the place where *A. menyharthii* came from.

The specimen at Kew is extremely poor, but it shows that the racemes were very short, densely flowered, and that it belongs to the *Saponariae*, and is related to *A. swynnertonii*.

* * *

24. *A. mitis* Berger in Engler's *Pflanzenr.* (*l.c.*) 226 (1908).

Described from a plant at La Mortola, without precise locality of origin, and with no figures or type material cited.

* * *

25. *A. oligophylla* Baker in *Journ. Linn. Soc.* 20: 272 (1883); Berger in Engler *Pflanzenr.* Liliac.–Aloin 263 (1908).

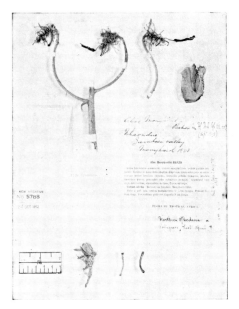

Fig. 554.

A. menyharthii Bak. Menyharth 1248, from Inhondue (Nhaondue), Zambezi Valley, type (K). *Photo: By courtesy The Director, Royal Botanic Gardens, Kew.*

CENTRAL MADAGASCAR: Without precise locality, Baron 1207 (K).

This is now *Lomatophyllum oligophyllum* (Bak.) H. Perrier in *Mém. Soc. Linn. Norm.* 1 (1): 10 (1926), et *Fl. Madag.* Liliac. 76 (1938).

26. *A. puberula* (Schweinf.) Berger from Aiderso, Barasio Valley, Eritrea – a natural hybrid between *A. camperi* Schweinf. and *A. trichosantha* Berger.

* * *

27. *A. pungens* Berger in *Pflanzenr.* (*l.c.*) 253 (1908).

Cultivated at La Mortola, without locality of origin, collector, figures or type material cited.

* * *

28. *A. princeae* Berger in Engler's *Bot. Jahrb.* 36: 64 (1905), in *Pflanzenr.* (*l.c.*) 263 (1908).

TANZANIA (Tanganyika): "Uhehe, Utschungwe Berge bei 1600m. ü.M., Frau Hauptmann Prince 1899 – Herb. Berlin."
Uhehe is a tribal area. Utschungwe Berge corresponds with the Uzungwa scarp near Dabaga (30 miles SE of Iringa) extending SW.
Habit of growth and leaves unknown, but sulcate rhachis, 5mm. pedicels, very narrow 30mm. perianth with outer segments triangular and only 3mm. long, suggests that this specimen might have been a species of *Kniphofia*. A photo of the type material does not disprove this possibility. The identity of *A. princeae* remains a mystery. (Fig. 555).

* * *

29. *A. riccobonii* Borzi in *Bollettino Orto Bot. Palermo* Part 2: 18–20 (1912), with figure.

A hybrid of *A. arborescens* Mill. and *A. capitata* Bak. which arose in the Botanical Gardens at Palermo in Sicily.

* * *

30. *A. sahundra* Bojer in *Hort. Maurit.* 347 (1837). *Nomen nudum.* See notes under *A. divaricata* Berger – Madagascar.

* * *

31. *A. schimperi* Todaro in *Hort. Bot. Panorm.* I: 70, t. 16 (1875) *non* Schweinfurth, is a garden hybrid, the parents being *A. saponaria* (Ait.) Haw. and *A. striata* Haw. Todaro's *t.* 16 shows this clearly. (*A. schimperi* Schweinf. (*non* Tod.) is a synonym of *A. percrassa* Tod.).

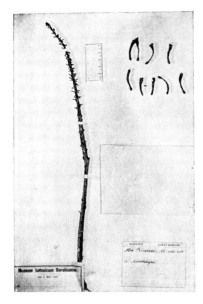

Fig. 555.

A. *princeae* Berger. The type specimen at Berlin-Dahlem.
Photo: By courtesy, the late Prof. G. Werdermann.

32. *A. schoelleri* Schweinf. in *Bull. Herb. Boiss.* 2: app. 2, 107 (1894).

ERITREA: On the plateau of Kohaito, 2600m., in the upper parts of the rivulet coming down from Andal, May 1894, Schweinfurth 158. – Berger states: "On the little river leading to the Eschka basin from Andal."
Described with flowers unknown. Schweinfurth considered it a possible form of *A. percrassa* Tod. The Kohaito plateau runs roughly north to south, east of Adi Caieh, about 110km. S of Asmara, at an altitude averaging 8,300 ft.

The names Eschka and Andal were not known to the Police or the Senior Divisional Officer at Adi Caieh, and were not found on any maps.

The present author was provided with armed guards against *shiftas* (bandits) and he visited several parts of the Kohaito Plateau, searching for *A. schoelleri*. He found many plants of *A. percrassa*, *A. elegans* and *A. camperi*, but nothing fitting the description of *A. schoelleri* without flowers. It seems *A. schoelleri* will remain imperfectly known, especially with flowers unknown.

*   *   *

33. *A. straussii* Berger in *Hortus Mortolensis* 370 (1912).

A garden plant without precise locality of origin. No type material or Herbarium specimen cited.

*   *   *

34. *A. trothai* Berger in Engler's *Bot. Jahrb.* 38: 86 (1905), in *Pflanzenr.* (*l.c.*) 240 (1908).

Described as *Stemless. Leaves* up to 60cm. long, only 3cm. broad, linear-ensiform. *Inflorescecne* simple, 1m. high. *Raceme* lax 30cm. *Bracts* 13mm. long. *Pedicels* 20mm. *Perianth* (dry) 40—45mm. long. (Fig. 556).

TANZANIA (Tanganyika): Uvinza, 5 days march to the east of Ujiji. Expedition of von Trotha, n. 66. 1896–97 (B).

Uvinza is on the Malagarazi River east of Kigoma, 47 miles SE of Kasula, in the Western Province. A map shows von Trotha's route from Bagamoyo on the coast westwards to Tabora, Uvinza, and Lake Tanganyika more or less along the present railway route. There are no roads running east and west of Uvinza today. Presumably *A. trothai* was collected west of Uvinza, and it has not been collected again. Its identity remains a mystery.

*   *   *

35. "*Vaotsohy, Vaotsoy*" Decorse in *Notes, Reconn. Explor.* 623 (1900). See notes under the synonymy of *A. divaricata* Berger (Group 8).

*   *   *

36. "*Vaombe*" Decorse in *Notes, Reconn. Explor.* 623 (1900). See notes under the synonymy of *A. vaombe* Decorse et Poisson.

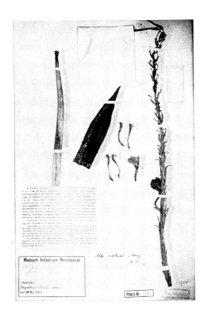

Fig. 556.

A. *trothai* Berger. The type specimen at Berlin-Dahlem.
Photo: By courtesy, the late Prof. G. Werdermann.

37. *A. variegata* Forskal in *Fl. Aeg. Arab.* 74 (1775) – *non L.* No locality given; no description of flowers; no material; epithet previously occupied.

* * *

38. *A. venenosa* Engler *Bot. Jahrb.* 15: 471 (1893).

Habit of growth and stem not stated. *Leaves* 35cm. long, 7cm. broad, *marginal teeth* 6—7cm. long and broad. *Inflorescence* copiously paniculate. *Racemes* 25—35cm. long. *Pedicels* 25mm. long. *Perianth* pale-red, 27—30mm. long.

LUNDA: Between Kimbundu and Nyangwe, 20 May 1882, P. Pogge 1460 (B).

The Lunda District is in the far NE corner of Angola. Kimbundu is now Mona Quimbundo, 38 miles SW of Henrique de Cavalho at about 9° 55′ S, 19° 58′ E. Nyangwe is a considerable distance away on the Lualaba River in the Congo. The expedition of Lieut. Wissmann and P. Pogge started at Mona Quimbundo in July 1881 and went NNE crossing the limit of the Lunda Kingdoms at about 6° 40′ S, 20° 40′ E. It seems that Pogge collected his specimen somewhere between Mona Quimbundo, Henrique de Cavalho, Vila Verissimo Sarmento and Portugalia near the Congo border, or it might have been across the border in the Lusambo Territory, of the Kasai Prov. in the Congo (Leo).

Because of shocking sandy tracks and other difficulties, the author was prevented from attempting to search for *A. venenosa* along the track to Portugalia.

This species has never been collected again, it seems, and its identity remains a mystery.

* * *

39. *A. vituensis* Baker in Th. Dyer *Fl. Trop. Afr.* 7: 458 (1898); Berger in Engler's *Pflanzenr.* 261 (1908).

Habit of growth not known. Leaves 30cm. long, 30—35mm. broad; *marginal teeth* 3—4mm. long, 10—12mm. apart. *Inflorescence* 40cm. long (simple or branched?). *Racemes* laxer below, denser upwards; length? *Pedicels* 5—6mm. long. *Perianth* yellow, 27mm. long. (Fig. 557).

KENYA: Witu, on sandy steppes, 31 March 1896, J. Thomas 113 (B).

The village of Witu is 173 miles northwards from Mombasa beyond the Tana River. There are no sandy steppes at or near Witu. The only Aloe seen (by the writer) near Witu was *A. rabaiensis* Rendle, a shrub. The former Sultanate of Witu stretched from the Tana River to beyond Lamu in the early days. The reference to Witu appears to apply to an area and not to the village of Witu.

Native name: "*Assai*". Local natives at Witu did not know this name.

A. vituensis is allied to *A. trichosantha* and allies in the Series *Verae* (Group 9). It has not been collected again and its identity remains unknown.

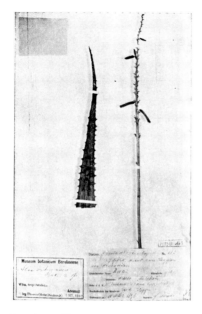

Fig. 557.

A. vituensis Bak. The type specimen. Thomas 113, Witu, Kenya, at Berlin-Dahlem.
Photo: By courtesy the late Prof. G. Werdermann.

40. *A. wollastonii* Rendle in *Journ. Linn. Soc. Bot.* 38: 235 (1908).

Leaves ensiform, not spotted, 15cm. long, gradually narrowing from a 2·5—3cm. broad base. *Racemes* 4—6cm. long. *Flowers* 3cm. long, constricted above the ovary, *outer segments* free 10mm.

UGANDA: "Ruwenzori SE, 3500 ft., flowers pink, Dr. A. F. R. Wollaston without number, 4 May 1906 (BM) – between Lake Ruisamba and the mountains proper."

Since Rendle compares his *A. wollastonii* with *A. amanensis* Berger and *A. lateritia* Engler, it seems to belong to the *Saponariae*.

Lake Ruisamba could not be traced on any map and no such name was known to the Authorities at Fort Portal when the present author made enquiries there. It seems that *A. wollastonii* could well be a form of *A. lateritia* Engler which grows in these parts. If this is the case, *A. lateritia*, having been described in 1898, has priority.

INDEX

1. Pre-Linnean Epithets

Aloe foliis spinosis confertis dentatis, vaginantibus planis maculatis. 145

Aloe Hispanica & Aloe vera vulgo. 145

Aloe sempervivum marinum, Fuchs. 147

Aloe vera vulgaris, Muntingius. 145, 148

Aloe vulgaris Caspar Bauhin. 145

Aloe Vulgaris B.P.H.L.H.A. etc. 145

Aloe vulgaris sive Sempervivum marinum. 145, 150

2. Aloe Species, Series Etc.

Note: **Names of good tropical species printed in Bold Type;** *Synonyms and Doubtful Species in Italics;* with good South African species printed in Roman. Some other plant names also included.

Aethiopicae Berger—Series, 3, 102

Aloe L., **1**

A. abyssinica Lam. ix, 202, 203, : 14, 294, **519-20**

—var. *peacockii* Bak., 203

—var. *percrassa* Bak., 271

A. abyssinica Berger (*non* Lam.) 203, 211

A. abyssinica Hook *f.* (*non* Lam.) 215

A. abyssinica Salm Dyck (*non* Lam.) 211

A. aculeata Pole Evans, x, 5, **241-44**, 392

—× *A. excelsa,* 244

—× *A. globuligemma,* 244

A. acutissima H. Perr., 393, 487, **495-97,** 503

—var. **antanimorensis** Reynolds, 487, **498-99**

A. adigratana Reynolds, 192, **215-16**

A. aethiopica (Schw.) Berger, 203, 207

A. agavefolia Tod., 520

A. albiflora Guillaumin, 391, 394, 405, **406-07**

A. amanensis Berger, 95, 530

A. ambigens Chiov., 520

A. amudatensis Reynolds, **76-78**

—× *A. tweediae,* 271

A. andongensis Bak., 330, **346-48**

—× *A. gossweileri* Reynolds, 348

A. andringitrensis H. Perrier, 450, **451-53**

A. angiensis De Wild., 95, 98

—var. *kitaliensis* Reynolds, 99

A. angolensis Bak., 305, 306, **310-11**

A. antandroi (R.Decary) H. Perr., 391, 486, **490-92** 493, 523

A. arabica Lam., 520

A. arabica Salm Dyck, 520

A. arborescens Mill., x, 6, 19, 25, 246, 322, **382-84,** 447, 521

—× *A. cameronii,* 384

—× *A. capitata,* 527

—× *A. inyangensis,* 382, 384

A. audhalica Lavranos et Hardy, 119, **143-44,** 156

A. babatiensis Christian et Verdoorn, 331, **358-59**

A. bainesii Th. Dyer, 384, 385, 388

A. bakeri Scott Elliot 391, 395, **414-17,** 423

A. ballii Reynolds, 10, **11-12**

A. ballyi Reynolds, 305, 306, **325-26**

A. bamangwatensis Schönland, 89

A. barbadensis Mill., 4, 119, **144-51,** 155, 524, 526

—var. *chinensis* Haw., 145

A. barteri Bak., xx, 41, 288, **292**

—var. *sudanica* A. Chev., 41

—var. *dahomensis* A. Chev., 14

—var. *lutea* A. Chev., 288

A. barteri Schnell (*non* Baker), 91

A. baumii Engler et Gilg., 89

A. bellatula Reynolds, 10, 394 **402-05,** 406, 440

A. beniensis De Wild, 259, 368

A. bequaerti De Wild, 95, 98

A. berhana Reynolds, 250, 274, **278-80**

A. betsileensis H. Perr., 392, 476, **481-82,** 483

A. boehmii Engler, 520

A. boiteaui Guillaumin, 391, 392, 395, **420-21**

A. boranensis Cufod., 234, 521

A. boscawenii Christian, 331, **364-66,** 525

A. brachystachys Bak., 521

A. breviscapa Reynolds et Bally, 250, 253, **266-68**

A. brunneo-punctata Engler et Gilg., 32, 35

A. buchananii Bak., 10, 11, **29-32,** 36

A. buchlohii Rauh, 392, 393, 430, **431-32**

A. buettneri Berger, 2, 36, **41-47,** 520, 523

A. bukobana Reynolds, 102, **109**

A. bulbicaulis Christian, 41, 44, 46,

531

A. bulbillifera H. Perrier, 392, 393, 450, **454-56**
—var. **paulianae** Reynolds, 392, 450, **456-57**
A. bullockii Reynolds, 36, **38-40**
A. bussei Berger, 522
A. calcairophila Reynolds, 392, 394, **408-10**
A. calidophila Reynolds, 158, 192, 209, 284, **217-18**
A. cameronii Hemsley, 331, **348-51**, 366
—var. **bondana** Reynolds, 331, 351, **353-54**
—var. **dedzana** Reynolds, 330, 331, **353**
—× *A. arborescens*, 353
—× *A. chabaudii*, 314, 353
—× *A. christianii*, 353
—× *A. excelsa*, 314, 353
—× *A. greatheadii*, 353
A. camperi Schweinf. ix, 1, 4, 192, 207, 209, **211-15**, 216, 520, 527, 528
A. campylosiphon Berger, 95
A. capitata Bak., 391, 392, 393, 461, **466-68**
—var. **cipolinicola** H. Perr., 462, **473-75**
—var. **gneissicola** H. Perr., 461, **469**
—var. **quartziticola** H. Perr., 461, **470-72**
—var. **silvicola** H. Perr., 461, **468-69**
—var. *trachyticola* H. Perr., 462
—× *A. arborescens*, 527
A. caricina Berger, 6
A. catengiana Reynolds, 331, **373-74**
A. cernua Tod., 466
A. chabaudii Schonl., 4, **102-05**, 114, 116
—× *A. aculeata*, 105
—× *A. cameronii*, 105
—× *A. excelsa*, 105
—var. **mlanjeana** Christian, 102, **105-06**
—var. **verekeri** Christian, 102, **107**
A. chimanimaniensis Christian, 19, 84
A. chinensis Bak., 145
A. chortolirioides Berger, 10, 13, 20
A. christianii Reynolds, 4, 183, 184, **186-90**, 230

A. classenii Reynolds, 249, **255-56**
A. commutata Engler, 94
A. comptacta Reynolds, 173, **179-81**
A. compressa H. Perr., 66, 393, 424, **425**
—var. **rugosquamosa** H. Perr., 424, **425-26**
—var. **schistophila** H. Perr., 424, **426-28**
A. concinna Bak., 333
A. confusa Engler, 162, **165-67**, 170
A. congolensis De Wild, et Th. Dur., 522
A. conifera H. Perr., 392, 476, **477-80**, 481
A. constricta Bak., 523
A. contigua (H. Perr.) Reynolds, 445
A. corbisieri De Wild., 32, 34, 35
A. crassipes Bak., 183, **184-86**
A. cremnophila Reynolds, 162, **163-65**, 330
A. cryptoflora Reynolds, 392, 476, **480-82**, 483
A. cryptopoda Bak., x, 4, 173, **181-83**, 224
A. dawei Berger, 6, 259, 330, 331, 345, **368-71**, 372, 382
A. debrana Christian, 272, 280
A. decorsei H. Perrier, 393, **450-51**
A. decaryi Guillaumin, 391, 523
A. decurva Reynolds, xiii, 241, **246-49**
A. defalcata Chiov., 524
A. deltoideodonta Bak., 391, 393, 432, **433-35**
—var. **brevifolia** H. Perr., 432, 434, **436-37**
—var. **candicans** H. Perr., 432, 434, **435-36**
—var. *contigua* H. Perr., 455
—var. *intermedia* H. Perr., 500
A. dependens Steud., 165
A. descoingsii Reynolds, 51, 392, 394, **410-13**
A. deserti Engler, 160, 179, 330, **337-40**
A. dhalensis Lavranos, 119, **140-43**, 156

A. divaricata Berger, 391, 483, 487, 493, **503-06**
—var. **rosea** (R. Decary) Reynolds, 487, **506**
A. doei Lavranos, 119, **130-31**
A. dorotheae Berger, 3, **69-71**
A. duckeri Christian, 76, **86-88**
A. edulis A. Chev., 91
A. elegans Tod., ix, 192, 200, **203-07**, 214, 274, 286, 520, 528
A. elgonica Bullock, 331, **359-62**
—× *A. lateritia*, 362
A. elizae Berger, 524
A. elongata Murray, 145
A. ellenbeckii Berger, 524
A. eminens Reynolds et Bally, 2, 6, 384, **287-88**
A. engleri Berger, 230
A. eremophila Lavranos, 119, **137-39**
A. erensii Christian, 48, 53, **59-61**
A. eru Berger, 211, 214
—var. *hookeri* Berger, 215
A. excelsa Berger, xiii, 248, 306, **314-16**
A. eylesii Christian, 26
A. forbesii Balf. *fil.*, 192, **193-95**
A. ferox Mill., 246
A. fievetii Reynolds, 392, 461, **464-66**
A. flava Persoon, 145
A. flexilifolia Christian, **362-64**
A. gillilandii Reynolds, 6, 305, 306, **311-14**
A. globuligemma Pole Evans, x, 5, 219, **223-24**
A. gloveri Reynolds, 340
A. gossweileri Reynolds, 219, 311, **371-73**
A. gracilicaulis Reynolds et Bally, 255, 306, **308-10**, 358
A. graminicola Reynolds, 6, 76, **78-80**
A. grata Reynolds, 102, **116-18**
A. greatheadii Schonl., 3, 47, 71, **82-84**, 392
A. greenwayi Reynolds, 69, **75**
A. guerrai Reynolds, 183, 186, 219, **228-30**
A. harlana Reynolds, 250, **275-77**

A. harmsii Berger, 524
A. haworthioides Bak., 391, 392, 394, **395-96,** 401, 464
—var. **aurantiaca** H. Perr., **397**
A. hazeliana Reynolds, 11, 19, **25-26**
A. helenae P. Danguy, 391, **513-15**
A. hemmingii Reynolds, 48, **51-53**
A. hendrickxii Reynolds, 330, **336-37**
A. hereroensis Engler, 3, **100**
—var. *orpeniae* (Schonl.) Berger, 100
A. hildebrandtii Bak., 330, **340-44**
—× *A. megalacantha* Bak., 341
A. howmanii Reynolds, xiii, 10, **17-19**
A. humbertii H. Perr., 391, **476-77**
A. humilis (L) Mill., 392
A. humilis (L) Mill. var echinata (Willd) Bak., 401
A. ibitiensis H. Perr., 433, 440, 442, **443-44**
A. imalotensis Reynolds, 392, 433, **445-47**
A. indica Royle, 145, 150, 524
A. inermis Forsk., 1, 122, 219, **220-23**
A. intermedia (H. Perr.), Reynolds, 487, 497, **500-03**
A. inyangensis Christian, 10, 17, 21, **22-25,** 26, 392
A. isaloensis H. Perr., 391, 487, **492-94**
A. itremensis Reynolds, 487, **499-500**
A. jacksonii Reynolds, 2, 3, 47, 48, **53-55,** 330
A. jex-blakeae Christian, 253
A. johnstonii Bak., 7
A. jucunda Reynolds, 2, **48-51,** 53, 413
A. keayi Reynolds, **286-88**
A. kedongensis Reynolds, 331, 345, **374-77**
A. kilifiensis Christian, 76, **80-82**
A. kirkii Bak., 524
A. kniphofioides Berger, 3
A. laeta Berger, 391, 433, **437-39**

—var. **maniaensis** H. Perr., 433, **440**
A. lanuriensis De Wild., 95, 98
A. lanzae Tod., 145
A. lastii Bak., 523
A. lateritia Engler, 3, 75, 76, 78, **95-99,** 392, 521, 530
—var. **kitaliensis** (Reynl.) Reynolds, **99-100**
A. lavranosii Reynolds, xx, 249, **250-53**
A. leachii Reynolds, 219, **226-27**
A. leptocaulon Bojer, 391, 490, 492, 525
A. leucantha Berger, 525
A. lomatophylloides Balf. f., 391, 508
A. littoralis Bak., x, 91, 120, 189, 305, 306, 311, **317-19**
—× *A. zebrina* Bak., 319
A. lugardiana Bak., 89
A. luntii Bak., 220
A. macleayi Reynolds, 283, 284, **298-300**
A. macrocarpa Tod., 76, **91-94,** 211, 392, 518
—var. **major** Berger, 94
A. macroclada Bak., 240, 391, 392, 398, 476, 481, **483-86**
A. macrospihon Bak., 66, 173, 174, **176-79**
—× *A. bukobana,* 179
—× *A. secundiflora,* 179
A. maculata Forskal, 526
A. madecassa H. Perr., 391, 433, **447-49**
—var. **lutea** Guillaumin, 391, **448**
A. magnidentata Verdoorn et Christian, 276, 294
A. marlothii Berger, 219
A. marsabitensis Verdoorn et Christian, 61, 116, 220, **303-05**
A. massawana Reynolds, 2, 3, 47, 120, **153-55,** 253
A. mawii Christian, 220, **237-41,** 392
A. mayottensis Berger, 391, 487, **506-08**
A. mcloughlinii Christian, 48, **64-66,** 276
A. medishiana Reynolds et Bally, 306, **308,** 310, 358

A. megalacantha Bak., 2, 5, 66, 162, 249, 276, 283, 286, **294-98**
—× *A. hildebrandtii,* 298
—× *A. mcloughlinii,* 298
—× *A. rigens,* 298
A. melsetterensis Christian, 84
A. menachensis (Schweinf.) Blatter, 119, **134-35,** 156
A. mendesii Reynolds, xx, 162, **170-72**
A. menyharthii Bak., 526
A. metallica Engler et Gilg., xx, 120, **151-53**
A. microdonta Chiov., 217, 220, 284, **300-03,** 524
—× *A. rabaiensis* Rendle, 302
A. microstigma Salm Dyck, 520
A. millotii Reynolds, 417, 486, **487-90,** 493
A. milne-redheadii Christian, 102, **109-11**
A. mitis Berger, 526
A. mketiensis Christian, 32, 35
A. modesta Reynolds, x, 10
A. monotropa Verdoorn, viii
A. monticola Reynolds, 250, 266, 276, **280-83**
A. morogoroensis Christian, 69, **71-75**
A. mubendiensis Christian, 249, **259-61,** 292
A. munchii Christian, xiii, 19, 306, **319-22**
A. musapana Reynolds, 10, 12, 19, **21-22,** 24, 392
A. mwanzana Christian, 176
A. myriacantha (Haw.) R & S., x, 2, **6-9,** 10, 17, 256, 392
A. mzimbana Christian, 102, **111-14,** 118
—× *A. christianii,* 114
—× *A. greatheadii,* 114
A. ngobitensis Reynolds, 345, **377-80**
A. ngongensis Christian, 366
A. niebuhriana, 119, **120-23,** 130
A. nuttii Bak., 10, 11, **32-36,** 86, 392
A. nyeriensis Christian, 6, 330, 345, 372, 377, 379, **380-82**
A. officinalis Forsk., 120, 143, **156-57**

—var. **angustifolia** (Schweinf.) Lavranos, 120, **157-58**

A. oligophylla Bak., 526-27

A. oligospila Bak., 271

A. ortholopha Christian et Milne-Redhead, 219, **234-36**, 241, 249

A. otallensis Bak., 120, **158**, 340, 521

—var. **elongata** Berger, 120, **158-60**, 521

—× *A. secundiflora*, 234

A. paedogona Berger, 41, 46, 47

A. pallidiflora Berger, 82

A. paludicola A. Chev., 41

A. palmiformis Bak., 331, **354-55**, 373

A. parallelifolia H. Perr., 395, **417-19**

A. parvula Berger, 391, 392, 395, **397-401**, 416

A. parvula H. Perr. (*non* Berger), 404, 405

A. peckii Bally et Verdoorn, 3, 47, 48, **61-64**

A. pendens Forskal, 162, **164-65**, 166

A. penduliflora Bak., 162, 170, **172-73**

A. percrassa Tod., ix, 2, 5, 214, 216, 249, 250, 256, **271-74**, 280, 434, 528

—× *A. camperi* Schw., 274

A. percrassa Schw. (*non* Tod.) 131, 134

—var. *albo-picta* Schw., 131

—var. *menachensis* Schw., 134

A. percrassa Berger (*non* Tod.), var. *saganeitiana* Berger, 203

A. perfoliata (var.) π *vera* L., 144

A. perfoliata L. (var.) γ *barbadensis* Ait., 144

A. perfoliata L. (var.) λ *vera* Willdenow, 144

A. perrieri Reynolds, 394, 404, **405-06**, 440

A. perryi Bak., 192, **195-99**

A. petricola Pole Evans, 392

A. pienaarii Pole Evans, 181

A. pirottae Berger, 48, **66-68**

A. platyphylla Bak., 89

A. plowesii Reynolds, 11, **15-19**

A. pole-evansii Christian, 368, 382

A. pretoriensis Pole Evans, 4, 183, 184, **190-91**

A. princeae Berger, 527

A. puberula (Schweinf.) Berger, 527

A. pubescens Reynolds, 119, **135-36**

A. pungens Berger, 527

A. rabaiensis Rendle, 331, 345, **366-68**, 377, 522

—× *A. microdonta*, 368

A. rauhii Reynolds, 392, 394, 413, **414**

A. retrospiciens Reynolds et Bally, 310, 330, 331, **356-58**

A. rhodesiana Rendle, 11, **26-29**

A. riccobonii Borzi, 527

A. richardsiae Reynolds, **36-38**, 39

A. rigens Reynolds et Bally, 119, **123-26**, 139

—× *A. megalacantha*, 125

—var. **glabrescens** Reynolds et Bally, 119, **126-27**

A. rivae Bak., 102, **114-16**, 158

A. rossii Tod., 433, 434

A. rubescens D.C., 145, 156

A. rubrolutea Schinz, x, 317

A. rubroviolacea Schweinf., 241, **244-46**

A. rupestris Bak., 314

A. rupicola Reynolds, 306, **322-24**, 118

A. ruspoliana Bak., 249, **253-55**, 524

—var. **dracaeniformis** Berger, **255**

A. sabaea Schweinf., 6, 314, 384, **385-87**

A. sahundra Bojer, 391, 483, 503, 506, 527

A. salm-dyckiana Schult.*f.*, 246

A. saponaria (Ait.) Haw., 76, **88-89**, 392

A. schelpei Reynolds, 283, **284-86**

A. schimperi Schweinf. (*non* Tod*)*, 271

A. schimperi Tod. (*non* Schweinf.) 527

A. schimperi Karsten et Schenck (*non* Tod.), 271

A. schinzii Bak., 317

A. schoelleri Schweinf., 528

A. schomeri Rauh, 392, 393, **429-30**, 432

A. schweinfurthii Bak., ix, 207, 259, 283, **288-92**

—var. **labworana** Reynolds, 283, **292-94**

A. schweinfurthii Gard. Chron. (*non* Bak.)., 288

A. schweinfurthii Hook.*f.* (*non* Bak.), 203, 288

A. scobinifolia Reynolds et Bally, 2, 3, 190, 192, **197-200**

A. secundiflora Engler, 5, 158, 219, 227, **230-34**, 271, 379, 392, 521

—× *A. otallensis* var. *elongata*, 234

A. sempervivoides H. Perr., 397, 406

A. sereti De Wild., 99, **256-59**, 292

A. serriyensis Lavranos, 119, **139-40**

A. sessiliflora Pole Evans, 249, 392

A. silicicola H. Perr., 450, **453-54**

A. sinana Reynolds, 192, **210-11**

A. sinkatana Reynolds, 192, **200-03**

A. solaiensis Christian, 95

A. somaliensis W. Watson, 48, 53, **56-58**

—var. **marmorata** Reynolds et Bally, 48, **58-59**

A. soutpansbergensis Verdoorn, x, 10

A. spicata Bak. (*non* L.*f.*), 211

A. spicata Bentley et Trimen (*non* L.*f.*), 211

A. splendens Lavranos, 120, **160-62**

A. squarrosa Bak., 330, **332-33**

A. stefaninii Chiov., 253

A. steudneri Schweinf., 250, **277-78**

A. straussii Berger, 528

A. striata Haw., 392, 442, 447

A. striatula Haw., 524

A. stuhlmannii Bak., 327

A. suarezensis H. Perr., 450, **458-61**

A. suzannae R. Decary, 391, 392, 476, **516-18**

A. swynnertonii Rendle, 19, 76, **84-86**, 526

A. tenuior Haw., 524

A. termetophila De Wild., 82

A. thraskii Bak., 515

A. tomentosa Deflers, 119, **127-29,** 131, 134, 268, 340

A. tororoana Reynolds, 165, 330, **334-36**

A. torrei Verdoorn et Christian, 10, 11, **12-15**

—var. *Wildii* Reynolds, 19, 20

A. trachyticola H. Perr. Reynolds, 393, 440, 461, **462-64**

A. trichosantha Berger, 119, 122, 126, 129, **130-34,** 136, 155, 211, 272, 461, 527, 529

—var. *menachensis* Schweinf., 134

—var. *albo-picta* Schweinf., 130

A. trivialis A. Chev., 288

A. trothai Berger, 181, 528

A. tweediae Christian, 250, **269-71**

A. turkanensis Christian, 219, **224-26**

A. ukambensis Reynolds, 250, **264-66**

A. vacillans Forsk., 120, 135, 143, 144, **155-56**

A. vahontsohy H. Perr., 503

A. vaombe Decorse et Poisson, 391, 392, 394, **508-11,** 512

—var. **poissonii** R. Decary, **511**

A. vaotsanda R. Decary, 391, **511-12**

A. vaotsohy Decorse et Poisson, 391, 503

—var. *rosea* R. Decary, 506

A. variegata Forskal (*non* L.), 529

A. venenosa Engler, 529

A. venusta Reynolds, **173-76,** 179, 181

A. vera "L.", 144, 149, 150, 155, 384, 483, 526

—var. *aethiopica* Schweinf., 203

—var. *angustifolia* Schweinf., 157

—var. *chinensis* Berger, 144

—var. *lanzae* Berger, 144

—var. *littoralis* Koenig, 144

A. vera Mill (*non.* L.), 145

—var. *officinalis* (Forsk.) Bak., 156

A. versicolor Guillaumin, 391, 395, 417, **421-23**

A. veseyi Reynolds, 4, 162, **168-70,** 172, 173

A. viguieri H. Perr., 391, 392, 433, **440-42,** 447, 492

A. vituensis Bak., 529

A. volkensii Engler, 6, 305, 306, 322, **327-29,** 366, 522

A. vulgaris Lam., 145, 524

A. wildii (Reynl.) Reynolds, 10, 17, **19-21**

A. wilsonii Reynolds, 101, **261-63**

A. wollastonii Rendle, 530

A. wrefordii Reynolds, 158, 192, **207-09**

A. yavellana Reynolds, 300, **344-46**

A. zanzibarica Milne-Redhead, **333-34**

A. zebrina Bak., x, 76, **89-91,** 311, 392, 523

Aquilaria agollocha Roxb., 150

Bowiea Haw., 1

B. myriacantha Haw., 6, 9

Bulbiformes Christian (Series), 2, 36

Busipho Salisb., 1

Catevala Medicus, 1

Gasteria antandroi R. Decary, 490

Graminialoe Reynolds, 2

Guillauminia albiflora (Guillaum.) Bertrand, 406, 407

Hereroenses—Series, 3, 100

Kumara Medicus, 1

Latebracteatae Berger Series, 4, 173

Leptaloe Stapf., 1, 2

L. myriacantha (Haw.) Stapf., 6

Lomatophyllum citreum Guillaumin, 421

L. oligophyllum (Bak) H. Perr., 527

Macrifoliae Sect., 524

Ortholophae Christian—Sect., 5, 219

Pachydendron Haw. (Sect.) 1, 4, 305

Pytas Salis., 1

Rhipidodendron Willd., 1

Sahoundra, 506

Saber, Sabr, Sabbara, 149, 150

Saponariae—Series, 3, 75, 392, 524

"*Vaombe*" Decorse, 391, 508, 528

"*Vaotsohy*" (*Vaotsoy*) Decorse, 391, 503, 528

Verae Berger—Series, 4, 47, 118

3. Personal Names Past and Present
(Alphabetically)

Adams, Dr. C. D., 49

Antony, Dr. Harold E., 238

Arthur, P. G., 329

Balfour, Prof. Isaac Bayley, 193, 196, 508

Ball, John, ix, 12, 19

Bally, P. R. O., ix, 9, 48, 51, 53, 59, 61, 67, 71, 96, 116, 125, 155, 163, 254, 265, 294, 308, 310, 326, 336, 358, 368, 377

Baron, Rev. R., 397, 433, 466

Beecher, Mrs. S. B., 78

Bell, A. J., 155

Bent, J. Theodore, 220

Benton, Police Officer, 266

Bequaert, Dr. J., 256, 258, 259

Bertram, E. C., 25

Bojer, 391, 483, 492, 506

Boscawen, Col. The Hon. M. T., 366

Bowie, James, 9

Brown, J. M., 105

Bruce, James, 519

Buchloh, Dr. Gunther, 432

Bullock, A. A., Kew, 39, 40

Bullock, E. J., Bulawayo, ix, 12, 19, 21, 22, 189, 314, 382

Burtt, B. D., 82, 86, 169

Cameron, Kenneth J., 354

Chabaud, John A., 105

Chief, Botanical Research Institute, Pretoria, xi, 147, 148, 195, 196, 281, 350, 437, 454, 475, 522 *et passim*
Christian, H. Basil, ix, 31, 73, 81, 86, 111, 189, 234, 236, 353, 365, 366, 380, 382 *et passim*
Classen, George A., ix, 256
Codd, Dr. L. E., ix
Cole, Miss Edith, 56
Collins, Jas., 196
Compton, Prof. R. H., ix, *et passim*

Dandy, J. E., 311, 354, *et passim*
Davies, H. F., 189
Dawkins, H. C., 336
Decorse, Dr. J., 503, 508
De Flacourt, Governor, Etienne, 391
Delap, H. A., 326
Descoings, Bernard, ix, 408, 411, 413, 421, 440, 444, 463, 473, 477, 488, 515
Dioscorides, Pedianos, 146, 149, 151
Director, Botanisches Museum, Berlin-Dahlem, 521
Director, Jardin Botanique de l'Etat, Brussels, 523 *et passim*
Director, Royal Botanic Gardens, Kew., ix, 93, 147, 164, 172, 206, 245, 272, 332, 342, 385, 395, 526, 527, *et passim*
Doe, Brian, 130
Ducker, H. C., 86
Dyer, Dr. R. A., ix, *et passim*

Erens, J., 61, 259, 303, 359

Fernandes, Dr. A., ix
Fievet, Gerard, 401, 427, 464, 480
Forskal, Peter, 122
Frederick V., King of Denmark, 122

Giess, W., 172
Gillett, Jan B., ix, 56, 159, 217
Gilliland, Prof. H. P., 153, 155

Gossweiler, John, 373
Greathead, Dr. J. B., 82
Greenway, Dr. P. J., x, 71, 75, 326, *et passim*
Guerra, Eng. Guilherme, x, 230
Guichard, Ken, 220
Guillaumin, Prof. A., 164, 391, 421, 448, 523

Hagos, Ato Tekle, Addis Ababa, 278
Hague, Mr. T. W., 160, 162
Hanbury, Sir Thomas, 277
Hardy, David, 475, *et passim*
Hemming, C. F., 53
Hendrickx, Fred L., 336, 337
Hendriques, Sr. C., 171
Hopkins, Dr. J. C., 234
Howman, Roger, 7
Humbert, Prof. H., xii, 421, 524

Jackson, T. H. E., 53, 55
Johnson, Sir Harry, 9

Keay, R. W. J., xii, 287, 288, 292
Kirk, Sir John, 170, 172, 173, 183, 334, 521, 523, 524, 525

Last, J. T., 525
Lavranos, John, xii, 122, 130, 140, 144, 160, 161, 220, 221, 252, 312
Leach, Larry C., xii, 13, 15, 88, 89, 155, 189, 226, 239, 240, 243, 244, 246, 285, 286, 314, 353, 384, *et passim*
Leandri, J., x
Lort-Phillips, Mr. & Mrs. E., 56
Lunt, W., 220

MacLeay, Dr. K. N. G., x, 93, 291
Maw, Capt. A. H., 241
Mc Dermid, E. M., 291
Mc Loughlin, Major A. G., 66, 377
Mecklenburg, The Duke of, 9
Meintjies, C., 139, 313
Mendes, Dr. E. J., Lisbon, xii, 34, 35, 149, 152, 170, 171, *et passim*

Mendonça, Prof. F. A., 311
Millot, Prof. J., xi, 399, 400, 403, 404, 448, 507, 520, *et passim*
Milne-Redhead, Edgar, xiii, 111, 173, 184, 186, 236, 240, 523, *et passim*
Mogg, Dr. A. O. D., 107
Moggridge, J. V., 82
Munch, Mr. & Mrs. R. C., xi, 19, 25, 26, 191, 247, 248, 320, 321

Niebuhr, Carsten, 122, 123

Paulian, Dr. Renaud, ix, 452, 456
Paulian, Madame, L., 456
Peck, Major, E. A., 61
Pedro, Senhor J. Gomes, 320
Penzig, Prof., 277, 278
Perrier de la Bâthie, H., 391, 392, 401, 404, 405, 406, 451, 453, 454, 455, 463, 466, 483, *et passim*
Perry, Wykeham, 196
Piers, C. P., 22
Plowes, D. C. H., xi, 17, 18, 24, 315, 317
Pole Evans, Dr. I. B., 61, 303, 359
Popov, George, 193, 195
Proctor, John, 38

Rauh, Prof. Dr. W., xi, 121, 123, 136, 139, 160, 397, 408, 411, 413, 414, 420, 423, 428, 430, 431, 464, 473
Rendle, Dr. A. B., 28
Richards, Mrs. H. M., xi, 38, 169
Robyns, Prof. W., xi, 258, 523
Rycroft, Prof. H. B., xi

Santos, Sr. R., 171
Schelpe, Dr. E. A., 13, 284, 285
Schönland, Dr. S., 82
Scott, Dr. Hugh, 312
Sheldrick, David, 260
Smuts, Field Marshal The Rt. Hon. J. C., 183
Smuts, Dr. N. R., xi, 174, 179
Souchier, B., 514

South African Council for Scientific & Industrial Research, Dedication, xi

Stent, Arthur J., 352

Stern, Dr. Wm. T., 149

Swynnerton, C. F. M., 28, 86

Taylor, Sir George, xi, *et passim*

Taylor, Hugh, 84, 114

Thompson, R. Campbell, 150

Torre, Dr. Rocha da, 13

Tweedie, Mrs. E. M., xi, 78, 208, 262, 263, 269, 270

Vaughan, Dr. R. E., 508

Verdoorn, Miss Inez C., xii

Vereker, L. S. A., 107

Vesey-FitzGerald, L. D. E. F., xii, 155, 169

Werdermann, Prof. G., 528, 529, 530

Whellan, J. A., 17, 19, 21, 26, 155, 236, 322

Wild, Dr. Hiram, xii, 19, 86, *et passim*

Williams, John, 61

Wilson, John T., xii, 208, 262, 271

Wreford Smith, H., 208